C000181368

Sarah Morgan is the bestselling author of ***Sleigh Bells in the Snow***. As a child Sarah dreamed of being a writer and, although she took a few interesting detours on the way, she is now living that dream. With her writing career she has successfully combined business with pleasure and she firmly believes that reading romance is one of the most satisfying and fat-free escapist pleasures available. Her stories are unashamedly optimistic and she is always pleased when she receives letters from readers saying that her books have helped them through hard times.

Sarah lives near London with her husband and two children, who innocently provide an endless supply of authentic dialogue. When she isn't writing or reading, Sarah enjoys music, movies and any activity that takes her outdoors.

Readers can find out more about Sarah and her books from her website: www.sarahmorgan.com. She can also be found on Facebook and Twitter.

Sarah Morgan

Summer Kisses

This edition published in Great Britain 2015
by Mills & Boon, an imprint of Harlequin (UK) Limited,
Eton House, 18-24 Paradise Road, Richmond, Surrey, TW9 1SR

ISBN: 978-0-263-91557-0

022-0215

Harlequin (UK) Limited's policy is to use papers that are natural, renewable and recyclable products and made from wood grown in sustainable forests. The logging and manufacturing processes conform to the legal environmental regulations of the country of origin.

Printed and bound by
CPI Group (UK) Ltd, Croydon, CR0 4YY

Flora

PROLOGUE

THEY were all staring.

He could feel them staring even though he stood with his back to them, his legs braced against the slight roll of the ferry, his eyes fixed firmly on the ragged coastline of the approaching island.

The whispers and speculation had started from the moment he'd ridden his motorbike onto the ferry. *From the moment he'd removed his helmet and allowed them to see his face.*

Some of the passengers were tourists, using the ferry as a means to spend a few days or weeks on the wild Scottish island of Glenmore, but many were locals, taking advantage of their only transport link with the mainland.

And the locals knew him. Even after an absence of twelve years, they recognised him.

They remembered him for all the same reasons that he remembered them.

Their faces were filed away in his subconscious; deep scars on his soul.

He probably should have greeted them; islanders were sociable people and a smile and a 'hello' might have begun to bridge the gulf that stretched between them. But his firm mouth didn't shift and the chill in his ice blue eyes didn't thaw.

And that was the root of the problem, he brooded silently as he studied the deadly rocks that had protected this part of the coastline for centuries. He wasn't sociable. He didn't care what they thought of him. He'd never been interested in courting the good opinion of others and he'd never considered himself an islander, even though he'd been born on Glenmore and had spent the first eighteen years of his life trapped within the confines of its rocky shores.

He had no wish to exchange small talk or make friends. Neither did he intend to explain his presence. They'd find out what he was doing here soon enough. It was inevitable. But, for now, he dismissed their shocked glances as inconsequential and enjoyed his last moments of self-imposed isolation.

The first drops of rain sent the other passengers scuttling inside for protection but he didn't move. Instead he stood still, staring bleakly at the ragged shores of the island, just visible through the rain-lashed mist. The land was steeped in lore and legend, with a long, bloody history of Viking invasion.

Locals believed that the island had a soul and a personality. They believed that the unpredictable weather was Glenmore expressing her many moods.

He glanced up at the angry sky with a cynical smile. If that was the case then today she was definitely menopausal.

Or maybe, like the islanders, she'd seen his return and was crying.

The island loomed out of the mist and he stared ahead, seeing dark memories waiting on the shore. *Memories of wild teenage years; of anger and defiance*. His past was a stormy canvas of rules broken, boundaries exploded, vices explored, girls seduced—*far too many girls seduced*—and all against an atmosphere of intense disapproval from the locals who'd thought his parents should have had more control.

Remembering the vicious, violent atmosphere of his home,

he gave a humourless laugh. His father hadn't been capable of controlling himself, let alone him. After his mother had left, he'd spent as little time in the house as possible.

The rain was falling heavily as the ferry docked and he turned up the collar of his leather jacket and moved purposefully towards his motorbike.

He could have replaced his helmet and assured himself a degree of privacy from the hostile stares, but instead he paused for a moment, the wicked streak inside him making sure that they had more than enough time to take one more good look at his face. He didn't want there to be any doubt in their minds. He wanted them to know that he was back.

Let them stare and speculate. It would save him the bother of announcing his return.

With a smooth, athletic movement, he settled his powerful body onto the motorbike and caught the eye of the ferryman, acknowledging his disbelieving stare with a slight inclination of his head. He knew exactly what old Jim was thinking—*that the morning ferry had brought trouble to Glenmore.* And news of trouble spread fast on this island. As if to confirm his instincts, he caught a few words from the crush of people preparing to leave the ferry. *Arrogant, wild, unstable, volatile, handsome as the devil...*

He pushed the helmet down onto his head with his gloved hands. Luckily for him, plenty of women were attracted to arrogant, wild, unstable, volatile men, or his life would have been considerably more boring than it had been.

From behind the privacy of his helmet, he smiled, knowing exactly what would happen next. The rumours would spread like ripples in a pond. Within minutes, news of his arrival would have spread across the island. Ferryman to fisherman, fisherman to shopkeeper, shopkeeper to customer—it would take no time at all for the entire population of the island to be informed of the latest news—that Conner MacNeil had come in on the morning ferry.

The Bad Boy was back on the Island.

CHAPTER ONE

'THE waiting room is packed and you've had five requests for home visits.' Flora handed Logan a prescription to sign, thinking that he looked more tired than ever. 'Given that they were all mobile and none of their complaints sounded life-threatening, Janet's managed to persuade them all to come to the surgery because it just isn't practical for you to go dashing around the island at the moment when you're running this practice on your own. What happens if we have a genuine emergency? You can't be in five places at once. We can't carry on like this, Logan. *You* can't carry on like this. You're going to drop.'

Logan looked at the prescription. 'Gentacin ear drops?'

'Pam King has an infection. She has her ears syringed regularly, but this time the whole of the canal is looking inflamed. There didn't seem any point in adding her to your already buckling list. I've taken off half your patients and if I can sort them out, I will. Otherwise I'll have to push them back through to you.'

'You, Flora Harris, are a miracle.' Logan signed the prescription. 'And persuading you to come back here as my practice nurse was the best thing I ever did. When Kyla and

Ethan left, I couldn't imagine how we were going to cope. I lost nurse and doctor in one fell swoop.'

'Well, I've only solved one half of your problem. You still need to find a doctor to replace Ethan. Any progress?'

'I think so.'

'Seriously?' Flora picked the prescription up from his desk. 'You've found someone?'

'Ask me again at lunchtime. I'm expecting someone on the morning ferry.'

'Oh, that's fantastic.' Relieved, Flora relaxed slightly. 'Is he or she good? Well qualified?'

'It's a he.' Logan turned back to his computer. 'And, yes, he's extremely well qualified.'

Flora stared at him expectantly. 'And…?'

'And what?'

'Aren't you going to tell me any more?'

'No.' He tapped a few keys and frowned at the screen. 'How are you finding Glenmore, Flora? I haven't really had a chance to ask you and you've already been here for a month. Everything going all right? Have you settled into Evanna's cottage?'

'Yes, thank you.' *Hadn't they been discussing the new doctor?* Why were they suddenly on the subject of her cottage? Why was he changing the subject? 'Evanna's cottage is beautiful. I love it.' It was true. She'd never imagined she'd live anywhere so pretty. 'You can see the sea from the bed…' she blushed '…but, of course, you already know that, given that the two of you are married. I'm sure you spent plenty of time in her cottage.'

'Actually, we didn't.' Logan glanced at her, amused. 'We usually stayed at mine because there was more room. Are you finding the work very different from the practice in Edinburgh?'

'Not really, but everything takes four times as long because this is Glenmore and people like to chat.' Flora gave a helpless shrug. 'I always seem to be running late.'

'You need to cut them off when they gossip.' Logan turned his attention back to the computer screen, searching for something. 'That's what the rest of us do.'

'I haven't worked out how to do that without appearing rude. I don't want to offend them. They're all so nice and they mean well.' Flora picked up the prescription and moved towards the door. 'Anyway, I'd better let you carry on. At this rate you'll still be here at midnight. And so will I.'

As she left the room and returned to her own consulting room she suddenly remembered that Logan hadn't given her any more clues as to the identity of the new doctor. On an island where no one kept a secret, Logan appeared to have one. Why? What possible reason could he have for being so cloak and dagger about the whole thing?

Who exactly had he appointed?

Conner parked the motorbike and dragged the helmet from his head. The rain had stopped and the sun fought a battle with the clouds, as if to remind him that the weather on Glenmore Island was as unpredictable as ever.

It was July and still the wind blew.

That same wind had almost landed him in jail at the age of sixteen.

Tucking his helmet under his arm, he strolled into the surgery. *Nice job, Logan*, he thought to himself as he took in his surroundings in one casual glance. Sleek, clean lines and plenty of light. Despite the early hour, the waiting room was already crowded with patients and he saw heads turn and eyes widen as he passed.

Without adjusting his pace, he ignored the reception desk and made for the first consulting room. As he approached the door a patient walked out, clutching a prescription in her hand. She took one look at him and stopped dead, her open mouth reminding him of a baby bird waiting to be fed.

'Conner MacNeil.' Her voice trailed off in a strangled squeak and he lifted an eyebrow, a sardonic expression in his eyes as he observed her mounting discomfort.

If he'd been in any doubt as to the islanders' reaction to his return, that doubt had now gone.

'Mrs Graham.' He was cool and polite, his neutral tone a direct contrast to her shock and consternation. He moved past her, knowing that he should cut short the encounter, but he couldn't quite help himself and he turned, the devil dancing in his eyes. 'I hope your beautiful garden is thriving. If I remember correctly, it's always at its best in July.'

Her soft gasp of outrage made it obvious that her memories of their last meeting were as clear as his and a smile played around his hard mouth as he walked into the consulting room without bothering to knock.

Mrs Graham's garden.

He still remembered the girl...

He pushed the door shut with the flat of his hand and the man at the desk looked up.

'Conner.' Logan rose to his feet, welcome in his eyes as he stretched out his hand. 'It's been too long.'

'Not long enough for some,' Conner murmured, thinking of Mrs Graham who, he was sure, at that precise moment was still glaring angrily at the closed door. 'Prepare yourself for a riot. The locals will be arming themselves any minute now.' He shook the hand of the man who had been part of his boyhood.

'Kate Graham recognised you, then? I seem to recall that you were stark naked the last time she saw you.'

The devil was back in Conner's eyes. 'Mrs Graham had extremely tall delphiniums in her border,' he recalled. 'She only saw my face.'

Logan laughed out loud. 'You have no idea how pleased I am to see you. You're looking good, Conner.'

'I wish I could return the compliment.' Conner's dark brows drew together in a frown as he studied his cousin, taking in the faint shadows and the lines of strain. 'You've looked better. Island life obviously doesn't suit you. You need to leave this backwater and find yourself a proper job.' But his tone was light because he knew that the medical care that his cousin delivered on this remote Scottish island was of exceptional quality.

'There's nothing wrong with island life, just the lack of medical staff. To run this place effectively we need two doctors and two nurses.' Logan rubbed his fingers over his forehead. 'It's been tough since Kyla and Ethan left. I lost a doctor and a nurse in one blow.'

Conner thought about his cousin. 'I never thought Kyla would leave this place.'

'She married an Englishman with itchy feet.'

'There's treatment for that.'

'Yeah.' Logan grinned. 'Anyway, it's only temporary and I've replaced Kyla. Now you're here, so we're back on track.'

'If I were you, I'd postpone the celebrations until the whole island gets wind of your little plan. The jungle drums will start beating soon.'

'They're already beating.' Logan picked up his coffee-mug and then realised that it was empty and put it down again. 'My phone has been ringing and you've only been on the island for twenty minutes. You certainly know how to make a lasting impression, Conner MacNeil. What exactly did you do on that ferry?'

'Travelled on it. Apparently that was more than enough.' Conner stretched his legs out in front of him and put his helmet down on the floor. 'There's going to be a rebellion. If looks could kill, I'd be in your mortuary right now, not your consulting room. The natives will probably return to their roots and take up arms to defend themselves from the unwelcome invader. They're preparing themselves for rape and pillage.'

'Ignore them. You know what the islanders are like.' Logan reached for a pack of papers. 'They don't like change. Can you read this lot quickly and sign? Just a formality.'

'And you know how much I love formality,' Connor drawled softly, but he leaned forward to take the papers, grimacing when he saw the thickness of the documentation. 'Life's too short to wade through that much bureaucracy. What does it say? *Conner MacNeil must not steal, destroy property or otherwise harass the citizens of Glenmore*?'

'All that and the fact that all single women under the age of thirty are now considered to be in danger.' Logan's eyes gleamed as he handed his cousin a pen. 'The men of the island are locking up their wives and daughters as we speak and Mrs Graham is probably shovelling fertiliser on her delphiniums to increase their height and preserve her modesty and yours. Sign the back page.'

'Single women under the age of thirty? Why thirty? That doesn't give me nearly enough scope. I've always preferred experience to innocence.' Conner flipped straight to the back of the sheaf of papers and signed with a casual flourish.

Logan lifted an eyebrow. 'Aren't you going to bother to read what you just signed?'

'I'm presuming it's a load of rules and regulations.'

'And knowing that, you're prepared to sign? I thought you hated rules and regulations.'

'I do, but I trust you and I admire what you've built here on Glenmore.' Conner handed the papers back to Logan, a faint smile on his mouth. 'I promise to do my best for your patients. I'm *not* promising that I won't bend the rules a little if it proves to be necessary.'

Logan reached for an envelope. 'I bend them all the time. It's the only way to get things done. It's good to have you here, Conner.'

'I don't think everyone is going to agree with you. Judging from the shock on the faces I've seen so far, you didn't warn them in advance.'

'Do I look stupid?' Logan slipped the papers into the envelope and dropped it into the tray on his desk. 'I was waiting until you showed up.'

'Did you think I wouldn't?'

'Reliability isn't your middle name. I wasn't sure you'd actually do this when the time came.'

Connor gave a humourless laugh. 'Then that makes two of us.'

'But you did, so now I can break the happy news to the inhabitants of Glenmore. How have you been? Tell me, honestly.' Logan hesitated. 'It must have been hard…'

'Coming back? Why would you say that?' Conner was surprised to find that his voice sounded so harsh. 'You know how much I love this place.'

Ignoring the sarcasm, Logan watched him steadily. 'Actually, I was talking about leaving the army.'

The army?

Conner realised that since he'd stepped off the ferry, he'd given no thought to the life he'd just left. All he could think about was Glenmore and how it felt to be back. The bad memories poured into him like some dark, insidious disease, gradually taking possession of his mind. 'Leaving the army isn't my problem at the moment.' he growled. 'And, anyway, I don't believe in living in the past when there's a perfectly good future to be getting on with.'

'Are you going to sell the house?'

'You get straight to the point, don't you?' Conner rose to his feet and paced across the room, keeping his back to his cousin as he rode the pain. 'Yes.' He turned, his eyes fierce. 'Why would I keep it?'

'So that you have a place on Glenmore?'

'If I'd wanted that,' Conner said softly, 'why would I be renting your barn?'

'Good point.' Logan gave him a sympathetic look. 'This must be hard for you, I know.'

'Nowhere near as hard as it's going to be for the locals.' Conner studied a picture on the wall. 'They're going to think that you've lost your mind, appointing me as the locum.'

'They'd be less shocked if you told them the truth about what you've been doing since you stormed off Glenmore all those years ago.'

'Island gossip has never interested me.'

'You sound like Flora. Her clinics are taking twice as long as they should because she doesn't like to interrupt people when they're chatting.'

'Flora?'

'My practice nurse. She replaced Kyla.'

'Flora Harris?' Conner turned, the pain inside him under control. 'Daughter of Ian Harris, our island solicitor? Niece of our esteemed headmistresses?'

Cloudy dark hair, soft brown eyes, an impossibly shy and awkward teenager, and as innocent as the dawn...

Logan's eyes narrowed. 'You didn't ever...'

'Fortunately for her, there were enough wild teenage girls on the island who were more than happy to experiment, without me having to corrupt the saintly Flora. Anyway, she didn't take her nose out of a book for long enough to discover the existence of sex.'

'She isn't saintly. Just shy.'

'Maybe. But definitely not the sort of girl who would skip classes in favour of a practical session on human reproduction.' Conner rolled his shoulders to ease the tension. 'I'm not surprised she's a nurse. It would have been that or a librarian. Does she know I'm the new doctor?'

'Not yet.'

'She won't approve.'

'Even if she doesn't, she would never say so. Flora is sweet, kind and incredibly civilised.'

'Whereas I'm sharp, unkind and incredibly uncivilised. I'm willing to bet that the first thing she does, when she finds out about me, is remind you that I blew up the science lab.'

'I'd forgotten about that.' Momentarily distracted, Logan narrowed his eyes. 'What did you use—potassium?'

'Too dangerous. They didn't keep it at school.' Restless, Conner paced across the room again and scanned the row of textbooks on the shelf. 'But they did keep sodium. That was good enough.'

'It should have been in a locked cupboard.'

'It was.'

Logan laughed. 'I'm amazed you weren't expelled.'

'Me, too. Very frustrating, given how hard I applied myself to the task.' Conner suppressed a yawn. 'So I'm going to be working with Flora. The excitement of this place increases by the minute.'

'She's a brilliant nurse. She was working in Edinburgh until last month but we persuaded her to come back. And now you've joined us. I've been thinking—we should tell the islanders what you've been doing with your life.'

'It's none of their business.'

Logan sighed. 'I don't see why you're so reluctant to let people know that you're a good guy.'

'Who says I'm a good guy? If you wanted a good guy for the job then you've appointed the wrong man.' Conner turned, a ghost of a smile on his face. 'You'll have a hard job convincing Flora, Mrs Graham and any of that lot on the ferry that there's a single decent bone in my body.'

'Give them time. How soon can you start?'

'That depends on how soon you want to clear out your surgery.' Conner unzipped his jacket. 'I can guarantee that they won't be queuing up to see me. I'm assuming that, by appointing me, you want to encourage your patients to deal with their ailments at home. We both know they won't be coming to the surgery once they know who the doctor is. Which means I get to lounge around all day with my feet up while you pay my salary.'

'That's rubbish. You know as well as I do that the women will be forming a disorderly queue all the way to the harbour.' Logan's expression was serious. 'Tell them the truth about yourself, Con. It will help them understand you.'

'I don't need them to understand me. That's always been the difference between us. You *are* a nice guy. I'm not. You care about them. I don't.'

'So why are you here?'

'Not out of love for the islanders, that's for sure. And I'm here because…' Conner shrugged '…you rang me. I came. Let's leave it at that.' He didn't want to think about the rest of it. Not yet. He frowned, his attention caught by one of the photographs on the wall. 'Isn't that little Evanna Duncan? Are you two together?'

'She's Evanna MacNeil now,' Logan's tone was a shade cooler as he corrected him. 'I married her a year ago and if you so much as glance in her direction you might just discover that I'm not such a nice guy after all.'

'Seducing married women has never been on my list of vices.' Conner turned and looked at his cousin. 'She always adored you. Children?'

'Evanna is due in five weeks.' Logan hesitated. 'And I have a daughter from a previous marriage. Kirsty. She's two.'

'So, you're a regular family man.' Conner saw the shadows in Logan's eyes but he knew better than to ask questions. He had plenty of shadows of his own, *dark corners that he kept private.*

Logan's gaze didn't waver. 'What about you? Wife? Children?'

'I'll assume that wasn't a serious question.'

'I was just hoping you had a reason not to wreak havoc across the female population of Glenmore over the summer. Just don't touch the patients, it's strictly frowned on and definitely against the rules.' Logan rose to his feet. 'Use the consulting room across the corridor. Do you want to shave or change before you start?'

'And ruin the opportunity to shock everyone? I don't think so. I'll stay as I am.'

'I've just broken the news of your arrival to Janet, our receptionist. She's already lined up some patients. Is there anything you need to know before you start?'

'Yes.' Conner paused, his hand on the door. 'If I'm not allowed to seduce the patients, how am I supposed to relieve the boredom of being trapped on Glenmore?'

'I don't suppose you'd consider a round of golf?'

'No.'

'I didn't think you would. Well, I'm confident you'll find something or someone to distract you.' Logan gave a resigned laugh. 'Just steer clear of Mrs Graham's garden, that's all I ask.'

She needed to talk to Logan quickly.

Flora nipped across the corridor and tapped lightly on the door. Without waiting for an answer, she walked into his consulting room and immediately collided with a tall, dark-haired man whose body seemed to be made of nothing but rock-hard muscle. She stumbled slightly but his hands came out and steadied her, his strong fingers digging into her arms as he held her.

'I'm *terribly* sorry,' she apologised breathlessly, catching her glasses before they could slide down her nose, 'I had no idea Logan had a patient with him.'

'Hello, Flora.' His lazy, masculine drawl was alarmingly familiar and her eyes flew wide as she tilted her head back to take a proper look at him.

'Oh!' Her heart started to beat in double time and she felt decidedly faint. Her knees weakened and from a distance she heard Logan's voice.

'Flora, you remember my cousin Conner?'

Remember? *Remember?* Well, of course she remembered! She might be short-sighted, but she was still a woman! And it didn't matter how many rules or hearts he'd broken, there wasn't a woman alive who would forget Conner MacNeil once she'd met him.

Especially not her.

And he would have known how she'd felt because arrogance and Conner had gone hand in hand. Even as a young boy he'd known exactly what effect he had on the girls and had used it to his advantage.

But it wasn't a boy who was standing in front of her now. It was a man. And his effect on the opposite sex had grown proportionately.

Determined not to boost his ego by revealing her thoughts, Flora screwed up her face and adopted what she hoped was a puzzled expression. 'Conner...Conner... The name *is* familiar—were you below me at school? Or were you above me?'

His blue eyes glinted with wicked humour. 'I don't recall ever being above or below you, Flora,' he murmured softly, 'but that may be my defective memory.'

She felt the heat flare in her cheeks and remembered, too late, that anyone trying to play word games with Conner was always going to lose. His brain and his tongue worked in perfect unison whereas hers had always been slightly disconnected. Without fail she thought of the perfect thing to say about two days after the opportunity to say it had passed.

'Well, you do look vaguely familiar,' she said quickly, stepping back and concentrating her attention on Logan to cover up how unsettled she felt. A moment ago she'd been happily existing in the present, enjoying her life. The next she'd been transported back to her childhood and it was a lonely, uncomfortable place. If this was time travel, then she wanted none of it.

She'd had such a desperate, agonising crush on Conner. *A crush that had been intensified by the fact that her father had forbidden her to mix with him.* 'Sorry to disturb your reunion, but Amy Price just rang me. Heather has chickenpox.'

'And?' Logan frowned. 'Tell her to buy some paracetamol and chlorpheniramine from the pharmacy.'

'I'm not worried about Heather. I'm worried about your wife. Evanna saw the child in clinic yesterday.'

'And the child would have been infectious.' Understanding dawned and Logan cursed softly. 'Has Evanna had chickenpox?'

'I don't think so. That's why I thought you ought to know straight away. I remember talking about it with her a few months ago. She was telling me that her mother sent her off to play with everyone who had chickenpox, but she never caught it.'

'Chickenpox is a disease that you don't want to catch in the third trimester of pregnancy.'

'That's what I thought.'

Somehow she was managing to have a normal conversation with Logan, but her head and senses were filled with Conner. In some ways he'd changed, she mused, and yet in others he hadn't. The muscular physique was the reward of manhood but other things—*the air of supreme indifference and the ice-blue eyes*—had been part of the boy.

What was he doing here, anyway? Like everyone else, she'd assumed he'd never show his face on the island again.

Logan walked to his desk. 'I'll call Evanna now.'

'I've already done it. She's about to start her clinic, but she'll come and talk to you first. I thought you might want to delay your first patient or pass him across to the new doctor when he arrives.'

'Relax. She's probably immune.' Conner leaned his broad shoulders against the doorframe, watching them both with an expression that could have been amusement or boredom. 'Do a blood test and check her antibody status.'

She was wrong, Flora realised with a flash of disquiet. *There was nothing of the boy left.* There were more changes than she'd thought, and some were so subtle that they weren't immediately obvious. Those ice-blue eyes were sharper and more cynical, and his arrogance had clearly developed along with his muscles. *What did he know about antibody status?* Or was he one of those people who watched all the medical soaps on television and then assumed they were qualified to diagnose?

To make matters worse, Logan was nodding, encouraging him. 'Yes—yes, I'll do that, but if she's not immune…'

'Then you just give her zoster immunoglobulin. What's the matter with you?' Conner's brows drew into a frown as he looked at his cousin. 'This is why I'm careful not to fall in love. It fries your brain cells and obliterates your judgement.'

'There's nothing wrong with Logan's judgement.' Fiercely loyal, Flora immediately flew to Logan's defence and then wished she hadn't because Conner switched his gaze from Logan to her and his attention was unsettling, to say the least.

Apparently unaware of the change in the atmosphere, Logan rubbed his hand over the back of his neck. 'When you love someone, Conner,' he said, 'you lose perspective.'

Conner's eyes held Flora's. 'I wouldn't know. That's one mistake I've never made.'

She swallowed, every bit as uncomfortable as he'd clearly intended her to be. Was he trying to shock her? He'd had women, she knew that. Probably many. Was she surprised that he'd never found love? *That he considered love a mistake?*

'True love is a gift, given to few,' she murmured, and Conner's mouth tilted and his blue eyes glinted with sardonic humour.

'True love is a curse, bestowed on the unlucky. Love brings weakness and vulnerability. How can that be a gift?'

Flustered, she cleared her throat and looked away. *What was he doing here?* Why had he returned to Glenmore with no warning, looking like the bad guy out of a Hollywood movie? His hair was dark and cropped short and his jaw was dark with stubble. He was *indecently* handsome and the only thing that marred the otherwise faultless symmetry of his features was the slight bump in his nose, an imperfection which she assumed to be the legacy of a fight. He looked tough and dangerous and the impression of virile manhood was further intensified by the width and power of his shoulders under the black leather jacket.

He wasn't attractive, Flora told herself desperately. How could he possibly be attractive? He looked…rough. Rough and a little menacing. She thought of the conventional, bespectacled lawyer she'd dated for a while in Edinburgh. He'd always let her through doors first and had been completely charming. His hair had always been neat and tidy and she'd never, ever seen him anything other than clean-shaven. He'd almost always worn a suit when they'd dated and his legs hadn't filled his trousers the way that Conner's did. And then there had been his smile. His cheeks had dimpled slightly and his eyes had been kind. *Nothing like Conner's eyes.* Conner's eyes were fierce and hard, as if he was just waiting for someone to pick a fight so that he could work off some pent-up energy.

Her heart thudded hard against her chest. Conner MacNeil wasn't charming or kind. He was— He was…unsuitable. Dangerous. A woman had to be mad to look twice at a man like him.

Why, she wondered helplessly, *was the unsuitable and the dangerous always so much more appealing than the suitable?*

'We need to get on.' With a huge effort of will, she broke the connection and turned her attention back to Logan. 'We've a busy surgery this morning. What happened to the new doctor? Did he show up? You didn't tell me who he is or when he or she can start.'

'You heard the woman.' Logan turned to Conner. 'Go and do your job.'

Conner shrugged and a slight smile touched his mouth. 'Prepare for chaos.'

It took Flora a moment to understand the implications of their conversation. 'You can't— Conner?' Her voice cracked. 'But Conner isn't—' She broke off and Conner lifted an eyebrow.

'Don't stop there,' he prompted softly. 'I'm keen to hear all the things I'm not.'

Not suitable. Not safe. Not conventional. Not responsible... She could have drawn up a never-ending list of things he was not. 'I— You're not a doctor. You *can't* be a doctor.'

He smiled. 'Why? Because I didn't hand in my homework on time?'

'You didn't hand in your homework at all. You were hardly ever at school!'

'I'm flattered that you noticed.' His soft observation was a humiliating reminder that she'd always been aware of him and he'd never even noticed her.

She was probably the only girl on Glenmore who hadn't been kissed by Conner MacNeil.

She turned away, horrified that after all this time she still cared that she'd been invisible to him. 'You're forgetting that my aunt was the headmistress.'

'I've forgotten nothing.' There was something in his tone that made her glance at him and speculate. There was resentment there and—*anger*?

He'd always seemed angry, she remembered. *Angry, moody and wild.*

Was that why he was back? Was he seeking revenge on the people who had disapproved and eventually despaired of him?

'Ann runs a wonderful school.' She felt compelled to defend her family. 'The children all adore her and they get a fantastic education.'

'There's more to education than sitting in rows in a classroom with a book in front of you.' Conner leaned nonchalantly against the table, his glance speculative. 'Still the same Flora. Conventional. Playing everything by the rules. I presume that all your affairs are still with books?'

His comment stung. He made her feel so—so—*boring*. Plain, boring Flora. And that was what they'd called her at school, of course. *Boring Flora*. Hurt, she clawed back. 'Rules are there for a reason and if you're really a doctor then I hope you've read a few books yourself along the way, otherwise I pity your patients.' She stopped, shocked at herself and aware that Logan was gaping at her in amazement.

'Flora! I've never heard you speak to anyone like that before. Usually I have to drag a response from you. What is the matter with you?'

'I don't know. I— Nothing.' Flora's cheeks were scarlet and she blinked several times and adjusted her glasses. She didn't know what was the matter. She didn't know what had come over her. *She didn't know why she felt so hot and bothered.* 'Sorry. I apologise.'

She felt miserably uncomfortable and mortified that she'd embarrassed Logan. The only person who didn't seem remotely embarrassed was Conner himself. He simply laughed.

'Don't apologise. I much prefer to be around people who say what they think. I'm sure most of the inhabitants of Glenmore will share your sentiments and express them far more vociferously.' He turned to Logan. 'I did warn you that this wouldn't work. It isn't too late to change your mind.'

'Of course I'm not going to change my mind.' Logan sounded exasperated. 'Flora, Conner's credentials are—'

'Irrelevant,' Conner interrupted smoothly, and Flora bit her lip.

She knew she ought to say something nice and welcoming, but her brain just didn't seem to be working with its normal efficiency. Seeing Conner again without warning was shocking, confusing and—*thrilling*?

Horrified, she quickly dismissed that last emotion and pressed her fingers to her chest, wishing that her heart would slow down. It was not, definitely not, thrilling that he was back on the island. If she'd been asked to choose the least suitable man to be a doctor on Glenmore, it would have been Conner MacNeil.

Over the years, she'd thought of him often.

Too often.

She'd wondered where he was and what he was doing. She'd imagined him languishing in some jail, maybe in a foreign country; she'd imagined him sitting by a pool in a tax haven, having made piles of money by some unspeakably dubious means.

Never, in her most extravagant fantasies, had she imagined him training as a doctor and never, in those same dreams, had she imagined him returning to Glenmore.

One thing she knew for sure; the calm, tranquil routine of Glenmore Island was about to be overturned.

She didn't know what sort of doctor Conner was going to prove to be, but she knew it wasn't the sort that the islanders were used to seeing.

CHAPTER TWO

CONNER buzzed for his first patient and braced himself for the reaction.

He wasn't disappointed.

The first man who walked through his door took one look at him, gave a horrified gasp and immediately backed out, muttering that he'd 'wait for the other doctor'.

Conner watched him leave, his handsome face expressionless. Clearly people had long memories and he understood all about that. *He hadn't forgotten a single minute of his time on Glenmore.*

With a dismissive shrug, he buzzed for the next patient and the moment Susan Ellis walked through the door, he prepared himself for a repeat performance. If he had any supporters among the islanders—*and he was beginning to doubt that he had*—this lady wouldn't be among them. She ran the shop at the harbour and she had reason to know him better than most.

'Good morning, Mrs Ellis.' He kept his tone suitably neutral but her face reflected her shock at seeing him.

'Conner MacNeil! So the rumours are true, then.' She glanced behind her, obviously wondering if she'd wandered into the wrong building, and Conner lifted an eyebrow.

'Is there something I can help you with, Mrs Ellis?' *Perhaps this wasn't going to work after all.*

'I don't know. I'll have to think about it.'

It was on the tip of his tongue to tell her to think quickly because there was a queue of patients waiting but then he realised that the queue was probably dwindling by the second so a slightly longer consultation wasn't likely to matter.

'If you'd rather see Logan, go ahead. My feelings will remain intact.'

'I'm not thinking about your feelings,' she said tartly. 'I'm thinking about my health. I assume Logan knows you're here?'

'You think I broke a window and climbed in? Looking for drugs, maybe?'

She gave him a reproving look. 'Don't give me sarcasm, Conner MacNeil. I'm not afraid to admit that you wouldn't leap to mind as someone to turn to in times of trouble.'

Clearly recalling the details of their last encounter, Conner relented slightly. 'I don't blame you for that.'

She studied him from the safety of the doorway, her mouth compressed into a firm line of disapproval. 'So you've mended your ways. Are you really a doctor?'

'Apparently.'

'There's plenty on this island who will be surprised to hear that.'

'I'm sure that's true.' Conner kept his tone level. 'Are you going or staying? Because if you're staying, you may as well sit down. Or we can carry on this consultation standing, up if that's what you would prefer.'

'Not very friendly, are you?'

'I presumed you were looking for a doctor, not a date.'

Susan Ellis gave a reluctant laugh. 'You always were a sharp one, I'll give you that.' After a moment's hesitation she closed the door and sat down gingerly on the edge of the seat, as if she hadn't quite decided whether she was going to stay or not. 'I'm not sure if I can talk about this with you.'

Conner sighed. *It was going to be a long day.* 'As I said, if you'd rather see Logan, I quite understand.'

She fiddled with the strap of her handbag and then put it on the floor in a decisive movement. 'No,' she said firmly. 'I've never been one to live in the past. Times change. People change. If you're a doctor then— I don't suppose you'll be able to help me anyway.'

'Try me.'

'It's hard to put a finger on when it all started, but it's been a while.' She glanced at Conner and he sat in silence, just listening. 'Probably been almost a year. I'm tired, you see. All the time. And I know doctors hate hearing that. You're going to say it's just my age, but—'

'I haven't said anything yet, Mrs Ellis. You speak your lines and then I'll speak mine.' He could have been wrong but he thought he saw her shoulders relax slightly.

'Fair enough. Well, I feel washed out and exhausted a lot of the time. It doesn't matter how well I sleep or how much rest I take, I'm still tired.' She hesitated and then sighed. 'And a little depressed, if I'm honest. But that's probably because I just feel so…slow. If this is getting old, I want none of it.'

'Have you gained weight?'

She stiffened. 'Are you going to lecture me on my eating?'

'Are you going to answer the question?'

Susan shifted self consciously, automatically pulling in her stomach and straightening her shoulders. 'Yes, I've gained weight, but I suppose that's my age as well. You just can't eat so much when you get older and it's hard to change old habits. Aren't you going to make notes? Logan always keeps meticulous notes.'

'I prefer to listen. I'll do the writing part later.' Conner stood up and walked towards her, his eyes concentrating on her face. 'Your skin is dry. Is that usual for you?'

'Didn't used to be but it's usual now. My hair's the same.' She tilted her face so that he could take a closer look. 'Observant, aren't you?'

'Sometimes.' Having looked at her skin, Conner took her hands in his and examined them carefully. Then he looked at her eyelids. 'You have slight oedema. Can I take a look at your feet?'

'My feet?'

'That's right.' He squatted down and helped her slip her shoes off.

'I never thought I'd have Conner MacNeil at my feet.'

'Savour the moment, Mrs Ellis. Do they bother you?'

'They're aching terribly and I wouldn't be surprised if they're a bit swollen…' She wiggled her toes. 'I assumed it was the heat.'

Conner examined her feet and ankles. 'From what I've seen, Glenmore is in the middle of a typical summer. Wind and rain. I'm not expecting any cases of heatstroke today.' He was sure that her feet were swollen for a very different reason.

'We had sunshine last week. You know Glenmore—the weather is always unpredictable. A bit like you.' She looked at him, her gaze slightly puzzled. 'You're very gentle. I hadn't expected that of you.'

'I prefer not to leave marks on my victims.' A faint smile on his face, Conner rose to his feet. 'The swelling isn't caused by heat, Mrs Ellis. I can tell you that much.' He washed his hands and picked up the IV tray that Flora had left on the trolley. 'I'm going to take some blood.'

'Is that really necessary?'

'No. I just want to cause you pain.'

His patient laughed out loud. 'Revenge, Conner?'

'Maybe. You called the police that night.'

'Yes, I did.' Susan stuck out her arm. 'You were out of control. Only eight years old and helping yourself to what you wanted from my shop.'

He ran his fingers gently over her skin, searching for a vein. 'I needed some stuff and I didn't have the money to pay.'

'And how often did I hear that from the children? Plenty of them did it.' Her laughter faded and she shook her head as she watched him. 'But I remember you. You were different. So bold. A real rebel. Even when John, our island policeman, gave you a talking to, you didn't cry. It was as if you were used to being shouted at. As if you'd hardened yourself.'

Conner didn't falter. 'You have good veins. This shouldn't be hard.'

'You're not going to excuse yourself, are you?'

'Why would I do that?'

'Because we found out later that there were things happening in your house.' She spoke softly. 'Plenty to explain why you were the way you were.'

Suddenly the room felt bitterly cold. Conner slipped a tourniquet over her wrist. 'Everyone's family is complicated. Mine was no different.'

'No?' Susan looked at him for a moment and then sighed. 'I remember how you looked on that day. You just stood there, all defiant, your chin up and those blue eyes of yours flashing daggers. Oh, you were angry with me.'

'As you said, you'd called the police.'

'But it didn't have any effect. You were never afraid of anyone or anything, were you, Conner MacNeil?'

Oh, yes, he'd been afraid. *'Don't do it. Don't touch her—I'll kill you if you touch her.'*

With ruthless determination Conner pushed the memory back into the darkness where it belonged. 'On the contrary, I was afraid of my cousin Kyla.' Keeping his tone neutral, he tightened the tourniquet and studied the woman's veins.

'She had a deadly punch and a scream that would puncture your eardrums.'

'Ah, Kyla. We all miss her. It's not good when islanders leave. It's not good for Glenmore.'

Swift and sure, Conner slipped the needle into the vein. 'Depends on the islander, Mrs Ellis. There are some people that Glenmore is pleased to see the back of.' He released the tourniquet and watched as the blood flowed. 'I'm checking your thyroid function, by the way.'

'Oh. Why?'

'Because I think hypothyroidism is a possible explanation for your symptoms.' Having collected the blood he needed, he withdrew the needle and covered the area with a pad. 'Press on that for a moment, would you? If you leave here with bruises, that will be another black mark against me.'

She looked down at her arm. 'That's it? You've finished? You're good at that. I barely felt it.' The expression in her eyes cooled. 'I suppose you have a lot of experience with needles.'

Conner picked up a pen and labelled the bottles. 'I'm the first to admit that my list of vices is deplorably long, Mrs Ellis, but I've never done drugs.'

Her shoulders relaxed. 'I'm sorry,' she said softly. 'That was uncalled for. If I've offended you…'

'You haven't offended me.' He dropped the blood samples into a bag, wondering what had possessed him to take the job on Glenmore. He could have come in on the ferry, sorted out his business and left again.

'Hypothyroidism, you say?'

'There are numerous alternative explanations, of course, but this is a good place to start.'

'I don't know whether to be relieved or alarmed. I was expecting you to tell me it was nothing. Should I be worried?'

'Worrying doesn't achieve anything. If we find a problem, we'll look for a solution.' He completed the necessary form and then washed his hands again. 'I'm going to wait for those results before we look at anything else because I have a strong feeling that we've found the culprit.'

'You're confident.'

'Would you prefer me to fumble and dither?'

She laughed. 'You always were a bright boy, Conner MacNeil. Too bright, some would say. Bright and a rebel. A dangerous combination.'

Conner sat back down in his chair. 'Call the surgery in three days for the result and then make another appointment to see me. We can talk about what to do next.'

'All right, I'll do that. Thank you.' Susan picked up her bag, rose to her feet and walked to the door. Then she turned. 'I always regretted it, you know.'

Conner looked up. 'Regretted what?'

'Calling the police.' Her voice was soft. 'At the time I thought you needed a fright. I thought a bit of discipline might sort you out. But I was wrong. You were wild. Out of control. But what you needed was a bit of love. People to believe in you. I see that now. What with everything that was happening at home—your mum and dad. Of course, none of us knew the details at the time, but—'

'You did the right thing calling the police, Mrs Ellis,' Conner said in a cool tone. 'In your position I would have called them, too.'

'At the time I was angry that they didn't charge you.'

'I'm sure you were.'

It was her turn to smile. 'Now I'm pleased they didn't. Can I ask you something?'

'You can ask. I don't promise to answer.'

'There was a spate of minor shoplifting at that time but everyone else was taking sweets and crisps. You took the oddest assortment of things. What did you want it all for?'

Conner leaned back and smiled. 'I was making a bomb.'

* * *

'He blew up the science lab!' Flora stood in front of Logan, trying to make him to see reason.

'Funny.' Logan scanned the lab result in front of him. 'Conner said that you'd bring that up.'

'Of course I'm bringing it up. It says everything about the type of person he is.'

'Was.' Logan lifted his eyes to hers. 'It tells you who he was. Not who he is.'

'You really think he's changed?'

'Are you the same person you were at fifteen?'

Agonisingly shy, barely able to string a sentence together in public. Flora flushed. 'No,' she said huskily. 'Of course not.'

Logan shrugged. 'Perhaps he's changed, too.'

'And what if he hasn't? What sort of doctor is he going to make?'

'An extremely clever one. Most people wouldn't have had such a good understanding of the reactivity series to cause that explosion. Anyway, I thought you were relieved that I'd found another doctor.'

'I was, but I never thought for a moment it would be— I mean, *Conner*?' Flora's expression was troubled. 'He's right, you know. The locals won't be happy. What if they make life difficult for him?'

'They always did. He'll cope. Conner is as tough as they come.'

'I can't believe he's a doctor. How did you find out? I mean, he vanished without trace.'

'I stayed in touch with him.' Logan lifted his gaze to hers. 'He's my cousin, Flora. Family. I knew he was a doctor. When I knew I needed help, he seemed the obvious choice.'

'Are you sure? He used to be very unstable. Unreliable. Rebellious. Disruptive.' *Attractive, compelling, addictive.*

'You're describing the teenager.'

'He created havoc.' she looked at him, wondering why she had to remind him of something that he must know himself. 'He was suspended from school *three times*. If there'd been an alternative place for him to go, I'm sure he would have been expelled. Not only did he blow up the science lab, he set off a firework in the library, he burned down the MacDonalds' barn—the list of things he did is endless. He was wild, Logan. Totally out of control.' *And impossibly, hopelessly attractive.* There hadn't been a woman on Glenmore who hadn't dreamed of taming him. Herself included.

She'd wanted to help.

She'd wanted...

She pushed the thought away quickly. She'd been a dreamy teenager but she was an adult now, a grown woman and far too sensible to see Conner as anything other than a liability.

'His parents were going through a particularly acrimonious divorce at the time. There were lots of rumours about that household. My aunt—his mother—left when he was eleven. That's tough on any child.' Logan turned his attention back to the pile in his in-tray. 'Enough to shake the roots of any family. It's not surprising he was disruptive.'

'He isn't interested in authority.'

Logan threw the pen down on his desk. 'Perhaps he thinks that those in authority let him down.'

Flora bit her lip. 'Perhaps they did. But if that's the case then it makes even less sense that he's back. He couldn't wait to get away from Glenmore the first time around and he stayed away for *twelve years*.'

'Is it that long?' Logan studied her face thoughtfully. 'I haven't been counting, but obviously you have.'

'It was a wild guess,' Flora muttered quickly, 'but either way, it's been a long time. And the question is, why has he picked this particular moment to come back?'

'Why does it matter? If he turns out to be a lousy doctor,

I'm the one who will pay the price. Or is there more to this than your concern for the reputation of Glenmore Medical Centre? Is this personal, Flora?' Logan's voice was gentle. 'Is there something going on that I should know about?'

'Don't be ridiculous.' Flora rose to her feet swiftly, her heart pounding. 'And I think it's obvious to everyone that I'm not his type. I've never been attracted to unsuitable men.' A painful lump sat in the pit of her stomach. *He'd never looked at her. Not once.*

'Then you're probably the only woman on the island who wasn't,' Logan said mildly, 'if I recall correctly, Conner had quite a following, and the more reprehensible his behaviour, the bigger the following.'

'I suppose some of the girls found him attractive because he was forbidden territory.' Flora wished her heart would slow down. 'I still can't believe he's a doctor.'

'I know you can't. You didn't exactly hide your astonishment,' Logan said dryly and Flora felt a twinge of guilt.

'I didn't mean to be rude but weren't *you* surprised when you found out?'

'No.' Logan rolled his shoulders to ease the stiffness of sitting. 'Conner always was ferociously clever.'

'He hated school. He was barely ever there.'

'And he still managed straight As in every subject. As I said—we all let him down. He was too clever to be trapped behind a desk and forced to learn in a prescribed pattern. People were too conventional to notice the brain behind the behavioural problems.'

Flora gave a puzzled frown. She'd never thought of it that way before. 'Well, he obviously learned to study at some point. Where did he train, anyway?'

'In the army.'

'In the—' Stunned, Flora swallowed. 'He was in the *army*?'

'Army medic.' Logan flipped through a pile of papers on his desk and removed a file. 'Read.' He handed it to her. 'It's impressive stuff. Perhaps it will set your mind at rest about his ability and dedication.'

'But the army requires discipline. All the things Conner doesn't—'

'Read,' Logan said firmly. 'The patients might doubt him to begin with, but I don't want the practice staff making the same mistake. The man's qualifications and experience are better than mine. Read, Flora.'

Flora opened the file reluctantly. After a moment, she looked up. 'He's a surgeon?'

'Among other things. I did tell you that the man was clever.'

Her eyes flickered back to the page. 'Afghanistan? That doesn't sound very safe.'

'No.' Logan's voice was dry. 'But it sounds very Conner. I don't suppose anything safe would hold his interest for long.'

'Which brings me back to my original question.' She dropped the file back on his desk. 'What's he doing back on Glenmore? He hates Glenmore and if he still needs adrenaline and excitement in his life, he's going to last five minutes on this island.'

'I don't think it's any of my business.' Logan leaned back in his chair. 'He's back, that's all I need to know.'

'It's going to be like putting a match to a powder keg. And I'm just worried he'll let you down in the middle of the summer tourist season. You and all the islanders.'

Logan's gaze followed her. 'They let him down. This is his chance to even the score or prove himself. Either way, he's family, Flora, and I'm giving him this opportunity. It's up to him what he chooses to do with it.'

Flora bit her lip. Family. On Glenmore family and community was everything. It was what made the island what it was. But Conner had rejected everything that Glenmore stood for. He'd walked away from it.

So why was he back?

CHAPTER THREE

CONNER WATCHED as Flora entered the room. Her eyes were down and she was clutching a bunch of forms that he assumed were for him.

Probably from Logan, he thought, *finding an excuse to engineer peace.*

The fact that she seemed reluctant to look in his direction amused him. As a teenager she'd been impossibly shy. He remembered her sitting on her own in the corner of the playground, her nose stuck in a book. What he didn't remember was her ever stringing more than two words together. But today, in Logan's surgery, she'd been surprisingly articulate.

He gave a cynical smile.

It seemed his presence was enough to encourage even the mute to speak.

'The lamb enters the wolf's den unprotected,' he drawled softly, and watched as the heat built in her cheeks. 'I never saw you as a risk-taker, Flora. Aren't you afraid I might do something evil to you now we're on our own?'

'Don't be ridiculous.' She adjusted her glasses and put the forms on his desk. 'Logan wanted you to have these.'

No, Conner thought to himself. *Logan wanted us to have*

a moment together because he doesn't want his staff at odds with each other.

He heard her take a deep breath and then she looked at him.

As if she'd been plucking up courage.

'So...' She cleared her throat. 'How is it going? Any problems so far?'

'No problems at all. The locals are refusing to see me, which means I don't have to spend my time listening to the boring detail of people's minor ailments.' He studied the slight fullness of her lower lip and the smooth curve of her cheeks. *She was pretty*, he realised with a stab of shock. She was also wonderfully, deliciously serious and he couldn't resist having a little fun with her. 'And it's really interesting to make contact with all the girls I...grew up with.'

As he'd anticipated, she flushed. What he hadn't expected was the sudden flash of concern in her eyes. *The kindness.* 'The patients are refusing to see you?' She sounded affronted. 'That's awful.'

'Don't worry about it. I'm allergic to hard work and it gives me more time to spend on the internet.'

'You're just saying that, but you must feel terrible about it.'

'I don't give a damn.'

She gave a faint gasp and blinked several times. 'You don't need to pretend with me. I'm sure you're upset. How could you not be?'

'Flora,' he interrupted her, amused by her misinterpretation of the facts, 'don't endow me with qualities that I don't possess. To feel terrible I'd have to care, and I think we both know that my relationship with the islanders is hardly one of lasting affection.'

'You're very hard on them and perhaps that's justified, but you need to see it from their point of view. Everyone's a bit shocked, that's all. No one was expecting you because Logan didn't say anything to anyone.'

'Given that this is Glenmore, I expect he'll be struck off for respecting confidentiality.'

Her sudden smile caught him by surprise. 'They do gossip, don't they? Everything takes three times as long here because of the conversation. I can't get used to it.' Her smile faded. 'Logan told me about what you've done—your training. That's amazing. I had no idea.'

Conner sat in silence and she spread her hands, visibly uncomfortable with the situation.

'I'm *trying* to apologise. I didn't mean to be rude. It was just that…' She gave an awkward shrug. 'Anyway, I really am sorry.'

'Never apologise, Flora.'

'If I'm wrong, then I apologise,' she said firmly. 'Don't you?'

'I don't know.' Enjoying himself, he smiled. 'I've never been wrong.'

Derailed by the banter, she backed away slightly and then stopped. 'I'm apologising for assuming that you weren't qualified for the job. For thinking that you being here would just cause trouble.'

'It *will* cause trouble,' Conner drawled softly, 'so you weren't wrong.'

'You knew it would cause trouble?'

'Of course.'

His answer brought a puzzled frown to her face. 'If you knew that, why did you come back?'

'I thrive on trouble, Flora. Trouble is the fuel the drives my engine.'

This time, instead of backing away, she looked at him. Properly. Her eyes focused on his, as if she was searching for something. 'You're angry with us, aren't you? Is that why you're here?' She fiddled with her glasses again, as if she wasn't used to having them on her nose. 'To level a score?'

'You think I became a doctor so that I could return to my roots and exterminate the inhabitants of Glenmore, one by one?'

'Of course not. But I know you're angry. I can feel it.'

Then she was more intuitive than he'd thought. Raising his guard, Conner watched her. 'I'm not angry. If people would rather wait a week to see Logan, that's fine by me.'

'But it must hurt your feelings.'

'I don't have feelings, Flora. Providing I still get paid, I don't care whether the patients see me or not. It's Logan's problem.' He could tell she didn't like his answer because she frowned and shook her head slightly.

'I can't believe that you're not at all sensitive about the way people react to you.'

'That's because you're a woman and women think differently to men.' This time his smile was genuine. 'Do I look sensitive?' He watched as her eyes drifted to his shoulders and then lifted to his jaw line.

'No.' Her voice was hoarse. 'You don't.' And then her eyes lifted to his and the atmosphere snapped taut.

Conner felt his body stir.

Well, well, he thought. *How interesting.* Sexual chemistry with a woman who probably didn't know the meaning of the phrase. His gaze lowered to her mouth and he saw that her lips were soft and bare of make-up. He had a sudden impulse to be unforgivably shocking and kiss her.

'Well, if you're sure you're fine…' She was flustered. He could tell she was flustered.

Normally he had no qualms about making a woman flustered but somehow with Flora it seemed unsporting. She might be older but she obviously wasn't any more experienced. With an inner sigh and lingering regret, he backed off. 'I'm fine,' he said gently. 'But thank you for asking.'

He wondered idly if she'd ever had sex.

A boyfriend?

'My consulting room is next door.' Apparently unaware of what had just happened between them, she suddenly became brisk and efficient. 'Evanna is still doing a morning clinic, but if you need a nurse to do a home visit then ask me because she's too pregnant to be dashing around the island. You know your way around, so that shouldn't be a problem. If there's anything you're not sure of, ask.'

'I'll do that.'

If she had a boyfriend, it was someone tame and safe, he decided. Someone who hadn't taught her the meaning of passion.

'Well—I've held you up long enough. Morning surgery can be a long one.' Her gaze slid to his legs, encased in black leather. 'You know, people might feel more comfortable with you if you changed.'

'I am who I am, Flora.'

'I meant your clothes.' She pushed her glasses onto the bridge of her nose. 'You could change your clothes.'

'Why would I want to do that?'

'Because the patients expect a doctor to look like a doctor.'

'Flora.' He failed to keep the amusement out of his voice. 'It wouldn't matter whether I was wearing a set of theatre scrubs or a white coat, the inhabitants of Glenmore would still struggle to believe that Bad Conner is a doctor. Just as *you're* struggling.'

'I'm not. Not any more. But I don't see why you should confirm their prejudices by dressing like a biker.' She flushed. 'Do you always have to antagonise people? Break the rules?'

'Yes. I think I probably do.' Conner watched her. 'Just as you always like to please people and do everything that is expected of you. In our own ways we're the same, you and I. We're both working hard to meet society's expectations of us.'

She looked at him, her dark eyes reproachful. 'There's nothing wrong in being part of a community.'

'True. But neither is there anything wrong with *not* being part of it,' he said gently. 'Do you really think the way I'm dressed is going to compromise my ability as a doctor?'

'No. Of course not. It's just that you look—' She broke off and he knew he shouldn't follow up on that comment but he couldn't help himself.

'How do I look, Flora? Tell me. I want to know what you think of the way I look.'

She looked hot and flustered. 'I-intimidating,' she stammered, eventually. 'I wouldn't want to bump into you on a dark night.'

'Is that right?' Conner gave a slow smile and gave up trying to subdue his wicked streak. 'In that case, we'll have to make sure that we leave the lights on, angel.'

He was impossible and she was never going to be able to work with him.

Flora tried to concentrate on the dressing and not reveal how shaken she was by her encounter with Conner. He'd played with her, toyed with her carelessly, like a predator having fun with its prey before a kill. And as usual she hadn't been able to think of the right thing to say because she'd been trying to sort out surgery business and he'd been—well, he'd been Conner. Selfish, indifferent and supremely cool. Just the thought of him seeing patients—*or not seeing patients*—in the room next door unsettled her.

She shook her head and studied the skin around the leg ulcer. 'You still have a degree of varicose eczema, Mrs Parker. Are you using the cream Dr MacNeil gave you?'

'The steroid cream? No, I forget.'

Flora studied the skin, checking for infection. 'Is this tender when I press?'

'No more than usual.'

'There's no erythema and your temperature is fine.' Talking to herself, Flora made a judgement. 'We'll leave it for now but do me a favour and try the cream, would you? If it isn't looking better in a week or so, I'm going to ask one of the doctors to look at it.'

'As long as it's Logan.' Mrs Parker's mouth clamped in a thin line of disapproval. 'I'm not afraid to say that I almost fainted dead away when I saw Conner MacNeil stroll into the surgery this morning. Bold as brass. Not even trying to hide his face.'

'Why would he hide his face, Mrs Parker?' Flora swiftly finished the dressing and applied a compression bandage. 'He's a doctor and he's come to—' *create havoc?* '—help Logan.'

'Help? Help? This is the boy who was so much of a handful that his mother left home! Can you imagine how badly the boy must have behaved for his own mother to give up on him? His father stayed, of course, but he was driven to drink by Conner's antics. Died five years ago and did his son bother turning up to his funeral? No, he didn't.'

Flora flew to Conner's defence. 'He's a man now, not a boy. And no one knows what happened in his childhood, Mrs Parker.' He hadn't told anyone.

She paused for a moment, lost in thought as she remembered the love of her own family. Just what had Conner endured? She remembered the day she'd walked along the cliffs to his house.

She remembered the shouting.

'Well, I tell you this much,' Mrs Parker said firmly. 'That boy isn't capable of warmth or sensitivity and he doesn't care about anyone but himself. I still don't believe he's a doctor.

He never did a day's studying in his life and as for the way he dresses—well, I mean, Logan's always smart in trousers and a shirt, but Conner hadn't even shaved! He looked—'

Handsome, Flora thought helplessly as she fumbled with the bandage. *He'd looked impossibly, outrageously handsome.*

'Dangerous,' Mrs Parker continued with a shudder, watching as Flora finished the dressing. 'Who in their right minds would trust him with a medical problem? He causes more problems than he solves. Not too tight, dear.'

'It has to be quite tight because we need the pressure on the ankle.'

'I couldn't believe it when I heard Janet booking patients in to see him. I said to Nina Hill, "Well, that's going to be interesting to watch. Now he'll get his comeuppance because no one will see him."' Having delivered that prediction, Mrs Parker paused expectantly and Flora glanced up at her, realizing that some sort of response was required.

'They'll see him, Mrs Parker,' she said quietly. 'That was then and this is now. Conner is well qualified. And it's great news that Logan finally has help. Super.'

'Super?' Mrs Parker gaped at her. 'You think it's great news?'

Far too loyal to reveal her own reservations, Flora secured the bandage. 'Of course. Logan is barely managing on his own. We need another doctor on the island.'

'Well, don't imagine for one moment that Conner MacNeil will make a difference! Even if he *is* a doctor now, which frankly I doubt because everyone knows that these days you can fake everything for a price, there won't be a soul on this island who will trust his opinion.'

Flora took a deep breath and tried to speak. 'Mrs Parker, you really shouldn't—'

'Anyway, enough of that conversation.' Mrs Parker apparently didn't even notice the interruption. 'I refuse to waste the air in my lungs on Conner MacNeil when there are so many more important things going on around us. I meant to say to you, John Carter was seen talking at the school gate with Meg Watson. Now, *that's* an interesting match, if you ask me. She's a single mother and he's…'

Realising that a two-way conversation wasn't required, Flora stood up and washed her hands, only half listening as Mrs Parker regaled her with all the latest island gossip.

How could Conner not be hurt by the negative reaction of the islanders?

Was he really as indifferent as he seemed?

If it were her, she'd be completely mortified.

She tugged a paper towel out of the holder and dried her hands, part of her brain listening to Mrs Parker while the other half thought about Conner. He'd built a shell around himself, and who could blame him?

'So what do you think, dear?'

Realising that this time Mrs Parker was waiting for a response, Flora turned. 'I honestly don't know,' she said truthfully. 'I couldn't give an opinion.' And even if she could, she wouldn't. 'Don't forget it's important to walk when you have a venous ulcer.'

'Yes, yes, I can't possibly forget because you keep telling me.' The elderly lady put her foot on the floor and tested it gingerly. 'Oh, that's much more comfortable. You're a wonderful nurse, dear. Simply wonderful.'

But a useless gossip, Flora thought wryly. 'That's very kind of you, Mrs Parker.'

'Not kind at all. I'm only saying what everyone else is saying.' Angela Parker slipped on her shoes. 'We're all so thrilled that you've come back to the island to take over from our Kyla. Only yesterday I was saying to Meg in the café that we could have ended up with some mainlander with no idea how things work on Glenmore but, no, Dr MacNeil managed to tempt you back. When your father died I thought you might never return but then Nina reminded me that your aunt is here. Did you miss it when you were away?'

Flora felt a sudden shaft of pain as she thought of her father. *She still missed him.* 'Well, I suppose I—'

'Of course you did and now you're back, which is perfect. And Logan has been in desperate need of a practice nurse since Kyla and Dr Walker left, and what with poor Evanna being so pregnant.' Without waiting for Flora to respond, Mrs Parker forged ahead like a ship in a force-nine gale. 'Well, we all know that Dr MacNeil is worried about her, given the tragedy with his first wife. Not that Evanna should have a problem in that direction. She's a girl with good childbearing hips.'

Flora winced and hoped that no one repeated that comment to her friend and colleague. 'Logan doesn't seem worried,' she lied, 'and Evanna is a midwife, so if anyone understands her condition, she does!'

'Do you really think she should still be working, this close to having that baby?'

Aware that whatever she said would be spread around the island by nightfall, Flora once again kept her answer suitably neutral. 'She isn't on her feet that much. She's just doing the odd morning clinic.' She sat down at her desk and updated the notes on the computer. 'It's fortunate that their house is attached to the surgery. At least she doesn't have to come far to work and I do all the community calls so she doesn't have that to cope with.'

'You see? That's what I mean. It's great that you're back.' Angela Parker picked up her bag and stood up. 'Everywhere I go I hear people saying, "Have you seen our Flora? Doesn't she look well?"'

An intensely private person, Flora felt herself shrink slightly inside. 'People are talking about me?'

'Of course,' Angela said cheerfully. 'A new nurse on Glenmore is big news. People are thrilled. We're all hoping you'll meet a nice young man and then you'll be a permanent fixture on the island. Glenmore is a good place to raise a family, dear.'

A family? 'I think it's a bit soon to be thinking of that,' Flora said faintly, deciding that it was time to end the conversation before gossip about her 'wedding' reached the pub. 'Your leg is healing well, Mrs Parker. Make an appointment to see me again on your way out.'

'Yes, I'll do that. I certainly won't be seeing Conner, that's for sure.' She sniffed. 'I value my health far too much for that.'

Flora opened her mouth to reply and then realised that no reply was expected because Angela Parker was once again answering her own question.

'I think this time Logan will discover he's made a mistake.' She slid her bag over her arm. 'If he's not careful, he'll find himself handling the summer singlehanded and that won't be an easy task with a toddler and a new bairn.'

Knowing that to comment on that statement would trigger a conversation she didn't have time for, Flora stood up, worried that she'd never finish her clinic if all her patients had as much to say as Angela. 'It was nice to see you. Don't forget to put that leg up when you're sitting down.'

'I always do that.' Angela opened the door. 'Take care of yourself and give me regards to your aunt.'

'I'll do that, Mrs Parker.' Flora waited for the door to close behind her and then sank back into her chair. A quick glance at the clock on the wall confirmed that she was now running *seriously* late and she gave a despairing shake of her head. She still hadn't adjusted to how long each appointment took on Glenmore. Everyone had something to say and a consultation involved so much more than it did on the mainland.

'Problems?' Logan stood in the doorway, a question in his eyes. 'Angela Parker was with you a long time. Is her leg giving her trouble?'

'She still has some signs of eczema around the ulcer but that's because she isn't using the cream you gave her. She's not pyrexial and there's no pain or tenderness to speak of and no obvious signs of cellulitis or infection. I'll keep an eye on it. If it isn't looking any better next week, I'll give you a shout.'

Logan walked into the room and closed the door behind him. 'If there's no sign of healing in another month or so, I'll refer her for a biopsy. We need to exclude malignancy.'

'I think it is healing, it's just that she doesn't do much to help it along.'

'So why are you looking so worried? I can't believe that Mrs Parker's leg ulcer is responsible for that frown on your face.'

'I'm hopeless at this job,' Flora confessed simply. 'Absolutely hopeless.'

'That's utter nonsense.' It was Logan's turn to frown. 'You're a brilliant nurse.'

'It's not the nursing that worries me, it's the rest of it. The gossip, the chat, the rumour machine.' Flora waved a hand in a gesture of despair. 'I'm just no good at it. I've never been any good at just chatting. When I did the clinic in Edinburgh, patients just wanted me to dress their leg or take their blood. On Glenmore, I'm supposed to have an opinion on everything from the Carpenters' divorce to Janey Smith's speeding fine.' She brushed her hair out of her eyes and shot him a helpless look. 'I don't know how to handle it. I don't want to join in, I have no intention of revealing confidential information, but I don't want to look rude. How do you do it? How do you cope?'

'I say "That's interesting" a hundred times a day and if they're really rambling on I adopt my "this could be something serious" look and that soon focuses their minds back on their medical problem. The skill is to cut them off tactfully.'

'I definitely need to work on that skill,' Flora muttered. 'And I confess that I *hate* the idea that everyone is talking about me.'

'This is Glenmore,' Logan said easily. 'Of course people are talking about you. They're talking about everyone. But it's mostly friendly talk. People care and that's what makes this island so special. You've been in the city for too long. You've forgotten what island living is all about. You'll adjust.'

'But the talk isn't friendly about Conner, is it?' Troubled, Flora looked at him. 'They're being horrid to him. I mean, I know I was shocked to see him and even more shocked to discover that he's a doctor, but boycotting his surgery...'

'Some of the patients saw him and word will spread.' Logan smiled. 'Providing he isn't too outrageous. Don't worry about Conner. He can look after himself.'

'Maybe.' She suddenly noticed the dark shadows underneath his eyes. 'You look really, really tired, Logan. Is there anything I can do to help?'

'You're already doing it. Being tired is part of the job description when you work here, as you're fast discovering.' He rubbed his fingers over his forehead. 'And on top of that I was up in the night with little Helen Peters because she—'

'Had a nasty asthma attack,' Flora finished his sentence with a laugh, 'and before you ask, the reason I know is because Mrs Abbott mentioned it when she came in to have her ears syringed and *she* heard it from Sam when she was buying fish on the queue this morning and Sam knew because—'

'He lives across the road from the Peters' sister.' Logan

looked amused. 'Relax, Flora. This is how things work on Glenmore. Don't knock it. Sam was the one who called me because there were lights on all over the house and he went across the road to see if he could help.'

Flora's eyes softened. 'That was kind.'

'People are kind here. Don't worry—you'll soon get back into the swing of it. And they'll get used to Conner.'

'I hope you're right. So what happened to little Helen? Did you change her medication?'

'No, but I talked to her mum about exercise.' He frowned. 'It was sports day yesterday. I'm confident that the physical exertion is what triggered it. Any chance that you could you pop in and see them today? It was pretty scary for everyone and I think they'd appreciate an extra dose of reassurance. You might want to have a conversation about lifestyle.'

'I'll pop in, no problem.' This was the Glenmore she knew and loved. Where else would the medical team find time for that sort of visit? That level of care and attention was what made the island special. And she was doing the job she'd been trained to do. Feeling more relaxed, Flora added Helen's name to her list of afternoon calls.

'I'll see you later.' Logan opened the door to leave and Conner strolled in.

Flora's world tilted and her insides knotted with an almost unbearable tension. 'Conner.'

He stepped aside to let Logan pass. 'Isn't Angela Parker a little old to be training for the Olympics? She took one look at me and ran as if the hounds of hell were after her. What's the matter with her leg?'

'Venous ulcer. She's supposed to be mobilising but she doesn't do enough of it.'

'Then perhaps I should stand behind her more often. She ran so fast I could have entered her in the Derby.'

He was so confident, so easy with a situation that most

people would have found agonisingly awkward. He really didn't seem to care that the locals had been distinctly unwelcoming. *But if he'd cared, he wouldn't be the man he was.*

Flora cleared her throat. 'Mrs Parker was a little surprised to discover that you're now a doctor.'

Conner smiled. 'Sweet Flora, always coating the truth with honey. Come on, angel. Tell me what she said. The truth. It will be good for you. And my shoulders are broad. I can take it.'

She knew his shoulders were broad—in fact, she was far, far too conscious of his body.

'She doesn't believe you're a doctor and she values her health too much to see you.'

'And I value my sanity far too much to see her, so both of us are happy. If her health is that good, she doesn't need a doctor anyway. So I'm spared.'

'It's not funny.' Ignoring the amusement in his eyes, Flora kept her head down and put a box of vaccine back in the fridge. 'You have no idea what things are like here! We're overwhelmed with work and every day the ferry brings more tourists. Logan needs help. He's barely had time to see his wife and daughter since Ethan left and the baby is due in a few weeks. He needs someone he can trust.'

'And you think he can't trust me?'

'I don't think that's relevant.' Desperate to make him understand, she turned to face him. 'If the patients won't see you, then it doesn't matter what Logan thinks.'

'Relax. The tourists will see me. I'll talk to Janet and make sure she allocates me a surgery full of patients who know nothing about my wicked past.'

'Conner—'

'I wasn't expecting a hero's welcome, Flora.' He gave a faint smile. 'And now you'll have to excuse me. There's a bit of a rush on. Patients are fighting to see me and I don't want to disappoint them.'

Her heart bumped against her chest and she didn't understand it. She couldn't possibly find him attractive. It was ridiculous to find him attractive. *So why were her legs shaking so much she needed to sit down?*

CHAPTER FOUR

'GLENMORE is in an uproar. Eight patients refused to see him this morning and insisted on waiting for Logan.' In the café near the harbour, Flora leaned across the table and helped herself to one of Evanna's sandwiches. 'These are delicious. Why aren't you eating them?'

'Because there's no room in my body for anything except the baby.' Evanna shifted in her seat, obviously uncomfortable. 'They refused to see him? Really? Oh, poor Conner, that's dreadful. Were his feelings hurt, do you think?'

'Does he have feelings?' Flora glanced out of the window, watching idly as groups of tourists walked from the ferry towards the beach. 'Since when did Conner MacNeil care what people think of him? He is Mr Tough Guy.'

'Deep down, I'm sure he cares.'

'If he cared he wouldn't have done his surgery wearing black leather and half an inch of stubble.' Flora winced as a toddler tripped over a fishing rod and fell hard onto the pavement. She watched the mother scoop up the child and offer comfort. 'Believe me, he has no intention of modifying his behaviour to please anyone. He was as defiant and confrontational as ever.' *And sexy. Indecently sexy.*

'If he didn't care, he'd be living in his parents' old house up on the cliffs.'

Flora was silent for a moment. She hadn't given any thought to where Conner was living. 'And he's not?'

'Logan gave him the barn.'

'I thought it was let for the summer.'

'It is. To Conner. When Logan thought he might be coming back, he kept it free for him. I suppose he knew Connor wouldn't want to stay in his parents' house.' Evanna shrugged. 'Who can blame him? I don't suppose it has any nice memories for him. By all accounts, he had a pretty miserable childhood.'

'Then why didn't he sell it after his father died?'

'He hasn't been here to sell it. Perhaps he'll deal with it this summer.'

'Break his final tie with the island? Do you think that's why he's come back? To sell the house?'

'I wouldn't think so. He could have done that with one call to the island estate agent. Perhaps he's laying old ghosts.' Evanna gave a suggestive smile. 'Or maybe he's laying old girlfriends.'

'Evanna!' Struggling between shock and laughter, Flora sent a weak, apologetic smile towards the tourists eating lunch at the next table. 'If you're going to make obscene comments, lower your voice. We still have to work here after Conner's gone.'

'And life will be considerably more boring.'

'Pregnancy has driven you mad.'

'You might be right.' Evanna shifted in her seat. 'I can't remember what it's like not to be fat and exhausted.'

'I think Conner is trying to shock them on purpose. I suspect he wants to provoke a reaction from them.' Flora looked at her and smiled. 'Do you want to know something funny?'

'Not too funny.' Evanna patted her enormous bump gently. 'I have to be economical with laughter at the moment. Go on.'

'Mrs Ellis saw him.'

'As a patient? You're joking.'

'I'm not. I expected her to walk straight back out and call the police, but she was in there for ages and she came out smiling.'

'So he even charmed her.' Evanna sighed wistfully. 'You see? It doesn't matter how badly he behaves, women just can't help themselves. It's the danger, I suppose. The fact that he's a bit volatile and unstable just adds to his appeal. If you had a date with Conner you never quite knew whether you were going to end up in bed or in a jail cell.'

Flora gasped. 'What exactly do you know about dates with Conner? There is no way your parents would have allowed you anywhere near him.'

'Didn't stop me dreaming.' Evanna sipped her tea. 'I had fantasies, just like you.'

'I did not have fantasies.'

'Now you're lying.' Evanna grinned placidly. 'Every woman dreams about the local bad boy.'

'Conner is well educated.'

'Which makes him all the more attractive,' Evanna sighed.

'My idea of a perfect date never involved a close encounter with the police,' Flora said lightly, 'and I don't believe yours did either. You were always crazy about Logan.'

'That didn't stop me looking. I suppose that's part of the reason Conner was so attractive,' Evanna said simply. 'He was forbidden. Are you seriously telling me you've never had a few fantasies about Conner?'

'Never.' Keen to end what was increasingly becoming an uncomfortable conversation, Flora finished her sandwich and glanced at her watch. 'I have to go. Little Helen Peters had an asthma attack in the night. I'm going to call on her on my way back to the surgery.'

Evanna yawned. 'Yes. Poor Logan was up and down in the night. First it was Helen, then it was our Kirsty.'

'How is she?'

'We've moved her from a cot to a bed in preparation for the arrival of her sibling.' Evanna patted her swollen abdomen gently. 'And she's just discovered that she can leap out whenever she likes and come in with us. Which is fine, except she sleeps like a starfish, arms and legs stuck out at angles designed to cause maximum discomfort to those sharing the space.'

Flora laughed. 'She's gorgeous. Who is looking after her today?'

'Meg had her this morning and I'm going home right now.' Evanna stood up and winced. 'I can't believe this is how it feels to be thirty-five weeks pregnant. Remind me to be more sympathetic next time I run the antenatal clinic. Give little Helen a kiss from me.'

'I will. Why didn't you tell me that Logan had appointed Conner as the doctor?'

'Neither of us were sure he'd turn up. It didn't seem worth mentioning until we knew for sure.'

'So you really don't know why he's back, Evanna?' Flora tried to keep her tone casual.

'No. Logan hasn't said any more to me than he has to you.'

Flora reached for her bag. 'No pillow talk?'

'Are you kidding? Our pillow talk revolves around me telling him how uncomfortable I am and him trying not to phone for an air ambulance.'

'Is he that nervous?'

'He's hiding it quite well but, yes, he's nervous. Of course. His first wife died in childbirth and none of us are likely to forget that, myself included.' Evanna breathed out heavily.

'He wants me to go and stay on the mainland, but the baby's not due for another five weeks and if it was two weeks late I could be stuck over there for seven weeks. Even if I wanted to, which I don't, it just isn't practical. There's Kirsty to think of. I don't want her unsettled.'

'No. Well…' Flora leaned forward and gave her friend a hug, carefully avoiding her bump. 'We're all keeping an eye on you and we can get you over to the mainland at the first sign of movement.'

'That's the plan.' Evanna stroked her bump. 'Just hope the baby is listening.'

Flora drove with the windows down, humming to herself and enjoying the breeze and the sunshine. She loved Glenmore at this time of year. Wild flowers clustered on the banks of grass at the side of the road and in the distance she could see the jagged silhouette of the ruined castle.

She waved at Doug MacDonald who was out on his bike and then caught sight of Sonia Davies pushing a buggy on the pavement.

'Sonia!' She slowed to a halt and called out to the young mother. 'Everything OK? How's Rachel?'

'She's beautiful.' Sonia pushed the buggy over to the car. 'I'm due in clinic later this week for another immunisation.'

Flora nodded. 'She's twelve months, isn't she? So that will be the Hib booster. *Haemophilus influenzae.*'

Sonia handed Rachel a rattle to play with. 'I hope she doesn't freak out. It's different when they're babies, isn't it? They don't know what's happening and it's over in a flash.'

'She'll be fine. Have you booked her in for Thursday afternoon?'

'Yes.' Sonia jiggled the pushchair. 'No sign of Evanna having the baby yet, then?'

'She has a few weeks to go yet.'

'I bet Dr MacNeil is nervous.' Sonia gave a little frown. 'We all know how uneasy he gets when women get near their due date. When he had to deliver me on the island last year, he was horrified. Never saw him look nervous before that night. I still think that if Evanna hadn't been there, he would have done a runner.'

'I'm sure he wouldn't, although we all know that he prefers babies to be born on the mainland. I'm sure he'll be packing Evanna off on that ferry in good time. And I'd better go. I have a visit to do before my afternoon clinic.' Flora slid back into her car. 'See you later in the week, Sonia.'

She carried on up the coast road, called in on Helen to check on her and offer reassurance to her mother. Then she drove to the medical centre, parking next to a sleek black motorbike.

She gave a faint smile. That explained the black leather. A motorbike.

She couldn't imagine Conner with anything else. He was a man who always chose to live his life on the wrong side of risk.

Janet was at the reception desk, trying to find an appointment for a patient. 'Flora has had a cancellation so she can see him straight away, Mrs Gregg,' she was saying. 'I'll put you in with her. If she thinks Harry should see a doctor urgently, she'll arrange it.'

Looking anxious, Mrs Gregg took Harry by the hand and led him to the chairs in the waiting room.

Flora walked up to the desk. 'Problems?'

'Just the one problem. People don't want to book in with Conner.' Janet sighed and rubbed her fingers over her forehead. 'I can't believe that Logan has done this to us in the middle of summer. His afternoon surgery is bursting at the seams and how many does Conner have? Two people.'

'Two? That's all?'

'No one wants to see him, Flora.' Janet looked exhausted. 'I'm sure he's a very good doctor, but all anyone round here remembers is a boy with a lot of problems. They don't trust him.'

Remembering what Logan had said to her, Flora straightened her shoulders. 'His qualifications are excellent.'

'Well, maybe he'd like to put them above my desk in neon lights.'

'It's only his first day. People will settle down,' Flora said firmly, hoping that she was right. 'I thought the women, at least, would be queuing up.'

'I'm sure they will, but not for his medical skills,' Janet said dryly. 'If Logan was looking for help, I think he was looking in the wrong place. Anyway, the Greggs are back from holiday and Harry isn't well. He has a rash and Diane is worried. Your first patient has cancelled so I've put them in with you. If you're worried, perhaps you can persuade them to see Conner, but I don't hold out much hope.'

'Leave it with me. If you see Logan can you tell him that I popped in to see Helen and she was fine?' Flora walked to the waiting area. Harry was sitting on his mother's lap and his eyes were closed.

'Hello, Nurse Harris.' Diane gave her a tired smile. 'Janet said you might fit us in.'

'Of course.' Flora touched the little boy's forehead with a gentle hand. 'He's very hot.'

'I've spent the past two nights trying to bring his temperature down.' Diane clearly hadn't slept for days and her face was pale and drawn. 'But it's the rash that's really worrying me. It's spreading.'

'I'll take a look.'

The woman gave her a grateful smile and gently eased Harry onto the floor. 'You're too big for Mummy to carry now,' she murmured, taking his hand. 'Just walk as far as the consulting room, then you can sit down again.'

Harry murmured a protest but trotted along the corridor towards Flora's consulting room.

'Tell me what happened. I'd like to know when Harry first became ill.' Flora flicked on her computer and stowed her bag under the desk. 'Presumably it started on holiday?'

'Three days ago he developed this rash. One minute he was fine and the next he had a temperature, neck stiffness, headache.' Diane swallowed. 'He's gone from well to ill really fast and that's— Well, I'm worried.'

Understanding that she didn't want to say too much in front of the child, Flora nodded. 'And you think the rash has spread?'

'Oh, yes. Definitely.'

Flora washed her hands. 'I'll take a look, if that's all right.'

'I'm just going to take your T-shirt off, Harry.' Diane reached forward and lifted his T-shirt carefully over his head. 'I want to show Nurse Harris.'

Harry gave a moan of protest. 'I'm really, really cold.'

'That's because you have a temperature,' Flora said gently, lifting his arm slightly and turning him towards the light. 'When did you first notice the rash, Mrs Gregg?'

'Well, it didn't look like this at first. It started with just one red spot under his arm and then it spread. Then his temperature shot up and he's been feeling boiling hot ever since.' Diane pushed her son's hair away from his face and touched his forehead. 'He's hot now.'

Flora examined the rash carefully. It was scarlet and circular and she'd never seen anything like it before. 'Did you see a doctor when you were away?'

'Yes, but he said it was just a virus.' Diane rolled her eyes, her worry evident. 'Perhaps it is, but I wanted a proper opinion. It isn't until you leave Glenmore that you realise how good the medical care is on this island. I was hoping to see Dr MacNeil, but Janet says his surgery is full.'

Flora checked Harry's temperature and recorded it. 'Logan isn't the only doctor working at Glenmore now,' she said carefully, and Diane pursed her lips.

'If you're talking about Conner MacNeil, I'm not interested. I remember the time he set off that firework in the school library.'

'That was a long time ago, Mrs Gregg.' Flora checked Harry's pulse and blood pressure. 'He trained in the army. His qualifications are excellent.'

'I don't care. I—'

'Didn't you ever do anything you shouldn't when you were young?'

'Well, I—I suppose…'

'I know I did.' Flora shrugged. 'And I also know I wouldn't want to be judged as an adult by how I was as a child. People change, Mrs Gregg. And everyone deserves to be given chances. Logan wouldn't have taken Conner on if he didn't trust him. I'd like him to see Harry. I don't recognise this rash and the fact that he has a temperature makes it worth exploring further.'

Mrs Gregg hesitated and then glanced at Harry, clearly torn. 'I don't suppose Conner will know any more than that doctor on the mainland.'

'Let's give it a try—see what he says? I'll see if he's free,' Flora said cheerfully, trying not to reveal that the chances of Conner having a patient with him was extremely remote.

Hoping that she wasn't making a mistake, she went across the corridor and tapped on his door. 'Conner?' She walked in and found him absorbed in a website on the internet. She peered closer. 'Wetsuits?'

'I'm planning to do some sailing. It looks as though I'm

going to have plenty of time on my hands.' He swivelled his head and looked at her. 'Are you here to relieve my boredom?'

She flushed. 'I have a patient that needs to be seen by a doctor.'

'And?'

'You're a doctor.'

'Am I?' He lounged back in his chair, his ice-blue gaze disturbingly direct. 'So why am I sitting in an empty consulting room?'

'Because this is Glenmore and it takes folks a while to get used to change. The last time they saw you, you were stirring up trouble all over the island. I don't suppose anyone imagined you'd become a doctor. So will you see Harry Gregg?'

Conner's eyes narrowed. 'Diane's son?'

'Yes. He's eight years old and a really nice little boy. Very lively usually, but not today. Diane is frightened.'

'She always did have a tendency to overreact. I remember she slapped my face once.'

'You probably deserved it.'

He smiled. 'I probably did. So what do you think, Flora? Paranoid mother?'

Flora shook her head. 'I think it's something that needs looking at. The child is poorly, there's no doubt about that. And he has a really weird rash. I've never seen anything like it before.'

Conner rose to his feet. 'Is she going to slap my face again or run away screaming in horror if I walk into the room?'

'I've no idea.' Flora gave a weary smile. 'Let's try it, shall we? Harry needs to see a doctor and I'd rather it was sooner than later.'

Diane looked up as they walked into the room. 'Dr MacNeil.'

'Diane.' Conner's greeting was cursory, his eyes focused on the boy, who was now sitting on his mother's lap, his head on her chest. 'Hey, sport.' He hunkered down so that he was on the same level. 'What's going on with you?'

Harry opened his eyes but didn't move his head. 'Feel bad.'

'His temperature is thirty-nine degrees.' Flora gently lifted Harry's arm so that Conner could see. 'He's had this rash for three days.'

'Feel horrible,' the boy muttered, and Conner nodded.

'Well, we need to see what we can do about that.' He studied the rash in silence, his blue eyes narrowed slightly. 'Circular rash.'

Diane watched his face. 'You're going to tell me that it's just a virus and that I shouldn't have bothered you.'

Conner lifted his gaze to hers. 'You were right to bring him. Harry? Do you mind undressing down to your underpants? I want to take a proper look at this rash.'

Flora helped the child undress and Conner examined his skin carefully and questioned Diane in detail.

'It started under his arm when we were on holiday,' she told him. 'Just a red spot. And then it grew bigger and it turned into that weird thing he has now.'

'Where did you go on holiday?'

Flora glanced at him in surprise. She wouldn't have expected Conner to be interested in small talk.

'Mainland.'

'Highlands?' Conner ran a finger over the rash, his expression thoughtful. 'Were you walking?'

'Yes.' Diane looked at him. 'How do you know?'

Conner straightened and reached for Harry's T-shirt. 'It fits with what I'm seeing. You can get dressed now. I've seen all I need to see.' He gently pulled the T-shirt over the boy's head. 'Were you camping?'

'Yes. We spent a few nights in a forest. It was lovely.'

'Lots of deer around?'

'Actually, yes.' Diane frowned. 'How do you know that?'

'Because Harry has Lyme disease.' Conner washed his hands. 'He was almost certainly bitten by a tick, which is why he started off with one red spot. Did you see an insect?'

'No.' Bemused, Diane shook her head. 'No, I didn't. But we've been camping every year since he was born and we've never had a problem. Lyme disease? What is that? I've never even heard of it.'

'It's not that common in this country, although the number of cases is increasing. Ticks are tiny insects and they feed by sucking blood from animals such as deer. Some ticks get infected with the bacterium that causes Lyme disease and if they bite a human then they pass the disease on.'

Diane looked at him in a mixture of horror and amazement. 'And you're sure Harry has it? How do you know?'

'Because his symptoms fit the history.'

Flora felt the tension leave her. Clearly Conner hadn't been making small talk about holidays, he'd been verifying the cause of the symptoms he was seeing. Logan was right. Conner was a good doctor. *A clever doctor.* And Diane appeared to have forgotten that she'd ever had reservations about seeing him.

'You've seen this Lyme disease before?'

'When I was stationed overseas.' Without waiting for an invitation, he sat down at Flora's computer and hit a few keys, bringing up a list of antibiotics. 'The rash that Harry has is fairly typical.' He scrolled down, searching for the one he wanted. 'It starts as a single circular red mark and it gradually spreads. It isn't always painful or itchy and some people don't even notice it, depending on where they were bitten.'

'Is there any treatment?'

'Yes.' Conner's eyes were fixed on the screen. 'I'm going to give Harry some antibiotics.'

'And will they work?'

'They should do because we've caught it early. You did the right thing, bringing him in.'

'The doctor on the mainland thought it was a virus.' Diane's mouth tightened with disapproval. 'Virus is a word doctors use when they haven't got a clue what's going on.'

'You might be right. I usually say "I don't know" but that phrase doesn't win you many friends either. In fairness to your guy on the mainland, Lyme disease is not a condition every doctor will have seen.' Conner printed off the prescription and handed it to Diane. 'Make sure Harry finishes the course.'

'I'll do that.' She slipped the prescription into her bag and hesitated. 'Thank you.' She looked Conner in the eye. 'I wasn't sure about seeing you…'

'I don't blame you for that.' As cool as ever, Conner rose to his feet. 'Make an appointment to see Logan in a few days. Harry needs to be followed up. We need to be sure that the antibiotics are working.'

Diane took Harry's hand in hers. 'Why should I see Logan? Are you going to be busy?'

Conner gave a faint smile. 'On current form? Probably not. But it's important that the patients have faith in the doctor they see.'

'I agree.' Diane walked towards the door. 'Which is why we'll be making that appointment when you're doing surgery. Thank you, Dr MacNeil. I knew I could rely on a Glenmore doctor to get the diagnosis right.' The door closed behind her and Flora smiled happily at Conner.

'I think you're a hit. That was pretty impressive. I predict that once word spreads, your surgery will be crammed with patients.'

'And I'm supposed to rejoice about that?'

'Maybe not. But Logan will. So, tell me about Lyme disease because I'm feeling horribly ignorant.'

'What else do you want to know? You get bitten by a tick that clings on once it bites. Then it sucks your blood—'

'Don't!' Flora pulled a face. 'You're telling it like a horror story. If you carry on like that I'll never set foot outside again.'

It was the wrong thing to say to Conner. He leaned against the desk and gave a wicked smile. 'As I was saying, they suck your blood and slowly become more and more engorged—'

'You do it on purpose, don't you? Try and shock people.'

'I admit it's an extremely stimulating pastime.'

'You might not find it so funny when I'm sick,' Flora said sweetly, and his smile widened.

'Nurses aren't supposed to have delicate constitutions.'

'Doctors aren't supposed to be bloodthirsty.'

'I'm just delivering the facts.'

'Well…' She was horribly aware of just how strong his shoulders were and how much he dominated her tiny room. 'Could you deliver them with slightly less gruesome relish?'

'Where was I?' He angled his head slightly. 'Oh, yes, they were engorged with blood. Anyway, the bacteria that cause Lyme disease are usually carried in the gut and only travel to their mouth once they've been feeding for about twenty-four hours. So if you remove the tick as soon as you're bitten, you're unlikely to be infected.'

Flora shuddered. 'So you're telling me that a method of prevention is to drag this greedy, engorged creature off your skin?'

'You remove it before it's engorged. And you don't drag. If you drag, you'll just leave the mouth stuck in your body.'

'Enough!'

'The best thing is to smother it with Vaseline. It suffocates and then you can remove it with a pair of tweezers. You shouldn't use your fingers—'

'I wouldn't touch it with a bargepole! And I'm never venturing outside again without full protective clothing.'

Conner's eyes flickered to the neck of her uniform. 'You don't need to overdo it. The tick that carries the bacteria likes areas where there are wild deer.'

Her heart started to beat just a little bit faster. 'And that's why you were so interested in where the Greggs went on holiday?'

'The symptoms fitted. The fact that they'd been camping in a forest in warm weather made it highly possible that he'd contracted the disease. Ticks like warm weather and people wear less then so they're more likely to be bitten.' His eyes lifted to hers and the tension between them increased.

'Why haven't I heard of it?'

'Obviously there haven't been any cases on Glenmore. It's sensible to take precautions if you're walking or camping in an area where infected ticks are known to live.' His eyes dropped to her mouth, his gaze lingering. 'Wear long sleeves and trousers, use a tick repellent spray—all the obvious things.'

They were talking about medical matters and yet there was a sudden intimacy in the atmosphere that she didn't understand. It circled her like a forcefield, drawing her in, and when the phone rang suddenly she gave a start.

He was between her and the desk and she waited for him to move to one side so that she could answer it, but he stayed where he was. Left with no choice, she was forced to brush past him as she reached for the receiver. 'Yes? I mean…' Flustered by the fact that he was standing so close to her, she stumbled over the words. 'Nurse Harris speaking— Oh, hello, Mr Murray.' Struggling to concentrate, she listened as the man on the other end spoke to her. 'Well, no, I hadn't heard of it either, but—' She broke off and listened again before finally shaking her head. 'You'd better speak to him yourself.'

She sighed and handed the receiver to Conner. 'It's Mr Murray, the pharmacist down on South Quay. He has a question about the prescription you just gave Harry.'

Relaxed and confident, Conner took the phone from her, his gaze still locked with hers. 'MacNeil.'

Flora felt as though someone had lit a fire inside her body. She should look away. She knew she should look away but she just couldn't help herself. There was something in his ice-blue eyes that insisted that she look.

'That's right, Mr Murray, the dose is large.' He listened, his eyes still fixed on hers. 'Yes, I do know that I'm not treating a horse.'

Flora frowned and mouthed, 'A horse?' But Conner merely lifted a hand and trailed a finger down her cheek with agonising slowness.

'No, believe it or not, I'm not trying to kill him, Mr Murray,' he drawled softly, his finger lingering near her mouth. 'I'm treating a case of Lyme disease. If you look it up I think you'll find that the dose I've given him is appropriate…Yes, even in a child.' He brushed her lower lip with his thumb as he continued to field a tirade from the island pharmacist. 'Yes, I do remember the incident with the firework. Yes, and the barn—No, I don't blame you for questioning me, Mr Murray.' His hand dropped to his side and she sensed a sudden change in him. 'Of course, you're just doing your job.'

Finally he replaced the receiver. 'Apparently it isn't just the patients who have a problem trusting my judgement.'

His tone was flat and Flora stood still, wanting to say something but not knowing what. 'It was an unusual prescription.'

'You don't need to make excuses for them, Flora.' Conner straightened and walked towards the door, his face expressionless. 'You'd better carry on with your surgery. You have patients lining the waiting room.'

She stared after him as he left the room, wanting to stop him. She wanted to say something that would fix things because she sensed that beneath his bored, devil-may-care attitude there was a seam of pain buried so deep that no one could touch it.

The islanders were wary of him, that was true, but what did he think of them?

Remembering Logan's words, Flora bit her lip. When had anyone given Conner MacNeil a chance? When had anyone given him the benefit of the doubt? Why should he bother with any of them when they'd never bothered with him?

It was going to take more than one or two successful consultations to fill his consulting room with patients because no one believed that Conner MacNeil could be anything but a Bad Boy.

It was going to take a miracle.

CHAPTER FIVE

THE miracle didn't happen.

A few of the locals reluctantly agreed to see Conner, but the majority refused, choosing to wait a week to see Logan rather than be forced to consult the island rebel.

'It's ridiculous,' Flora told Evanna crossly a week after Conner had arrived on Glenmore. They were sitting on a rug on the beach, watching Kirsty dig in the sand. Finally the wind had dropped and the sun shone. 'They tell Janet it's urgent, and then say they'd rather wait than see Conner. I mean, just how urgent can something be if it can wait a week? Frankly, it would serve them right if a bit of them dropped off.'

'Well, to be fair to them, Conner was a bit wild and crazy,' Evanna said mildly, picking up Kirsty's sunhat and putting it back on her head. 'We just need to give them time to realise that he's changed.'

'Time isn't on our side. Glenmore needs another doctor. A doctor the patients will see! Your baby is due in four weeks,' Flora reminded her. 'If the patients don't stop demanding to see Logan, you won't get a look-in.'

Evanna sighed. 'I know. He's shattered. He used to always get home before I put Kirsty to bed. Now I'm lucky if he's home before *I'm* in bed.' She lifted her face to the sun. 'It's hot today.'

'I gather from Logan that your blood result was all right.' Flora lifted a bottle of water out of her bag and took a sip. 'That's a relief all round.'

'Yes, I was already immune to chickenpox, so that's one less problem to contend with.'

Flora was still pondering the problem of Conner. 'It isn't as if he's a useless doctor. He's brilliant. You should have seen him with Harry Gregg.' She leaned forward and helped Kirsty ease the sand out of the bucket. 'There! A perfect castle.' She smiled as Kirsty clapped her hands with delight. 'And he's diagnosed Mrs Ellis.'

'Yes, she told me he's given her thyroxine. He certainly seems to know what he's doing.'

'So why hasn't word spread? Why won't the islanders see him?'

'Because they see the boy and not the man? I'm guessing, but I suppose they just don't trust him.' Evanna hesitated. 'Apparently Finn Sullivan refused to rent him a yacht a few evenings ago.'

Flora stared at her. 'Are you serious?'

'Yes, but it's not all black. I saw Conner kicking a football around with the kids on the beach yesterday. They think he's *so* cool. And several women have made appointments to see him, but I don't think he was too thrilled about that.'

'He certainly wasn't.' Flora brushed sand from Kirsty's face. 'He strode up to Janet and said, "I'm not a bloody gynaecologist" or something equally unsympathetic. And Janet pointed out that as we didn't have a female doctor, he was expected to see female problems.'

'And what was Conner's response to that?'

'I don't know because he lowered his voice but Janet went scarlet.'

Evanna laughed. 'I don't suppose there was much call for gynecology in the army. According to Logan, he was dealing with a lot of trauma. Anyway, it's time we helped him settle in, which is why I've invited him to join us for lunch later.'

Flora's heart bumped hard against her chest. 'He's coming to lunch? I thought it was just your family. Logan, Meg and a few others.'

'Conner is family. I thought it might be a good idea to remind people of that.'

'Oh.' Flora concentrated on Kirsty. 'Well, that's great. Really nice of you, Evanna. So we should go back to the house. Start getting ready.' She rose to her feet and picked Kirsty up. 'Come on, sweetheart. Let's get the sand off your feet and take you home. Who knows? Your daddy might even be there.'

Conner's feet echoed on the cracked wooden floorboards and he glanced around him, feeling the memories swirl. The house smelled of damp, but that wasn't surprising because it had been years since the light and air had been allowed to pour unrestricted through its doors and windows.

He'd always hated this house and nothing had changed. It was as if the walls had absorbed some of the anger and hatred that had been played out in these rooms.

He tried to feel something positive, but there was nothing that wasn't dark and murky, and he gave a soft curse and strode out of the front door and back into the sunshine, drawing the clear air deep into his lungs.

Just walking into the house had made him feel contaminated.

He shouldn't have come.

He should have just paid someone to sell the damn place.

Beneath him the sea crashed onto the rocks and he sucked in a breath, drinking in the wildness of it—the savage beauty.

Everything about this part of Glenmore was angry. The coast, the sea, the wind, the house…

Him?

Conner stood for a moment, battling with uncomfortable thoughts until some inner sense warned him that he wasn't alone.

He turned swiftly and saw her.

Flora was standing only metres away from him, the wind lifting her brown curls and blowing them around her face, her expression uncertain.

'Sorry.' Her voice faltered and it was obvious that she couldn't decide whether to stay or retreat. 'I didn't mean to disturb you.'

He wished she hadn't, because he was in no mood for company and his desperate need for isolation fuelled his temper. 'Then why did you?'

Flora flinched at his directness, but she didn't retreat. 'You were supposed to be at Logan and Evanna's for lunch. We assumed you'd forgotten.'

'I needed some space.'

'Oh.' She took a breath. 'It's just that…you didn't ring or anything.'

'No.'

'I was worried.'

'Why?' *Since when had anyone worried about him?*

'This business with the islanders,' she shrugged, embarrassed and awkward. 'It's horrible. I thought by now they would have accepted you.'

'It's not important.'

'Of course it's important! Evanna told me that Finn wouldn't rent you a boat—'

When he didn't answer, she gazed at him in exasperation. 'Don't you *care*?'

He could feel the blood throbbing in his veins. 'What are you doing here, Flora?'

'When you didn't show up, I thought I'd bring lunch to you.'

It was then that he noticed the basket by her feet. He could see a bowl of strawberries, thick whipped cream and another bowl, this one piled high with bronzed chicken legs. And white and red checked napkins.

A traditional picnic.

It was all so civilised and in such direct contrast to this place and everything he was feeling that he felt his tension levels soar.

He wasn't feeling civilised. He wasn't feeling civilised at all.

In fact, he was in an extremely dangerous mood.

'It's pretty here,' she ventured hesitantly, glancing over to the rocks and the tiny beach. 'This is the only house on the island that has its own private beach.'

'Flora, if you have any sense, you'll leave right now.'

Her eyes flew to his. Widened. 'I've made you angry.'

There was something different about her but he couldn't work out what it was. 'I was angry before you arrived. I know you mean well, but I don't wish to take a trip down memory lane and I especially don't want to do it holding anyone's hand,' he said harshly. 'How did you know where to find me?'

'I went to your barn first and you weren't there.' She captured a strand of hair as it danced in the breeze. 'And I saw Mrs North picking blackberries in the lane outside and she said she'd seen you coming in this direction.'

Conner's mood darkened still further. 'Now I know why they don't bother with CCTV on Glenmore. They have locals stationed on every street corner.'

'I shouldn't have come. I really am sorry.' Flushed and flustered, Flora lifted the basket and stepped forward. She pushed the basket into his hands, her smile brief and shy. 'Take it. Evanna is an amazing cook. Her chicken is delicious and the strawberries are freshly picked from the Roberts' farm. If you're not hungry now, you can eat it later.' Without waiting for him to reply, she turned and walked quickly away from him, her long flowery skirt swirling around her body, outlining the soft curve of her hips.

He'd offended her. *Or had he frightened her?*

Conner watched her for a moment and then looked down at the basket and swore long and fluently. The day was *not* turning out as he'd planned. He lifted his gaze from the strawberries and stared after her retreating figure with a mixture of exasperation and anger.

He didn't care that he'd offended her.

He really didn't care.

It wasn't as if he'd invited her here. He hadn't asked her to follow him.

Caught in an internal battle, he opened his mouth to speak, changed his mind and closed it again, then growled with frustration and called out to her. 'Do you like strawberries?'

She stopped and turned—slowly. 'Yes. I love them.'

But she didn't move and even from this distance Conner sensed her wariness and remembered what Logan had said about her being shy.

'Good. Because there's a large bowlful in this basket and I hate them.' He dumped the basket on the ground and looked at her expectantly, but she still didn't move.

'Just eat the chicken, then.'

Realising that she wasn't going to walk to him, he strolled towards her and suddenly saw what was different about her. 'You're not wearing your glasses.'

She lifted a hand to her cheek and shrugged self-consciously. 'Contact lenses. I don't usually wear them at work.

I'm not a morning person and I'm never awake enough to risk putting my fingers into my eyes.' She looked over his shoulder at the basket, which now lay abandoned on the soft grass. 'I can take the strawberries with me, if they offend you that much.'

'Or you can sit down and eat them here.'

Her eyes narrowed. 'I didn't think you were looking for company.'

'If the strawberries aren't eaten, I'll hurt Evanna's feelings.'

A smile touched her mouth. 'I thought you didn't care about other people's feelings, Conner MacNeil.'

'I don't, but if I upset her, Logan will give me a black eye. And then the locals will think I've seduced someone's wife or girlfriend. And I'm already in enough trouble.'

She laughed, as he'd intended. 'You told me that you thrive on trouble.'

'That's just habit. I've never known anything else.'

Her laughter faded and she stared up into his face. 'I shouldn't have come here. It's personal for you. Stressful. And you don't want to talk about it, do you?'

He gave a twisted smile. 'Let's just say that if I talk, you wouldn't like the language I'd choose to use.'

'Use whatever language you please. I'm not as shockable as you seem to think I am.'

'It would be all too easy to shock you, Flora.' He thought of what his life had been and then he looked down at her gentle eyes and her soft mouth and wondered why he'd stopped her walking away. 'I'm not the type of man who eats strawberries with girls in flowered skirts.'

'You don't like my skirt?'

'You look…' He gave a faint smile as he searched for the word that best described her. 'Wholesome. Like an advert for that whipped cream in the basket.'

'It's Evanna's whipped cream. And I don't see what my skirt has to do with anything. Do you always push people away?'

'I don't have to. They usually run all by themselves.'

'Well, I can't run in these shoes.'

'Is that right? In that case, you can sit down and help me eat this damn picnic.'

'Where?' Flora glanced towards the house and he made an impatient sound.

'No way.' *He wasn't going back in there.* Instead, he took her hand, scooped up the basket and then led her down the path to the tiny cove at the bottom. The path was steep and stony but she didn't falter, confident and sure-footed despite her comment about her shoes.

She was a local girl, he remembered. *She'd spent her childhood playing on these cliffs and exploring Glenmore's rocky shores.*

As they reached the sand, she slipped off her shoes and stooped to pick them up. 'It's pretty here. Really sheltered.'

'Haven't you been here before?'

'No.'

'Why not?'

'Honestly?' She hesitated. 'This beach is part of your property and we were too afraid of your father. Even Kyla.'

Conner gave a bitter laugh. 'Lovely man, my father.' He sat down on the sand and then glanced at her with a frown. 'Did you bring something to sit on?'

She smiled and sat down on the sand next to him. 'This is perfect.' She reached into the basket and then glanced at him, her eyes twinkling. 'Napkin?'

'Of course,' he said sarcastically. 'I'd hate to drop anything on my tuxedo.'

She laughed and passed him the bowl of chicken instead. 'Try this. I guarantee it will taste better than anything you've ever eaten before, tuxedo or no tuxedo. I bumped into Diane Gregg in the supermarket this morning. She said Harry is feeling much better.'

'Yes. I saw him in surgery yesterday. One of the advantages of being treated like a leper is that I have plenty of time for the patients that do want to see me.' He bit into the chicken and flavours exploded on his palate. 'You're right—this is good.'

'I have a boat, if you want to sail.'

Conner lifted an eyebrow. 'Are you making a pass at me?'

The colour poured into her cheeks. 'Of course not.'

'But you're offering to lend me your boat?'

'Yes.' She delved into the basket and pulled out some crusty bread. 'Or we could sail together. You can sail it singlehanded but it's more fun with two.'

'I didn't know you sailed.'

'I suspect there's quite a lot about me that you don't know,' she said calmly, and Conner gave a surprised laugh.

'And what do you think the locals will say when they see you consorting with Bad Conner?'

Flora broke the bread in two and handed him half. 'I suppose it might be sensible to avoid getting into trouble, just in case the lifeboat crew refuse to help.'

'You'd be all right. They'd pick you up and leave me in the water.'

'No problems, then. Lemonade?'

Conner winced. 'Are you serious? What is this—nursery food?'

'It's home-made. Evanna makes it.' She poured him a glass and he heard a dull clunk as ice cubes thudded into the glass. 'It's very refreshing.'

He took the glass and stared at it dubiously. 'If you say so.'

'You'd probably prefer beer.'

'I don't drink.' He felt her eyes on his face and when she spoke her voice was soft.

'Because of your father.' Her quiet statement required no response and so he didn't give one.

They ate in silence and he found himself glancing at her occasionally and noticing things about the way she looked. Like the fact that she had tiny freckles on her nose and that her eyes were incredibly pretty.

'You should ditch the glasses,' he said softly, and she blinked awkwardly.

'Oh...' She concentrated on the chicken and suddenly he was reminded of a baby kitten he'd found abandoned when he'd been a child. It had been so soft and vulnerable that he he'd been afraid to touch it in case he harmed it. So he'd placed an anonymous call to the vet's surgery and had then hidden behind a tree, watching until they'd picked it up.

Flora had that same air of vulnerability.

They finished the picnic in silence and she packed everything away tidily in the basket. 'There's a good wind. I always find there's nothing better than sailing to clear the mind and put everything into perspective.'

'Flora—'

'Don't pretend you don't want to sail, because I know you tried to hire a boat from Finn at the sailing school. I'm offering you my boat. With or without myself as crew.'

He stared out to sea. 'I was going to clear the house out this afternoon.'

'There's no worse job in the world,' she said softly. 'After Dad died, it took me six months to even go into the house. I just couldn't face all those memories. And mine were happy ones. Are you sure you don't want to talk about this?'

'I wouldn't know what to say. I've been away for twelve years. But it seems even that isn't long enough.' Conner took a mouthful of his drink and choked. 'That is truly disgusting.'

Flora laughed. 'Some people prefer it with sugar.'

'The only way I'd drink it is topped up with gin. And given that I don't touch alcohol, there's no chance of that.' Pulling a face, he emptied his glass onto the sand. 'Where's your boat moored?'

'South Quay.'

His eyes narrowed. 'In full public view.'

'Yes.' She scrambled to her feet and brushed the sand from her skirt. 'We need to go via my house so that I can change, but that will only take a minute.'

'You seriously want to sail? I thought you hated being the focus of people's attention.'

'I won't be the focus,' she muttered, carefully stacking everything back into the basket. 'You will.'

She was being kind, he realised. Trying to show solidarity in front of the locals.

He probably ought to refuse but just as he opened his mouth to do just that, the wind gusted and he glanced at the waves breaking on the beach. 'It's a perfect afternoon for a sail.'

'Then what are you waiting for?' She walked towards the path. 'Are you coming, Dr MacNeil? Or would you rather spend the afternoon being moody?'

She'd never had so much fun. The wind was gusting at five knots and Conner was a born sailor, with a natural feel for the wind and the sea and blessed with nerves of steel. And although they came close several times, he didn't land them in the water.

As the water sprayed over the bows, Flora laughed in delight. 'Who taught you to sail?'

'Taught myself. Sank two boats in the process. Probably why Finn won't rent me a boat. I always loved being on the water. The sea was the place where everything came together.' He tightened the mainsheet as he turned the boat into the wind. 'Ready about,' he called. Flora released the jib sheet and they both ducked under the boom as the boat came swiftly around. The wind caught the sails and the boat accelerated smoothly away, the sea sparkling in the summer sunshine.

It was hours before they finally turned the boat back towards the jetty and Flora felt nothing but regret. 'Do you ever feel like just sailing away and never looking back?'

'All the time.' He adjusted the sail. 'What about you?'

'Oh, yes.' She gazed dreamily up at the sky, loving the feel of the wind and the spray on her face. 'I love being on the boat. It's just so easy and comfortable. No people. No problems.'

'You are full of surprises, Flora Harris.' Conner laughed. 'I never imagined you were a sailor.'

'I bought her with the money Dad left me when he died. He was the one who taught me to sail. I was hopeless at team sports at school because I was too shy. No one ever picked me. I think Dad realised that sailing would suit me. I love the freedom of the boat. And the fact that you're away from people.' She closed her eyes and let the sun warm her skin. 'I'm always tense around people.'

'You're still incredibly shy, aren't you?'

She opened her eyes. 'Yes. But I've learned to act. That's what you do as an adult, isn't it? You act your way through situations that would have paralysed you as a child.'

'Was it that bad?'

'Yes.' Her simple, honest response touched him.

'I didn't realise. I just thought you were studious.'

Flora stared at the quay, measuring the distance. 'If I was absorbed in a book then no one bothered with me, and I preferred it that way. I liked being inconspicuous.'

'So why did you come back to Glenmore? Logan said you

were working in Edinburgh before this. I would have thought it was easier to be inconspicuous in a city.'

'It's also very lonely and I missed the scenery and the sailing. Coming back here seemed like the right thing to do.'

'And was it?'

She glanced at him. 'I don't know. Even though I know they mean well, I can't get used to the fact that everyone knows what everyone is doing.'

They approached the jetty and she released the jib sheet and the sail flapped in the wind. Conner turned the boat head to wind and brought her skilfully into the quay.

'She's pretty.' He ran a hand over the mast and Flora felt her heart kick against her chest.

She wished she were the boat.

He leapt over the foredeck onto the quay and secured the boat to the jetty while Flora de-rigged the boat, wishing they could have stayed out on the water. Now that they were on dry land she was suddenly aware that she was with Conner MacNeil and that all the locals were watching them.

As usual, Conner was totally indifferent. 'I had no idea your father encouraged you to indulge in such dangerous pastimes. My impression was that he kept you under lock and key. He was strict.'

'Not strict, exactly. Protective.' Flora stepped off the boat and onto the quay. Hot after the exertion, she removed her hat and her hair tumbled loose over her shoulders. 'My mother died when I was very young and I think he was terrified that something would happen to me, too. He never relaxed if I was out.'

'I don't remember you ever going out. All my memories of you have books in them.'

Flora laughed. 'That was partly my fault. I was painfully shy and books stopped me having to talk to people.'

'So why aren't you shy with me, Flora?'

Her eyes flew to his, startled. It was true, she realised. She'd had such fun she hadn't once felt shy with him. Not once. 'I'm never shy when I'm sailing.'

But she knew that it had nothing to do with the sailing and everything to do with the man.

She felt comfortable with Conner.

Unsettled by that thought, she looked across the quay at the throngs of tourists who were milling around on their way to and from the beach. 'Can I treat you to a hot fudge sundae? Meg's café is calorie heaven.'

'I don't think so.' He checked that the boat was securely tied. 'I just upset the balance of Glenmore. I'm like you. Better with the boat than people. I've never been any good at platitudes and all the other false things people say to each other.'

It was so close to the way she felt that for a moment she stood still. Who would have thought that she and Conner had so many similarities? 'But you came back.'

He gave a careless shrug. 'It was time.'

But it wouldn't be for long, she knew that.

Suddenly she just wanted to drag him straight back on the boat and sail back out to sea. On the water she'd had glimpses of the person behind the bad boy. He'd been relaxed. Good-humoured. Now they were back on dry land his ice-blue eyes were wary and cynical, as though he was braced for criticism.

A commotion on the far side of the quay caught her eye and she squinted across the water. 'I wonder why the ferry hasn't left yet.' Flora glanced at her watch. 'It's five past four. Jim always leaves at four o'clock sharp. He's never late.'

'Obviously he is today.'

'What are they all staring at?' An uneasy feeling washed over her. 'Something is happening on the quay. Conner, I think someone must have fallen into the water.'

A woman started screaming hysterically and Flora paled as she recognised her.

'That's Jayne Parsons, from the dental surgery. Something must have happened to Lily. It must be little Lily in the water.' She started to run, dodging groups of gaping tourists as she flew towards the other side of the quay.

And suddenly she could see why people were staring.

Blood pooled on the surface of the water and Flora felt a wave of nausea engulf her as she realised just how serious the situation was.

Her hand shaking, she delved in her pocket for her mobile phone and quickly rang the coastguard and the air ambulance. Then she caught Jayne by the shoulders before she could throw herself into the water after her child. 'No! Wait, Jayne. What happened? Is it Lily?'

'She fell. One minute she was eating her ice cream and the next...Oh, God, she fell.' Jayne's breath was coming in hysterical gasps and out of the corner of her eye Flora saw movement, heard a splash and turned to see Conner already in the water.

A local who had seen the whole incident started directing him. 'She went in about here. Between the quay and the boat. I guess the propeller...' His voice tailed off as he glanced towards Jayne and the woman's eyes widened in horror as she focused on the surface of the water and saw what Flora had already seen.

The blood.

Jayne started to scream and the sound had a thin, inhuman quality that cut through the summer air and brought horrified silence to the normally bustling quay. Then she tried to launch herself into the water again and Flora winced as Jayne's flying fist caught her on the side of her head. She was too slight to hold the woman, her head throbbed and she was just about to resign herself to the fact that Jayne was going to jump when two burly local fishermen came to her aid.

They drew a sobbing, struggling Jayne away from the edge of the quay and Flora gave them a grateful nod. Whatever happened next, Jayne being in the water would only make things worse.

Oblivious to the audience or the building tension, Conner vanished under the water. Time and time again he dived, while strangers and locals stood huddled in groups, watching the drama unfold.

Offering what comfort she could, Flora took Jayne's hand. 'Conner will find her,' she said firmly, praying desperately that she was right. 'Conner will find her.' *If she said it often enough, perhaps it would happen.*

'Conner?' Shivering violently and still restrained by the fishermen, Jayne looked at Flora blankly, as if she hadn't realised until this point who was trying to rescue her daughter. 'Conner MacNeil?'

'He's in the water now,' Flora said gently, wondering whether Jayne was going into shock. Her eyes were glazed and her face white. 'He's looking for her, Jayne.'

'Conner? When has he ever put his life on the line for anyone? He won't help her. *He won't help my baby.*' Her eyes suddenly wild with terror, Jayne developed superhuman strength, wrenched herself from the hold of the two men and hurled herself towards the edge of the quay once again.

The two men quickly grabbed her and she wriggled and pulled, struggling to free herself. 'Get the coastguard, anyone— Oh, God, no, no.' She collapsed, sobbing and Flora slid her arms round her, this time keeping her body between Jayne and the quay.

'Jayne, you're no help to Lily if you fall in, too. Leave it to Conner. You have to trust Conner.'

'Who in their right mind would trust Conner MacNeil?'

'I would,' Flora said simply, and realised that it was true. 'I'd trust him with my life.'

'Then you're obviously infatuated with him,' Jayne shrieked, 'like every other woman who comes close to him.' But she sagged against Flora, her energy depleted by the extravagant surge of emotion.

Infatuated?

Dismissing the accusation swiftly, Flora stared at the surface of the water but there was no movement and a couple of tourists standing next to her started to murmur dire predictions. She turned and glared at them just as there was a sound from the water and Conner surfaced, the limp, lifeless body of the child in his arms. He sucked in air and then hauled himself onto the concrete steps with one hand, his other arm holding the child protectively against his chest.

Lily lay still, her soaked dress darkened by blood, her hair streaked with it.

Flora felt panic, jagged and dangerous. Oh no, please no.

There were no signs of life. None.

Next to her Jayne started to moan like a creature tormented and then the sound stopped as she slid to the concrete in a faint.

'Leave her,' Conner ordered, climbing the steps out of the water, the body of the child still in his arms. Lily's head hung backwards and her skin was a dull grey colour. 'Someone else can look after her and at the moment she's better off out of it. Get me a towel, Flora. With the blood and the water, I can't see what we're dealing with here.'

A towel?

Feeling sick and shaky, Flora scanned the crowd and focused on two tourists who were loaded down with beach items. 'Give me your towel.' Without waiting for their permission, she yanked the towel out of the bag, spilling buckets and spades over the quay. Then she was on her knees beside Conner.

Lily lay pale and lifeless, her tiny body still, like a puppet that had been dropped. Blood spurted like a fountain from a wound on her leg.

'It's an artery.' With a soft curse Conner pressed down hard. 'I'm guessing she gashed it on the propeller as she fell. She's lucky the engine wasn't on.' He increased the pressure in an attempt to stop the bleeding. 'She's stopped breathing.'

Flora almost stopped breathing, too. Panic pressed in on her and without Connor's abrupt commands she would have shrivelled up and sobbed, just as Jayne had. Perhaps he realised that she was on the verge of falling apart because he lifted his head and glared at her, his blue eyes fierce with determination.

'Press here! I need to start CPR. Flora, *move*!'

She stared at him for a moment, so stunned by the enormity of what was happening she couldn't respond.

'Pull yourself together!' His tone was sharp. 'If we're to stand any chance here, I need some help, and you're the only person who knows what they're doing. Everyone else is just gawping.'

Flora felt suddenly dizzy. She'd never seen so much blood in her life. She'd never worked in A and E and all the first-aid courses she'd attended had been theoretical. *She didn't know what she was doing.*

And then she realised that *he* did. Conner knew exactly what he was doing and she knelt down beside him.

'Tell me what you want me to do.'

'Press here. Like that. That's it—good.' He put her hands on the wound, showed her just how hard he wanted her to press, and then shifted slightly so that he could focus on the child's breathing. With one hand on her forehead and the other under her chin, he gently tilted Lily's head back and covered her mouth with his, creating a seal. He breathed gently, watching as the child's chest rose.

Then he lifted his mouth and watched as Lily's chest fell as the air came out. 'Flora, get a tourniquet on that leg. She's losing blood by the bucketload.'

'A tourniquet?' Flora turned to the nearest tourist. 'Get me a bandage or a tie, something—anything—I can wind around her leg.'

The man simply stared at her, but his wife moved swiftly, jerking the tie from the neck of a businessman who had been waiting to take the ferry.

Flora didn't dare release the pressure on Lily's leg. 'If I let go to tie it, she's going to bleed.' Feeling horribly ignorant, she sent Conner a helpless glance. 'I haven't done this before. Do I put it directly over the wound?'

'Above the wound. You need a stick or something to twist it tight. Tie it and leave a gap and tie it again.'

Flora swiftly did as he instructed. The towel was soaked in blood and her fingers were slippery with it and shaking.

'The bleeding's not stopping Conner,' she muttered, and he glanced across at her, his expression hard.

'You need to tighten it. More pressure. Get a stick.'

She glanced at the uneven surface of the quay. 'There's no stick!'

'Then use something else!' He glared at the group of tourists standing nearest to them. 'Find a stick of some sort! A kid's spade, a cricket stump—anything we can use.'

'The blood is everywhere.' Flora tried to twist the tie tighter but the bleeding was relentless and she felt a sob build in her throat. It just seemed hopeless. Completely hopeless. 'She's four years old, Conner.' She was ready to give up but Conner placed the heel of his hand over the child's sternum.

'She's hypovolaemic. She needs fluid and she needs it fast.' He pushed down. 'Where the *hell* is the air ambulance?'

Someone thrust a stick into Flora's hand and she looked at it with relief. Perhaps now she could stop the bleeding. 'Do I push it under the tie and twist?'

'On top.' Conner stopped chest compressions and bent to give another rescue breath. 'Between the two knots. Twist. Make a note of the time—we can't leave it on for more than ten minutes. But if we're not out of here in ten minutes, it will be too late anyway.'

He covered Lily's mouth with his again and Flora followed his instructions, placing the stick between the first and second knots and twisting until it tightened.

'The air ambulance has just landed on the beach,' Jim, the ferryman, was by her shoulder, his voice surprisingly steady. 'What can I do, Flora?'

'I don't know. Keep the crowd away, I suppose. How's Jayne?'

'Out cold. Might be the best thing. Someone's looking after her—a nurse from the mainland on a day trip.'

Conner returned to chest compressions. 'Jim—get over to the paramedics. I want oxygen and plasma expander. And get them to radio the hospital and warn them. She's going to need whole blood or packed cells when she arrives. I want her in the air in the next few minutes. We don't have time to play around here.'

'Will do.' Without argument, Jim disappeared to do as Conner had instructed and Flora lifted the edge of the towel.

'The bleeding's stopped.' She felt weak with relief and Conner nodded.

'Good. We'll release it and check it in about ten minutes. If the bleeding doesn't start again we can leave it loose, but don't take it off—we might need it again.' He bent his head to give Lily another life-saving breath and Flora saw the paramedics sprinting along the quay towards them.

'They're here, Conner.'

Conner wasn't listening. His attention was focused on the child. 'Come on, baby girl,' he murmured softly, 'breathe for me.' His eyes were on her chest and Flora watched him, wondering. Had he seen something? Had he felt a change in her condition?

'Do you think she—?'

And at that moment Lily gave a choking cough and vomited weakly.

'Oh, thank God,' Flora breathed, and Conner turned the child's head gently and cleared her airway.

'There's a good girl. You're going to be all right now, sweetheart.'

He spoke so softly that Flora doubted that anyone else had heard his words of comfort and she felt a lump block her throat as she watched him with the child.

So he was capable of kindness, then. It was there, deep inside him, just as she'd always suspected.

But then he lifted his head and his eyes were hard as ever. 'Get some blankets, dry towels, coats—something to warm her up,' he ordered, and then looked at the paramedics. 'Give her some oxygen. I want to get a line in and give her a bolus of fluid and then we're out of here.'

'How much fluid do you want?'

Conner wiped his forearm across his brow, but he kept one hand on the child's arm. *Offering reassurance.* 'What's her weight? How old is she? We can estimate—'

'I know her weight exactly,' Flora said. 'I saw her in clinic last week. She's 16 kilograms. Do you want a calculator so that you can work out the fluid?'

'Start with 160 mils of colloid and then I'll reassess. I don't want to hang around here.' Conner released Lily's hand and started looking for a vein, while one of the paramedics sorted out the fluid and the other gave Lily some oxygen.

The child was breathing steadily now, her chest rising and

falling as Conner worked. Occasionally her eyes fluttered open and then drifted closed again.

'She's got no veins,' Conner muttered, carefully examining Lily's arms. 'Get me an intraosseous needle. I'm not wasting time looking for non-existent veins. We need to get her to hospital. We've messed around here long enough.'

The paramedic dropped to his knees beside Conner, all the necessary equipment to hand. 'You want an intraosseous needle?'

'Actually, just give me a blue cannula. She might just have a vein I can use here.' Conner stroked the skin on the child's arm, focused. 'One go—if it fails, we'll get her in the air and I'll insert an intraosseous needle on the way.'

Flora leaned forward and closed her fingers around the child's arm, squeezing gently and murmuring words of reassurance. Lily was drifting in and out of consciousness and didn't seem aware of what was going on.

There was a commotion next to them but Conner didn't seem to notice. He didn't look up or hesitate. Instead, he applied himself to the task with total concentration, slid the needle into the vein and then gave a grunt of satisfaction. 'I'm in—good. That makes things easier. Let's flush it and tape it—I don't want to lose this line.'

The paramedic leaned towards him with tape but just at that moment Jayne launched herself at Conner and tried to drag him away. *'What are you doing to my baby?'* Her face was as white as swan's feathers, her eyes glazed with despair. 'Let me get to her— I need to hold her— *Get him away from her.*'

'Jayne, not now.' Flora quickly slid an arm round her shoulders and pulled her out of the way so that the paramedic and Conner could finish what they'd started.

'But she's dead,' Jayne moaned, and Flora shook her head.

'She's not dead, Jayne,' she said firmly. 'She's breathing.'

'Not dead?' Relief diluted the pain in Jayne's eyes but then panic rose again as she saw Conner bending over her child. *'What's he doing to her? Oh, God, there's blood everywhere.'*

'Lily cut herself very badly,' Flora began, but Jayne began to scream.

'Get him away from her! *Get him away from my baby! I don't trust him!'*

'You should trust him. He's the reason the bairn's breathing now.' It was Jim who spoke, his weatherbeaten face finally showing signs of strain. Gently but firmly he drew Jayne away from Flora. 'Flora, you help Dr MacNeil. Jayne, you're staying with me. And you'd better remember that Conner MacNeil is the reason Lily is alive right now. I know you're upset, and rightly so, but you need to get a hold. The man is working miracles.'

Conner straightened, conferred with the paramedics and together he and the crew transferred Lily's tiny form onto the stretcher. Then he wiped his blood-streaked hands down his soaked shorts. His handsome face was still damp with sea water and the expression in his ice-blue eyes cold and detached as he finally looked at Jayne. 'We're taking her to hospital.'

Jayne crumpled. 'I'm sorry, I'm so sorry.' Tears poured down her cheeks as she looked from him to Lily's still form. 'Can I come with you? Please?'

Conner took a towel that a tourist tentatively offered him. 'That depends on whether you're likely to assault me during the flight.' He wiped his hands properly, watching as Jayne breathed in and out and lifted a hand to her chest.

'I—I really am sorry.'

'No, you need to understand.' Conner handed the towel back, his voice brutally harsh. 'This isn't over. If she arrests during the flight, I'll be resuscitating her. Can you cope with that? Because if you can't, you're staying on the ground.'

Jayne flinched but for some reason his lack of sympathy seemed to help her pull herself together and find some dignity. 'I understand. Of course. And that's fine. I'm just grateful that you…' She swallowed and nodded. 'Do everything,' she whispered. 'Everything. I just—I just want to be near her. And with her when we get there. I— Thank you. Thank you so much. Without you…' Her eyes met Conner's for a moment and he turned his attention back to Lily.

'We're wasting time. Let's move.'

In a matter of moments the helicopter was in the air and Flora watched as it swooped away from Glenmore towards the mainland.

Suddenly she realised how much her hands were shaking.

She stared down at herself. Her shorts were streaked with blood and Lily's blood still pooled on the grey concrete of the quay. 'Someone get a bucket and slosh some water over this,' she muttered to Jim, and he breathed a sigh and rubbed a hand over his face.

'I haven't seen anything like that in all my time on Glenmore.'

'No. I suppose it was because the quay was so crowded. She must have been knocked off the edge and into the water.'

'I didn't mean that.' Jim stared into the sky, watching as the helicopter shrank to a tiny dot in the distance. 'I meant Conner MacNeil. He was in the water like an arrow while the rest of us were still working out what had happened. And he just got on with it, didn't he?'

'Yes.' Flora cleared her throat. 'He did.'

'Logan says he was in the army.' Jim pushed his hat back from his forehead and scratched. 'I reckon if I was fighting in some godforsaken country, I'd feel better knowing he was around to pick up the pieces.'

'Yes. He was amazing.'

'He's not cuddly, of course.' Jim held up five fingers to a

tourist who tentatively asked whether or not the ferry would be running. 'Five minutes. But in a crisis which do you prefer? Cuddly or competent?'

Flora swallowed, knowing that Jim was right. Conner's ice-cold assessment of the situation had been a huge part of the reason Lily was still alive. He hadn't allowed emotion to cloud his judgement, whereas she…

Suddenly Flora felt depression wash over her. The whole situation had been awful and she was experienced enough to know that, despite Conner's heroic efforts, Lily wasn't out of danger. 'I'd better go, Jim. I need to clean up.'

'And I need to get this ferry to the mainland.' Jim gave a wry smile and glanced at his watch. 'It's the first time the Glenmore ferry has been late since the service started. Nice job, Flora. Well done.'

But Flora knew that her part in the rescue had been minimal.

It had been Conner. All of it. He'd been the one to dive into the water. He'd pulled Lily out. And when she'd been frozen with panic at the sight of Lily's lifeless form covered in all that blood, he'd worked with ruthless efficiency, showing no emotion but getting the job done. Nothing had distracted him. Not even Lily's mother. He'd had a task to do and he'd done it.

CHAPTER SIX

SHE COULDN'T relax at home so she went back to the beach with her book and when it was too dark to read she just sat, listening to the hiss of the waves as they rushed forward onto the beach and then retreated.

She wanted to know how Lily was faring, but Conner wasn't answering his mobile and she didn't want to bother the hospital staff.

Shrieks of excitement came from the far corner of the beach where a group of teenagers had lit a fire and were having a beach party. Flora watched for a moment, knowing that she was too far away for them to see her. They weren't supposed to light fires but they always did. This was Glenmore in the summer. She knew that sooner or later Nick Hillier, the policeman, would do one of his evening patrols and if they were still there, he'd move them on. Back home to their parents or the properties they rented for a few weeks every summer.

'What's a nice girl like you doing on a beach like this? It's late. You should be home.' The harsh, familiar male voice came from directly behind her and she gave a gasp of shock.

'Conner? Where did you come from? I thought you'd still be on the mainland.'

'Hitched a lift back on a boat.'

'How's Lily?'

'Asking for her dolls.'

Flora felt a rush of relief and smiled. 'That's wonderful.'

'If it's wonderful, why such a long face?' He sat down next to her and there was enough light for her to see the dark stains on his shirt and trousers. It was a vivid reminder of just what he'd achieved.

'It would have been a very different outcome for Lily if you hadn't been there.'

'Someone else would have done it.'

'No. No, they wouldn't. And I was no use to you at all. I'm sorry. I was completely out of my depth. I've never seen anything like that before.' Just the thought of Lily's body, lifeless and covered with blood, made her feel sick.

'You were fine.' He reached behind him for a pebble and threw it carelessly into the darkness. There was a faint splash as it hit the water.

'Conner, I wasn't fine.' She'd been thinking about it all evening and becoming more and more upset. 'You always imagine that you'll know what to do in an emergency, but I didn't. I didn't know! I mean, I suppose I knew the theory but nothing prepares you for seeing a little girl you know well, covered in blood and not breathing. I—I just couldn't concentrate.'

'That happens to the best of us.'

She was willing to bet it had never happened to him. 'I've never even tied a tourniquet before.'

'Join the army,' he suggested, and reached for another stone. 'You get to tie quite a few. Believe me, it's a talent I'd willingly not have to use ever again. You were fine. Stop worrying.'

'There was so much blood.'

'Yeah—it has a habit of spreading itself around when you hit an artery.'

'It didn't worry you.'

'Blood?' He shrugged. 'No, blood doesn't worry me—but emotion…' He gave a hollow laugh and threw the stone. 'Now that's a different story. When they discharge her from hospital, you're the one that's visiting.'

She curled her toes into the soft sand. 'I remember Jayne from school.'

'Me, too. I think I might have kissed her once.'

'You kissed everyone.' *Except her.* She turned to look at him. Fresh stubble darkened his jaw and in the dim light he looked more dangerous than ever.

He flung another stone and then leaned back on his elbows, watching her through narrowed eyes. 'What the hell are you doing out here at this hour, Flora Harris? You should be tucked up in bed, having exhausted yourself with a fat book.'

Flora drew a circle in the sand with her finger. 'You think I'm so boring, don't you?'

'Trust me, you don't want to know what I think.'

'I already know.' Her heart thumping, she looked at him. 'I'm probably the only girl on Glenmore that you haven't kissed, so that says quite a lot.'

'It says that I still had some decency, despite what the locals thought of me. You weren't exactly the kind of girl to indulge in adolescent groping.' Conner glanced towards the crowd on the beach, barely visible in the darkness. 'You didn't do late-night beach orgies. I suppose you were studying.'

'Yes, I probably was.' Flora thought of the life she'd led. 'Dad hated me being out too late. He always worried about me.'

'You were a good daughter. You never once slipped off the rails, not even for a moment. That's good. Be proud of it.'

'It was easy to stay on the rails because my rails were

smooth and consistent. I lost Mum but I still had Dad.' She glanced at him, hesitant about saying something that would upset him. 'It must be very stressful for you, coming back here after so long. You had such a difficult childhood and all the memories are here.'

'Actually, I think I probably had an easier childhood than you. Everyone expected you to do well, so you had to work hard and deliver or risk disappointing them. No one expected anything but trouble when I was around, so I could create havoc and meet their expectations at the same time.' He sat up and flung another stone. 'Your father expected you to be home before dark because he loved you and worried about you, so you didn't dare go out and paint the town red in case you upset him. My father didn't give a damn what I did as long as it didn't involve him.'

'You must be very upset and angry with your mother for leaving.'

'Not at all.' His tone was cool. 'He beat her every day of their marriage. She had no choice but to get out. She should have done it sooner. Probably would have done if it hadn't been for me.'

Flora was so shocked by his unexpected confession that it took her a moment to respond. 'Oh, Conner…' She'd heard rumours, of course, but no one had ever known for sure. 'But she left you there. With him.'

'She had no choice about that. If she'd taken me, he would have followed. Her only chance was to go before he killed her.'

Flora sat for a moment, trying to imagine what it must have been like, and failing. She'd only ever known love. 'Did he ever…?' Her voice trailed off and she shook her head and looked away. 'Sorry, it's none of my business and I know you hate talking about personal stuff.'

'Did he ever hit me? Is that what you were about to ask?'

He lay back on the sand and stared into the darkness. 'Just once. And I was so angry I stabbed a hole in his leg with a kitchen knife. I was six years old at the time. After that he left me alone. I think he was always a bit worried I'd empty the contents of the science lab into his tea. Did you know that science was the only subject I never skipped? I went through a phase of making bombs—blowing everything up. You probably remember that phase. Everyone on Glenmore does.'

Flora hesitated and then reached out and touched his arm, because it seemed like the right thing to do. 'I can't imagine what it must have been like for you.'

'It was amazing fun. I was causing explosions all over the place and no one could stop me.' He showed no emotion but she wasn't fooled.

'So if it's that easy and you care so little, why haven't you come home before now?'

'Good question.' He was silent for a moment and then he laughed. 'Perceptive, aren't you? Yes, I suppose I'm back here because I wanted to see how it felt to be home.'

'And?'

'It feels every bit as bad as I thought it would.' He spoke calmly and turned his head to look at her. 'So now I've spilled my guts, what happens next? I cry into your soft bosom and get in touch with my feelings?'

'In case you hadn't noticed, I'm pretty flat-chested so that won't work.' She kept her tone light because she sensed that was what he wanted. 'I suppose I just want you to know that, well, that I'm a friend—if you need one.'

'A flat-chested friend.' He gave a slow smile. 'I've never had one of those before. Do you know what I really fancy right now?'

Her heart thumped wildly. 'I hardly dare ask.'

'A cigarette.'

It wasn't what she'd wanted him to say and she let out a

breath, not knowing whether to laugh or cry. *Drop the fantasies*, Flora. 'I didn't know you smoked.'

'I don't. At least, not for years. I just need something to relieve the tension. I'll have to find another way.'

Flora stiffened. *He was talking about sex*, she knew he was. And there was no doubt in her mind that there were any number of women on Glenmore who would be only too delighted to offer him the distraction he wanted.

And he was stuck on the beach with her.

Boring Flora.

He looked at her. 'I suppose it's a waste of time asking if you have any cigarettes?'

'Complete waste of time,' she said lightly. *Boring, staid Flora.*

'Anything to drink?'

'I have a small bottle of mineral water in my bag.'

'Mineral water?' He laughed. 'You really know how to live, don't you? Nothing like a few minerals to get a person into a party mood. Tell me, Flora Harris, what do you do to release tension? Read a chapter of *War and Peace*?'

She smiled. 'If I can't sail, then I swim.'

'You swim?'

'In the sea. Every morning. I love it. It relaxes me.'

'You take your clothes off?'

'No, I swim in my uniform.' Flora glanced at him in amusement. 'Of course I take my clothes off. What did you think?'

'I've no idea. I've made a point of never picturing you without clothes on.'

'Thanks.'

His eyes narrowed. 'If you're taking that as an insult then you're even more naïve than I think you are.'

'I'm not naïve.'

'Yes, you are. The reason I don't picture you without

clothes is because then I'll start thinking about you in a way that would make Logan punch me.'

Her heart was racing. 'Logan isn't my keeper.'

'Good point.' He rose to his feet and tugged her up beside him. 'Come on, then, Flora Harris. We'll try the swim. See if it works.'

'Now?' Her voice was an astonished squeak. 'It's one in the morning.'

'Less crowded than one in the afternoon.'

She gave a strangled laugh. 'Yes, I suppose it is. I don't have a costume.'

He gave a wicked smile and slowly undid the buttons on his shirt. 'The point of skinny dipping is that you don't need clothes.' His hands dropped to the fastening at the waistband of his trousers and her cheeks warmed as she caught a glimpse of taut, muscular stomach and dark male body hair.

'For goodness' sake, Conner…'

'What? You just said "Of course I take my clothes off." So that's what I'm doing.'

'Obviously, I wear a costume.'

'Obviously.' He grinned. 'Because you wouldn't be you if you didn't. But me being me, I'm not going to bother.' Completely unselfconscious, he stepped out of his trousers and boxer shorts and Flora gave a nervous laugh, keeping her eyes firmly fixed on the horizon.

'You're going to get yourself arrested, Conner MacNeil.'

'It's dark. No one knows we're here.' His hands were on the hem of her T-shirt. 'Come on, Flora. Take a risk. Live a little. Get naked with me.'

Take a risk. Live a little.

Suddenly the world opened up in front of her and her heart thundered in her chest. 'I am *not* swimming naked with you.'

'If the water is as cold as I suspect it's going to be, you're at no risk from me, darling, but if it makes you feel better you can leave your underwear on.' He gently pulled the T-shirt over her head and slid her shorts down her legs.

As his fingers brushed her skin and she shivered.

She knew she should stop him, but she couldn't, and when he closed his hand firmly over hers and dragged her down to the water's edge, she didn't resist.

And then the water touched her feet and she stopped dead. 'Oh, my goodness, that's cold.'

'Don't be a wimp.' He jerked her forward. 'This was your idea and you're not bottling out now. Anyway, what are you complaining about?' Conner kept walking, long steady strides that took him deeper into the sea. 'It's like bathwater. I can't imagine why anyone would travel all the way to the Mediterranean when we have this on our doorstep.' He gave her no choice but to wade in with him and she picked her way gingerly through the dark, swirling water, catching her breath as the waves licked higher and higher on her legs.

'I'm not sure if I like doing this in the middle of the night.' She peered towards her feet. 'Do you think there are jellyfish?'

'No. It's long past their bedtime. They're all curled up asleep with hot-water bottles.' The water was halfway up his thighs now and as a wave washed over him at waist level, he cursed fluently. 'I think we've just discovered a whole new non-surgical method of vasectomy. If any of my sperm survive this experience, it will be a miracle.'

Flora giggled helplessly and wondered what had come over her. *What was she doing?* She was standing in the sea at one o'clock in the morning with Conner MacNeil, the most dangerous, unsuitable man she was every likely to meet.

And she was having the time of her life.

'This is freezing. I don't think I can go in any further.'

'The only way to do this is quickly. If you do this every

morning then I have new respect for you, Flora. You're twice the woman I thought you were, flat chest or no flat chest.'

'It's bracing. It wakes me up.'

'No surprise there. If this didn't wake you up, you'd have to be dead.'

'It's colder tonight.' She clutched him tightly, afraid that the waves would knock her over, and he steadied her and then released her hand.

'All right, let's do this…' He dived forward into the waves and she had a brief glimpse of powerful male muscle and strong legs before he vanished from sight.

She rubbed her hands down her arms, knowing that the goose-bumps had nothing to do with the cold water and everything to do with the way her body had felt next to his. *How was it possible to feel hot when she was standing waist deep in freezing seawater?*

She followed him into the waves, wondering why she'd never swum in the moonlight before. In all the years she'd lived here and swum here, she'd never done this. And it was fabulous. Magical. The stars and the moon shone in the clear sky and the water glistened.

And she felt daring and more alive than she'd ever felt.

She was so enchanted by her surroundings that she gasped with shock when Conner emerged next to her.

There was just enough light for her to see the outline of his face and the faint glitter in his eyes as he reached out and pulled her against him. 'I can't believe I'm skinny dipping with Flora Harris. Looks like I've finally corrupted you.'

'I like being corrupted.' She kept her voice light, trying not to reveal how it felt to be this close to him. She could feel the hardness of his thighs against hers and, despite his complaints about the cold water, a building pressure against her abdomen. 'And I'm not naked.'

'Not yet.'

'Conner…' To keep her balance she placed her hands on his shoulders and felt the smooth swell of hard male muscle under her fingers.

His mouth was dangerously close to hers. 'I've been thinking about what you said.'

Thinking? *How could he think?* 'What did I say?'

'That you were the only female on the island that I haven't kissed.'

'I was wrong.' She was so aware of him that could barely speak, 'I'm fairly sure you haven't kissed Ann Carne, and Mrs Parker may have escaped, too.'

'Good point.' He lifted his hands and cupped her face gently. 'Nevertheless, it's only fair to warn you that I might be about to corrupt you further. You might want to run for the beach. I'll give you a two-second start.'

Her heart pounded like the hooves of a racehorse on the home stretch. 'Two seconds doesn't sound like much.'

'It's all you're getting. Take it or leave it.'

She couldn't take her eyes from his and the anticipation was agonising. 'I'll leave it. I can't run in these waves.' *He was going to kiss her.*

Finally, after what seemed like a lifetime, Conner MacNeil was going to kiss her.

'If you can't run, then you're trapped.' His head moved closer but he didn't touch her. Instead, his mouth hovered tantalisingly close to hers, the expression in his eyes knowing and wickedly sexy as he prolonged the torture for both of them. Her stomach tumbled and her senses hummed and when finally he brushed his lips over hers, she knew that this was the most perfect and exciting thing that had ever happened to her. His lips were cool and the tip of his tongue gently caressed her lower lip.

Heat exploded inside her and she made a soft sound in her throat and leaned against him, seeking more. Her eyes closed, but still she saw stars as everything inside her erupted with excitement.

His fingers closed hard around her arms and his body shifted against hers.

'Hell, Flora...' This time his mouth came down hard, his kiss sending bolts of electricity through her body, and she clutched at him for support as he drew the fire from deep inside her with the skilled, sensual stroke of his tongue. And she kissed him back, her tongue toying with his in a kiss that was both intimate and erotic. His hands dropped from her face and slid down her back, pulling her against him in a movement that was unmistakably possessive.

It was a kiss with promise and purpose but before she had the chance to discover where it was leading, there was a shout.

With a groan of frustration and anger Conner dragged his mouth from hers and Flora clutched at him for support, dizzy and disoriented from the kiss. It took her a moment to realise that the sound was coming from the beach behind them.

'Conner? Conner MacNeil, is that you? It's Jim—Jim from the ferry and a few of the lads. We wanted to buy you a drink.'

'Oh, my goodness.' Flora shrank with embarrassment. 'They can't possibly see us, can they? It's too dark.'

Conner stared down at her for a moment, his lashes lowered, his eyes as cool and defiant as ever. 'Do you care?'

Flora didn't answer because she genuinely didn't know the answer to that. This was her island. And it was her reputation on the line. She should care, she knew she should. But his kiss had changed everything. It was as if her life had reached a crossroads and she didn't know which path to take—the safe one was back on the shore and the dangerous one was here, in the sea, with Conner's hard male body pressed against hers.

'Flora?' His voice was even and she wondered how he could sound so normal after what they'd shared. She felt far from normal. She felt churned up, confused—*different*.

She breathed in and out. She knew that it was too dark for them to have recognised her, but if she walked out of the water with Conner...

She wanted to say, *Damn the lot of them,* and carry on kissing him, but something held her back. 'I—I don't know, Conner.' Her fingers tightened on his arms. 'I suppose I do care. I have to work with these people. I'll still be living on this island long after you've left.'

He released her abruptly. 'Of course you will. Stay here. I'll get them away from you and you can get home before anyone is any the wiser. I guess that's more chivalrous than escorting you home.' He spoke with a careless indifference and she felt a flash of desperation as she sensed his withdrawal and felt her new self slipping away.

Suddenly she wished desperately that she hadn't spoken. *The person who had spoken had been the girl she'd been all her life, but now she wasn't sure if she was that girl any more. She didn't know if she wanted to be that girl.*

She wanted to be daring and careless of the consequences, like him. She wanted to live in the moment and not think about what other people thought. She wanted to kiss Conner MacNeil and enjoy every second of the excitement.

Without his hands to steady her, she almost stumbled as a wave hit her from the back and the shower of cold water seemed symbolic.

It was over.

Her moment of wild living had passed and she was back to being boring Flora. Sensible Flora. A girl who would never swim half-naked in the sea with a very unsuitable man.

But did she really want to be that girl?

'Conner, wait.' She grabbed his arm. 'I don't care about them. I don't care if they see us.'

It took him a moment to reply and when he did, his voice was rough. 'Yes, you do, angel. And quite right, too. How are you going to have a proper conversation with Mrs Parker if word gets round that you've been cavorting in the waves with Bad Conner? Be grateful to the locals. You've been saved from total corruption by the brave and persistent citizens of Glenmore.'

She didn't know what to say to rescue the situation so she tried to joke about it. 'Isn't it typical? The first time I try to be wild, I have an audience.'

He laughed, then lifted a hand and drew his thumb slowly over her lower lip, the intimacy of the gesture in direct contrast to his words. 'I've had more excitement being shot at in the desert.' His tone was sarcastic but the look in his eyes made her dizzy.

'I'm sure.'

His smile faded. 'You're not made for this, Flora, and both of us know it. You need a man you're not ashamed to be seen with, so let's end this now before we both do something that will keep the locals talking for years. I'll swim to the other side of the beach and meet them there. Stay in the water until I'm out and they won't see you. Can you make your way home safely?'

'Of course. Do I look helpless?'

'No, you look sexy.' He gave a wicked smile and lowered his mouth to hers once more, his lips and tongue working a seductive magic that made the world spin. Then he lifted his head reluctantly and gave a resigned shrug. 'Sorry about that. Just couldn't help myself. Once bad, always bad, or so it would seem. You just had a lucky escape, Flora Harris. Five more minutes and we would have been in the middle of a practical scientific experiment involving frozen body parts and libido.' Without giving her time to respond, he called to the men on the shore. 'Back off, guys. I'll be with you in a minute.' And then he plunged back into the waves and swam away from her with a powerful crawl.

Nodding to the locals who were toasting his health, Conner raised his glass to his lips and tried to decide whether he should be grateful or just punch them.

Five minutes more and he would have been completing the corruption of Flora.

So he should be grateful, obviously. If he'd followed the episode to its natural conclusion, Flora would now be steeped in embarrassment and regret.

He remembered her anguished gasp when she'd realised that they'd been spotted. Even in the semi-darkness he'd been able to see the burning colour of her cheeks.

Narrow escape for her. And for him, he told himself firmly. It was hard enough being back on Glenmore, without having that on his conscience.

He drank deeply, trying to obliterate the memory of the way she'd tasted and the way her body had felt pressed against his. She'd been lithe, slender, slippery from the seawater—

'Conner MacNeil, am I drunk or are you really sitting there drinking cranberry juice?'

Conner looked at Jim. 'You are drunk. And I am sitting here drinking cranberry juice.'

Jim focused on the glass in his hand. 'It looks disgusting.'

'It is disgusting.' *But not as disgusting as Evanna's home-made lemonade*, he thought with wry humour. Something stirred inside him as he remembered Flora standing on the grass, clutching a picnic basket.

'When I offered to buy you a drink…' Jim lifted a finger and waggled it in his direction '…I meant a *proper* drink. A man's drink. What are you? Wimp or man?'

Dismissing thoughts of Flora's soft mouth, Conner gave a careless lift of his shoulder. 'Wimp, obviously.'

'Leave the man alone.' Nick Hillier, the island policeman, slapped Conner on the back. 'A hero can relax in any way he chooses. Personally, I'm just glad it's not alcohol. It will save me the bother of arresting him for drink-driving later.'

Jim hiccoughed lightly. 'Your old man knew how to drink.'

An uncomfortable silence fell on the group of men who'd had less to drink than Jim, but Conner simply nodded. 'He certainly did.'

Jim sniffed. 'Couldn't have been easy, living with that. Duncan MacNeil had one hell of a temper.'

'You want me to cry on your shoulder?'

Jim shuddered. 'You know what I want? I want to know who the girl was, Conner. That's what I want.' He winked at the others and Conner slowly lowered his glass to the table.

So they *had* seen. 'No one.'

'Bet she was pretty. You always did get the pretty ones. Hey, everyone…,' Jim raised his voice to attract maximum attention. Then he hiccoughed again and lifted his glass in salute. 'Conner was in the waves with "no one".'

'At least "no one" can't nag at you,' someone muttered, and Jim gave a snort.

'She was real enough.'

'We can torture it out of him.' Nick suggested. 'You have the right to remain silent—'

'And I intend to,' Conner drawled, his face expressionless. Inside, a slow anger burned. *Anger towards himself and what he'd so nearly done.* If they'd seen that it was Flora, what would that have done to her reputation? She was decent and sweet and, as she'd pointed out, she was going to be working on this island long after he'd turned his back on it for ever. She was also a shy and private person who would have hidden in a hole in the ground rather than have her name tossed carelessly around a group of men in a pub.

And with his selfish actions, he'd almost destroyed everything she'd worked for.

And not just by exposing her to gossip.

He lifted his glass again, remembering the shyness and the desperate excitement in her eyes in the last seconds before he'd given in to impulse and kissed her. She'd wanted him, badly. He should have been flattered but instead he felt…disgusted with himself. Disgusted with himself for not walking away. He had no idea how much sexual experience she'd had, but he was willing to bet that her lifestyle didn't encompass meaningless affairs, and that was all he could offer her.

He stared at the bunch of locals gathered around the table, laughing and joking at his expense.

He should be grateful to them.

If it weren't for them he'd now be suffering from regret instead of sexual frustration. And Flora… Flora would have assured him in that polite voice of hers that everything was fine, but deep down she'd have been horrified at herself for indulging in a moment of madness with a delinquent like him.

Or worse—she'd be looking at him with those huge, brown eyes of hers, wanting things from him that he'd never, ever be able to deliver.

Conner drained his glass, knowing that probably for the first time in his life he'd done the right thing.

With a humourless laugh he studied the empty glass in his hand, sure of one thing. If doing the right thing felt this bad, he wasn't going to make a habit of it.

CHAPTER SEVEN

'HE SAVED the child, can you believe that? Anyway, I always knew there was good in him. It's not surprising he went off the rails with everything that he had to contend with at home.' Angela Parker watched as Flora tightened the bandage. 'I mean, his mother left when he was only ten years old. And his father was a drunk. A *violent* drunk, some say. Shocking, really shocking. It's no wonder he was wild. The poor boy.'

'Yes, Mrs Parker. I mean, no.' Flora was barely listening. Her mind was on other things. Although part of her was delighted and relieved that the entire island was now treating Conner as a hero, another part of her felt as though something inside her had been ripped out.

It was just because she was tired, she told herself. But she knew that wasn't true. It had nothing to do with lack of sleep and everything to do with the kiss she'd shared with Conner.

The kiss that had been interrupted.

The kiss that she'd totally messed up.

She kept reliving that moment and wishing she'd done things differently. She wished she'd yelled out, *It's me, Flora Harris, Jim. Yes, I'm kissing Conner so could you just all go away and let us get on with it?* She wished she hadn't been embarrassed. She wished she'd held onto the moment instead of letting it slip from her fingers. She wished…

She wished Conner felt something for her.

But he didn't.

In fact, not only had he not mentioned it, he hadn't even talked to her. Several days had passed and he'd been so busy fielding patients eager to consult him about his various problems that she'd barely seen him in the distance, let alone put herself in the position where a conversation might be possible.

At first she'd managed to convince herself that he was just very busy. She'd lingered in the surgery long after the patients had left, hoping that he'd seek her out, and she'd sat in her empty cottage at night, waiting for a knock on the door or the ring of the phone.

She'd thought up a million reasons for the fact that he hadn't come near her, but in the end she'd run out of reasons. And still he hadn't disturbed her solitude.

And she couldn't blame him for that, could she? Not after she'd made it perfectly clear that she'd be embarrassed to be caught with him. It was hardly surprising that he was now avoiding her and she wished she'd done everything differently.

She had no backbone.

She was pathetic.

'Well?' Angela peered down at her. 'You've been staring at my leg for ages, dear. Is something wrong?'

'No, nothing,' Flora said quickly, and Angela nodded.

'If you're worried, perhaps I should make an appointment with Conner.'

Remembering how fast Angela had run from Conner just a couple of weeks ago, Flora gave a faint smile. That was the other reason she was finding it hard to put him out of her head. Everywhere she went, people were talking about

Conner. And he treated their attention with as much careless indifference as he'd treated their disregard.

'Your leg is looking much better, Mrs Parker. The inflammation has settled and I think it's healing now. Keep up the good work.'

And she had to pull herself together and accept the person she was. She just wasn't someone who could cavort half-naked in the moonlight with the island bad boy. She cared too much what people thought.

And that was why a relationship between her and Conner would never work.

She cared. And Conner didn't give a damn. The more he shocked people, the happier he was.

Even that night on the beach had probably just been a game to him, seeing if his seduction skills were good enough to persuade boring old Flora to kiss him.

He wasn't interested in anything more, and she couldn't blame him for that.

She was boring Flora, wasn't she? The type of girl who kept her knickers on even when she swam in the sea at night.

Not the sort of girl who would hold Conner MacNeil's attention for more than two minutes.

Trying to block out Angela's endless chatter, Flora finished the dressing, washed her hands, completed her notes and saw the woman to the door.

Then she went across and tapped on Logan's door. 'How's Evanna?'

'Still pregnant. No change. She's going to the mainland for a check at the end of the week.'

'And presumably you can go with her now, given that the entire population of Glenmore thinks that Conner walks on water.'

'I know. It's brilliant. Overnight my life has changed.' He smiled at her. 'I actually managed to have breakfast with my wife and daughter this morning. Conner should be a hero more often. I could resign and grow my own vegetables.'

'I'm so pleased it's all worked out. His surgery is so full now Janet's having to turn people away.'

'Conner's a good doctor.'

'Yes.' She thought of him with Lily. *His sure touch. His skill. His incredible focus when the entire world around him had been panicking.*

And then she thought of his kiss. Equally sure and skilled. Did he do everything well?

She gave a little shiver and Logan glanced at her.

'Are you all right? You're a bit pale.'

'I'm fine. Absolutely fine.' Just confused. *Frustrated. Out of her depth.* She'd never felt like this before and she didn't know what to do about it. Her previous relationships had been boringly uncomplicated. She'd been out with two men and neither of them had caused this degree of turbulence to her insides. 'Tell Evanna to call me if she needs anything.'

'I'll do that.' Logan studied her closely. 'Are you sure you're all right?'

'Really, I'm fine,' Flora lied. 'Just a little tired.'

'Right.' Logan watched her. 'If you're sure.'

Flora returned to her consulting room and worked her way through her patients, only half listening to the steady stream of Glenmore chatter.

She'd just seen her last patient when the door opened and Conner stood there.

Flora felt her stomach flip and looked at his face, hoping to see something that suggested he felt the same way, but there was nothing. His handsome face was expressionless, his attitude brisk and professional.

'Lily is being discharged today. You should call on her and her fussy mother—do all the touchy-feely stuff that I can't be bothered with.'

She tried not to feel hurt or disappointed. *What had she expected?* 'You could go yourself. They'd want to thank you. Jayne is so grateful, she can't stop crying.'

'All the more reason to stay away. The one body fluid I'm no good with is female tears.' He gave a faint smile. 'If Lily bleeds again, phone me. Otherwise it's just emotional support and someone else can do that bit. Someone better qualified than me.'

He wasn't comfortable with emotion.

Flora thought of the things he'd told her in the velvet darkness. She thought about the mother who had left him and the father who hadn't cared. And she suspected that he'd been exposed to more extremes of emotion in his childhood than most people experienced in a lifetime.

Was that why he backed away from it now?

Was that why he was backing away from *her*?

'I'll call on her.'

'Good.' His eyes held hers for a moment—lingered—then his mouth tightened and he turned to leave.

But there had been something in that look that made it impossible for her to let him walk away. 'Conner!' Something burst free inside her and she just couldn't help herself. 'Wait. Can we talk?'

Conner paused, his hand on the door, a man poised for flight. 'What about?' But he knew what it was going to be about and he kept his tone cool and his face expressionless because he also knew what he needed to do. *And it was going to be the hardest thing he'd ever done.*

He stood still, hoping she'd lose courage. And perhaps she almost did because she watched him closely and then gave a confused little smile that cut through him like the blade of a knife.

Don't say it, Flora. Don't say it and then I won't have to reject you.

She rubbed her hands nervously down her uniform and took a deep breath. 'All I wanted to say was that…well, you—you really don't have to avoid me.'

'Yes, I do.' He kept his answer blunt, knowing that it was the only way.

'Why? Because you kissed me?' She shrugged awkwardly. 'Do you ignore every woman you kiss?'

'No, normally I corrupt them totally before I ignore them. You escaped lightly.'

'Is that supposed to make me feel lucky?' The colour bloomed in her cheeks but she didn't back off. 'Because it doesn't.'

Her response almost weakened him and Conner reminded himself ruthlessly that this time he was doing the right thing, not the easy thing.

He watched her for a moment, his eyes fixed on her face. Then he closed the door, slowly and deliberately, giving them privacy. 'It should make you feel lucky. If they hadn't turned up I would have taken you, Flora.' His voice dangerously soft, he closed the distance between them in a single stride. *Shock tactics.* Perhaps shock tactics would work. 'You would have been mine. That's how close you came.'

She shivered with excitement. 'Yes…'

'And then I would have dumped you, because that's what I do with women. And you would have cried.'

She swallowed. 'Maybe.'

Definitely.

Unable to help himself, Conner lifted a hand to touch her but then saw the trust shining in her dark eyes and took a step backwards, letting his hand drop to his side. 'You're the sort of woman who deserves to wake up next to a good man.' His hand curled into a fist. 'That isn't me, Flora.'

'You're a good man.'

'No.'

'Why do you say that?'

'Because a good man wouldn't do what I'm about to do,' he muttered, knowing that he'd lost the fight. He reached out a hand, yanking her against him and crushing his mouth against hers.

A kaleidoscope of colours exploded in his head and any hope of pulling away vanished as she wrapped her arms around his neck and pressed closer. He kissed her roughly but she gave back willingly and her mouth was sweet and warm under his.

And since when had sweetness had any place in his life?

He released her so suddenly that she swayed dizzily. 'Conner—'

'Don't.' With a rough jerk he disengaged himself from her arms. 'Don't offer yourself to me, Flora.'

'Why not?' Clearly sensing the tension and anger boiling inside him, she lifted a hand to his cheek, pushing aside her natural shyness. 'It's what I want.'

'No, it isn't what you want.'

She stood, looking hurt and vulnerable. 'It is. I want you.'

The blood throbbing in his veins, Conner turned away from her, knowing that he couldn't say what he had to say if he was looking at her. None of the things he'd ever done in his life had ever felt as hard as this and he steeled himself to do what had to be done. 'Well, I don't want you.' His tone was rock steady. 'I'm sorry if that hurts, but it's better to be honest up front. I don't want you, Flora. There's no chemistry there at all.'

Her soft gasp was like a punch in the gut. 'Conner—'

'You kiss like a child, Flora. You don't even turn me on.' This time he altered his tone so that he sounded careless, even a little bored. Then he gave a dismissive shrug and strolled towards the door. 'I suggest you find someone of your own age to practise on.'

Then he left the room, slamming the door so hard that the entire building shook.

Only when he was safely within the privacy of his consulting room did Conner finally release the emotion he'd kept firmly locked inside. He let out a string of expletives and thumped his fist against the wall. Then he sank onto his chair and stared at the door, willing himself not to walk back through it and tell her that he hadn't meant a single word he'd just said. Because if he did that—*if he sought her out and apologised*—he wouldn't be righting a wrong, he'd be making things worse.

Yes, he'd hurt her.

He'd hurt her so badly that he felt physically sick at the thought, and he knew that her gasp of pain and the shimmer of tears in her eyes would stay with him for a long time.

But he also knew that the pain would be infinitely greater if he took their relationship any further.

His eyes slid to the doorhandle and he gritted his teeth and looked away, ruthlessly ignoring the urge to go back and comfort her. Talk to her. What was there to say? He'd already said it. And better now than later. Better a small amount of private pain than public humiliation when the entire island discovered their affair.

They'd tear her apart and he wasn't going to let that happen to her.

There was a tap on the door and he looked up with a growl of impatience, furious at having been disturbed. 'What?' He barked the word and the door opened slowly and a woman peeped nervously into the room.

'Janet said to come straight through.'

'What for?'

She blinked. 'Surgery? I have an appointment with you.'

Conner stared at her blankly and then realised that kissing Flora had actually driven everything out of his head. *Everything, including the fact that he was supposed to be seeing patients.*

'Of course. Sorry.' He managed something approximating a smile. 'Come in.' And then he recognised her. Agatha Patterson, the elderly lady who lived in the converted lifeboat cottage on the beach. 'I expect you've come to exact your revenge. I seem to remember raiding your flower-beds one night.'

'You gave them to that girl—the pretty blonde one. I still remember how pleased she was.'

Conner gave a faint smile. 'That was at least sixteen years ago so I'm guessing you're not here because you're worried about your memory. Am I supposed to apologise for helping myself to your flowers?'

'Goodness, I don't want an apology! I should be the one thanking you.' Agatha closed the door and walked stiffly into the room. 'You livened up my life. You were always down on the beach below my property. I liked watching you.'

Remembering some of the things he'd done on the beach below her house, Conner inhaled sharply. 'How much could you see?'

'Well, my eyes were better in those days, of course.' She chuckled and walked slowly towards the chair, her body bent in the shape of a question mark. She was a grey-haired lady with a jolly smile and a twinkle in her eye that hinted at a lively past. 'I was always amazed by how successful you were. Quite the lad, Conner MacNeil.'

Conner gave a reluctant laugh. 'All right, that's probably enough of that conversation. Did you want to ask me something or are you just here to threaten me with my wicked past?'

'Oh, no, nothing like that. I heard what you did for little Lily, by the way. I think you're amazing.'

'Thanks.' *So amazing that he'd left a woman crying in the room opposite.* 'What can I do for you, Mrs Patterson?'

'Well, funnily enough, it's my eyes I've come about. They're incredibly sore.'

'Too much watching people on the beach,' Conner said in a wry tone, and she gave a delighted smile.

'There's been hardly any action since you left. These days everyone is too worried about being arrested. Not that you ever worried about that sort of thing. Anyway, I wouldn't normally bother you with anything so pathetically trivial, but my eyes are so sore that the pain is reducing the time I can spend on the internet.'

Conner stared at her. 'The *internet*?'

'And if you're thinking of telling me to reduce the time I spend on the computer, you needn't waste your breath. I'm careful never to do more than eight hours a day.'

Conner glanced at his own computer screen, searching for the information he wanted. 'You're…eighty-six, Mrs Patterson. Is that right?'

'Eighty-seven next week.'

'And you're spending…' he cleared his throat, intrigued by his patient '…*how long* on the internet?'

'No more than eight hours a day.' She curled her fingers around the strap of her bag. 'Given the chance, I'd spent longer, but with my eyes the way they are…'

Conner gave a disbelieving laugh. 'I have to ask this—just what are you doing on the internet, Mrs Patterson?'

'Everything,' she said simply. 'I mean, for an old lady on her own like me, it's a doorway to a whole new exciting life. Last week I spent a morning looking around a new exhibition in a fancy gallery in London, just by clicking my mouse, then I spent an afternoon gazing at a beach in Australia—

amazing webcam, by the way, you should try it. Last month I spent an entire week in Florence—I visited somewhere new every day. But it's not just travel and art, it's food, conversation. I just *love* chat rooms.' She leaned forward and winked at him. 'I bet you didn't know there was a chat room for the over-eighties.'

Conner started to laugh. 'No, Mrs Patterson. I didn't know that. Do you party?'

'Like you wouldn't believe.' Her smile faded. 'But these eyes of mine…'

'Yes.' He shook his head and stood up. 'All right, let's take a look, although why I would want to fix your problem just so that you can spy on me, I don't know. It's probably dry-eye syndrome. You're spending too long on the computer. And that's something I've never had to say to an eighty-six-year-old before.'

'So, which young lady's heart are you breaking at the moment, you bad boy?'

Conner stilled, thinking of Flora. 'No one. I'm being boringly good.'

'You mean you don't want to tell me.' Agatha gave him a conspiratorial wink. 'That's good. When you care about a girl's reputation, it means it's serious.'

Conner stared at her. *Serious?* 'Trust me, Agatha, it isn't serious.'

'Ah—so there is someone.'

Realising that he'd just been outmanoeuvred by an eighty-six-year-old woman, Conner gave a silent laugh and examined her eyes, trying not to remember how Flora had looked when he'd said that she didn't turn him on.

Why on earth had she believed him?

Hadn't she seen that his words and his body had contradicted each other?

Apparently not, which just proved how naïve she was.

And proved that he'd been right to walk away.

He was absolutely *not* the man for her.

'Is everything all right?' Agatha looked at him anxiously. 'You seem very grim-faced.'

'I'm fine. Everything is fine.'

And it should have been.

He'd ended a completely unsuitable relationship before it had started. He should have been feeling good about himself. But he was experiencing his first ever attack of conscience.

He'd hurt women before. Plenty of them. And it had never particularly bothered him. He'd always thought it more cruel to let a woman delude herself and spend hours waiting by the phone for a call that wasn't going to come.

Fast and sharp, that's how he would have wanted it, so that's how he'd delivered it.

The difference was that he wasn't doing this for himself. He was doing it for Flora and there was a certain irony in the fact that his first truly unselfish act was causing her pain. And he was in agony.

Suddenly realising that Agatha was watching him closely, he pulled himself together. 'Do you have the central heating on at home?'

'Of course. This is Glenmore.' Her tone was dry. 'Without central heating I'd be too cold to sit at the computer.'

'Try logging on to somewhere warm,' he drawled, examining her eyes carefully. 'Mauritius is nice at this time of year. Central heating can make the irritation and redness a little worse. Tear secretion does reduce with age, Mrs Patterson.'

'So do all the other secretions, Dr MacNeil.' She gave him a saucy wink and Conner shook his head and started to laugh.

'I can't believe we're having this conversation. What were you like at twenty, Agatha?'

'I would have given you a run for your money, that's for sure.' She leaned forward, a twinkle in her eyes. 'You wouldn't have been able to walk away from that beach after a night with me.'

'I have no trouble believing you. All right, this is what we're going to do. I'm going to start by giving you artificial tears to use. It they don't make a difference, I can refer you to an ophthalmologist on the mainland for an opinion.'

'Can I contact him by email?'

Conner grinned and sat back down in his chair. 'I'm sure he'd be delighted to hear from you. Try the drops first. They might do the trick.' He studied his computer screen, clicked on the drug he wanted and printed off a prescription.

'You're a handsome one, aren't you?' Agatha gave a cheeky smile. 'If I'd seen you sixty years ago, you wouldn't have stood a chance.'

'Now, that's a pick-up line I haven't heard before.' Conner took the prescription out of the printer and stood up. 'Try these. If you have no joy, come back to me.'

'I certainly will.' She took the prescription, folded it and tucked it into her handbag. Then she stood up. 'The beach is still nice, you know. If you fancied paying a visit.'

Conner laughed. 'Get out of here, Agatha.'

'I'm going. I'm going.' And she left the room with slightly more bounce and energy than she'd shown when she'd entered it.

Flora began to wish that Glenmore was larger and busier. After her last humiliating encounter with Conner she was the one avoiding him, if such a thing was possible on an island as small as this one.

She arrived at work, hurried to her consulting room and then straight out on her calls. She didn't spend time in the staffroom and if she needed a doctor's advice on a patient, she sought out Logan.

It should have helped, but it didn't. She felt dreadful.

On the outside she looked as she always had—a little paler perhaps, but pretty much the same. But on the inside…on the inside she was ripped to shreds. She was *mortified* that she'd misinterpreted his actions and felt foolish beyond words for ever believing that a woman like her—*boring Flora*—could ever be attractive to a man like Conner.

He was a woman's dream, wasn't he?

She might be relatively inexperienced, but she wasn't blind. Women's eyes followed him wherever he went. That wicked, careless streak that defied the opinion of society was one of the very things that made him so appealing. He was his own person. As strong of mind as he was of body.

And she had to put him out of *her* mind and move on.

So she concentrated on work and succeeded in avoiding contact with him until one afternoon a thirteen-year-old boy with a cheeky smile and long, lanky limbs tapped on her door.

Recognising him immediately, Flora waved a hand towards the empty chair. 'Hi, Fraser, come on in. How are the summer holidays going?'

'Too fast.' The boy gave a shrug and stood awkwardly just inside the door.

Aisla, his mother, gave him a gentle push towards the chair. 'For goodness' sake, she isn't going to bite you!' She rolled her eyes at Flora. 'Honestly, these teenagers. They're men one minute and boys the next. He's terrified you're going to tell him to undress.'

Fraser shot his mother a horrified look, gave a grunt of embarrassment and slunk into the chair.

Flora smiled at him. 'What's the problem, Fraser?'

'It's my legs. Well, this leg mostly.' He stuck it out in front of him and frowned down at the mud and the bruises. 'I was doing football camp up at the school but I've had to stop.'

'Both the doctors are fully booked but Janet said you'd take a look and decide what we need to do,' Aisla said quickly. 'I don't know whether he needs an X-ray or what.'

'Did something happen? Did you fall?'

'I fall all the time. It's part of football.' Fraser rubbed his leg and Aisla gave a long-suffering sigh.

'I can vouch for that. You should see the colour of his clothes. I swear that all the mud of Glenmore is in my washing machine.'

Flora smiled and dropped to her knees beside Fraser. 'Let me take a look—show me exactly where it hurts. Here?'

'Ow!' Fraser winced. 'Right there. Have I broken it?'

'No, I don't think so. Nothing like that. I'm going to ask Logan to take a quick look.'

'Don't waste your time. He's just gone on a home visit,' Aisla told her wearily. 'We were in Reception when Janet took the call and he came rushing out. Some tourist with chest pain on the beach.'

'Oh.' Flora's heart rate trebled. 'Well, we could wait until he's back, I suppose. He might not be long.'

'I want to see Conner,' Fraser blurted out. 'He knows everything about football. Can we ask him to look at my leg?'

Just the sound of his name made her palms damp. 'With Logan out, he'll be very busy.'

'Is it worth just trying? Perhaps he'd see Fraser if you ask him.' Aisla's expression was worried. 'It's just that, if he thinks it should be X-rayed, I'm going to need to make some plans.'

'Of course I'll try. Wait there a moment.' Hoping she didn't look as reluctant as she felt, Flora left her room and took several deep breaths. Across the corridor a patient left Conner's room and Flora felt her knees turn to liquid.

She couldn't do it. She really couldn't face him.

She turned backwards to her room and then realised that

she couldn't do that either. How could she tell Aisla that she was too pathetic to face Conner?

Taking a deep breath, she walked briskly over to his door and rapped hard, before she could change her mind.

Keep it brief and to the point, she told herself. Professional. And don't look at him. *Whatever you do, don't look at him.*

'Yes?' The harsh bark of his voice made her jump and she wondered how any of the patients ever plucked up courage to go and see him. Closing her eyes briefly, she took a deep breath and opened the door.

'I just wanted to ask if you'd see a patient for me. Thirteen-year-old boy complaining of pain in his leg. It's tender and there's swelling over the tibial tubercle.' She adjusted her glasses, still not looking at him. 'He's been at football camp so it's possible that he's injured himself, but I'm wondering whether it could be Osgood-Schlatter disease.'

'Reading all those books has obviously paid off.'

She had the feeling that he was intentionally trying to hurt her and she didn't understand it. He wasn't unkind, she knew he wasn't. Why would he want to hurt her? 'Obviously I'm not qualified to make that diagnosis.' Suffering agonies of embarrassment, she cleared her throat. 'He's in my room now. He's suffering from an attack of hero-worship and is desperate for your opinion on his leg.'

'Ah…' He spoke softly. 'Patient pressure. And I'm willing to bet you tried Logan first.'

'Fraser is Logan's patient so he was the logical first choice.'

'And nowhere near as terrifying as facing me. How much courage did it take for you to knock on my door?'

She stiffened. 'Please, don't make fun of me, Dr MacNeil.'

'Do I look as though I'm laughing?' With a low growl of impatience, he rose to his feet. 'There are things I need to say to you, Flora.'

'You made your thoughts perfectly clear the last time we

spoke. If you could just see the patient and give me your opinion, I can take it from there.' Terrified that she was about to make a fool of herself, Flora turned and walked quickly back to her room, her heart thundering in her chest. Aware that Conner was right behind her, she concentrated on Fraser. 'Dr MacNeil will take a look at you, Fraser.'

Conner threw her a dark and dangerous look that promised trouble for the next time they were alone. 'Can you lie on the couch, Fraser? I want to examine you properly.' He waited as Fraser winced and limped to the couch and then examined the boy, his hands gentle.

'It's not my hip, it's my leg,' Fraser muttered as Conner examined his joints.

'But your hip is attached to your leg,' Conner observed in a mild tone, 'so sometimes a problem with one can cause a pain in the other. Does this hurt?'

'No.'

'This?'

'Ow! Yes, yes.' Fraser swore and his mother gasped in shock and embarrassment.

'Fraser Price, you watch your language! Where did you learn that?'

'Everyone says it,' Fraser mumbled. 'It's no big deal.'

'It's a big deal to me!'

'I bet Conner swore when he was my age.'

'He's Dr MacNeil to you,' Aisla said sharply, and Conner cleared his throat tactfully and examined the other hip.

'I can't remember that far back. Is this OK? I'm going to bend your knee now—good. Do you play a lot of sport?'

'Yes, all the time. Just like you did.' Fraser grinned. 'Football, beach volleyball, loads of different stuff.'

It wasn't just the women who adored him, Flora thought helplessly, *it was the children, too.* They thought he was *so* cool.

Aisla looked at Conner. 'Do you think we need to have it X-rayed?'

'No.' Conner straightened. 'You can sit up now, Fraser. I'm done. As Nurse Harris correctly assessed, you have something called Osgood-Schlatter disease. It's a condition that sometimes affects athletic teenagers, particularly boys. There's inflammation and swelling at the top end of the tibia—here.' He took Fraser's hand and placed it on his leg. 'Can you feel it?'

'Yes.' Fraser winced. 'So will it go away?'

'Eventually. But you're going to need to play a bit less football.'

'How much less?'

'You need to cut down on your physical activity, because that will only make things worse.'

'All of it? Everything I do?' Fraser sounded appalled and Conner put a hand on his shoulder.

'It's tough, I know. But basically you need to stop doing anything that aggravates your condition. Ideally you should avoid sport altogether until your bones have fully matured, but I appreciate that's asking a bit much. A compromise would be to stop if you feel that whatever you're doing is making it worse.' He glanced at Aisla. 'He can take anti-inflammatories for the pain. If it doesn't improve, we can immobilise it for a short time and see if that helps. Failing that, we can refer him to an orthopaedic consultant for an assessment.'

Fraser slumped. 'No football?'

'Try cutting back. That will allow the pain and swelling to resolve. Anything that makes it worse, stop doing it.'

'Will it go?'

'Once your bones have fully matured. Unfortunately, the more active you are, the worse the symptoms are likely to be.'

Fraser looked grumpy. 'I'll have to spend the summer playing on game machines.'

'I don't think so,' his mother said dryly. 'You can read a few books.'

'Books!' Fraser's face went from grumpy to mournful. 'It's my holiday! Why would I want to spend it staring at a book?'

Aisla walked towards the door. 'Thanks, Dr MacNeil. Flora. We're grateful.'

Conner waited for the door to close behind him. 'I don't know which upset him more—the prospect of cutting back on football or the thought of reading books.'

'It was a close-run thing.' Careful not to look at him, Flora changed the paper on the couch. 'Thank you for seeing him.'

'Your diagnosis was correct. Well done. That was very impressive.'

'Thank you. I'm pleased all that studying paid off.' Although she didn't look at him, she knew he was watching her. She could feel him watching her.

'Flora…' His voice was husky. 'I know you're hurt and I'm sorry.'

'I thought you never apologised.'

'Well I'm apologising now,' he said testily, and she shrugged.

'You don't have to apologise for not finding me attractive,' Flora said stiffly, and heard him inhale sharply.

'I know you won't believe me, but I was doing you a favour.'

'Really? It's doing me a favour to kiss me and then tell me I'm boring?'

'I should never have kissed you in the first place.'

'So why did you?' She breathed in and out, forcing air into her lungs. 'Not once, but twice. The kiss on the beach—all right, let's say that was an accident. But you kissed me again, didn't you? If I'm so boring, why did you do that? Were you just teasing me? Doing me a favour, giving boring old Flora a thrill? Did you just do it to hurt my feelings? It was patronizing, Conner. You made me— I was…' She couldn't even say the words. 'If you didn't want me then you should have just left me alone. Or are you so bad that you just have to cause hurt?'

'Bad? You think I'm bad?' He pressed her against the wall, his body hard against hers. 'I'll show you what bad is, Flora.' He brought his mouth down on hers with punishing force, kissing her with raw, explosive passion, the slide of his tongue explicitly sexual and unbelievably seductive.

And she melted. Her head spinning from his skilled assault on her senses, she kissed him back, feeling fire dance inside her belly. She wasn't capable of thought or speech—all she could do was respond to his demands. She did so willingly and when he finally lifted his head she stared at him, mute.

'I've been called bad by a lot of people,' he said hoarsely, his hands planted either side of her head so that she couldn't escape his gaze, 'and most of it has been justified. But I'm damned if I'm accepting that criticism when it comes to you, Flora Harris. If I was as bad as people think, we would have already had sex.'

She was dizzy with need, unable to make sense of what he was saying. 'But you don't find me attractive.'

'No?' He slid his hands over her bottom and pulled her into him so that she felt the hard ridge of his arousal pressing against her. 'What I really want to do right now is strip you naked and take you hard and fast until we're both so exhausted that neither of us can move. And then I want to do it again. And again. Do you understand me?'

She gave a little whimper of shock and his eyes darkened.

'I'm not talking about marriage, or friendship or any of those soft, woolly things. I'm talking about sex, Flora. Sex.' He released her suddenly and took a step backwards, a look of disgust on his face. 'And that isn't the sort of person you are, which is why I'm going to let you go now. I'm going to walk out of that door into my consulting room and you're not going to follow me. You are a woman who deserves a conventional relationship with a reliable guy. I'm neither of those things.'

She licked her lips, shaken by everything he'd said to her. 'I don't think you should tell me what I want.'

'You're too naïve to play this game.'

'I am not naïve. I'm not naïve, Conner.' There was tearing agony inside her. *He was going to walk away from her again.* 'Would it make a difference if I told you that I'm not a virgin? Is that what's worrying you?'

He inhaled sharply and turned away, his profile tense. 'Don't tell me that.'

'I just thought it might make a difference.'

A muscle worked in his cheek. 'It doesn't. And you might find this hard to believe, but the desire *not* to hurt you is the reason I walked away. And it's the reason I'm about to walk away again. Because there are some rules that even I won't break.' He ran a hand over his face and then strode out of the room, leaving her shaking so badly that she could hardly stand.

He wanted her?

She sank onto her chair, staring at the door. He'd pulled back out of consideration for her? He didn't find her repulsive?

She wasn't 'boring Flora'?

Her fragile, bruised confidence recovered slightly and her mind started to race.

CHAPTER EIGHT

CONNER lay sprawled on the huge sofa in the barn, mindlessly flicking through the sports channels on the television. On the floor next to him was a bottle of whisky and a half-filled glass. He stared at it blankly and was just about to pick up the bottle and do what needed to be done when someone hammered hard on the front door.

Conner reached for the remote control and increased the volume on the television, determined to ignore whoever it was who mistakenly believed that he might be in need of company.

There was no second knock, so he picked up the whisky bottle, satisfied that his unwelcome visitor had decided to go and bother someone else.

He stared at the television screen for a moment, too emotionally drained to find an alternative mode of entertainment. After a few moments some deep-seated instinct warned him that he wasn't alone and he turned his head slowly.

Flora stood in the doorway.

She was wearing a coat belted at the waist and raindrops glistened like diamonds on her dark hair. 'You didn't answer your door.'

Whisky sloshed over his shirt and it took him a moment

to reply, the speed of his mind and his tongue dulled by the shock of seeing her there. 'I didn't feel like company.'

'Well, that's tough because there are things I need to say to you.' She stepped into the room, her eyes burning with a fire that he'd never seen before. 'That was quite a speech you made earlier, Conner MacNeil. You said a lot of things.'

What was she doing here? 'They were things that needed saying.'

'I agree. And I've been thinking about those things.' She breathed in and out, her chest rising and falling under her raincoat. 'You've made a lot of assumptions about me.' Water clung to her eyelashes and cheeks and her hair, as dark as mahogany, curled around her face. She looked pretty and wholesome and he had to force himself not to look at her soft mouth.

If he looked, he was lost.

'You shouldn't be here, Flora.'

Her eyes slid to the whisky bottle. 'Oh, Conner…' Her gentle, sympathetic tone scratched against his nerve endings.

'Go home.'

'Why? Because you're drunk?'

He licked his lips and discovered they were dry. 'I'm not drunk.'

But she didn't seem to be listening. It was as if she was in the middle of a rehearsed speech. 'You're worried in case you lose control and behave badly?' She stepped closer, the blaze in her eyes intensifying. 'What would you say if I told you that I *want* you to behave badly, Conner? In fact, I want you to be as bad as you can possibly be.'

The breath hissed through his teeth. 'For God's sake, Flora…'

'People say you're super-bright. Shockingly intelligent—brain in a different stratosphere to most people's, and all that. I'm not sure if they're right or not. What I do know is that you're certainly very slow when it comes to knowing what I want.'

His hand tightened around the glass. 'I said, *go home*!'

'Why? So that you can get slowly drunk on your own? I don't think that's the answer.'

'Well, you wouldn't, would you?' He gave a mocking smile. 'I'm willing to bet you've never been drunk in your life, Flora Harris.'

'You're right, actually. I haven't.' Her tone was calm. 'I never saw the point. There are other ways to solve a problem.'

'What makes you think I'm solving a problem?'

Her eyes flickered to the bottle. 'If you're not solving a problem, why are you drinking?'

'Actually, I'm not drinking.'

But she still wasn't listening. 'I don't know what you're searching for but you won't find it in the bottom of a whisky bottle.'

He gave a cynical smile. 'My father did.'

'You're not your father, Conner.' She spoke quietly. 'Which is why I'm standing here now.' She let the coat slip from her shoulders and underneath she was naked apart from the skimpiest, sexiest underwear he'd ever seen. 'You think I'm a good girl, Conner? You think you're not allowed to touch me?'

The glass slipped from his hand and the whisky spilled over the floor. Conner didn't notice because every neurone in his brain had fused.

Her body was all smooth lines and delicate curves, her legs impossibly long and her small breasts pressing against the filmy lace of her bra.

He stared at her in tense silence. 'I didn't think I'd drunk anything,' he muttered to himself in a hoarse voice, 'but perhaps I'm wrong about that. For a moment there I thought Flora Harris was standing in front of me in her underwear.'

She made an exasperated sound and removed the bottle from his hand. 'You've had enough.' Her subtle, floral perfume drifted towards him and he leaned his head back against the sofa with a groan.

'Believe me, I haven't had enough. I haven't even started. But if I'm still imagining Flora naked, perhaps it's time I did. I need the image to fade to black.'

'It won't fade because it's real. *I'm* real. Oh, for goodness' sake, Conner, I came here to seduce you and you're—you're…' She sighed with frustration and put the bottle on the floor, spilling some of the contents in the process. 'Why did you open a bottle of whisky?'

'Because of you.'

'Me? *I'm* the reason you're drunk?'

'I'm not drunk. But for a brief moment it seemed like a good idea. I thought it might take my mind off ravishing you,' he mumbled, and she made a sound that was somewhere between a moan and a giggle.

'Why do you need to do that? I *want* you to ravish me. I'm desperate for you to ravish me.'

He squinted up at her. 'Am I dreaming?'

'No, you're not dreaming!' She gave a sigh and shook her head. 'You're going to take a cold shower and while you're doing that I'm going to make you a jug of very strong coffee.'

Conner rubbed his eyes with the tips of his fingers and shook his head. 'You don't need to do that. And coffee stops me sleeping.'

'Good.' She sounded more exasperated than ever. 'I don't want you sleeping. I want you awake when I seduce you. I've spent most of my life listening to other women telling me what an amazing lover you are, and just when I'm about to find out what all the fuss is about, you pass out on me.'

'I'm not going to pass out.'

'Get in that shower, Conner MacNeil, or I swear I'll throw a bucket of freezing water over you right here!'

He ran a tongue over his lips. 'You look like Flora but you're not acting like Flora. Flora never swears. She's a really sweet girl.'

'Sweet? I'll show you sweet.' She grabbed his arm and yanked. 'Stand up! You're too heavy for me to pull you.'

He wondered if she'd be as confident if she knew he was as sober as she was.

Aware that his body was betraying his emotions in the most visible way possible, Conner stood up and gave a wry smile. 'I spilt half the bottle over myself when you walked through the door, so a shower might be a good idea. A freezing one, to kill my libido.'

'I don't want you to kill your libido.' Her voice was sultry and she pulled him against her and stood on tiptoe. 'Kiss me, Conner. And then go and take that shower. I want you sober enough to remember this. I don't want to wake up tomorrow and have you mouthing all sorts of excuses about being too drunk to know what you were doing.'

He knew exactly what he was doing and it felt incredible.

He groaned as he felt her silky smooth body pressing against his. He just couldn't help himself and he brought his mouth down on hers, stars exploding in his head as her tongue met his. 'You taste fantastic.'

She pulled away from him, her eyes soft and her cheeks pink. 'Where's your bathroom?'

'I don't need a cold shower.'

'Yes, you do.'

'Where is Flora? I think you've hit her on the head and stolen her identity.' He ran a hand through his hair as she tugged him towards the bathroom and hit a button on the shower. 'Flora isn't a forceful woman.'

'There's lots you don't know about Flora.'

He was starting to agree with her, especially when she reached up and yanked impatiently at his shirt, scattering buttons around the bathroom floor. Then he felt her fingers slide into the waistband of his jeans.

His hands covered hers and he gave her a sexy smile, astonished and delighted by her new-found confidence. 'Careful, angel. That's the danger zone and Flora would never wander into the danger zone.'

She gave him a gentle push and he swore fluently and then sucked in a breath as freezing water sluiced over his back. '*That* is cold.'

'Good—it's supposed to be cold. Stay in there until you can walk in a straight line unaided and tell me your name and date of birth. I'll be in the kitchen when you're ready.'

Her hand shaking, Flora rummaged through his fridge and found a packet of fresh coffee. She spooned a generous quantity into a cafetière and topped it up with hot water.

Then she sat at the table, listening to the rushing sound of the shower.

He was taking a long time.

Was it safe to have left him there? Had he drowned?

Or maybe she'd totally misread the situation and he was spending a long time in there in the hope that she'd give up and go home.

Her nerve faltered and she caught her lower lip between her teeth.

What on earth did she think she was doing?

He was absolutely right. She wasn't the sort of woman who stripped off and issued invitations to men. Neither was she the sort of woman who made coffee for a man while dressed in silk underwear.

With a whimper of panic she was just about to sprint back into the sitting room and retrieve her coat, when he walked into the kitchen. He'd knotted a towel around his waist but droplets of water still clung to the dark tangle of curls that shadowed his chest. His shoulders were broad and powerful and his arms strong and muscular. He had a body designed to make a woman think of nothing but sin, but what really caught her attention was the look in his eyes. Lazy, sexy and ready for action.

Her nerve fled completely and she decided to follow. 'Coffee on the table,' she muttered as she backed towards the door.

A hand shot out and closed around her wrist, his fingers like bands of steel as he yanked her back towards him. 'Oh, no, you don't.' His voice was cool and rock steady. 'You told me to shower. I've showered.'

'You can't possibly have sobered up that quickly.'

'I was never drunk.'

She stared at him. 'I saw the bottle.'

'I admit I considered it. That's how low I felt.' His eyes held hers for a long moment. 'But if there's one thing that being around my father taught me, it's that drink solves nothing. I was about to pour it down the sink when you walked in.'

'You smelt of alcohol.'

His smile was faintly mocking. 'When you took your coat off, I spilled most of it.'

Her heart thumped as she re-examined the facts. He hadn't been drunk. He'd been sober. She swallowed hard, all her courage leaving her. Somehow her belief that he was drunk had made him less intimidating and now, knowing that he hadn't touched a drop, she felt suddenly shaky.

'I should probably leave now. I've just remembered that I—'

'What?' His mouth was dangerously close to hers, his tone low and impossibly sexy as he curved an arm around her waist and trapped her against him. 'What have you just remembered, Flora?'

She could hardly breathe. 'Flora? Who's she? Oh, I remember—she's the woman I left her locked in her cottage when I stole her identity. I need to go and let her out.'

He gave a slow smile and his head lowered towards hers. 'Too late, sweetheart.' He paused, his mouth tantalisingly close to hers, 'You are most definitely Flora. A whole new Flora. A standing-naked-in-my-kitchen Flora.'

'In my underwear…'

His lips brushed hers, a deliberately erotic hint of things to come. He gave a low, appreciative murmur. 'You taste good. Whatever happens in the next few hours, don't dig your fingernails into my shoulders. If this is a dream, I don't want to be woken up.'

Her entire body was throbbing but still the nerves fluttered in her stomach. He was so sure and confident, whereas she… 'I made you coffee.'

'I don't want it.' His mouth slid down her neck and lingered at the base of her throat, his tongue tasting her skin. 'I want you, sweetheart.'

Her pulse was thundering and she tilted her head back with a gasp. 'Conner…'

'You came here to seduce me…' His lips moved slowly along her shoulder. 'You want to know what sort of lover I am.'

As she felt his hands slide confidently down her back, she gave a shiver. 'I thought you didn't find me attractive.'

'I always found you attractive. But you were always off limits as far as I was concerned. Despite what everyone thought of me, that was the one line I was never prepared to cross.'

'But you're crossing it now.'

'No. *You're* crossing it.' He lifted his head and looked

down at her, his ice-blue eyes compelling. 'This was your decision, Flora. You made it by coming here.'

He was giving her the chance to change her mind. But she didn't want to do that. 'Yes.'

'So…' His hand slid slowly down her back and cupped her bottom. 'You came here to seduce me.'

She couldn't breathe. 'Yes.'

He gave a slow smile. 'Carry on, angel. I'm all yours.'

Was that it? *Was that all the help he was going to give her?* For a moment her courage faltered but then she looked at his gorgeous naked body and couldn't help herself. She leaned forward and pressed her mouth to his chest, while her fingers trailed slowly across the hard muscle of his abdomen and lower still until they brushed against the top of the towel that was all that was between her and his straining manhood.

'All right, commercial break,' he said roughly, scooping her up into his arms as if she weighed nothing, 'If you carry on like that, this whole event is going to be very short-lived. You need to slow things down, angel. Make me beg.'

Beg?

She had no idea how to make a man beg. Flora clamped her mouth shut, judging it wise not to confess as much at this point. The problem with playing the seductress was that you were expected to follow through.

He carried her up a flight of stairs to the bedroom. Dusk was falling but there was enough light for her to see open fields and the jagged ruins of Glenmore Castle.

'It's a wonderful view,' she breathed, and he gave a lazy, confident smile as he deposited her in the centre of the bed.

'The only view you're going to be looking at has me in it.' He delivered a lingering kiss to her mouth and then lay down beside her and rolled onto his back, arrogantly sure of himself, his gaze direct.

And she understood. He wanted active, not passive. He

was giving her the chance to change her mind but she had no intention of doing that.

She wanted this. *She wanted him.* And this time she wasn't going to blow it. The whole of Glenmore could sing and dance outside his bedroom window and it wouldn't make any difference.

Aware that he was waiting for her to make the first move, she reached out a hand and stroked his shoulder, shivering slightly as she felt smooth skin and powerful male muscle.

He lay still, his eyelids lowered, watching and waiting, and suddenly she felt desperately nervous and impossibly excited.

'You can stop whenever you want,' he murmured, but he sounded less cool and composed than usual and the edgy quality to his voice gave her courage.

'I'm not stopping. You have an amazing body,' she said huskily, and her eyes slid shyly to his and her insides tumbled and warmed. He was so outrageously sexy that it was hard not to stare and even harder not to touch. She leaned forward and kissed his cheek, feeling the roughness of male stubble under her lips. Then she ran a finger over his nose, exploring the bump. 'How did you break it? Were you fighting?'

'Rugby.' He turned his head and kissed her fingers. 'I'm not quite the animal everyone seems to think I am.'

'Aren't you?' She trailed her finger over his mouth and then replaced it with her lips and he slid a hand behind her head and held her there while they kissed. His mouth was hot and purposeful and she felt the excitement flash through her body, turning her from willing to desperate.

Her hand slid over his shoulder, tracing flesh and hard muscle, and then lowered her head and rubbed her cheek over the roughness of his chest and breathed in his erotic scent. Her hand lingered low on his abdomen and she felt his muscles clench in an involuntary response.

She allowed her fingers to linger in that dangerous place,

teasing and promising, and then she bent her head and kissed his shoulder, using lips and tongue to discover and explore his body, gradually moving lower until her mouth rested where her hand had been. His muscles quivered under her gentle touch and she heard the sharp hiss of his breath as she teased him with her tongue. He sank his fingers into her hair and then released her instantly. She glanced up at him and saw that his eyes were closed and his jaw was clenched. Desire burned deep inside her and she bent her head again and closed her mouth over him and he made a choking sound.

'Flora...'

She lifted her head. 'Sorry—am I hurting you? Your face is sort of…twisted.'

'You're not hurting me,' he said hoarsely, 'but—'

'Good.' She lowered her head again and used her tongue and her lips until he gave a harsh groan, grabbed her and rolled her onto her back.

'You have to stop. I'm not going to last five minutes if you…' He closed his eyes and breathed deeply, tension etched in every line of his handsome face. 'Give me a minute. Just give me a minute.'

'Did I do something wrong?' She was suddenly covered with embarrassment. 'I—I haven't actually done it before…'

He shifted so that he was half on top of her, one leg pinning her to the mattress. 'You're full of surprises, do you know that? If you've never actually done it before, where did you—?' His voice cracked and he cleared his throat. 'Learn those tricks?'

'From a book.'

'A book?' He gave a shaky laugh. 'A book. Typical Flora.' He bent his head and kissed her mouth expertly and her body trembled and ached in response.

And he hadn't even touched her yet.

Desperate for him to do so, her hips moved against him

and he put a hand on her hip to steady her. Only then did she realise that at some point he'd removed her underwear. And she hadn't even noticed. She was about to ask him about it when he lowered his head and drew her nipple into his mouth.

Sensation shot through her and she tried to move against him, but he held her firmly while he lavished attention on both her breasts. The pleasure was so intense it was almost unbearable, and when he finally lifted his head, her cheeks were flushed and her limbs were trembling. For a moment he just looked at her and she thought that she was going to be the one to beg, and then she felt his hand between her thighs and the expert stroke of his fingers as they discovered the heart of her.

His touch was so intimate that for a moment she stiffened and instantly felt him pause. And the fact that he'd paused made her realise just how much care he was taking with her.

'Conner—please— I don't think I can wait.'

With a skilled, knowing fingers he found exactly the right place and caressed her gently until the excitement grew from a slow ache to a maddening turmoil of sensation. As his exploration grew bolder and more intimate, she arched and writhed, silently begging for the possession that her body craved.

'Look at me, Flora.' He shifted over her, slid a hand under her bottom and she felt the blunt tip of his erection brushing against her. For a moment she couldn't breathe, the excitement and anticipation so great that her entire body was trembling with need. And then he eased forward slowly and she gasped because it took her body a moment to accommodate him.

He paused, his breath warming her neck. 'Am I hurting you?'

'No.'

'Relax, angel.' He closed his mouth over hers, kissed her

deeply and moved forward, driving deeper inside her. 'Relax for me.'

But she didn't want to relax. She wanted— *She wanted...*

Excitement exploded inside her and she rose instinctively to meet his thrusts.

Her heart thudded wildly and she curved her hands over his bottom, urging him on. 'Conner, Conner…' She looked into his eyes and saw primitive need blazing there.

He slowed the pace, his eyes holding hers. 'Are you OK?'

'Yes…' Talking was difficult. 'It's just that you look—' She broke off and moaned as he moved again in an agonisingly slow rhythm.

'How do I look?'

'Sort of—scary.'

'I'm trying not to lose control.' He gave a wry smile. 'And it's pretty hard.'

'Then stop trying.' She breathed the words against his mouth and felt him tense. 'I'm not delicate, Conner. Make love to me the way you want to make love to me.'

His eyes darkened and his breathing quickened. 'I never want to hurt you, Flora.'

'You won't hurt me.' But the fact that he cared enough to be careful with her increased the feeling of warmth growing inside her. 'I'm OK. I've never been so OK,' she murmured, and his mouth flickered into a half-smile and he surged into her again, this time going deeper.

And she felt the change in him. He shifted his position, altered the rhythm, and her body hummed and fizzled and then tightened around his in an explosion of ecstasy so intense that it drove him to his own completion.

Flora lay in his arms, stunned and breathless. 'I—I had no idea that it would be like that.'

He turned his head, a frown on his face. 'You told me you weren't a virgin.'

'Technically I wasn't.' Her voice was soft and her eyes were misty. 'But I suppose it depends on your definition. I've never done that before. Never felt like that before.'

'I don't think I want to hear about your past lovers.' He folded her back against him in a possessive gesture and she smiled, feeling warm and protected and—just amazing.

'Lover. Just the one.'

'I definitely don't want to hear this,' Conner muttered darkly. 'Knowing you, it must have been serious.'

'I suppose it was a serious attempt to discover what all the fuss was about. He was a lawyer—very proper. Predictable. Chivalrous.'

'All the things I'm not.' Conner's arms tightened. 'He sounds like the perfect mate. You should have stuck with him.'

She lay in the semi-darkness, staring at his profile, thinking of the care he'd taken with her. 'I didn't love him.'

'Oh, please.' He made an impatient sound and she turned her head.

'It's true. I know you don't believe in love, but I do. And I didn't love him. My feelings just weren't right. There was no chemistry.' She gave a short laugh. 'That's what you said to me.'

'I was lying.' Conner bent his head and kissed her. 'And if you weren't so naïve, you would have known I was lying, because I had a massive erection as I said it.'

She gasped and then gave a strangled laugh. 'Conner MacNeil, why must you always try and shock?'

'The fact that you're shocked proves my point. You're naïve.'

'I'm *not* naïve. And it's hardly surprising that I didn't notice anything because I was so upset, I was trying not to look at you. And it wasn't hard to believe you when you said I didn't turn you on, because I know I'm not sexy.'

It was Conner's turn to laugh. 'Angel, if you were any sexier you'd have to carry a government health warning.'

She slid her arm over his stomach and rested her chin on his chest. 'Really?'

'You need to ask?' He guided her hand down his body and gave her a wicked smile. 'You currently have a hold on the evidence.'

She smiled. 'Do you know what's amazing? I don't feel at all shy with you.'

'I'd noticed. Permit me to say that your behaviour tonight would have thoroughly shocked the inhabitants of Glenmore.'

'I don't care about them,' she said honestly, and he stroked her hair away from her face, his expression serious.

'Yes, you do, and I don't blame you for that. Glenmore is your home. Talking of which…' He frowned suddenly and then released her and sprang out of bed. 'Where did you park?'

'Sorry?'

'Your car. Where did you park your car?'

She frowned. 'Outside your barn. Where else?'

'Someone could see it.' He reached down and pulled her gently to her feet. 'You have to leave, angel.'

'Now?' Bemused, she slid her arms around his neck. 'I—I assumed I'd stay the night.'

'At least eight islanders drive past my barn on the way to work in the morning. I don't want them seeing your car.' He gently unhooked her arms from his neck and retrieved her underwear from the floor. 'You need to leave, Flora.'

His words made her feel sick and her heart bumped uncomfortably. 'So—that's it?'

He slid her arms into her bra and fastened it with as much skill as he'd shown unfastening it. 'No, of course that's not it.' He lowered his head and kissed her swiftly. 'Are you busy tomorrow night?'

'No.'

He smiled and winked at her. 'Then you can cook me dinner. Meet me here at eight o'clock.' Then he frowned. 'On second thoughts, your place is probably better. Evanna's cottage is off the main road.'

She felt a rush of excitement and anticipation but tried to hide it. 'Why can't *you* cook *me* dinner?'

'Because I'm rubbish in the kitchen and I'm assuming you'd rather not be poisoned,' he drawled, sliding her silk knickers up her legs and then giving a tormented groan. 'Why am I dressing you when all I want to do is *un*dress you?'

'I don't know,' she said breathlessly. 'Why are you?'

'Because I care about you. I care about your reputation.'

She looked at him curiously. 'That doesn't exactly sound like Bad Conner.'

'You've corrupted me,' he said roughly. And then he took a deep breath, stepped back and lifted his hands. 'Get out of here. Your coat is downstairs. For goodness' sake, remember to button it or you'll give everyone a cheap thrill. Go, quickly, before I change my mind.'

CHAPTER NINE

FLORA tried, she *really* tried, to keep their relationship secret. She made a point of not gazing at him when they were in public together and she kept their interaction brief and formal. But inside she trembled with insecurity when he didn't glance at her and she knew why.

No relationship of Conner's had ever lasted. Why should theirs be any different?

But even knowing that it was probably doomed, she wouldn't have changed anything. And if she spent her days racked with doubt as to his feelings, when night came she was left in no doubt at all.

Every evening he arrived at her cottage and spent time with her until the early hours. They ate, talked and made love, but he never stayed the whole night and Flora didn't know whether she felt frustrated by that or grateful.

On the one hand she was slightly relieved not to be the subject of local gossip, but on the other hand she was greedy for time with him. She loved the fact that he talked to her and sensed that he said things to her that he'd never said to anyone else.

Occasionally the conversation turned to the topic of his father. 'It's hardly any wonder you virtually lived wild,' she murmured one night as she lay with her head on his shoulder. 'I don't suppose there was much to go home to.'

'It wasn't exactly a laugh a minute.' He stroked a hand over her hair. 'After my mother left, he was pretty much drunk from the moment he woke up in the morning to the moment he keeled over at night. I stayed out of his way. Half the time I didn't even go home. I slept on the beach or borrowed the MacDonalds' barn. That was fine until the night I lit a fire to keep warm and the wind changed.'

Flora's heart twisted. 'I guessed things were bad. I went up there once, to look for you. And he yelled at me so violently that my legs shook for days.'

His arms tightened around her. 'Why were you looking for me?'

'After your mother left, I was worried about you. And I thought I understood what you were going through. How arrogant was that?' She sighed and kissed him gently. 'I suppose because I'd lost my mother, too, I thought I might be able to help you. But of course our situations were entirely different because I still had my dad.'

'I didn't want to be helped. I just wanted to be angry.'

'I don't blame you for being angry.' She rubbed her cheek against his shoulder. 'Was it the army that stopped you being angry?'

'They taught me to channel my aggression. Running thirty miles with a pack on your back pretty much wipes it out of you.'

'So they helped you?'

'Yes, I suppose they did.' He kissed the top of her head. 'You're such a gentle person, I don't suppose you've ever been angry.'

'Of course I have. Anger is a human emotion. But I didn't have reason to be angry—not like you. I feel so bad for you. The locals should have done something.'

'What could they have done? And, anyway, I didn't exactly invite assistance.'

'You basically grew up without parents.' She raised herself on one elbow, her expression soft as she looked down at him. 'Why did you become a doctor?'

'I don't know.' His eyes closed again. 'I spent my whole life on Glenmore being angry. I suppose it was a bit of a vicious circle. They thought the worst of me so I gave them the worst. And then I left and suddenly I was with people who didn't know me. And I realised that I was tired of living my life like that. I went to an army recruitment day and it all happened from there.'

'Did you ever hear from your Dad?'

'No. And I never contacted him either.'

'But you kept in touch with Logan.'

Conner's eyes opened. 'Logan is a good man. Always was. He was the one who told me about my father's cirrhosis. He arranged for his admission to hospital on the mainland and he did all the paperwork when he died. Logan did all the things I should have done.' He hesitated. 'He was also the one who thought I should come back and tie up some loose ends. Sell the house, bury some ghosts—that sort of thing.'

'I'm glad you came back.'

He looked at her. 'I'm not good for you, Flora,' he murmured, stroking his hands over her hair and then pulling her down so that he could kiss her. 'I'm just going to hurt you.'

'I'll take that chance.'

'Relationships are destructive, terrible things.'

'I can understand why you'd think that, given everything that happened with your parents, but theirs was just one relationship, Conner. My parents' relationship was different.'

'Your mother died and your father was devastated,' he said softly. 'In its own way, that relationship was as traumatic as the one my parents had. Both ended in misery.'

'It was traumatic, that's true. But what my father and mother shared was so special that I know Dad wouldn't have changed things, even if he'd been able to foresee what was going to happen. True love is rare and special—a real gift. You don't turn that away, even if it comes with pain.'

'Love is a curse, Flora Harris, not a gift.'

'No, Conner.' She kissed him gently. 'The best thing that can happen to anyone is to be truly loved. Whatever happens in adult life, every child deserves to be loved unconditionally by their parents, and that didn't happen to you. And I'm guessing you haven't experienced it as an adult either, given the way you stomp through relationships.'

'Don't be so sure.' He lifted an eyebrow. 'Do you want to know how many women have told me that they love me?'

'Actually, I don't.' She laughed, trying to ignore the queasy feeling in her stomach that his words had induced. 'And I was talking about love, not sex.'

'All right, it's *definitely* time that you stopped talking.' He rolled her swiftly onto her back and came down on top of her, pinning her still with his weight. 'If the only thing on your mind is love, I'm going to have to do something brutal.' But his eyes were gentle and she giggled softly.

How did he feel about her?

How did she feel about him?

She really didn't know.

Their relationship was the most thrilling, exciting thing that had ever happened to her, but at the same time she knew that there couldn't be a happy ending.

But for the time being she was just going to live in the present.

And that was what she did.

But rumours were gradually spreading across Glenmore.

* * *

A few weeks into their relationship, Flora was in the pub with the rest of the medical centre staff, including an extremely pregnant Evanna.

'At the weekend I'm taking you over to the mainland.' Logan raised his glass to his wife. 'That baby is going to come any time now.'

'No hurry.' Evanna glanced at Flora. 'Are you going to manage?'

'Of course.'

'Hey, Conner.' Jim wandered over to their table and slapped Conner on the shoulders. 'How are you doing?'

Flora studied her grapefruit juice intently, careful not to look at Conner.

'I'm good, Jim.' Conner leaned back in his chair and stretched his legs out under the table. 'And you?'

'Bit tired.' Jim winked at him. 'Woken up by that bike of yours at three in the morning every night this week. Thought to myself, Young Conner's been out on the hunt.'

Flora felt her face flame, but Conner simply stifled a yawn, apparently unflustered. 'Just relieving the boredom of being stuck on Glenmore, Jim. Do you blame me?'

'No, but I envy you.' Jim gave a delighted laugh. 'Go on, lad. Tell us the name of the lucky girl. Knowing you, it's someone different from the girl you were hiding in the waves the night we saw you on the beach.'

'Of course. That was weeks ago and I'm not into long relationships.' Conner didn't falter but Flora's breathing stopped and inside she suffered an agony of embarrassment.

People were talking. Of course they were. How could she have imagined otherwise?

How long would it take for people to put two and two together?

And how would she cope with being on the receiving end of everyone's nudges and winks?

This time *she'd* be the one that everyone was talking about when they bought their apples in the greengrocer on the quay. *She'd* be the subject of speculative glances when she took her books back to the library.

Flora tightened her fingers round her glass and tried to breathe steadily and slow her heart rate, but inside she was shrinking because she knew only too well what they'd all be saying.

That Conner MacNeil had seduced her and that it wouldn't last five minutes.

She took a large slug of her drink and then realised that Conner was looking at her, his gaze curiously intent. Unable to look away, she slowly put her glass down on the table.

He gave a faint smile and something in that smile worried her. He looked…resigned? *Tired?*

She looked away quickly, telling herself that she was reading something into nothing. Of course he was tired. They were both tired. Neither of them slept much any more. Because they weren't able to conduct their relationship in daylight, they'd become nocturnal.

'I'm going to have to make a move.' Evanna rose to her feet with difficulty, a hand on her back. 'I never realised how uncomfortable these chairs are.'

Conner drained his glass. 'I don't suppose any chair is comfortable when you're carrying an elephant around in your stomach.'

Evanna laughed good-naturedly and Flora reached for her bag, grateful for the change of subject.

Jim was back with the lads, laughing about something that had happened to the lifeboat crew, and Conner was listening to Logan talking about his plans to extend the surgery.

For now, at least, it appeared that their secret was still safe. Although how long it would take for the locals to realise that she was the girl that Conner was seeing was anyone's guess.

And then what would happen?

* * *

Restless and angry with himself, Conner paced the length of his consulting room and back again.

Why had he ever let things go this far?

Buzzing for his first patient, he decided that he had to do something about the situation. Fast. Before it exploded in his face.

'Dr MacNeil?' Ann Carne stood in the doorway and Conner gave a reluctant laugh.

'If there's one thing I don't need this morning, it's an encounter with my old headmistress.' *And Flora's aunt.*

'I don't see why. Nothing I said ever worried you when you were young,' Ann said crisply, closing the door behind her and making her way to the chair. 'And I don't suppose that's changed just because you've grown up. And, anyway, it seems that no lecture is needed. You've made quite an impression since you returned to Glenmore, Conner.'

'Bad, I'm sure.'

'You know that isn't true.' She looked at him steadily. 'Evidently you're a reformed character. I've come to find out if you're as good a doctor as they say you are.'

Conner sighed. 'Is this like classroom testing?'

'You flew through every exam you ever bothered to take, Conner MacNeil. But while we're on that subject, there's something I want to say, so I may as well get it out of the way before we start.' Ann took a deep breath. 'We didn't help you enough. *I* didn't help you. That's been on my conscience for many years.'

Conner's eyes narrowed. 'I sense that this conversation is about to make both of us extremely uncomfortable so why don't we just skip straight to the part where you tell me your symptoms?'

'In a minute.' Her voice was quiet and Ann shook her head slowly, a hint of sadness in her eyes. 'You were the brightest, most able boy that ever passed through my school, Conner MacNeil.'

'And we both know I passed through it as quickly as I could,' Conner drawled lightly. 'I made a point of not resting my backside on the chair long enough to get bored.'

'You had a brilliant brain, but you were so disruptive and angry that it took me a long time to see it. Too long. By the time I realised the extent of your abilities it was too late to harness them because you were almost totally wild. You were off the rails, fighting everyone. No one could get through to you. Not the teaching staff. Not your father.' She paused and took a deep breath. 'We didn't know how bad things were for you at home. You covered it up so well. We thought your father was the one struggling with you, not the other way round.'

'I certainly didn't make his life a picnic.'

'He let you down. We all let you down.'

Conner kept his expression neutral. 'This is history and you know I hated history. Science was my subject. I never saw the point of lingering in the past.'

'There's a point when the past is affecting the future.'

'It isn't.'

'Isn't it? Are you married, Conner MacNeil? Are you living with some warm, kind, stable woman who is carrying your child?'

Conner sat for a moment, eye to eye with his old headmistress. 'My marital status has nothing to do with my father.'

'Of course it does. Are you pretending that it didn't affect you? Your wild behaviour was a reaction to everything that was happening at home, I see that now.' She shook her head again. 'I've been teaching for thirty-one years and you were the only child who passed through the doors of my school that I just couldn't cope with. The island couldn't cope with you. We all let you down and for that we owe you an apology.'

'I don't suppose the people whose property I destroyed would agree with you.

'You certainly left your mark on the place. And you're still leaving it, although this time the damage is more subtle.' Ann straightened her shoulders. 'My niece is in love with you. I suppose you know that?'

Conner swore softly and Ann's mouth tightened.

'Behave yourself! Just because you're a grown man, it doesn't mean that I'm prepared to accept that sort of language.'

'What are you going to do? Put me in detention?' Conner gave a short laugh. 'Did she tell you that?'

'No. In fact, I doubt she even knows herself. But I've heard the way she talks about you. Her eyes sparkle and every story that falls from her lips involves something you've done. Every other word she speaks is your name. So what are you going to do about it, Conner?'

Conner rubbed his fingers over his forehead. 'I expect I'll walk out and leave her crying. That's what I usually do.'

'Perhaps.' Ann's tone was calm. 'Or perhaps you'll see sense and realise that a warm, soft, kind woman like Flora is just what you need.'

'It doesn't matter what I need. I do know that whatever *she* needs, it isn't me.'

Ann smiled. 'So you've learned to think about someone other than yourself. That's good, Conner. And don't underestimate Flora. She's shy, not weak. There's more to her than meets the eye.'

Conner's hand dropped. 'So I've discovered.' He thought of Flora half-naked in the sea. Flora turning up at his barn wearing only underwear under her coat. *Flora riding him lightly, her brown curls tumbling over her shoulders.*

Ann was giving him the look she reserved for very naughty students. 'I just thought someone should tell you that you don't have to live up to your reputation. From what I've seen, Bad Conner has a good side. Why not develop it?'

Conner gave a mock shudder. 'That sounds like the lecture you gave me when you told me I should be interested in algebra.' He stirred. 'All right, enough. Is there a medical reason that you're here?'

'I have asthma. Or so they say. Started two years ago, out of nowhere. Completely ridiculous at my age, but there you are. Anyway, Logan started me off on an inhaler, and Dr Walker—he was your predecessor—gave me another one but they're not working any more.'

'And you say that because…?'

'I'm breathless all the time. Wheezing. Tight chest.' She sighed. 'I tried to walk the cliff path yesterday and had to sit down and look at the view instead. You're going to say that I shouldn't be exercising at my age—'

'Exercise is important at every age.' Conner studied his computer screen and his face broke into a slow smile. 'Well, Miss Carne, I see you were a smoker for fifteen years. I wonder how much money I could make selling that information?'

'I haven't touched one for sixteen years,' she said briskly, 'and everyone has to have a vice.'

'I couldn't agree more. I couldn't survive without my vices.' Conner stood up and took a peak-flow meter out of the drawer. 'Have you been monitoring your own peak flow?'

'Yes. Of course. I'm a teacher. I do everything by the book.' She delved into her bag and pulled out a chart. 'Here.'

He scanned it. 'This shortness of breath—is it just on exercise or when you're doing daily tasks?'

'Exercise. But I can't do as much.'

'And have you had a chest infection? Anything that might have been a trigger?'

He questioned her carefully, listened to the answers and then checked her inhaler technique. 'You should be inhaling slowly and then holding your breath for ten seconds.'

'That's what I'm doing.'

Conner questioned her further and then sat back down and looked at the computer screen. 'You're already taking salbutamol and an inhaled steroid. I'm going to add in a long-acting drug and see if that helps. If it does, you can carry on taking it. If it doesn't, we might increase the dose of your inhaled steroid.'

'I'm not wild about taking yet another drug.'

'If your symptoms stabilise, we can reassess in a few months.'

'So I should come back and see you in a few weeks?'

'Yes, or sooner if things don't settle.' He handed her the prescription and she took it with a smile of thanks.

'You've done well with your life, Conner.' She walked towards the door and paused. 'Do the right thing by my niece.'

The right thing.

Conner watched as she left the room and closed the door behind her.

What exactly was the right thing?

The rumours grew from soft whispers to blatant speculation until all the inhabitants of Glenmore had the same question on their lips.

Who was the woman that Conner MacNeil was seeing?

'She lives up your way,' Meg told Flora as she sprinkled chocolate onto a cappuccino. 'People have heard his motorbike roaring down the lanes late at night. Do you want anything to eat with this? Croissant? Chocolate muffin?'

'No, thanks.' Flora handed over the money and took the coffee, just wanting to escape before the conversation could progress any further.

'I mean, who lives near you? Who is likely to catch our Conner's eye? Tilly Andrews? No, it couldn't possibly be her.' Meg frowned as she rang up the amount on the till. 'I just can't imagine.'

'Me neither. Thanks for this, Meg.' Almost stumbling in her haste to make her exit, Flora backed towards the door while Meg pondered.

'I don't see why everyone is so interested anyway. This is Conner we're talking about. He'll have left the island or moved on to the next woman before we've identified the current one.' She wiped the side with some kitchen paper. 'You be careful out there today. There's a storm brewing. Jim reckons it's going to be a big one.'

'Is that right?' Not wanting to think about Conner leaving the island, Flora backed out of the door and took her coffee to the quay, where she sipped it slowly, watching the tourists pick their way off the ferry, most of them a pale shade of green after a rough sea crossing. Beyond them, the sea lashed angrily at the harbour walls and the sky turned ominously dark, despite the fact it was only lunchtime.

Flora sighed. Wild summer storms were a feature of Glenmore but that didn't mean that they welcomed it. If the ferry stopped running then the tourists didn't come, and if the tourists stopped then so did the money that contributed so much to the island economy. They were already in August and the summer months would soon be over.

And then Conner would be gone.

And she'd always known that, hadn't she? She'd always known that his presence on the island was only temporary.

Determined not to think about that, Flora finished her coffee and threw the empty container in the bin. She was not going to ruin the present by worrying about the future.

They still had the rest of summer together.

Climbing into her car, she drove back to the surgery, knowing that she was facing a full clinic now that Evanna had finally stopped work.

She worked through without a break and was just tidying up after her last patient when Conner walked into the room.

As usual her heart jumped and her mood lifted. Just seeing him made her want to smile. 'The weather's awful. There's a strong chance you're going to be trapped indoors tonight, Dr MacNeil.'

'Is that right?'

'Do you fancy being trapped indoors with me?'

'I might.' He pulled her against him and kissed her hungrily. 'As long as you promise to put your book away for half an hour.'

'That depends...' she curled her arms round his neck. '...on whether there is something more exciting to do than read.'

'Is that a challenge?'

'Do you need one?'

His answer was to kiss her again and she sank against him, her body erupting in a storm of excitement. They were lost in each other, absorbed, transported, and neither of them heard the click of the door behind them.

'What the—?' Logan's voice penetrated the fog of excitement that had anaesthetised her brain, and Flora opened her eyes dizzily, trying to remember where she was.

'Logan.' She said his name breathlessly and snatched her hands guiltily away from Conner's chest.

Logan gave a low growl of anger. 'Damn you, Conner, *what the hell do you think you're doing*?'

'Kissing your practice nurse.' Conner's tone was cool, almost bored. But he released his grip on her bottom and shrugged. 'Caught red-handed.' His gaze slid to Flora and he gave a faint smile. 'Or perhaps I should say red-faced.'

Flora froze as Logan turned his disbelieving gaze on her. *'Flora?'*

She stood, trapped in the headlights of his disapproval. *This was it, then.* The moment that had been inevitable.

The moment of discovery.

She waited to feel embarrassed, but nothing happened.

Tentatively, she examined the way she felt. Did she want the floor to open up and swallow her? No, she didn't. Did she wish she could turn the clock back? Absolutely not.

Flora frowned slightly, wondering why Logan's incredulous glance had so little effect on her. And then she looked at Conner—at the hard lines of his handsome face—and everything inside her disintegrated. Everything she'd thought she was, *everything she'd thought she wanted*—it all descended into rubble and she realised that the reason she wasn't embarrassed was because she didn't *care* what Logan thought. And the reason she didn't care what Logan thought was because she loved Conner.

She loved him.

Even though it was foolish and she was going to end up in tears, she was completely and utterly crazy about Conner.

She stood for a moment, shocked, exhilarated and absolutely terrified.

Then she turned to Logan, about to tell him that she didn't care what he thought, but something in his expression caught her attention. 'Logan? Is something wrong?'

Logan was glaring at Conner. 'You just can't help it, can you? You have to cause trouble. I ought to punch your lights out.'

'You're right,' Conner drawled, 'you probably should.'

'Stop it, both of you.' Flora was staring at Logan, her concern mounting as she noticed the unnatural pallor of his skin. 'Something has happened, hasn't it? Is it Kirsty? For goodness' sake, say something! You're scaring me.'

'Kirsty's fine.' Logan's voice was harsh. 'But Evanna's waters have broken.'

'Oh…' Flora immediately stepped forward and closed her fingers over his arm, her grip offering reassurance and support. 'It will be fine, Logan. Where is she?'

'In the car. I'm taking her to the ferry.' His breathing unsteady, Logan looked at Conner. 'I just came to tell you that the two of you are in charge. And then you—'

'Forget that,' Flora interrupted him. 'What's happening to Kirsty?'

'Meg is having her, but if she needs any help—'

'That's fine,' Flora said quickly. 'Of course.'

'You're taking Evanna to the ferry?' Conner frowned. 'The last thing I heard, the ferry wasn't going to run. There's a storm brewing, Logan.'

'I know there's a storm. And that's why we're getting off this island while we still can. I've already left it too late. We should have gone last weekend but Evanna is so damn stubborn.'

'But—'

'I know what I'm doing,' Logan said harshly, yanking open the door. 'Just keep an eye on the place while I'm gone.' He glared angrily at Conner. 'And try not to kiss anybody else.'

Janet appeared in the doorway, her face white. 'Logan, you have to come. Evanna says she wants to push. I've helped her out of the car and back into the house.'

'No!' Logan raked a hand through his hair, his voice sharp with panic. 'That isn't right. I don't want Evanna in the house. I want her on the ferry. And if the ferry isn't running, we'll call the air ambulance—'

Flora took control. 'If she wants to push, Conner should take a look at her.'

'I don't want him anywhere near my wife!' Logan rounded on him like a wounded animal and Conner's eyes narrowed.

'Relax. My taste has never run to heavily pregnant women.'

Flora sighed with exasperation and waved Janet away. 'Get me a delivery pack, Janet. Evanna's room. Tall cupboard on the right, top shelf. You two…' She turned to Logan and Conner, her eyes flashing with exasperation. 'Enough. All this testosterone is starting to get on my nerves and I can't concentrate. Logan, listen to me.' Stepping forward, she closed her hand over his wrist, her voice crisp. 'You are in no fit state to assess your wife's progress in labour. Conner and I will do that.' She could feel his pulse thundering under her fingers. 'We'll do that now. If Evanna is going to have this baby imminently, we need to be prepared.'

Conner looked as though he was about to speak and Flora silenced him with a glare, her instincts warning her that he was about to say something Logan didn't need to hear.

'She's not having our baby on this island.' Logan inhaled deeply and looked at her, his eyes bright with fear. *'I am not losing my wife!'*

CHAPTER TEN

'IT WOULD really help if someone could tell me what is going on here,' Conner drawled as he and Flora followed Logan through the surgery to the door that connected with their house. 'My cousin, who I always considered to be of sound mind, appears to have lost the plot. Given that he isn't usually prone to bouts of hysterics, I'm assuming there's a reason.'

Flora paused until Logan was out of earshot. 'He hasn't told you what happened to his first wife?'

'I never asked.'

Flora rolled her eyes. 'Men! OK. Well, to keep it brief, Logan was married before. His first wife died in childbirth, here on Glenmore. There was a terrible storm and he couldn't get her off the island and she…' Flora bit her lip. 'Well, she died. There isn't time to tell you more than that. There was nothing anyone could do, but don't try telling Logan that because he still blames himself.'

'Right.' Conner lifted his eyes and stared at his cousin's retreating shoulders. 'So we can expect him to be very relaxed and calm about the whole thing.'

'If he can't get Evanna off Glenmore for the delivery, he'll probably have a breakdown. We have to be very, very sensitive about this whole situation,' Flora said quietly, and Conner shot her a look, his expression faintly mocking.

'Sensitive? Perhaps I should just leave right now.'

'Don't be ridiculous. We need a plan. You can deliver the baby, I'll reassure Evanna and Logan—'

'No way.' Conner lifted his hands and stopped her in mid flow. 'I don't deliver babies. The only thing I know about babies is how *not* to produce them.'

Flora stared at him. 'Are you telling me you've never delivered a baby before? You're a doctor.'

His gaze was sardonic. 'There isn't a great deal of need for obstetrics in the army. Of course I've delivered a few babies but let's just say that my experience in that area is limited.'

'Mine, too. But we mustn't let them know that.' Flora bit her lip and thought fast. 'It doesn't matter. I can deliver the baby as long as it's straightforward. If there's a problem, you'll have to help. It will be fine. What they really need is reassurance. We just need to be confident. Really confident. Babies come by themselves…' she glanced at him doubtfully '…usually.'

'I can do confident,' Conner said, a trace of humour in his eyes, 'but I can tell you now that Logan isn't going to let me touch his wife.'

'Logan is traumatised. He'll do what we tell him.' She pushed him through the door and he lifted an eyebrow.

'I didn't know you were capable of being so dominating. Don't ever expect me to believe you're shy after this performance.'

Flora shrugged. 'You don't know me at all, do you?'

'Evidently not.'

They found Evanna in the breakfast room, a huge sunny room at the back of the house that adjoined the kitchen and looked over the garden.

'You can't possibly want to push,' Logan was saying in a hoarse voice, his arm round Evanna's shoulders. 'This is your first baby. First babies take ages. Days sometimes.'

Evanna's face was pale and streaked with sweat. 'Not all first babies take ages.' She broke off and Flora could see that she was struggling with pain.

Agitated, Logan stood up. 'I'm calling the air ambulance.'

'The wind's too strong,' Conner said in an even tone. 'They can't fly. I've already rung them.'

Evanna lifted a hand and touched Logan's face. 'You have to calm down,' she urged softly. 'You're panicking and I need you.'

'I'm not panicking,' Logan said tightly. 'I'm sorry.'

'Don't be sorry. I understand—and I love you.'

'All right—enough.' Conner pulled a face. 'You're making me feel ill. Flora, did I hear you asking Janet for a delivery pack? I presume such a thing exists on this godforsaken island?'

'We have everything,' Logan growled, his hair roughened from the number of times he'd run his fingers through it. 'I made sure. I've got the equipment to do a Caesarean section if it's necessary.'

'It's not going to be necessary,' Conner said calmly, washing his hands. 'Evanna, I'm going to take a look and see what's happening. Logan, go and check on Kirsty.'

Logan's jaw tightened. 'I'm not leaving her.'

Conner inhaled deeply and let the water stream off his hands into the sink. 'Leave the room, Logan. All this drama is giving me a headache.'

'No.'

Conner dried his hands and then pulled on the gloves Flora handed him. 'I can't concentrate with you hovering, ready to shout abuse at me.'

'What do you know about delivering babies?'

'I'm full of surprises.' Conner turned away from Logan and concentrated on Evanna, his smile gentle. 'The problem is that no one on this island trusts me.'

She gave a wan smile. 'I trust you, Conner.'

'It's all going to be fine, you know that, don't you?'

She swallowed. 'Yes…' Her voice faltered but she returned his smile. 'Of course it is. Have you—have you ever delivered a baby before?'

'Do you think I'd be here now if I hadn't? I love delivering babies,' Conner said smoothly, moving to her right side and glancing at Flora, his gaze faintly mocking. 'Delivering babies is my favourite thing.'

Evanna clutched his arm. 'You really have done it before?'

'Loads of times,' Conner said easily, and Logan snorted.

'Oh, for goodness' sake! I suppose you're going to try and convince us that the army is popping out babies all the time.'

'Of course not.' Conner's gaze didn't flicker. 'But the locals are. And they always came to us for help.'

Evanna gave a low moan and reached for Flora's hand. 'Actually, Logan, I think you should ring Meg and check on Kirsty. She was a bit off colour this morning.'

'But—'

'Logan!' Evanna's voice was surprisingly firm. 'You have to let Conner do this. We're wasting time. *I tell you this baby is coming now, whether you like it or not.*'

Flora realised that it was the first time ever she'd heard Evanna raise her voice and Logan took several deep breaths, his face a mask of indecision. 'All right—but I'll be back.' He strode away from them and Conner crouched down beside Evanna.

'Are you comfortable there?'

'I don't think I'd be comfortable anywhere,' she gasped, wincing as another contraction hit her. 'Wait a minute. I can't— Oh, Conner, I want to push—really…'

'Just hold on.' Flora dropped to her knees beside her friend. 'We're going to take a look, see if we can see the baby's head. We need to assess what's happening.'

'I can tell you what's happening,' Evanna muttered, her teeth gritted. 'I'm a midwife. This baby is coming. I think it's called precipitate labour.'

'Well, that's good news,' Conner said lightly. 'If there's one thing I can't stand, it's hanging around.'

Janet hurried into the room with the delivery pack.

'Open it,' Conner ordered brusquely. 'We're both wearing sterile gloves.'

'Open it fast,' Flora said calmly. 'I can see the head. In fact, I'd say it will crown with the next contraction.' *It was too quick*, she thought to herself. *Much too quick.* 'Don't push, Evanna. Can you take some shallow breaths? Pant? That's brilliant. Janet, put the central heating on.'

Janet stared at her. 'It's the middle of the summer.'

'It's not that warm in here and it's stormy outside. The temperature will drop and I want to heat the room a bit. And warm some towels.' *Just in case.*

Evanna groaned. 'I have to push. I can't not push. You have no idea. I've got another contraction coming— I can feel the head, Flora.'

'I know. It's brilliant,' Flora said cheerfully, ignoring Conner's ironic glance. She used her left hand to control the escape of the head and then gently allowed it to extend, remembering the deliveries she'd observed in her training. 'It's all fine, Evanna. The head is out.' *And terrifying.*

'Is he breathing? Is the cord round the neck? It's too fast. Logan was right,' Evanna gasped, tears trickling out of her eyes.

'That's nonsense, Evanna,' Flora said. She gently felt for the cord and her heart plummeted when she felt something. Struggling not to panic, she slid her fingers under it and slipped it over the baby's head. Only then did she start to breathe again. 'Everything is fine, Evanna. And there's nothing wrong with having a baby at home, you know that. You're a midwife!'

Suddenly aware that Conner was right by her side, Flora glanced at him. 'Is someone going to call Logan? He should be here for the next bit.'

'No.' Evanna grabbed his hand. 'It will be too much for him.'

But the decision was taken out of their hands because Logan appeared in the doorway, his face grey. 'Oh, God—what can I do?'

'Pour yourself a whisky and hold Evanna's hand,' Conner advised, and Flora glanced at him.

'Actually, you can draw up the Syntometrine so that Conner can give it.'

Evanna gave another gasp. 'Flora, I've got another one coming.'

'Great.' Flora smiled at her, concentrated on delivering the anterior shoulder and then the baby slithered out, red-faced and bawling. 'Little boy. Congratulations.' She lifted the wriggling bundle onto Evanna's abdomen and covered him with the warmed towels that Janet quietly handed her.

'Oh, Logan…' Tears spilled down Evanna's cheeks as she curved her arm protectively around the baby.

Logan stared down at his wife and son, his eyes bright. He didn't speak. Then he lifted a hand and pressed his fingers to his eyes, clearly struggling for control.

Conner rose to his feet. 'She's fine,' he said softly. 'They're both fine. Your family is safe. You can relax.' He hesitated for a moment and then reached out a hand and closed his fingers over his cousin's shoulder. Flora felt a lump build in her own throat as she saw the gesture of support and reassurance.

Who said Conner wasn't capable of forming relationships?

Who said that he wasn't capable of feeling?

Knowing that her work wasn't finished, Flora turned her attention back to the delivery. She clamped the cord twice, divided it and then attached a Hollister clamp near the umbilicus. 'Two normal arteries, Evanna,' she murmured. 'Everything is looking good here.' She gently applied traction to the cord and the placenta slid out into the bowl.

'I'll check it.' Logan stepped forward to help, his face regaining some of its colour. 'I'm feeling fine now. Thank you. Both of you.'

'He's already feeding, Logan.' Evanna sounded sleepy and delighted at the same time. 'What are we going to call him?'

They murmured together and Flora's eyes misted as she watched them with their new son. Logan's hands were gentle, his face softened by love, and Evanna looked as though she'd won the lottery.

Feeling a lump in her throat, Flora glanced towards Conner. He was standing at the French windows, staring out across the garden, his shoulders tense and his features frozen.

She wondered what he was thinking.

Was he remembering his own family, and the contrast they must have made to the scene playing out in front of him?

They'd shared enough secrets in the stillness of the night for her to know that he would be less than comfortable with such undiluted domesticity.

Wanting to help, she stood up and swiftly cleared everything away. 'We're going to leave the two of you alone for a few minutes,' she said to Logan. 'We'll be next door if you need us.' She washed her hands quickly and then touched Conner's arm.

He turned, his face expressionless. 'Yes?'

'I don't think we're needed here.' She gestured with her head. 'Let's go next door.'

'Sure.' With a faint shrug he followed her through to the surgery and they walked into her room. But he didn't reach for her or make any of his usual wry, disparaging comments. Instead, he seemed distant. Remote. 'So—I didn't know you were a midwife.'

'I'm not. That's the first baby I've ever delivered.'

Conner gave a short laugh. 'You're full of surprises. I never would have known.'

'Do you want to know the truth? I was always terrified that this baby would come when Evanna was on the island and I knew Logan would panic. So I read a few books, asked Evanna a few questions…' Flora shrugged, wishing that he'd relax with her. 'I had a nasty moment when I felt the cord but it was all fine. And it helped knowing you were there.'

'I was as much use as a hog roast at a vegetarian supper,' he drawled. 'You did it all.'

'That's not true. You were strong,' she said softly. 'You gave Evanna confidence, and if something had happened to her or the baby, you would have known what to do. You're good in an emergency.'

He looked at her for a moment and then looked away. 'Well, they're both all right, and that's all that matters.' He glanced at his watch. 'I'd better get going, or Logan will be grumbling that I haven't finished my paperwork.'

Flora felt a flicker of desperation.

Something had changed between them and she didn't know what it was.

She wanted to say something about Logan and Evanna. She wanted to show him that she understood how hard it must be for him, but he was cool and remote, discouraging any sort of personal intrusion into his thoughts or feelings. And, anyway, she didn't want to have that conversation here, where they could be interrupted at any moment. 'Are you busy tonight?'

'Why do you ask?'

Her heart skipped. 'Because I thought you might fancy skinny-dipping in the sea. It's a great form of relaxation.'

He stood for a moment and then he turned. His ice-blue eyes were serious and there was no hint of a smile on his mouth. 'I don't think so.'

Her heart plummeted. 'I'll take off my bra and knickers this time, if that would swing your decision.'

'No, Flora.' His voice held none of its usual mockery. 'I don't think that's a good idea.'

'Oh. I thought you— I thought we might—' She broke off, not knowing what to say. 'Of course. Sorry. I understand.'

Had he guessed how she felt about him?

Probably. Sooner or later it happened to every woman who spent time with him, she was sure of that.

He'd guessed, and now he was running for cover. She'd always known this moment would come, but that didn't make it any easier. In fact, the pain was so overwhelming that she turned away, not wanting to embarrass herself or him by saying anything else.

'This thing between us has to end, Flora. *Do you understand*?' He closed his hands around her upper arms and spun her towards him, his eyes fierce as he stared into her face. 'Do you?'

Even though she'd sensed this moment was coming, she felt totally unprepared. 'Yes,' she croaked. 'I understand, Conner.' If he didn't want to be with her, she couldn't change that. And she didn't want to make him feel bad by showing how much she was hurting. 'We've been together for over a month.' She gave a tremulous smile. 'That's probably a record for you. Don't feel guilty. We had a great time. I had a great time.'

He gritted his teeth. 'Don't cry.'

'I'm not going to cry.' *At least, not until she was on her own.*

And she wasn't going to admit that she loved him either,

because that would just make the whole situation even more embarrassing for both of them.

And what was the point of it?

His fingers tightened on her arms. 'We never should have started this,' he said hoarsely. '*I* never should have started it.'

'You didn't. I did. And, Conner, you're hurting me.'

'Sorry.' He released her instantly and let out a breath. 'Sorry.'

'You don't have to look so tormented.' Though it took all her courage, she was determined to say it. 'You never promised me anything. You haven't done anything wrong. It was just a bit of fun.'

'And will it be fun when the locals work out who the woman is that I've been seeing? No, it won't.' His tone impatient and full of self-loathing, he turned away from her and strode towards the window. 'I can't believe I thought for a moment we could have a secret affair on an island like Glenmore. I'd forgotten what the place was like. You can't sneeze without someone counting the microbes.'

'I didn't think you cared what people say about you.'

'I don't. But I care about what people say about *you*. I saw your face, Flora,' he said roughly, 'when you were looking at that baby. You watched Evanna and Logan and you wanted what they have. Admit it.'

'I admit it,' she said simply. 'Who wouldn't want that, Logan? Someone to love. A family. Isn't it what everyone wants?'

His hands dropped to his sides. 'I can't do this. I'm sorry, Flora.'

'Is this because of Evanna and Logan?' Suddenly she couldn't just let him walk away. 'Talk to me, Conner. I know you're upset about what just happened and I can imagine it must be very hard seeing all that family stuff when your own family life was so desperately bad, but—'

He jerked away from her and strode towards the door. 'Enough.'

'Please, talk to me, Conner. I can see you're upset. Come over later. Even if we don't…' She stumbled over the words. 'If we're not still together, I'm still your friend. '

He paused with his hand on the door and then he turned slowly. And then he looked at her and his eyes were bleak and empty. 'People are already talking.'

'I know.'

'They're going to find out, Flora,' he said roughly. 'Nods. Winks. Whispers. Everyone wondering what a girl like you is doing with a man like me. And you'll hate it. You hate being the focus of attention. Take that first night—you were mortified when Jim and the others turned up on the beach.'

'Well of course I was.' She defended herself. 'I was in my underwear!'

'It was more than that. You didn't want people gossiping about you. And the whispers have started all over Glenmore. Do you think I haven't heard them? In the pub the other night, you almost cracked your glass because you were so terrified that Jim had discovered just who I'd been visiting in the dead of night. Knowing this place, people are grilling you every time you go to buy eggs or milk. Am I right?'

'Yes, but—'

'And you'll hate that because you're so shy. And I don't want people breathing your name and mine in the same sentence.' His knuckles whitened on the doorhandle. 'You know what people say about me. I'm bad Conner. People expect me to go the same way my father went.'

'I keep telling you that you are *not* your father.'

'No, but you deserve to be with a man you're not ashamed to be seen with.'

'I'm not ashamed of what we share, Conner.'

'Yes, you are, because you're not the sort of woman to indulge in wild affairs, especially not with men like me. When Logan walked in and caught us kissing, you jumped like a kangaroo on a hot plate and your cheeks were the colour of strawberries.'

'Well, of course! But that wasn't about you, it was about me. I'm not used to…' she shrugged self-consciously '…kissing and stuff in public.'

'And you're not going to get used to it. I have no intention of dragging your reputation down into the dirt. You have to live here after I've left.' He took her face in his hands and looked at her. 'So far the only person who knows is Logan and he won't say anything. Our secret should be safe.'

Confused, she shook her head. 'Is that why you're ending it? Because of what people might think of me?'

'Look me in the eye and tell me you haven't spent years dreaming about finding the right man, about having babies and being a family here on Glenmore.'

Incurably truthful, Flora nodded. 'I have imagined that, of course, but—'

'Of course you have. And you deserve that. You'll be a great mother.' With a faint smile he lifted her hand to his lips in an old-fashioned gesture and then cursed softly and dragged her against him. 'Sorry, but I think I'm going to be bad one more time.' He lowered his mouth to hers and kissed her slowly and thoroughly until her heart was hammering and her legs were weak. Then he lifted his head and smiled. 'Now, go away and find a man who is going to make you happy.'

Without giving her a chance to reply, he turned and left the room, leaving her staring after him with a head full of questions and a heart full of misery.

'Conner is in such a foul mood,' Evanna murmured, tucking the baby expertly onto her shoulder and rubbing his back. 'The rumour is that whoever he was seeing has dumped him.

I told Meg that's *completely* ridiculous because when in this lifetime did a woman ever dump Conner? Flora, are you listening to a word I'm saying?'

'Yes. No.' Flora lifted her fingers to her throbbing head. 'Sorry—I didn't really hear you. What did you say?'

Three days had passed since Conner had ended their relationship. Three days in which she hadn't eaten or slept. She felt as though part of her had been ripped out.

'I was just talking about Conner.' Evanna frowned. 'I can't believe a woman has dumped him because what woman in their right mind would dump him? On the other hand, I haven't seen any broken-hearted women around the place. Everyone is behaving as they usually behave. What's the matter with you? Why are you rubbing your head?'

'Bad night.' Flora curved her mouth into something that she hoped resembled a smile. 'Too much on my mind.'

She missed him so much.

She missed sleeping in his arms, she missed their long, intimate conversations in the darkness of the night, and she missed the way he made love.

He'd ended it because he thought she wanted to get married and have children. Or had he ended it because he was afraid that the ever-increasing rumours would hurt her? She wasn't sure any more. She'd replayed their last conversation in her head so many times that she felt as though her brain had turned into spaghetti.

Evanna looked guilty. 'It's our fault. Logan and I are so wrapped up in little Charlie and you and Conner are working so hard covering for the pair of us. How has he been with you? Moody?'

'I don't see that much of him. We do our own clinics.' Flora stood up quickly. 'Great to see you and Charlie looks great, too, and—'

'Flora...' Evanna peered closely at her. 'What is the matter with you? You're behaving very oddly. Is it the baby?' Her voice softened. 'Has it made you all broody? I know how much you want your own family and it *will* happen. One day you're going to meet the man of your dreams and have a family of your own.'

'Yes.' Flora felt as though her face was going to crack. 'Absolutely.' And she realised that her dream didn't seem so clear any more.

What she wanted was to be with Conner.

And if he didn't want to get married or have a family—well, she'd live with that.

But he didn't want *her*, did he?

He'd ended the relationship.

Evanna's hand stilled on the baby's back. 'I wish you'd tell me what's wrong.' She frowned. 'Flora?'

Flora looked at Evanna and Charlie. And she thought of Logan and what they shared.

And then she thought of what she'd had with Conner.

Had he at any point actually said that he didn't want her? No. Yet again she ran through the conversation in her head, trying to remember every last detail. What he'd said was that he wasn't the right man for her. That she wouldn't want to be seen with him in public.

And when he'd said that, she hadn't argued with him because, as usual, she hadn't known what to say. She'd let him walk away because she hadn't thought of the right thing to say at the right time.

But suddenly she knew exactly what she wanted to say.

Maybe he didn't want her any more, but she needed to find out. And she didn't care about pride because some things were more important than pride.

Panic fluttered inside her. 'Evanna, where is Conner, do you know?'

'He went to the Stag's Head for a drink with Logan.'

Flora glanced at the clock on the wall. Seven o'clock. The chances were that most of Glenmore would be in the Stag's Head at this hour on a Friday night. She stood up. 'I'm really sorry to abandon you, but I'm going for a drink. There's something I need to say to Conner.'

The Stag's Head was crowded with locals and heads turned as Flora opened the door and paused, her eyes scanning the room.

'Hey, Flora.' Ben smiled at her from behind the bar. 'You look like a woman in need of a drink. What can I get you?'

'In a minute, Ben, thanks.' Finally she spotted Conner and just at that moment he lifted his eyes and saw her. Ice-blue melded with brown and for a moment she just stood still, her heart pounding and her cheeks flaming red, unable to look away or move.

'Hi, Flora,' a couple of the locals called out to her, and she gave a vague smile but didn't respond.

If she didn't do this right away, she'd lose her nerve.

She let the door close behind her and wove her way through the chattering throng towards his table.

His eyes narrowed, but his gaze didn't shift from hers and from behind her came the sound of wolf whistles and good-natured laughter.

'Hey, Conner, looks like our Flora's got something to say to you.'

'Have you been a naughty boy, Con?'

The cat calls and teasing continued and Flora stopped next to him, realising with a flash of desperation that her plan was never going to work. She *did* have something to say, but the pub was so noisy that no one was ever going to hear her. *And she needed them to hear.*

'Flora?' Conner's voice was wary and for a moment she just looked at him, wondering how she was going to do this.

She opened her mouth to speak and then closed it again, thinking rapidly.

Executing a rapid change of plan, she leaned forward, took his face in her hands and kissed him. He stiffened with shock and his mouth remained immobile under hers. Then he started to pull away from her, so she slid onto his lap, straddling him, her hands clasping his head, keeping his mouth against hers.

A stunned silence had descended on the pub and although she didn't turn her head to look, Flora knew that everyone was staring at them. And that was hardly surprising because she was creating the biggest spectacle that Glenmore had seen for a long time. Which had been her intention.

Despite the tension in his body, she felt Conner's mouth move under hers and then felt the skilled stroke of his tongue. It was as if he couldn't help himself and, as always, the chemistry flashed between them. But his lapse was short-lived and this time when he pulled away he removed her hands at the same time, clasping her wrists firmly.

He stared at her, his blue eyes blazing. *'What do you think you're doing?'*

The noise around them had ceased. The low hum of chatter had died, the laughter was silenced and there was no clink of glasses.

'I'm kissing you, Conner,' Flora said clearly. 'I'm kissing you, just as I've kissed you every day for the past month. Only this time I'm doing it in public, so there's no confusion about the facts.'

His mouth tightened and he muttered something under his breath, but she covered his lips with her fingers.

'No. You had your say the other night. Now it's my turn to talk,' she said calmly, and then she slid off his lap and turned to face everyone. And for a moment her courage faltered because what seemed like a million faces were staring at her.

Her gaze slid over the crowd.

She saw Nick and, behind him, Meg. She saw Janet and Jim.

It seemed that everyone was in the Stag's Head.

'You've all been wondering who Conner has been seeing for the last month. Well, it's me,' she said simply, speaking clearly and raising her voice slightly so that everyone could hear her. 'I'm the lucky woman.'

'Flora, for crying out loud.' Conner rose to his feet, dislodging her arm from his shoulder. 'Have you been drinking?'

'No. I'm completely sober.' She smiled up at him, aware that everything she felt shone in her eyes. Then she took his hand and turned back to face the islanders—the people she spent her life with. 'I know what you're all thinking. You're thinking that Bad Conner has lived up to his name again, that obviously he seduced good, sensible Flora because she'd never do anything as reckless as have a wild, passionate affair with a man who is obviously going to walk off into the sunset, leaving her broken-hearted and very possibly pregnant.'

The locals were too shocked to respond so Flora just ploughed on.

'You're wrong. *I* seduced *him*. And I'm not embarrassed about that because I've discovered that—' She broke off as the door to the pub opened and Evanna walked in, holding the baby.

'Charlie and I suddenly had a horrible feeling that we were missing something important so I called a babysitter for Kirsty.'

As if emerging from a trance, Logan rose to his feet and walked over to his wife. He took the baby from her and tipped one of the lifeboat crew out of his chair so that she could sit down.

Flora smiled at her friend. 'Good timing. I was just about

to tell everyone that I've discovered that I don't really want what I thought I wanted. Up until a month ago I thought I wanted a man who loved me, a home, children—all the usual things. And then Conner came back.'

Conner's eyes were on hers and he shook his head. 'Stop now, before you make things worse.'

'Things can't get any worse for me, Conner.' Flora touched his cheek gently. 'I've discovered that not being with you is the worst it can get. You're all I want.' She was speaking just to him now, suddenly oblivious to her audience who stood watching, paralysed with surprise and fascination. 'You're all I want, Conner MacNeil. And I want you as you are, for as long as you want to be with me. I know you don't want babies or a family. I know you don't want anything permanent. And that's all right. If all we ever share is hot sex, that's fine.'

Someone in the crowd gulped and she wasn't sure whether the shocked sound had come from Meg or Evanna because she wasn't paying attention.

She was watching Conner.

'I love you,' she said, her eyes misting as she looked at him. 'And I know that probably scares you. I don't think anyone has ever loved you properly before and I want you to know how I feel. And I know you don't feel the same way about me and that's fine. I understand. If I'd been as badly hurt as you were as a child, I wouldn't risk my heart either. But I'm giving you mine, Conner, for as long as you want it. And I'm telling you that in public so that there's no mistake about it. I love you so much. And I'm not ashamed of that. I don't care who knows because I'm proud of what you've become and I'm proud that I'm the one you've spent time with since you've been on Glenmore. And if turns out that you've had enough of me, I'll accept it.' She shrugged. 'But I won't accept you ending our relationship because you're worried about what people might think of me. I don't care what anyone thinks. I just care about you. Us.' She stopped and Logan cleared his throat.

'That's got to be the longest speech you've ever made, Flora Harris.'

Conner stared at her, his face unusually pale. But he didn't speak.

Flora looked at him expectantly. 'Aren't you going to say something? You're the one who's slick with words, Conner MacNeil, not me. You always know what to say.'

Still he didn't answer her. It was as if he'd been turned to stone and she gave a sigh of frustration.

'Did you hear what I said? I'm in love with you.' On impulse, she pulled out a chair, stood on it and turned to face the crowd. 'Flora Harris loves Conner MacNeil!'

Ben cleared his throat and scratched his head. 'We heard you the first time, Flora. We're waiting to hear what Conner has to say. But apparently he's been struck dumb.'

Finally Conner moved. He rose slowly to his feet, gently lifted Flora off the chair and lowered her to the floor as if she were made of porcelain. 'I thought you were shy.'

'I am shy.'

He stroked a strand of hair away from her eyes with a gentle hand. 'I've got news for you, angel. Shy girls don't stand on chairs in pubs and declare undying love.'

'They do if they mean it,' she said softly, and his hand dropped to his side.

'There are things I need to say to you.'

Her heart fluttered. Rejection? Or a stay of execution? 'Then say them.'

'Not here.' He glanced at their audience. 'I think you've had enough of a show for one night.' And then he closed his hand over hers and led her from the pub and out into the darkness.

'Where are we going?' Flora hurried to keep up with him but he didn't answer and eventually they reached the quay where her boat was moored. 'You want to go sailing in the dark?'

'No, but I want to sit and look at her for a minute. Boats always calm me.' He sat down on the edge of the quay and tugged at her hand. 'Sit down.'

She sat, her heart pumping, the surface of the quay rough beneath her legs. 'Are you angry?'

'How could I possibly be angry?' He gave a short laugh, his eyes on the boats. 'I'm not angry. But I can't accept what you're offering, Flora.'

'I love you, Conner. Nothing you do or say is going to change that fact.'

'You don't really want an affair. It isn't who you are.'

'I want *you*. And if an affair is what's on offer then that's what I'll take.' She hesitated and then put her hand on his thigh and left it there. 'There's no pressure on you, Conner. I know you were more than a little spooked by seeing Logan and Evanna. I know that family life isn't what you want—'

'You're wrong.' His voice was hoarse and he covered her hand with his and then gripped it tightly. 'I was spooked, that's true, but I was spooked because in my mind I kept seeing *you* sitting there, holding a baby. And I wanted that baby to be mine.'

His words were so unexpected that for a moment she assumed she must have imagined them. She stared blankly at the boat, afraid to breathe, move or do anything that might disturb the atmosphere. *Afraid to look at him.*

Then, finally, she dared to turn her head. 'What did you say?'

'You heard me.'

Stunned, Flora could do nothing but stare. 'I don't understand.'

'Neither do I. I've spent my entire life running from relationships. I've never given anyone the opportunity to hurt me. But you crept up on me, Flora Harris.' He gave a lopsided smile. 'Somehow you sneaked in under my radar. With you, I didn't feel angry any more. You're the only person I've ever met whose company I prefer to my own.'

She could hardly breathe. 'But if you felt like that, why didn't you tell me? Why did you end our relationship? *Why did you walk away?*'

'Because I'm not a good catch.' He lifted her hand to his lips and kissed it. 'As far as commitment goes, my track record is appallingly bad. What woman in her right mind would take a chance on me?'

'I would,' Flora said softly. 'I would, if you asked me to.'

He was silent for a moment and when he spoke his voice was husky. 'You would? You're not worried about my past?'

'I'm more worried about my future. I can't imagine what it will be like if you're not part of it.'

'Knowing who I am doesn't make a difference?'

'I love who you are,' she said simply. 'You're a man who has done tremendous things with his life, despite the most appalling start. Most people would have crumpled. Most people would have repeated the pattern they'd seen at home or allowed the past to dictate their present. You did neither of those things. You trained as a doctor. You give to others, even though you were given so little yourself.'

He was silent for a moment and then he cleared his throat and gave her a wry smile. 'Now, this is the sort of hero-worship I think I could live with,' he drawled softly, standing up and pulling her up after him. 'I'm still afraid you're going to lose your nerve any minute and change your mind.'

'I won't do that. I love you, Conner. What I feel for you isn't something I can turn on and off.'

'I make women miserable, Flora.'

'You don't make *me* miserable. These last weeks has been the happiest of my life.'

He hesitated. 'What would you say if I told you that I don't want to stay on Glenmore?'

She lifted a hand to his face, gently exploring the roughness of his jaw with her finger. 'I'd say that's fine. And I'd ask you where you want to go.'

His gaze flickered from her face to the boat. 'I want to sail. Just the two of us. And when you're too pregnant to move around the boat, we'll find some dry land and make a home.'

She felt the lump building in her throat. 'That sounds good to me.'

'You don't mind leaving Glenmore?'

'I want to be wherever you are.'

He closed his eyes for a moment and then lowered his head so that his forehead brushed hers. 'If you'll do this, *if you'll trust me with your heart,* I swear I won't let you down, angel.'

'I know you won't let me down.'

His breath warmed her mouth. 'I don't deserve you. You're such a good person.'

'Actually, you're wrong about that. I have an *extremely* bad side,' she murmured, giving a soft gasp as his lips brushed the corner of her mouth. 'Several less-than-desirable qualities, in fact.'

'Name a few.' His body was pressed against hers and it was becoming harder and harder to concentrate.

'I'm useless at gossip.'

'That's a quality.'

'I'm insatiable in the bedroom.' She tilted her head back and gave him a wicked smile. 'The problem with good girls,

Conner MacNeil, is that when they discover what fun being bad can be, they never want to stop.'

'Is that right?' He curved his hands over her bottom and brought his mouth down on hers. And then he suddenly lifted his head and cursed softly.

'What's the matter?'

'What does a person have to do to get privacy on this island?' He stared over her shoulder and Flora turned to find what appeared to be the entire population of Glenmore gathered on the quay, watching.

Several of them held torches and Flora blinked as the beam from one almost blinded her.

'Well?' It was Jim who spoke and his voice carried the short distance across the quay. 'You can't expect to make a declaration like that in the Stag's Head and not tell us the ending. What's the ending? Has she said yes?'

Conner shook his head in disbelief. 'I can't believe this,' he muttered. 'The first and only time I propose to a woman and I have to do it with an audience.'

'You should be down on one knee, Conner MacNeil,' Ann Carne said primly, appearing at the front of the crowd, and Flora's heart stumbled in her chest.

'You don't have to propose—I don't want you to feel smothered by all this. We can just live together and—'

He put a finger over her lips, his eyes gentle. 'That isn't what I want. I want to make sure you're chained to me so that you can't run off easily when you realise what you've married.' He dropped to one knee and she gave an appalled gasp.

'Conner! You don't have to go that far! The seagulls are usually pretty busy above here. Kneeling could be a messy experience.'

'If I don't kneel, I'll never hear the last of it from the locals.' With an exaggerated gesture Conner took her hand in his. His eyes gleamed wickedly and he lifted an eyebrow in question. 'Well? How daring are you feeling? Can you bring yourself to marry a reprobate like me?'

'Conner!' There was a disgusted snort from Evanna. 'You're *supposed* to make it romantic. At the very least you're supposed to tell her that you love her.'

'I'm on my knees in seagull droppings,' Conner growled. 'I think that tells her quite a lot about my feelings.'

Half laughing, half crying, Flora looked down at him. 'You haven't said that you love me. I want to hear you say it. That's the really important bit.'

'I love you.' This time his voice was serious. 'I love you, Flora Mary Harris. Will you marry me?'

'Yes. Oh, yes. *Yes!*' She choked on the word and tears spilled down her cheeks.

Instantly Conner was on his feet, his expression horrified as he scooped her face into his hands. 'What's wrong?' He brushed the tears away with his thumbs. 'All my life I've been making women cry because I wouldn't say those words. Now, suddenly, I've said them and you're crying!'

'I'm crying because I'm happy.' She pressed her mouth to his. 'I'm happy and I love you. And, just for the record, my answer is yes.'

Torchlight wavered on her face. 'Speak up, Flora! We can't hear you at the back!'

Flora started to laugh. 'Yes,' she yelled in a voice so loud that Conner flinched. *'Yes, I will marry you.'*

There was a cheer from the crowd on the quay and Conner folded her into his arms. 'I hope you know what you're saying yes to, because you can't back out now.'

'I'm saying yes to everything,' Flora said softly, and this time her words were for him alone. 'Everything, Conner.'

'Everything?' His eyes held a wicked gleam. 'In that case,

I don't know about you,' he murmured against her mouth, 'but I think I could do with a bit more privacy for the rest of this conversation. Your place or mine?'

* * * * *

Jenna

CHAPTER ONE

'I CAN'T believe you've dragged me to the middle of nowhere. You must really hate me.' The girl slumped against the rail of the ferry, sullen and defiant, every muscle in her slender teenage frame straining with injured martyrdom and simmering rebellion.

Jenna dragged her gaze from the misty beauty of the approaching island and focused on her daughter. 'I don't hate you, Lexi,' she said quietly. 'I love you. Very much.'

'If you loved me, we'd still be in London.'

Guilt mingled with stress and tension until the whole indigestible mix sat like a hard ball behind her ribs. 'I thought this was the best thing.'

'Best for you, maybe. Not me.'

'It's a fresh start. A new life.' As far away from her old life as possible. Far away from everything that reminded her of her marriage. Far away from the pitying glances of people she'd used to think were her friends.

'I liked my old life!'

So had she. Until she'd discovered that her life had been a lie. They always said you didn't know what was going on in someone else's marriage—she hadn't known what was going on in her own.

Jenna blinked rapidly, holding herself together through will-power alone, frightened by how bad she felt. Not for the first time, she wondered whether eventually she was going to crack. People said that time healed, but how much time? Five years? Ten years? Certainly not a year. She didn't feel any better now than she had when it had first happened. She was starting to wonder whether some things just didn't heal—whether she'd have to put on the 'everything is OK' act for the rest of her life.

She must have been doing a reasonably good job of convincing everyone she was all right because Lexi was glaring at her, apparently oblivious to her mother's own personal struggle. 'You had a perfectly good job in London. We could have stayed there.'

'London is expensive.'

'So? Make Dad pay maintenance or something. He's the one who walked out.'

The comment was like a slap in the face. 'I don't want to live off your father. I'd rather be independent.' Which was just as well, Jenna thought bleakly, given Clive's reluctance to part with any money for his daughter. 'Up here there are no travel costs, you can go to the local school, and they give me a cottage with the job.'

That was the best part. A cottage. Somewhere that was their own. She wasn't going to wake up one morning and find it had been taken away from them.

'How can you be so calm and civilised about all this?' Lexi looked at her in exasperation. 'You should be angry. I tell you now, if a man ever treats me the way Dad treated you I'll punch his teeth down his throat and then I'll take a knife to his—'

'Lexi!'

'Well, I would!'

Jenna took a slow deep breath. 'Of course I've felt angry.

And upset. But what's happened has happened, and we have to get on with it.' Step by step. Day by day.

'So Dad's left living in luxury with his new woman and we're exiled to a remote island that doesn't even have electricity? Great.'

'Glenmore is a wonderful place. Keep an open mind. I loved it when I was your age and I came with my grandparents.'

'People *choose* to come here?' Lexi glared at the rocky shore, as if hoping to scare the island into vanishing. 'Is this seriously where you came on holiday? That's totally tragic. You should have sued them for cruelty.'

'I loved it. It was a proper holiday. The sort where we spent time together—' Memories swamped her and suddenly Jenna was a child again, excited at the prospect of a holiday with her grandparents. Here—and perhaps only here—she'd felt loved and accepted for who she was. 'We used to make sandcastles and hunt for shells on the beach—'

'Wow. I'm surprised you didn't die of excitement.'

Faced with the sting of teenage sarcasm, Jenna blinked. Suddenly she wished she were a child again, with no worries. No one depending on her. Oh, for crying out loud—she pushed her hair away from her eyes and reminded herself that she was thirty-three, not twelve. 'It *is* exciting here. Lexi, this island was occupied by Celts and Vikings—it's full of history. There's an archaeological dig going on this summer and they had a small number of places for interested teenagers. I've booked you on it.'

'You *what*?' Appalled, Lexi lost her look of martyred boredom and shot upright in full defensive mode. 'I am not an interested teenager so you can count me out!'

'Try it, Lexi,' Jenna urged, wondering with a lurch of horror what she was going to do if Lexi refused to co-operate. 'You used to love history when you were younger, and—'

'I'm not a kid any more, Mum! This is my summer holiday. I'm supposed to have a rest from school. I don't want to be taught history!'

Forcing herself to stay calm, Jenna took a slow, deep breath; one of the many she'd taken since her daughter had morphed from sweet child to scary teen. When you read the pregnancy books, why didn't it warn you that the pain of being a mother didn't end with labour?

Across the ferry she caught sight of a family, gathered together by the rail. Mother, father, two children—they were laughing and talking, and Jenna looked away quickly because she'd discovered that nothing was more painful than being around happy families when your own was in trouble.

Swallowing hard, she reminded herself that not every modern family had perfect symmetry. Single-parent families, stepfamilies—they came in different shapes. Yes, her family had been broken, but breakages could be mended. They might heal in a different shape, but they could still be sturdy.

'I thought maybe we could go fishing.' It was up to her to be the glue. It was up to her to knit her family together again in a new shape. 'There's nothing quite like eating a fish you've caught yourself.'

Lexi rolled her eyes and exhaled dramatically. 'Call me boring, but gutting a fish with my mother is *so* not my idea of fun. Stop trying so hard, Mum. Just admit that the situation is crap.'

'Don't swear, Alexandra.'

'Why not? Grandma isn't around to hear and it *is* crap. If you want my honest opinion, I hope Dad and his shiny new girlfriend drown in their stupid hot tub.'

Relieved that no one was standing near them, Jenna rubbed her fingers over her forehead, reminding herself that this was not the time to get into an argument. 'Let's talk about us for a moment, not Dad. There are six weeks of summer holiday left before term starts. I'm going to be working, and I'm not leaving you on your own all day. That's why I thought archaeology camp would be fun.'

'About as much fun as pulling my toenails out one by one. I don't need a babysitter. I'm fifteen.'

And you're still a child, Jenna thought wistfully. Underneath that moody, sullen exterior lurked a terrified girl. And she knew all about being terrified, because she was too. She felt like a plant that had been growing happily in one spot for years, only to be dug up and tossed on the compost heap. The only difference between her and Lexi was that she had to hide it. She was the grown-up. She had to look confident and in control.

Not terrified, insecure and needy.

Now that it was just the two of them, Lexi needed her to be strong. But the truth was she didn't feel strong. When she was lying in bed staring into the darkness she had moments of utter panic, wondering whether she could actually do this on her own. Had she been crazy to move so far away? Should she have gone and stayed with her parents? At least that would have eased the financial pressure, and her mother would have been able to watch out for Lexi while she worked. Imagining her mother's tight-lipped disapproval, Jenna shuddered. There were two sins her mother couldn't forgive and she'd committed both of them. No, they were better on their own.

Anger? Oh, yes, she felt anger. Not just for herself, but for Lexi. What had happened to the man who had cradled his daughter when she'd cried and spent weeks choosing exactly the right dolls' house? Jenna grabbed hold of the anger and held it tightly, knowing that it was much easier to live with than misery. Anger drove her forward. Misery left her inert.

She needed anger if she was going to make this work. And she *was* going to make it work.

She had to.

'We're going to be OK. I promise, Lexi.' Jenna stroked a hand over the teenager's rigid shoulder, relieved when her touch wasn't instantly rejected. 'We'll have some fun.'

'Fun is seeing my friends. Fun is my bedroom at home and my computer—'

Jenna didn't point out that they didn't have a home any more. Clive had sold it—the beautiful old Victorian house that she'd tended so lovingly for the past thirteen years. When they'd first married money had been tight, so she'd decorated every room herself…

The enormity of what she'd lost engulfed her again and Jenna drew in a jerky breath, utterly daunted at the prospect of creating a new life from scratch. By herself.

Lexi dug her hand in her pocket and pulled out her mobile phone. 'No signal. Mum, there's no signal!' Panic mingled with disgust as she waved her phone in different directions, trying to make it work. 'I swear, if there's no signal in this place I'm swimming home. It's bad enough not seeing my friends, but not talking to them either is going to be the end.'

Not by herself, Jenna thought. With her daughter. Somehow they needed to rediscover the bond they'd shared before the stability of their family had been blown apart.

'This is a great opportunity to try a few different things. Develop some new interests.'

Lexi gave her a pitying look. 'I already have interests, Mum. Boys, my friends, hanging out, and did I say boys? Chatting on my phone—boys. Normal stuff, you know? No, I'm sure you don't know—you're too old.' She huffed moodily. 'You met Dad when you were sixteen, don't forget.'

Jenna flinched. She had just managed to put Clive out of her mind and Lexi had stuffed him back in her face. And she wasn't allowed to say that she'd had no judgement at sixteen. She couldn't say that the whole thing had been a mistake, because then Lexi would think she was a mistake and that wasn't true.

'All I'm asking is that you keep an open mind while you're here, Lexi. You'll make new friends.'

'Anyone who chooses to spend their life in a place like this is seriously tragic and no friend of mine. Face it, Mum, basically I'm going to have a miserable, lonely summer and it's all your fault.' Lexi scowled furiously at the phone. 'There's still no signal. I hate this place.'

'It's probably something to do with the rocky coastline. It will be fine once we land on the island.'

'It is not going to be fine! Nothing about this place is fine.' Lexi stuffed the phone moodily back in her pocket. 'Why didn't you let me spend the summer with Dad? At least I could have seen my friends.'

Banking down the hurt, Jenna fished for a tactful answer. 'Dad is working,' she said, hoping her voice didn't sound too robotic. 'He was worried you'd be on your own too much.' Well, what was she supposed to say? Sorry, Lexi, your dad is selfish and wants to forget he has responsibilities so he can spend his summer having sex with his new girlfriend.

'I wouldn't have cared if Dad was working. I could have hung around the house. I get on all right with Suzie. As long as I block out the fact that my Dad is hooked up with someone barely older than me.'

Jenna kept her expression neutral. 'People have relationships, Lexi. It's part of life.' Not part of *her* life, but she wasn't going to think about that now. For now her priorities were remembering to breathe in and out, get up in the morning, go to work, earn a living. Settling into her job, giving her daughter roots and security—that was what mattered.

'When you're young, yes. But he's old enough to know better. They should be banned for everyone over twenty-one.'

Lexi shuddered. 'Thank goodness you have more sense. It's a relief you're past all that.'

Jenna blinked. She was thirty-three. Was thirty-three really past it? Perhaps it was. By thirty-three you'd discovered that fairy tales were for children, that men didn't ride up with swords to rescue you; they were more likely to run you down while looking at the pretty girl standing behind you.

Resolutely she blocked that train of thought. She'd promised herself that she wasn't going to do that. She wasn't going to generalise and blame the entire male race for Clive's shortcomings. She wasn't going to grow old bitter and twisted, giving Lexi the impression that all men were selfish losers. It wasn't men who had hurt her; it was Clive. One man—not all men.

It was Clive who had chosen to have a rampant affair with a trainee lawyer barely out of college. It was Clive who had chosen to have sex on his desk without bothering to lock the door. There were moments when Jenna wondered if he'd done it on purpose, in the hope of being caught so he could prove how virile he was.

She frowned. Virile? If she'd been asked for a word to describe Clive, it certainly wouldn't have been virile. That would have been like describing herself as sexy, and she would never in a million years describe herself as sexy.

When had she ever had wild sex with a man while still wearing all her clothes? No one had ever been that desperate for her, had they? Not even Clive. Certainly not Clive.

When Clive had come home from the office they'd talked about household accounts, mending the leaking tap, whether or not they should have his mother for the weekend. Never had he walked through the door and grabbed her, overwhelmed by lust. And she wouldn't have wanted him to, Jenna admitted to herself. If he had grabbed her she would have been thinking about all the jobs she still had to do before she could go to bed.

Blissfully unaware that her mother was thinking about sex, Lexi scuffed her trainer on the ground. 'There would have been loads for me to do in London. Cool stuff, not digging up bits of pot from muddy ground. I could have done my own thing.'

'There will be lots of things to do here.'

'On my own. Great.'

'You'll make friends, Lex.'

'What if I don't? What if everyone hates me?'

Seeing the insecurity in her daughter's eyes, Jenna hugged her, not confessing that she felt exactly the same way. Still, at least the people here wouldn't be gossiping about her disastrous marriage. 'They won't hate you. You make friends easily, and everyone on this island is friendly.' Please let them be friendly. 'That's why we're here.'

Lexi leaned on the rail and stared at the island mournfully. 'Change is the pits.'

'Change often feels difficult, but it can turn out to be exciting.' Jenna parroted the words, hoping she sounded more convincing than she felt. 'Life is full of possibilities.'

'Not stuck here, it isn't. Face it, Mum. It's crap.'

Ryan McKinley stood with his legs braced and his arms folded. His eyes stung from lack of sleep, he'd had no time to shave, and his mind was preoccupied by thoughts of the little girl with asthma he'd seen during the night. He dug his mobile out of his pocket and checked for missed calls and messages but for once there were none—which meant that the child was probably still sleeping peacefully. Which was what he would have been doing, given the choice.

As the ferry approached the quay, he slipped the phone

back into his pocket, trying not to think of the extra hour he could have spent in bed.

Why had Evanna insisted that *he* be the one to meet the new practice nurse? If he hadn't known that the woman had a teenage daughter, he would have suspected Evanna of matchmaking. He'd even thought of mentioning his suspicions to Logan McNeil, his colleague and the senior partner in the Glenmore Medical Centre. If she was planning something, Logan would probably know, given that Evanna was his wife. Wife, mother, midwife and—Ryan sighed—friend. She was a loyal, caring friend.

In the two years he'd been living on the island she'd done everything she could to end his hermit-like existence. It had been Evanna who had dragged him into island life, and Evanna who had insisted that he help out when the second island doctor had left a year earlier.

He hadn't been planning to work, but the work had proved a distraction from his thoughts, as she'd guessed it would. And it was different enough from his old job to ensure that there were no difficult memories. Different had proved to be good. The shift in pace and pressure just what he'd needed. But, as grateful as he was to his colleague's wife for forcing him out of his life of self-imposed isolation, he refused to go along with her need to see him in a relationship.

There were some things that wouldn't change.

'Hi, Dr McKinley. You're up early—' A pretty girl strolled over to him, her hair swinging over her shoulders, her adoring gaze hopeful. 'Last night was fun, wasn't it?'

'It was a good night, Zoe.' Confronted with the realities of living as part of a small island community, Ryan chose his words carefully. This was the drawback of living and working in the same place, he mused. He was her doctor. He knew about her depression and the battle she'd had to get herself to this point. 'You looked as though you were enjoying yourself. It was good to see you out. I'm glad you're feeling better.'

He'd spent the evening trying to keep the girl at a safe distance without hurting her feelings in front of her friends. Aware that her emotions were fragile, he hadn't wanted to be the cause of any more damage—but he knew only too well how important it was to keep that distance.

'I wasn't drinking alcohol. You told me not to with those tablets.'

'Probably wise.'

'I—' She pushed her thumbs into the pockets of her jeans, slightly awkward. 'You know—if you ever wanted to go out some time—' She broke off and her face turned scarlet. 'I shouldn't have said that. Millions of girls want to go out with you, I know. Sorry. Why would someone like you pick a screwball like me?'

'You're not a screwball.' Ryan wondered why the most difficult conversations always happened at the most awkward times. The ferry was docking and he was doing a consultation on the quay, within earshot of a hundred disembarking passengers. And, as if that wasn't enough, she was trying to step over a line he never allowed a patient to cross. 'You're suffering from depression, Zoe, and that's an illness like any other.'

'Yes, I know. You made me see that.' Painfully awkward, she rubbed her toe on the hard concrete of the quay. 'You've been great, Dr McKinley. Really great. I feel better about everything, now. More able to cope, you know? And I just wondered if—'

Ryan cut her off before she went too far and said something that couldn't be unsaid. 'Apart from the fact I'm your doctor, and I'd be struck off if I said yes, I'm way too old for you.' Too old. Too cynical. 'But I'm pleased you feel like dating. That's good, Zoe. And, judging from the way the men of Glenmore were flocking around you last night, you're not short of admirers, so I think you should go for it. Pick someone you like and get yourself out there.'

Her wistful glance told him exactly who was top of her list, and she gazed at him for a moment before giving a short laugh. 'You're refusing me.'

'Yes.' Ryan spoke firmly, not wanting there to be any mistake. 'I am. But in the nicest possible way.'

Zoe was looking at him anxiously. 'I've embarrassed you—'

'I'm not embarrassed.' Ryan searched for the right thing to say, knowing that the correct response was crucial both for her self-esteem and their future relationship. 'We've talked a lot over the past two months, Zoe. You've trusted me with things you probably haven't told other people. It's not unusual for that type of confidence to make you feel a bit confused about your own feelings. If it would help, you can change doctors.'

'I'm not confused, Dr McKinley. And I don't want to change doctors. You've got such a way with words, and I've never known a man listen like you—I suppose that's why I—' She shrugged. 'Maybe I will date one of those guys.' She smiled up at him. 'That archaeologist who's hanging around this summer is pretty cool.'

'Interesting guy,' Ryan agreed, relieved that she didn't appear to be too heartbroken by his rejection.

'What about you, Dr McKinley? Why are you waiting for the ferry? Are you meeting a woman?'

'In a manner of speaking. Our new practice nurse is arriving today. Reinforcements.' And he had a favour to ask her. He just hoped that Jennifer Richards was a big-hearted woman.

'A new nurse?' There was a wistful note to Zoe's voice.

'Well, I know Nurse Evanna needs the help. So what's this new nurse like? Is she young?'

'She's coming with her teenage daughter.' Why had Evanna wanted him to meet her? That question played on his mind as he watched the ferry dock. It could have been an innocent request, but he also knew that his colleague was obsessed with matching people up. She wanted a happy ending.

Ryan felt the tension spread across his shoulders. He knew life didn't often offer up happy endings.

Zoe's face brightened. 'If she has a teenage daughter, she must be forty at least. Maybe even older.' She dismissed the competition. 'Well, the ferry is on time, so you're about to meet your nurse.'

Shaking the sleep out of his brain, Ryan watched as a patchwork of people flowed off the ferry. Businessmen in suits, families clutching bulging beach bags, toddlers in pushchairs. A slightly overweight, middle-aged woman puffed her way towards him carrying a suitcase.

He didn't know whether to be relieved that Evanna clearly hadn't been matchmaking or disappointed that their new practice nurse didn't look fit enough to work a hard day at the surgery. 'Jennifer?' He extended a hand. 'I'm Dr McKinley. Ryan McKinley. Welcome to Glenmore Island.'

The woman looked startled. 'Thank you, but I'm Caroline, not Jennifer. I'm just here for a week with my husband.' She glanced over her shoulder towards a sweating, balding man, who was struggling with a beach umbrella and an assortment of bags, one of which popped open, spilling the contents onto the quay.

'Oops. Let me help you—' A slim girl put down her own suitcase, stepped forward and deftly rescued the contents of the bag, her pink mouth curving into a friendly smile as she stuffed everything back inside and snapped the bag firmly shut.

Ryan's gaze lingered on that mouth for a full five seconds before shifting to her snaky dark curls. The clip at the back of her head suggested that at one time her hair had been fastened, but it had obviously made an escape bid during the ferry journey and was now tumbling unrestrained around her narrow shoulders. She was pale, and there were dark rings under her eyes—as if she hadn't had a decent sleep in months. As if life had closed its jaws and taken a bite out of her.

He recognised the look because for months he'd seen it in his own reflection when he'd looked in the mirror.

Or maybe he was imagining things. Plenty of people looked tired when they first arrived on the island. It took time to relax and unwind, but by the time they caught the ferry back to the mainland they had colour in their cheeks and the dark circles had gone.

Doubtless this girl had worked all winter in some grey, smog-filled city, saving up her holiday for a couple of bracing weeks on a remote Scottish island.

Eyeing the jumper looped around her shoulders, Ryan realised that she obviously knew that summer weather on Glenmore could be unpredictable.

He watched her for a full minute, surprised by the kindness she showed to a stranger. With no fuss, she helped rearrange his possessions into a manageable load, making small talk about the problems of packing for a holiday in a destination where the weather was unpredictable.

Having helped the couple, the girl stood for a moment, just breathing in the sea air, as if she hadn't stood still for ages while the man and his wife carted themselves and their luggage towards the two island taxis.

'The brochures promise you a welcome,' the woman panted, her voice carrying across the quay, 'but I didn't imagine that the island doctor would meet everyone personally. He even shook my hand! That *is* good service.'

A faint smile on his lips, Ryan watched them pile into a taxi. Then he stared at the ferry, resisting the temptation to take another look at the girl. He hoped the nurse and her daughter hadn't missed the boat.

A hand touched his arm. 'Did I hear you say that you're Dr McKinley?' The girl with the tumbling black hair was beside him, cases by her feet, her voice smoky soft and her eyes sharp and intelligent. 'I'm Jenna.'

Ryan looked into her eyes and thought of the sea. Shades of aquamarine, green and blue blended into a shade that was uniquely hers. He opened his mouth and closed it again—tried to look away and found that he couldn't. So he just carried on staring, and he saw something blossom in the depths of those eyes. Awareness. A connection. As if each recognised something in the other.

Something gripped him hard—something he hadn't felt in a long time.

Shocked by the chemistry, Ryan inhaled sharply and prepared himself to put up barriers, but she got there first.

Panic flickered across her face and she took a step backwards, clearly rejecting what had happened between them.

And that was fine with him, because he was rejecting it too.

He didn't even know why she'd introduced herself. Was every passenger going to shake his hand this morning?

Ryan knew he needed to say something casual and dismissive, but his eyes were fixed on the sweet lines of her profile and his tongue seemed to be stuck to the roof of his mouth.

She wasn't a girl, he realised. She was a woman. A young woman.

Mid-twenties?

And she looked bone tired—as if she was ready to collapse into a big comfortable bed and sleep for a month.

'Sorry. I must have misheard—' Flustered, she adjusted

the bag that hung from her shoulder. 'I thought I heard you say that you're Dr McKinley.'

'I did.'

'Oh.' Her tone suggested that news was unwelcome. Then she stuck out her hand. 'Right, well, I'm Jennifer Richards. Jenna.' She left her hand hovering in the space between them for a moment, and then slowly withdrew it as he simply stared at her. 'What's wrong? Have I arrived on the wrong day? You look a bit…stunned to see me.'

Jennifer Richards? Stunned didn't begin to describe his reaction. Ryan cleared his throat and shook her hand, noticing that her fingers were slim and cool. 'Right day.' Wrong description. 'It's just that—my partner fed me false information. I was expecting a woman and her teenage daughter.' Someone about twenty years older. Someone who wasn't going to make his hormones surge.

'Ah—' She glanced towards the ferry, her smile tired. 'Well, I'm the woman, but the teenage daughter is still on the boat, I'm afraid. That's her, hanging over the side glaring at me. She's refusing to get off, and I'm still trying to decide how best to handle this particular situation without ruining my reputation before I even take my first clinic. I don't suppose you have any experience in handling moody teenagers, Dr McKinley?'

He cleared his throat. 'None.'

'Shame.' Her tone was a mixture of humour and weary acceptance. 'This is one of those occasions when I need to refer to my handbook on teenagers. Stupidly, I packed it at the bottom of the suitcase. Next time it's going in my handbag and if necessary I'll ditch my purse. I apologise for her lack of manners.' She flushed self-consciously and looked away. 'You're staring at me, Dr McKinley. You're thinking I should have better control over my child.'

Yes, he was staring. Of course he was staring.

All the men on Glenmore were going to be staring.

Ryan realised that she was waiting for him to say something. 'I'm thinking you can't possibly be old enough to be that girl's mother. Is she adopted?' Damn. That wasn't what he'd meant to say.

'No, she's all mine. I have sole responsibility for the behavioural problems. But it's refreshing to hear I don't look old enough. According to Lexi, I'm a dinosaur. And she's probably right. I certainly feel past it—particularly right now, when I'm going to have to get firm with her in public. Oh, joy.' The wind flipped a strand of hair across her face and she anchored it with her fingers. 'You're still staring, Dr McKinley. I'm sorry I'm not what you were expecting.'

So was he.

He wasn't ready to feel this. Wasn't sure he wanted to feel this.

Mistrusting his emotions, Ryan ran a hand over his neck, wondering what had happened to his powers of speech. 'You must have been a child bride. Either that or you have shares in Botox.'

'Child bride.' There was a wistful note to her voice, and something else that he couldn't decipher. And then she lifted her eyebrows as the girl flounced off the ferry. 'Well, that's a first. She's doing something I want her to do without a row. I wonder what made her co-operate. Lexi—' she lifted her voice slightly '—come and meet Dr McKinley.'

A slender, moody teenager stomped towards them.

Ryan, who had never had any trouble with numbers, couldn't work out how the girl in front of him could be this woman's daughter. 'Hi, there. Nice to meet you.'

Eyes exactly like her mother's stared back at him. 'Are you the one who gave my mum this job? You don't look like anything like a doctor.'

Ryan wanted to say that Jenna didn't look like the mother

of a teenager, but he didn't. 'That's because I didn't have time to shave before I met the ferry.' He rubbed his fingers over his roughened jaw. 'I am a doctor. But I didn't give your mother the job—that was my colleague, Dr McNeil.'

'Well, whatever you do, don't put her in charge of family planning. As you can probably tell from looking at me, contraception is *so* not her specialist subject.'

'Lexi!' Jenna sounded mortified and the girl flushed.

'Sorry. It's just—oh, never mind. Being in this place is really doing my head in.' Close to tears, the teenager flipped her hair away from her face and stared across the quay. 'Is there an internet café or something? Any way of contacting the outside world? Or are we using Morse code and smoke signals? Or, better still, can we just go home, Mum?'

Ryan was still watching Jenna. He saw the pain in her eyes, the exasperation and the sheer grit and determination. She looked like someone who was fighting her way through a storm, knowing that there was no shelter.

Interesting, he mused, that Glenmore so often provided a bolthole for the wounded.

He wondered what these two were escaping.

Sensing that Jenna was hideously embarrassed, he knew he ought to say something—but what did he know about handling teenagers? Nothing. And he knew even less about what to say to soften the blow of teenage rudeness. Assuming that something along the lines of *she'll be leaving home in another four years* wouldn't go down well, Ryan opted to keep his mouth shut.

He'd never raised a child, had he?

Never been given that option. Anger thudded through him and he stilled, acknowledging that the feelings hadn't gone away. He'd buried them, but they were still there.

Taking an audible breath, Jenna picked up their bags.

'We're renting a cottage at West Beach. Is there a bus that goes that way?'

'No bus. There are taxis, but before you think about that I have a favour to ask.'

'What favour can I possibly do you already?'

Ryan gently prised the suitcases from her cold fingers, sensing the vulnerability hidden beneath layers of poise and dignity. 'I know you're not supposed to officially start until tomorrow, but we're snowed under at the surgery. I'm supposed to exert my charm to persuade you to start early, only I was up three times in the night so I'm not feeling that charming. I'd appreciate it if you'd cut me some slack and say yes.'

'You do house-calls?'

'Is that surprising?'

'The doctors I worked with rarely did their own house-calls. It was the one thing—' She broke off and smiled at him, obviously deciding that she'd said too much.

'On Glenmore we can't delegate. We don't have an out-of-hours service or a local hospital—it's just the three of us.' He looked at her pointedly. 'Four now. You're one of the team.' And he still wasn't sure what he thought about that.

'Are you sure you still want me? You're sure you don't want to rethink my appointment after what Lexi just said?' Her tone was light, but there was vulnerability in her eyes that told him she was worrying about her daughter's comments.

Ryan was surprised that she was so sensitive to what others might be thinking. Out of the blue, his mind drifted to Connie. Connie hadn't given a damn what other people thought. She'd been so monumentally selfish and self-absorbed that it had driven him mad.

'Your qualifications are really impressive. We're delighted to have you here. And the sooner you can start the better.'

'I spoke to Evanna McNeil on the phone.' She turned her head and checked on her daughter. 'She's arranged for us to pick up the keys to the cottage this morning. I was going to spend the day settling in and start work tomorrow.'

'The cottage isn't far from here. And I know you were supposed to have today to settle in, but if there is any way I can persuade you to start work this morning that would be fantastic. There's a clinic starting at eight-thirty, and the girl who helps Evanna with the kids is off sick so she has to look after the children. I'd cancel it, but we're already overrun because we've been down a nurse for a few months.'

'But if the clinic starts at eight-thirty that's just half an hour from now.' Jenna glanced at her watch, flustered by his request, working out the implications. 'I want to help, of course. Normally I'd say yes instantly, but—well, I haven't made any arrangements for Lexi.'

'I'm not six, Mum. I'll stay on my own.' The girl looked round with a despairing look on her face. 'I'm hardly likely to get into danger here.'

Ryan had a feeling that the child would be capable of getting into trouble in an empty room, and Jenna was clearly of the same opinion because she looked doubtful.

'I'm not leaving you on your own until we've both settled in and found our feet. It's going to be OK, Lex.' Her gaze was fixed on her daughter's face and Ryan wanted to ask *what* was going to be OK. What had given her dark rings around her eyes? What was keeping her awake at night?

Why had she taken a job on a remote Scottish Island?

It didn't take a genius to sense that there was a great deal more going on than was revealed by their spoken communication. And he couldn't help noticing that no man had followed her off the ferry. If there was a Mr Richards, then he was keeping his distance.

With customary practicality, Ryan searched for a solution. 'Lexi can come too. The surgery is attached to the house. She can hang out with Evanna and the children. Evanna would be glad of the help, and it will give Lexi a chance to find out something about the island. And I can drive you over to the cottage at lunchtime. I'll even help you unpack to speed things up.'

'Mum!' Lexi spoke through gritted teeth. 'I'm not spending the morning looking after a couple of babies! I'd rather go to broken pottery camp, or whatever it's called!'

Ryan struggled to think like a teenager. 'Evanna has internet access, and the mobile signal is great from her house.'

Lexi gave a wide smile that transformed her face from sullen to stunning. 'Then what are we waiting for? Lead me to civilisation. Otherwise known as wireless broadband.'

CHAPTER TWO

'I NORMALLY see Nurse Evanna,' the old lady said, settling herself into the chair. 'She knows exactly what to do with my leg.'

Could today get any worse? Feeling mentally exhausted, Jenna scanned the notes on the screen.

Not only did her daughter not want her to be here, the patients didn't appear to want her either. And doubtless Dr McKinley was also regretting her appointment after that embarrassing scenario on the quay.

And to top it all, having not thought about sex for what seemed like the whole of her twenties, she'd looked into Ryan McKinley's cool blue eyes and suddenly started thinking about nothing but sex. She'd been so mesmerised by an alien flash of chemistry that she'd almost embarrassed herself.

Jenna cringed at the memory of just how long she'd stared at him. Who was she kidding? She *had* embarrassed herself. There was no almost about it.

And she'd embarrassed him.

Why else would he have been staring at her?

What must he have thought?

That she was a sad, desperate single mother who hadn't had sex for a lifetime.

He'd made all those polite noises about her looking too young to have a teenage daughter, but Jenna knew it was nonsense. People said that, didn't they? People said *You don't look thirty*, while secretly thinking you looked closer to forty. She shuddered, appalled at the thought that he might be sitting in his consulting room right now, formulating a strategy for keeping her at a distance. She needed to make sure he knew she didn't have designs on him—that a relationship with a man was right at the bottom of her wish list.

She was just trying to survive. Rebuild her life.

Knowing she couldn't afford to think about that now, Jenna concentrated on her patient. 'I understand that it's unsettling to have someone new, Mrs Parker, but Evanna has left detailed notes. If you see me doing anything differently, or anything that makes you feel worried, you can tell me.'

'You've a teenage daughter, I hear?' Mrs Parker dropped her bag onto the floor and slipped off her shoe. Her tights were the colour of stewed tea and twisted slightly around her ankles.

Jenna searched through the choice of dressings available to her, unsure what the surgery stocked. 'I only stepped off the ferry half an hour ago. Word travels fast.'

'Hard to have secrets on Glenmore. We're a close community.'

'That's why I chose to come here, Mrs Parker.' That and the fact she hadn't had much choice. She helped the woman onto the trolley. 'And I don't have any secrets.'

'Will your husband be joining you later?'

'I'm no longer married, Mrs Parker.' Jenna swiftly removed the old dressing, wondering why saying those words made her feel such a failure.

As if to reinforce those feelings, Mrs Parker pressed her lips together in disapproval. 'I was married for fifty-two years. In those days we sorted out our differences. We didn't give up.'

Great. Just what she needed. A lecture. Still, she was used to those from her mother. She'd grown up seeing her failings highlighted in neon lights.

'I admire you, Mrs Parker. I'm just going to check your blood pressure.'

Mrs Parker sniffed her disapproval. 'I'm here to have the dressing changed.'

'I know that. And I've already picked out what I'm going to use.' Reminding herself that building relationships was essential to the smooth running of the practice, Jenna was patient. 'But it's important to check your blood pressure every six months or so, and I can see from your notes that it hasn't been done for a while.'

'I don't see what my blood pressure has to do with the ulcer on my leg.'

'Sometimes ulcers can be caused by bad circulation rather than venous problems. I want to do an ankle blood pressure as well as taking it on your arm.'

Mrs Parker relaxed slightly. 'You obviously know what you're doing. All right. But I haven't got all day.'

Jenna checked her blood pressure, reminding herself that she'd always known this move wouldn't be easy. Not for her, nor Lexi.

'So you fell pregnant when you were still in school, by the looks of you.' Mrs Parker's lips pursed. 'Still, everyone makes mistakes.'

Jenna carefully recorded the blood pressure readings before she replied. 'I don't consider my daughter to be a mistake, Mrs Parker.'

There was a moment of silence and then the old lady gave a chuckle. 'Capable of standing up for yourself, are you? I like that. You're obviously a bright girl. Why have you moved all the way up here? You could be in some leading city practice. Or are you running away?'

Jenna sensed that whatever she told this woman would be all over the island by lunchtime, so she delivered an edited version of the truth. 'My marriage ended. I needed a change. And this place has a good reputation. Logan McNeil has built a good practice.' She didn't add that she would have taken the job regardless, because it was as far from Clive and her parents as it was possible to get without leaving the country.

'Logan is a good doctor. So's Ryan McKinley, of course. But we all know he won't be around for long. He's a real high-flier. Used to work as one of those emergency doctors.'

Emergency doctor?

Confused, Jenna paused. 'How long has he lived here?'

'Came here two years ago and bought the old abandoned lighthouse that Ewan Kinaird had given up hope of selling. Too isolated for everyone. But not for Dr McKinley. Apparently isolation was what he wanted, and he paid a fair price for it. Didn't see him for most of that first year. Turned up occasionally in the village to buy supplies. Kept himself to himself. Never smiled. Some thought he was antisocial. Others thought he was recovering from some trauma or other. Certainly looked grim-faced whenever I glimpsed him.'

Jenna felt guilty for listening. Part of her wanted to cover her ears but she didn't want to be rude. And she was intrigued by Ryan McKinley. When she'd met him he hadn't seemed antisocial. Nor had he shown signs of trauma. He'd talked. Smiled. But she knew a smile often hid a secret. 'So how does he come to be working as a GP?'

'That was Evanna's doing. Won't let anyone be, that girl—especially not if they're in trouble. She coaxed him into helping out after the last locum left them in the lurch. She had baby Charlie, and Logan was managing the practice on his own. When he was needed, Ryan stepped up. But we all know he won't stick. He'll be off to some high-flying job before the tide has turned.' Mrs Parker took a closer look at her leg. 'What's your professional opinion of this, then?'

'I'm just taking a look now.' Jenna wondered what trauma had made a doctor qualified in emergency medicine buy a secluded lighthouse on an isolated island. 'How did you find out he was a doctor?'

'Oh, he kept it quiet.' Mrs Parker peered at her leg. 'But Fiona Grange crashed her car into a ditch in the middle of a storm and he happened to be passing when it happened. Some say he's the reason she's alive. Bones smashed, she was unconscious, and the air ambulance couldn't take off. And there was Dr McKinley, cool as a Glenmore winter, stopping the bleeding, extracting her from the car—shocked everyone, he did. Went from hermit to hero in the blink of an eye. But there was no hiding his profession after that. And he's been a good doctor, although he's private. Keeps himself to himself. Some think he's unfriendly. A bit cold.'

Unfriendly? Jenna thought about the man who had met her at the quay. He hadn't been unfriendly. Tired, definitely. Guarded, maybe. She would have described him as cool, but not cold.

'I'm going to take a proper look at your leg now.' Trying not to think about Ryan McKinley, Jenna washed her hands and opened the dressing pack. 'Your blood pressure is fine. How long have you had this problem, Mrs Parker?'

'I had it last summer and it went away. But then it came back.'

'Did you wear your compression stockings?' She glanced down at the tan stockings that had been placed neatly on the chair.

'Not as much as I'm supposed to.'

'They're not that comfortable, I know.' Jenna cleaned the

wound and dressed it. 'That does look sore, you poor thing. Are you in a lot of pain?'

Mrs Parker relaxed slightly. 'I'm old. I'm always in pain. My bones ache every morning. The Glenmore winter is bitter. Like having your leg in the jaws of a shark.'

'I've only ever been here in the summer. My grandparents used to bring me. Tell me if this feels too tight.' Jenna bandaged the leg, applying most pressure to the ankle and gradually less towards the knee and thigh. 'Try and keep your leg up before you come and have that dressing changed next week. Have you tried putting a couple of pillows under your mattress? The aim is to let gravity pull the fluid and blood towards the heart. It will reduce the swelling. Can you move your ankle?'

'Yes. You've done a good job,' Mrs Parker said grudgingly. She stood up and put her stockings back on with Jenna's help. Then she reached for her bag. 'That dressing feels very comfortable, actually. But tell Evanna I'm sorry to have missed her.'

'I'll do that.'

Jenna watched as Mrs Parker walked slowly down the corridor, and then returned to the computer to type up the notes, sinking into the chair, exhausted. This was a huge mistake. She should have just bought a new flat in London, then she could have stayed in her job and Lexi could have stayed in her school.

Instead she'd chosen a small island where strangers were viewed with suspicion and where her life was going to be lived under a microscope.

She was an idiot.

Forcing herself to take several deep breaths, Jenna reminded herself that it was natural for the islanders to be wary of a new nurse. She just had to earn their trust.

Or maybe she should just buy another ferry ticket and get

off this island as fast as possible. She sank her head into her hands, and then sat up quickly as she heard a rap on the door.

Ryan walked in. 'I owe you an apology. I had no idea Mrs Parker was your first patient. Talk about baptism of fire.'

Somewhere between meeting her on the quay and starting his surgery he'd shaved and changed. The faded jeans had been replaced by smart trousers and the comfortable tee shirt by a tailored shirt. In the confines of her consulting room he seemed taller. And broader. Suddenly she had no trouble imagining him as a high-powered consultant in a busy emergency department.

Her throat suddenly felt dry. 'Yes, she was my first patient.'

'You're still alive?'

Oh, yes. She knew she was alive because she could feel her heart banging hard against her chest. 'We did OK.'

'But now you want to resign?' His voice was dry. 'You're about to buy a return ferry ticket and run back to London?'

Jenna sat rigid, terrified that he'd guessed how bad she felt. 'No.' Her voice was bright. 'I'm not even remotely tempted to run away.'

His smile faded and his gaze sharpened. 'I was joking.'

'Oh.' She turned scarlet. 'Of course you were joking. Sorry. I'm a bit tired after the journey.'

'The last nurse we appointed lasted three days. Didn't Evanna tell you?'

'She did mention something. Don't worry, Dr McKinley. I'm not a quitter.' Jenna said it firmly, reminding herself of that fact. 'And Mrs Parker was fine.'

'I know Mrs Parker, so you must be lying.'

Yes, she was and it seemed that these days she spent her life lying. Even her smile was a lie. 'Mrs Parker was wary at seeing someone new, and that's normal—especially at her age. She doesn't like change. I understand that.' Jenna concentrated on the computer, thinking that she was finding change terrifying and she was several decades younger than Mrs Parker.

'That leg of hers is slow to heal.'

Jenna thought about the old lady—remembered how much had been said in a short time. 'I don't know her, but at a guess I'd say she doesn't really want it to heal. She's lonely. Her leg gives her a reason to come up here and interact with people.'

'That's possible.' His eyes narrowed thoughtfully. 'Despite your college-girl looks, you're obviously very sharp.'

Accustomed to thinking of herself as 'past it', his compliment made her feel strange. Or maybe it hadn't been a compliment. 'I'm interested in people. I like looking for the reasons they do things. It's why I do the job.' Even as she said the words she realised the flaw in that theory. If she was so interested in why people did what they did, why hadn't she spotted the signs that her husband was cheating on her? Maybe she wasn't so observant after all. Or maybe she hadn't wanted to see what was under her nose.

Feeling the tension erupt inside her, Jenna hit a button on the computer and exited Mrs Parker's file, wishing she could control her thinking. She had to stop asking 'what if?' She had to move on. That was what she was doing here, wasn't it? She was wiping out the past. 'Why do *you* do the job, Dr McKinley?' Would he tell her that he was an emergency specialist in hiding?

He was leaning against the wall, his broad shoulders threatening the safety of the asthma poster stuck to the wall. 'At the moment I can't remember. You'd better ask me that question again when I haven't been up for half the night doing calls. I'm always in a snarly mood when I get less than three hours' sleep.'

'That's understandable. Could you sneak off and sleep at some point today?'

'Unfortunately, no. Like I said to you on the quay—it's

just the four of us. When we're busy, we're busy. We can't hand it over.'

'Who called you out last night? Locals or tourists?'

'One tourist with chest pains, a toddler with a febrile convulsion, and one of our own with a very nasty asthma attack.' He frowned. 'I called the mother a few moments ago to check on her and she told me the child is still asleep, but I'm going to call in later. I didn't like the look of her in the night. I gather you have an interest in asthma?'

'Yes. I ran a clinic in London.' Jenna was interested. 'Was there an obvious trigger? Did she have an infection or something?'

'They'd got themselves a dog from the rescue centre. I'm assuming it was that.'

'They didn't know that animal fur was a trigger?' Jenna pulled a face, understanding the ramifications of that statement. 'So is the dog being returned?'

'It's a strong possibility. They're thinking about it, but obviously the child will be upset.'

'It would be wonderful to have a dog,' Jenna said wistfully, and then sat up straight, slightly shocked by herself. A dog? Where had that thought come from? Why on earth would she want a dog?

'Maybe you could give this one a home?'

Jenna automatically shook her head. 'We can't have a dog. Cl—' She was about to say that Clive hated animals, but then she remembered that she wasn't married to Clive any more. His opinion didn't matter.

Glancing down at her left hand, she stared at the pale line on her finger that was the only remaining evidence that she'd once worn a ring. It still felt strange, seeing the finger bare. And it still brought a sting to the back of her throat.

'Something wrong?' His question made her jump.

'No. I was just thinking about your little asthma patient and the dog.'

'Right.' His gaze locked onto hers and she looked away quickly, thinking that Ryan McKinley was nothing like the men she usually met during her working day. For a start he was about two decades younger than the GPs she'd worked with in her last practice. She tried to imagine any of *them* extracting a seriously injured girl from the wreck of a car during a storm without the help of paramedics—and failed. Ryan McKinley was a different breed of doctor. And then there was the fact that he was indecently good-looking. Sexy.

A different breed of man.

'You look really stressed out.' Ryan spoke quietly. 'Is that Mrs Parker's doing? Or is it being thrown in at the deep end?'

'No! Not at all.' Oh, God, he'd noticed that she was stressed. And the one thing she absolutely couldn't afford to do was put a foot wrong in this job. 'I love being thrown in at the deep end. Anyway, I didn't ask why you were here. Did you want to talk to me? Is there something I can help you with, Dr McKinley?' Please don't let him say he'd changed his mind about hiring her.

'I wondered if you could take some bloods for me.' Ryan handed her a form, his eyes still on her face. 'Callum is fifteen and he's showing all the signs of glandular fever. I know you already have a full clinic, but I really need these results as soon as possible.'

'Of course you do.' As she took the form from him, Jenna's fingers brushed against his. She immediately snatched her hand away, feeling as though she'd touched a live wire. 'I'll do them straight away.' Without thinking, she rubbed her fingers, wondering whether she was doomed to overreact around this man.

'He's in the waiting room with his mum.' Ryan was looking at her fingers, and Jenna swallowed and dropped her hands into her lap.

'Fine. Great. I'll call him.'

'I appreciate it.' There was a tension about him that hadn't been there before. 'Your bikes have been delivered, by the way. I had them taken straight to the cottage. They'll be safe enough outside your front door.'

'Bikes?' Jenna had to force herself to concentrate. 'Bikes. Yes, of course. Evanna told me about this place that hires them for the summer, so I rang them. I thought it would be good for both of us to cycle.'

'I'm impressed. It's a good example to set to the patients.'

'So you'll try not to knock me off my bike when you're accelerating past in your Porsche?'

He gave a faint smile as he strolled towards the door. 'Are you accusing me of speeding or being a couch potato?'

'Neither. I'm sure you're very fit.' Her eyes slid to the hard muscle of his shoulders, clearly outlined by the smooth fabric of his casual shirt. Damn, she shouldn't have used the word *fit*. Wasn't that the word Lexi used when she found a boy attractive? 'I mean, you're obviously athletic—I mean, health-conscious—sorry, just ignore me…' Jenna had the distinct impression that he was laughing at her, but when she looked at him his expression was unreadable.

'Why would I want to ignore you?'

'Because I'm talking nonsense—' And he was super-cool, hyper-intelligent and nothing like the men she usually dealt with. She had no trouble believing Mrs Parker's assertion that he was a top doctor. He had an air of authority and command that she found mildly intimidating. 'The bikes will be great.'

'Does Lexi know you've ordered bikes?'

'Not yet.' She didn't know which impressed her more, the fact that he'd remembered her daughter's name or his uncannily accurate assessment of her character. 'Light the touch paper and stand well back. Which reminds me; I owe you an apology for her behaviour earlier.'

'What do you have to apologise for?'

'Lexi. She—' Jenna didn't want to reveal personal details, but she was unable to bear the thought he might think badly of her daughter. 'She's very mixed up at the moment. She didn't want to move from our home in London. It's been hard on her.'

He was silent for a moment, considering her words. She had a nasty feeling that he knew just how close to the edge she was. 'Glenmore has a very calming effect on people. It's a good place to escape.'

'Lexi didn't want to leave London.'

'Perhaps your needs are greater than hers at the moment,' he said gently. 'Does Lexi know you're living in a cottage on the beach?'

'No. There's only so much bad news that she can take at one time. She's going to hate me for not renting a house in the village.'

'That's not exactly a hub for entertainment, either.' He opened the door. 'When you've finished your clinic, knock on my door. I'll take you and your luggage over there.'

'I don't expect you to do that. If you have any spare time, you need to sleep.'

'I'll give you a lift.' He hesitated, his hand on the door. 'Give it a few weeks before you buy that ferry ticket. I predict that in no time this place will feel like home.'

He knew.

He knew how bad she felt. She'd done a lousy job at hiding her feelings. He knew she was panicking and having second thoughts.

Horrified that he was clearly aware of how close she was

to breaking, Jenna just sat there, not trusting herself to speak. Their eyes held, and then he gave a brief nod.

'Welcome to Glenmore, Jenna. We're very pleased to have you here.'

Ryan stood in front of his colleague, legs spread, hands dug in his back pockets. 'Tell me about Jenna.'

'Jenna?' Logan McNeil signed a prescription and glanced up, his expression interested. 'Why? Was it love at first sight? Your eyes met across a crowded ferry ramp?'

Remembering the flash of chemistry, Ryan rolled his shoulders to ease the tension. 'Just give me the facts, Logan.'

Logan put his pen down. 'She's been working as a practice nurse in England for the past six years, but I'm not holding that against her. Why are you asking? Has she killed a patient or something?'

'I'm worried about her.'

'Isn't that a little premature? She's been here for five minutes.'

And he'd been worried about her within thirty seconds of meeting her. She'd looked fragile and battered, as though she'd emerged from a terrible storm. 'Evanna asked me to meet her, remember? She looks as though she's holding it together by a thread.'

Suddenly Logan wasn't smiling. 'You're worried about her ability to do the job?'

'No. She handled Mrs Parker, which proves she's more than capable of doing the job. I'm worried about *her*!' Ryan shot him an impatient look. 'What do you know about her personal circumstances?'

With a sigh, Logan opened his drawer and pulled out a file. Scanning the papers, he paused. 'Divorced with a teenage daughter. That's all it says.'

Divorced.

Ryan prowled to the window of Logan's consulting room and stared across the fields. Remembering the white circle on her ring finger, he was willing to bet the divorce was recent. Was that why she was so pale and drawn? Divorce did that to people, didn't it? Was that why she jumped when a man touched her? 'Was her ex-husband abusive?'

'I have absolutely no idea. This is her CV, not a police statement. Are you sure you're not going a little over the top here? You seem very concerned about someone you only met a few hours ago.'

Ryan turned. 'She's a colleague,' he said evenly. 'It's in our interest to make sure she's happy here.'

'And that's all that's going on here?' Logan closed the file. 'You seem very interested in her.'

'I didn't say I was interested. I said it was in our interest to make sure she's happy.'

'Good. Then I'll leave it to you to make sure she is.' Logan pushed the file back in the drawer. 'Plenty of people get divorced, Ryan. It's a fact of life in our society. It doesn't mean she has problems. You could be barking up the wrong tree. Has she seen the cottage yet?'

'I'm taking her at the end of morning surgery.'

'Let's just hope she likes isolation, otherwise we'll be looking for a new practice nurse. Ted Walker has a flat vacant in the village if you think that would be better.'

'I know she's going to like the cottage.' He didn't know how he knew, but he did.

She was running—wounded—looking for a place to hide and recover.

And the cottage was the perfect place for her. Whether her teenager daughter would survive the isolation was another matter.

CHAPTER THREE

IT WAS the prettiest house she'd ever seen—one of four fishermen's cottages facing the sea, their front gardens leading straight down to a sandy beach.

The iron gate was rusty and creaked as she pushed it open, but Jenna felt a sudden feeling of calm and contentment. No more endless traffic jams and road rage. No more rush hour. No more litter on the streets and graffiti on the walls.

Just open space, fresh air, and the sound of the sea.

It was perfect.

Lexi gave a whimper of horror. 'This is it? It's the smallest house I've ever seen.'

Jenna felt the tension return to her stomach. 'Small, yes, but it's ours.' As long as she kept the job. The house came with the job. They had a home again. And it would be cheap to run.

Lexi was gaping at the tiny cottage. 'A whole summer here?'

'Yes.'

'You can't swing a cat.'

'We don't have a cat.' But they might have a dog. She'd been thinking about it ever since Ryan McKinley had mentioned the idea.

Lexi closed her eyes. 'Just kill me now,' she muttered, and Jenna searched for something to say that would cheer her up.

'Don't you think this is better than London?'

'Tell me that isn't a serious question—'

Jenna sighed. They'd come this far. They had to keep moving forward.

She walked up the path to the front door, her eyes scanning the pretty garden. She noticed a few weeds and her hands itched. It would be fun, she mused, to have a proper garden.

Lexi stared desperately at the house and then at the beach. 'Where's the nearest shop?'

'Walk straight down the road and you reach the harbour. If it's low tide you can walk along the beach.' Ryan strode up the path behind them, carrying both suitcases. He deposited them on the ground, gently removed the key from Jenna's hand and opened the door of the cottage.

'Sorry—I was miles away.' Jenna gave a smile of apology. 'It's so long since I had a garden. Our house in London just had a courtyard. I'm not used to so much outdoor space.' Enchanted, she stooped and touched some of the pretty pink flowers that clustered by the door. *'Armeria maritima.'*

Ryan raised his eyebrows, apparently amused. 'You're quoting the Latin names of plants at me?'

'My mother was a botanist. I grew up hearing Latin names. Some of them stuck.' She touched the flower with the tip of her finger. 'Sea pinks. They grow well in this climate, by the coast.'

Lexi rolled her eyes. 'Gosh, Mum, gripping stuff.'

Jenna flushed and stood up. 'Sorry. It's just so wonderful to have a garden.' Despite the knot in her stomach she felt better, and she was in no hurry to go indoors. Instead she breathed in the sea air and watched the plants waving in the breeze. The grass needed cutting, and there were weeds in the borders, but somehow that just added to the charm. She imagined herself lying on a rug on a warm Sunday morning, listening to the gulls and reading the paper.

When had she ever done that? Sundays were normally so busy, what with making a traditional Sunday roast for Clive and his mother, and then being expected to produce tea for the cricket club…

Aware that Ryan was watching her, Jenna flushed. She felt as though he could read her every thought, and that was disturbing because some of the thoughts she'd been having about him were definitely best kept private. 'When Evanna told me that the job came with a house, I never imagined it would be anywhere as perfect as this. I can't imagine why anyone would want to leave here. Who owns it?'

'Kyla—Logan's sister. Her husband, Ethan, was offered a job in the States. They'll be back at some point.'

But not soon. Please don't let it be soon.

A warm feeling spread through her, and for the first time since she'd left London Jenna felt a flicker of hope. Excitement. As if this might be the right decision after all.

She felt as if she belonged. She felt at home.

It's—so peaceful.' A gull shrieked above her and she laughed as she caught Ryan's eye. 'Well, not peaceful, perhaps, but the noises are different. Good noises. No car horns and revving engines. And everything is slow. I'm looking forward to just being still.' Realising that she probably sounded ridiculous, Jenna shrugged awkwardly. 'In London everything moves so fast. You get swept along with it so that sometimes you can't even take a breath—I hate the pace of it.'

'That's because you're so old, Mum.' Lexi fiddled with her phone. 'London was exciting. And our house was lovely.'

'London was noisy and smelly and our house was far too big for the two of us.' It was what she'd told herself when she'd realised that their house had been sold and she and Lexi no longer had a home. It was the only way she had coped.

Pushing away that thought, Jenna stepped into the hallway of the cottage. They had a home now, and she loved it. Light reflected off the polished wooden floor, and through an open door she could see a bright, cheerful kitchen. 'We lived right next to an underground station and every three minutes the house shook.'

'Yeah, it was so cool.' Lexi tossed her hair away from her face, her eyes still on her mobile phone. 'I was never more than ten minutes from the shops.'

But Jenna wasn't thinking about shopping. It seemed far away. And so did Clive and the whole sordid mess she'd left behind. 'This place is wonderful. We can have our breakfast outside on that little table.' She turned to look at the pretty garden, eyes slightly misty, imagination running free. 'Lexi, you can go for a swim, or a run on the beach.'

How could this be a mistake?

Maybe she hadn't done the wrong thing. They could be happy here—she felt it.

Lexi shot her a look of incredulous disbelief and checked her mobile phone. 'No signal again. How do people function around here?'

'You can usually get a signal if you walk up the hill towards the castle.' Ryan lifted their suitcases into the hallway and Lexi gave an exaggerated sigh.

'Fine. If the only place I can use my phone is at the top of a hill then I'm going to have to walk up it!' Making a frustrated sound in her throat, she stalked away.

Jenna opened her mouth to say *be careful* and then closed it again, leaving the words unspoken. She knew from experience that too much maternal anxiety was counterproductive.

But the guilt was back, eating away at her like acid, corroding her insides. She might have fallen in love with the cottage, but she knew this wasn't what Lexi wanted.

'It must be hard, letting them grow up.' Ryan was standing in the doorway, his thumbs hooked into the pockets of his trousers, a speculative look in his blue eyes as he watched her.

'You have no idea.' Keeping her tone light, Jenna walked past him into the garden, her gaze on Lexi as her daughter sauntered across the road and started up the hill. A dozen nightmare scenarios sped through her overactive maternal brain. To control them, she used black humour. *Say it aloud and it might not happen*. 'Are there any scary, dangerous individuals at large on Glenmore at the moment?'

'Well, you've already met Mrs Parker—they don't come much scarier or more dangerous than her. She's wanted in five counties.' His arm brushed against hers and Jenna felt her whole body tingle.

She stepped away from him, keeping her distance as she would from an electric fence. 'I was thinking more of axe-wielding murderers and rapists.'

'We had dozens of those last summer, but Mrs Parker saw them off. It's hard to commit a crime in a community that knows what you're planning to eat for supper.'

As Lexi's figure grew smaller, and then vanished from sight, Jenna felt a moment of panic. Catching his eye, she gave an embarrassed laugh. 'Yes, I know—I'm overreacting. It's hard to forget this isn't London. You must think I'm crazy. *I* think I'm crazy!'

'That isn't what I'm thinking.'

'It would be if you knew what was going through my mind. It's taking all my will-power not to charge after her and follow her up that hill.'

His gaze shifted from her face to where Lexi had disappeared. 'I don't know much about teenagers, but at a guess I'd say that probably isn't the best idea.'

'Well, I'd have to be discreet, of course.' She made a joke of it. 'I'd probably start by sprinting up the hill and then drop to my stomach and crawl so that she couldn't see me.'

'You're going to have a hell of a job beating off an axe-wielding murderer if you're crawling on your stomach.'

'Never underestimate a mother protecting her young.'

'I'll remember that.' He had a deep voice. Deep and male, with a slightly husky timbre that made her think things she hadn't thought for a long time.

Jenna breathed in slowly and stared at the ridge, trying not to think about his voice. 'I can't believe she made it up there so quickly. Lexi isn't really into exercise. It's amazing what the lure of a mobile phone signal can do to cure teenage lethargy. I hope she'll be OK.'

Ryan turned to her, and she noticed that the passing hours had darkened his jaw again. 'She's crossed the only road and she's still alive. She'll be fine. I'm not so sure about you.'

Her gaze met his and their eyes held.

The rhythm of her heart altered and the oxygen was sucked from the air. The world shrank to this one place—this one man.

Everything else was forgotten.

Mesmerised by those blue eyes, Jenna felt her body come to life, like the slow, sensual unfolding of a bud under the heat of the sun. Not the sultry, languid heat of summer sunshine but the fierce, rapacious scorch of sexual awareness. Like a volcano too long dormant after centuries of sleep, it exploded violently—blowing the lid on everything she believed herself to be. Excitement ripped through her like a consuming, ravenous fire, and in her newly sensitised state she found staring longingly at the firm lines of his mouth.

If she wanted to kiss him, she could…

She was a free woman now.

The shriek of a seagull brought her to her senses and Jenna took a step backwards.

What on earth was she thinking? If she did something crazy, like kissing him, he'd fire her from her job, Lexi would have a nervous breakdown, and she'd be more of an emotional wreck than she was already. And anyway, if she hadn't been able to trust someone she'd known for fifteen years, what chance was there with someone she'd known for fifteen minutes?

Jenna straightened her shoulders. 'You're right. I worry far too much about her. I intend to work on that this summer. I'm hoping it will be easier here.' Unfortunately her bright, businesslike tone did nothing to dissipate the strange turbulence inside her. She needed to be on her own, so that she could undo whatever she'd just done to herself by looking at him. And she was sure he was desperate to escape from her, albeit for different reasons.

'Thanks so much for the lift, Dr McKinley. I'm sorry to hold you up.'

'You're not holding me up.' Instead of leaving, as she'd expected, he walked back towards the house. 'Do you have any caffeine?'

Pulling herself together, Jenna followed him. 'Pardon?'

'Caffeine. I'm feeling tired, and there's still most of the day to get through.' Suppressing a yawn, he walked through to the kitchen without asking for directions or permission. 'I need coffee. Strong coffee.'

'I thought you'd need to dash off somewhere—lunch, house-calls…' She had thought he'd be anxious to escape from her—the desperate divorcee…

'We try not to do too much dashing on Glenmore.' Concentration on his face, he pulled open a cupboard and rummaged through the contents. 'It's bad for the heart. Which do you prefer? Tea or coffee?'

'Either. I mean—I haven't had time to shop.'

'The kitchen should be stocked.'

'Oh.' Jenna was about to ask who could possibly have

stocked the kitchen when the phone rang. She jumped. 'Who on earth can that be?'

'Why don't you answer it and see? Phone's in the hall.'

Jenna found the phone, answered it, and immediately wished she hadn't because it was her mother. 'Hi, Mum.' Oh, no, she absolutely didn't want to have this conversation with Ryan McKinley listening. Why, oh, why had she given her this number? 'No, everything is fine—' All her newfound tranquillity faded as her mother's cold disapproval trickled down the line like liquid nitrogen, freezing everything in its path. 'No, the doctors here don't care that I'm divorced.' She lowered her voice and turned away from the kitchen, hoping Ryan couldn't hear her above the hum of the kettle. 'No, the patients don't care, either—' She squeezed her eyes shut and tried not to think of Mrs Parker. 'And I'm not trying to ruin Lexi's life—it's kind of you to offer, but I don't think living with you would have been the best thing, Mum. I need to do this on my own—no, I'm not being stubborn—'

The conversation went the way it always went, with her mother stirring up every unpleasant emotion she could. Reminding herself to get caller ID, so that she could speak to her mother only when she was feeling really strong, Jenna gripped the phone. 'Yes, I know you're very disappointed with the way things have turned out—I'm not whispering—'

By the time the conversation ended her throat was clogged and her eyes stung. Whatever magic the cottage had created had been undone. The knot was back in her stomach.

All she wanted was moral support. Was that really too much to ask from a mother?

Knowing that she wasn't capable of going back into the kitchen without making a fool of herself, Jenna stood for a moment in the hallway, still holding the phone to her ear. It was only when it was gently removed from her hand that she realised Ryan was standing next to her.

He replaced the receiver in the cradle and curved his hand over her shoulder, his touch firm. 'Are you all right?'

Jenna nodded vigorously, not trusting herself to speak. But the feel of his hand sent a warm glow through her body. It had been so long since anyone had touched her. She'd been divorced for months, and even during her marriage there hadn't been that much touching. Clive had never been tactile. More often than not he'd had dinner with clients or colleagues, which had meant she was in bed and asleep long before him. Even when they had made it to bed at the same time he'd been perfunctory, fumbling, as if making love to her had been another task on his 'to do' list and not something to be prolonged.

She was willing to bet that Ryan McKinley had never fumbled in his life.

His broad shoulders were there, right next to her, and Jenna had a powerful urge to just lean against him for a moment and see if some of his strength could be transferred to her by touch alone.

They stepped back from each other at exactly the same time, as if each had come to the same conclusion.

Not this. Not now.

'I found the coffee.' His voice was rough. 'We need scissors or a knife to open this.'

Blinking rapidly to clear the tears misting her eyes, Jenna saw that he was holding a packet of fresh coffee in his free hand. 'Great.' Appalled to realise how close she'd come to making a fool of herself, she took the coffee from his hand and walked back into the kitchen. Keeping her back to him, she opened the drawers one by one until she found a knife.

He followed her. 'Does a conversation with your mother always upset you like this?'

'How do you know it was my mother?'

'I heard you say, "Hi, Mum".'

'Oh.' If he'd heard that, then he'd heard everything—which meant that there was no point in trying to keep the messy details of her life a secret. Jenna stared down at the knives in the drawer. 'Stupid, isn't it? I'm thirty-three. She shouldn't have an effect on me, but she does. She has a talent for tapping into my deep-seated fears—exposing thoughts I'm having but would never admit even to myself.' She closed her fingers around the handle of a knife. 'She thinks I've made the wrong decision, coming here.'

'And what do you think?'

'I don't know any more.' The tears were back in her eyes, blurring her vision. 'I thought I was doing the right thing. But now I'm worrying that what's right for me might be wrong for Lexi. I've uprooted her. I've dragged her away from everything familiar. We had to leave our home, but I didn't have to come this far away—' Taking the knife from the drawer, Jenna turned, wishing she hadn't said so much. 'Sorry. You wanted a cup of coffee, not a confessional. My call has held you up. If you want to change your mind and get on with your day, I quite understand.'

It was mortifying, having your life exposed in front of a stranger.

'I'm not leaving until I've had my coffee. I'm not safe to drive.' He leaned against the granite work surface, thumbs hooked in his pockets. 'Why did you have to move?'

'I'm divorced.' There seemed no point in not being honest. Why keep it a secret?

It had happened. There was no going back. She had to get used to it.

The problem was that once people knew you were divorced, they inevitably wanted to know why.

Jenna stared at the coffee in her hand, trying not to think about the girl with the long legs and the blond hair who had been lying on her husband's desk having crazy, abandoned sex. When had *she* ever had crazy, abandoned sex? When had *she* ever lost control? Been overwhelmed—?

'Careful! You're going to cut yourself—' A frown on his face, Ryan removed the knife from her hand. 'In fact you have cut yourself. Obviously this isn't a conversation to have while you're holding a sharp object. Let me look at that for you.'

Jenna watched as blood poured down her finger. 'Oh!'

Ryan took her hand and held it under the tap, cleaned it and then examined the cut. 'We need to find a plaster. Call me traditional, but I prefer milk in my coffee.' He was cool and calm, but Jenna was thoroughly embarrassed, and she tugged her hand away from his, dried it in a towel and applied pressure.

'Stupid of me. I don't know what I was thinking.'

'You were thinking of your ex-husband. Perhaps I should clear the knives out of the cutlery drawer.'

'You don't need to worry about me. I'm fine.'

'Obviously not, or your hand wouldn't be bleeding now. And no one emerges from divorce completely unscathed.'

'I didn't say I was unscathed, Dr McKinley. I said I was fine.'

'Ryan—' He handed her another piece of kitchen roll for her finger. 'Call me Ryan. Round here we tend to be pretty informal. Do you always pretend everything is OK when it isn't?'

'I'm just starting a new job. I don't want everyone knowing I have baggage.' She pressed her finger hard, trying to stop the bleeding, exasperated with herself. 'It won't affect my work.'

'No one is suggesting that it would. Everyone has baggage, Jenna. You don't have to wrap it up and hide it.'

'Yes, I do. For Lexi's sake. I've seen couples let rip at each other through their kids and there is no way I'm going to let that happen. I refused to let it be acrimonious. I refuse to be a bitter ex-wife.'

'So you grit your teeth and shed your tears in private?' Ryan took her hand and strapped a plaster to her finger.

'Something like that.' She'd bottled up the humiliation, the devastation, the sense of betrayal—the sense of failure. All those years people had been waiting for her to fail. And she'd failed in spectacular style.

Feeling the familiar sickness inside her, Jenna snatched her hand away from his. 'Sorry. I'm talking too much. If you're sure you still want it, I'll make you that coffee.'

'I'll make it. You press on that finger.'

Watching him perform that simple task with swift efficiency, Jenna couldn't help comparing him with Clive, who had never made her a cup of coffee in all the years they'd been together. 'Do you live far from the practice, Dr Mc— Ryan?'

'In the old lighthouse, three bays round from this one. You can walk there in twenty minutes along the coast path.'

Jenna remembered what Mrs Parker had said about him living like a hermit. 'The views must be fantastic. If I had a lighthouse, I'd have my bedroom right in the top so that I could look at the view.'

'Then we think alike.' He poured fresh coffee into two mugs. 'Because I have a three-hundred–and-sixty-degree view from my bedroom.'

For some reason Jenna had a vision of Ryan sprawled in bed, and she felt a strange flutter behind her ribs, like butterflies trying to escape from a net.

'Lucky you.' Her image of leaning against his shoulder for comfort morphed into something entirely different. Different and dangerous.

She stood up quickly. 'Why don't we drink this in the garden?' The fresh air would do her good, and the kitchen suddenly seemed far too small. Or maybe he seemed too big. Something was definitely out of proportion.

'Why did you have to leave your home?' He followed her outside and put the coffee down on the wooden table. 'Couldn't you have bought him out?'

'He sold the house.' She felt her hair lift in the breeze and breathed in deeply, smelling the sea. 'He put it on the market without even telling me. I was living there with Lexi, and then one morning I woke up to find three estate agents on my doorstep.'

'Did you get yourself a good lawyer?'

'Clive *is* a lawyer,' Jenna said wearily. 'And I didn't want Lexi seeing her parents fighting. I wanted it to be as civilised as possible.'

'Civilised isn't sending round estate agents with no warning.'

'I know. But if I'd created a scene it would have been worse for Lexi. Apparently what he did was legal. I was only eighteen when we married—I didn't check whose name the house was in. I didn't check a lot of things.'

'Legal, maybe—decent, definitely not.' His tone was hard and there was a dangerous glint in his eyes. 'Does Lexi know he made you sell?'

'Yes. I told her the truth about that. I'm not sure if that was the right thing to do or not. She was already very angry with Clive for going off with another woman. And furious with me for choosing to relocate to Scotland.'

'Why *did* you choose Scotland?'

'Because it's a long way from London…' Jenna hesitated. 'Clive doesn't want Lexi around at the moment. He's living the single life and he sees her as a hindrance. I thought it would damage their relationship for ever if she found out he doesn't want her there, so I picked somewhere so far away it would be a logistical nightmare for her to spend time with him. I didn't want her having another reason to hate him.'

Ryan watched her for a long moment. 'No wonder you're exhausted. Lexi's a lucky girl, having a mother who cares as much as you do.'

'I don't know. Maybe I care too much. Maybe I'm protecting her too much. Or maybe I'm protecting myself. I don't want to admit that the man I was married to for fifteen years can behave like that. Anyway, this is a very boring for you.' Tormented by guilt, and depressed after the conversation with her mother, Jenna took a deep breath. 'Sorry. I'm lousy company, I know. Take no notice. I'm just tired after the journey. I'm sure you're really busy.'

'Why didn't your mother want you to come here?'

Jenna watched the sunlight spread across the pretty garden. 'She wanted us to move in with her. She said it would save money.'

'Save money, but not your sanity. I gather you resisted?'

'Yes. I thought we'd be better off having a fresh start, away from everyone. Clive has another woman. Actually, it turned out he had several women throughout our marriage…' Her face was scarlet. 'I was the last person to know. That's another reason I wanted to get away. That and the fact that the girl he's started seeing is twenty-two. It was really difficult for Lexi.'

'And you, I should imagine.'

She didn't even want to think about how she'd felt. 'The hardest thing was seeing Lexi so hurt. I thought if we moved here we'd be right away from it. I thought it would be good—but at the moment she just hates me for dragging her away from her friends. She's worried no one here will speak to her. And I have no idea why I'm telling you all this.'

'Because I asked. And don't worry about no one speaking to her. This is Glenmore,' Ryan said dryly. 'There aren't enough people here for anyone to be ignored. It's a small community.'

'I hope she doesn't get into any trouble.' Jenna stared over her shoulder towards the grassy hill where Lexi had disappeared. 'I think she's very vulnerable at the moment.'

'If it's any consolation, there are not a lot of places to find trouble here. Mrs Parker aside, the crime rate on Glenmore is very low. When we do have trouble it's almost always tourists and nothing serious. Nick Hillier, the island policeman, has a pretty boring job. If there's a group of tourists drunk on the beach then it's an exciting day for him. You have nothing to worry about.'

'I'm a mother. Worrying yourself to death is part of the package. It never changes. From the moment they're born, you're worrying. When they sleep you check them every five minutes to see if they're breathing. Once I even woke Lexi up in the night just to check she was alive. Can you believe that?'

His eyes amused, Ryan reached for his coffee. 'Our new mothers' group will love you. They talk about that sort of stuff all the time and I just nod sagely and say it's all normal.'

'But you're secretly thinking they're a bit odd?'

'Waking a sleeping baby? I have mothers tearing their hair out because the baby doesn't sleep, so, yes, it seems a bit odd to hear mothers worrying when the baby does sleep.'

'Once you have children you worry about everything, from sharp knives to global warming. And it doesn't stop.' Jenna shook her head, finding it a relief to talk to someone. He was a good listener. 'Will they fall off that bike they're riding? Will they remember to look both ways when they cross the road? You want them to be polite to people, and then you're worried they'll be too polite and might go off with some stranger because they don't want to give offence–'

'Jenna, relax! You're going to give yourself a nervous

breakdown and you haven't even unpacked yet. You need to learn to chill.'

'Chill? What's that?' Jenna rolled her eyes in self-mockery. 'I don't know how to chill. But at work I'm sane, I promise. You must be wondering why on earth you gave me a lift. And a job.'

'Your job is safe. I can promise you that.'

'There's no such thing as safe.' She rubbed her finger over the table, following the grain of the wood. 'A year ago I had a husband, a home and a job. I lost all three.'

He was silent for a long moment. 'And now you have a home and a job again.'

There was something in his voice that made her look at him—made her wonder what personal trauma had driven him to this island.

'What I want is for Lexi to be happy.' Feeling calmer than she'd felt for ages, Jenna slipped off her shoes and curled her toes into the grass. 'I'm hoping that this will be a fresh start. I want it to feel like home.'

'If you need any help turning it into a home, give me a shout.' Ryan checked his watch and rose to his feet. 'I'm pretty good with a toolbox. Do you want any help unpacking? Is any of your furniture coming over?'

'No. No furniture.' Clive had claimed the furniture and all the belongings they'd collected over fifteen years of marriage. She hadn't had the strength to argue. She'd packed her clothes, a few books and not much else. 'I need to go shopping—oh, you said someone had stocked the place already?'

'When Evanna told the town meeting that you were coming, everyone from the village contributed.'

Jenna blinked. 'A group of people sat down and discussed my shopping list?'

'There's not a lot going on around here when the nightclubs are closed.'

'That's really kind.' Touched, Jenna made a mental note to thank everyone. 'Perhaps you could tell me the names. Then I can work out how much I owe everyone and pay them back.'

Ryan gave a faint smile, rolling up his shirtsleeves, revealing arms as strong as his shoulders. 'Oh, you'll pay. Don't worry about it. Everyone will claim a favour from you at some point. Usually at the most awkward, embarrassing moment, because that's how it works around here. One minute you're buying yourself a loaf of bread and the next you're giving an opinion on someone's rash.' He stood up. 'If we can do anything to help you settle in faster, let us know. The key to the back door is in the top drawer in the kitchen. It can be temperamental. If it jams, jiggle it slightly in the lock. And the shower turns cold if someone turns on a tap in the kitchen.'

'You know this house?'

'I stayed here for a few nights before I completed the sale on the lighthouse.'

'Oh.' Jenna had a disturbing image of him walking around the kitchen—showering in the bathroom. Naked.

Oh, God, she was losing it.

He raised an eyebrow. 'Are you all right?'

'Absolutely. How long should it take Lexi to get to the top and back? When do I start worrying?'

'You don't.' Ryan looked at the grassy ridge. 'She's on her way down now. I'll leave you to it. Surgery isn't until four. You can have a few hours to settle in. Spend some time together.'

'Yes.' Conscious that Lexi was approaching, Jenna lost her sense of calm. 'Thanks for the lift. And thanks for listening.'

He gave a brief nod and strolled out of her gate towards the sleek sports car that had transported her and her luggage from the surgery to the cottage. Without pausing in his stride, he exchanged a few words with Lexi as she sauntered past.

Watching anxiously from the garden, Jenna couldn't hear what he said, but whatever it was had Lexi smiling and that was an achievement in itself. Bracing herself for more complaints about her new home, she smiled at her daughter. 'Did you get a signal?'

'Yes, but everyone was out. Or maybe they're all still asleep after a night clubbing. Lucky them.' Lexi glanced over her shoulder as the sports car growled its way up the road away from them. 'What was he doing here, Mum?'

'He gave us a lift, remember?'

'An hour and a half ago.'

An hour and a half? Was that how much time had passed? Startled, Jenna glanced at her watch. 'Well—we were talking.'

'About what?' Lexi stared at her suspiciously and Jenna felt herself blush.

'About work,' she said firmly. 'I'm new to this practice, remember?'

'Oh. Right. I thought for one awful minute you—' She broke off and Jenna stared at her, heart thumping.

'What?'

'Nothing.' The girl gave a careless shrug, but Jenna knew exactly what she'd been thinking— *That her mother had been showing interest in a man.*

Jenna walked back into the cottage, feeling the burden of responsibility settle on her like a heavy weight. Whatever happened, she mustn't do anything to make her daughter feel more insecure than she already did.

'Dr McKinley was telling me that he lives in a lighthouse.'

'Dr McKinley is really hot.'

'Lexi! You're fifteen years old.' Appalled, Jenna cast a look at her daughter, but Lexi had her head in the fridge.

'Nearly sixteen. Old enough to know when a man is hot. Don't worry—I don't expect you to understand. You wouldn't know a good-looking man if you fell over him.' She pulled some cheese out of the fridge and then noticed the empty mugs on the kitchen table. Suddenly the tension was back. 'You invited him in for coffee?'

No, he'd invited himself in for coffee. 'He was up all night with patients.' Jenna adopted a casual tone. 'He was tired. It was the least I could do after he'd helped us.'

'Oh, Mum—' Lexi rolled her eyes, visibly cringing. 'Poor guy, being trapped by someone desperate divorcee. I suppose he was too polite to refuse.'

Wondering if Ryan saw her as old and desperate, Jenna picked up the empty mugs and washed them by hand. 'Of course he was being polite.' She didn't need her daughter to tell her that. 'I'm going to spend a few hours unpacking before I do the clinic this afternoon. Come and see your bedroom.'

They wandered upstairs and Lexi stared into the pretty bedroom. It had been decorated in keeping with the beach setting, with white New England furniture. A rug with bold blue and white stripes sat in the centre of the white floorboards. 'This is mine?'

'Yes. We can put your duvet cover on the bed and—'

'Sorting out the bed isn't going to make this my home.'

'Home is where family is,' Jenna said softly, 'and I'm here with you.' She felt a pang as she saw the vulnerability in Lexi's eyes.

'Well, that doesn't mean anything does it?' Her tone was flippant. 'I mean—Dad just walked out. What's stopping you doing the same?'

'I'm not going to walk out, Lexi. Not ever.' Jenna sank onto the edge of the bed, wanting to reassure her daughter. 'I know how difficult this has been for you—'

'No, you don't! You haven't got a clue—you have no idea how embarrassing it is that my Dad is having sex with a girl not much older than me!' Her voice rose. 'It's gross!'

Jenna resisted the temptation to agree. 'I told you—adults have relationships, Lexi.'

'*You* were in a relationship,' Lexi hissed. 'With each other. Marriage is supposed to be for ever—isn't that what you taught me?'

Jenna bit her lip. 'Ideally, yes.'

'So why didn't you try and fix it with Dad?'

'He didn't want to fix it. And—' Jenna thought about everything that had happened. *The way he'd treated her.* 'Not everything can be fixed.'

'Well, don't tell me you know how I feel, because you have no idea.' Lexi flounced out of the room and locked herself in the bathroom.

Jenna flopped onto the bed, feeling wrung-out and exhausted.

It was will-power that drove her downstairs to fetch the suitcases. Will-power that made her unpack methodically, finding homes for her pathetically small number of belongings. Unfortunately her will-power wasn't strong enough to stop her from thinking about Ryan McKinley.

It was only when she was hanging her clothes in her wardrobe that she realised that they'd spent an hour and a half together and he'd told her nothing about himself.

Nothing at all.

CHAPTER FOUR

JENNA leant her bike against the wall near the quay, waving to Jim the ferryman.

'Morning, Nurse Jenna. Finished your morning clinic?' A grey haired lady with a stick ambled past her on the pavement and Jenna smiled.

'Yes, all done, Mrs Hampton. How's the hip?'

'It's a miracle. I've had my first good night's sleep for four years. I was dreading the operation, if I'm honest—probably wouldn't have gone ahead with it if Dr McKinley hadn't encouraged me.'

'Nurse Jenna?' Someone touched her arm. 'Sorry to bother you—'

The impromptu conversations continued, so that by the time she'd walked along South Quay and up to the row of terraced houses that overlooked the water she was ten minutes late.

Ryan was already there and glancing at his watch, a brooding frown on his handsome face.

Jenna quickened her pace and arrived breathless, although whether that was from rushing the last few metres or from the sight of him, she wasn't sure. After two weeks working alongside him she knew that her body did strange things when Ryan was near. It didn't matter that they kept every exchange strictly professional. That didn't alter the chemistry. She hadn't said anything, and neither had he, but they both knew it was there.

Funny, Jenna mused, that she could even recognise chemistry when she'd been with one man all her life. 'I'm so sorry I'm late—I was waylaid.'

'You did a clinic on the quay?'

'How did you guess?' Laughing, Jenna removed the clip from her hair. Smoothing her hands over her curls, she twisted it into a thick rope and secured it firmly. 'There was a strong wind on the coast road. I must look as though I've been dragged through a hedge backwards.'

His eyes moved from her face to her hair. 'That isn't how you look.'

Colour stung her cheeks and she felt a shaft of awareness pierce low in her pelvis. 'Did you know Abby Brown is pregnant? I saw her eating a double chocolate fudge sundae in Meg's Café to celebrate.'

Ryan gave a wry smile. 'Let's hope she doesn't keep that up throughout the pregnancy. Are you ready?' But before he could press the doorbell the door opened and a woman stood there, a baby in her arms and a harassed look on her face. 'Hello, Elaine.'

'Oh, Dr McKinley—come on in.' The woman stood to one side and almost tripped over the dog which was bouncing in the hallway. As his tail hit the umbrella stand flying, the woman winced. 'Whatever possessed me to say yes to a dog? Not only does he make Hope's asthma worse, he knocks everything over.'

'He's beautiful.' Jenna bent down and made a fuss of the dog, and the animal leaped up and tried to lick her face, sensing an ally.

'Sorry—we've failed to teach him any manners.'

'I don't mind.' Giggling, Jenna pushed the dog down. 'What's his name?'

'We haven't decided—at the moment he's just called Black.'

Jenna tried to look stern. 'Sit!'

Black sat, and Ryan lifted an eyebrow. 'That's the first time I've seen that animal do as it's told.'

Elaine was astonished. 'You're so good with dogs! Do you have your own?'

'No.' Jenna stared at the black Labrador, who stared back, tongue lolling, tail wagging over the floor. It was a long time since anyone had looked at her with such adoration and unquestioning trust. 'I don't have a dog of my own.'

A family, she thought, didn't have to be a mother, a father and two children.

'You should think about getting one—you're obviously good with animals.' Elaine ushered them into the living room. 'Hope's on the sofa. She's had a much better night. We kept Black locked in the garden shed, and I vacuumed all the dog hairs this morning, but I haven't quite got my head round taking him back to the home.'

Jenna followed Ryan into the sitting room and noticed that the little girl's face brightened when she saw him.

'Dr Mac—I've been eating ice cream and jelly.'

'For breakfast?' Ryan pulled a face and sat down next to the child. He admired her doll, had a solemn conversation about which outfit she ought to wear for the day, and then pulled out his stethoscope. 'Can I listen to your chest?'

'It's all better.'

'So I hear. That's good. Can I listen?'

'OK.' With a wide smile, the little girl lay back on the sofa and waited.

His hands infinitely gentle, Ryan listened to her breathing, and watching him with the child made Jenna's breath catch. He focused entirely on the little girl, listening to every word she said as if she were the most important person in the room. 'I've been thinking about the attack she had, Elaine.' He folded the stethoscope and slid it back into his bag. 'You say she's using a normal inhaler, is that right?'

'Yes.'

'I think that might be the problem. I want to try her with a spacer—it's a device that relies less on technique, which is very useful for younger children. It makes sure they inhale the complete dose. To see you're taught to use it properly I've brought Nurse Jenna along with me.' Ryan gave a self-deprecating smile. 'I'm the first to admit that training children in inhaler technique probably isn't my forte, so I've called in the experts. Jenna used to do it all the time in her last job.'

Jenna removed the spacer from her bag and showed Hope's mother how it worked, explaining exactly what she had to do. 'It's really that simple.'

'She's due a dose now,' Elaine said. 'Could you check we do it right?'

Jenna watched, made a few suggestions, and explained to Hope exactly why it was important for her to take the drug.

'I breathe in that space thing every time?'

'Every time.'

'If I do that can I keep Black?'

Elaine sighed. 'No, sweetie. Black has to go.'

Hope's eyes filled with tears. 'But I love him. I can't send him back to that horrid place. I made him a promise. I promised him he had a home now.'

Feeling tears in her own eyes, Jenna blinked rapidly, feeling every bit of Elaine's anguish as a mother.

Elaine sank onto the sofa and shook her head. 'I have to take him back, Hope.' Her voice cracked. 'We can't keep him here. I can't risk going through what I went through the other night with you. I know it's hard, but we have no choice.'

'But I promised him he'd have a home and be loved.' Hope was sobbing now, great tearing sobs that shook her tiny body. 'I promised him, Mummy, and I can't break a promise. He'll be all on his own again. He'll think no one loves him.'

'I'll have him.' Jenna blurted the words past the lump in her throat and then stood in stunned silence, absorbing two things. Firstly, that she'd just got herself a dog, and secondly that making that decision had felt incredibly liberating.

For once she'd thought about herself. Not Clive. Not her mother. Herself.

Realising that everyone was looking at her, she shrugged. 'I'd like to have him. Really.' She looked at Hope. 'And I'll love him and give him a good home. So you won't have broken your promise…'

A tearful Elaine exchanged glances with Ryan. 'You want to take the dog?'

'I do.' Jenna spoke the words firmly, almost defiantly. Like a wedding ceremony, she thought with wry humour. *Do you take this dog...?* Only she knew without a flicker of doubt that the dog would never disappoint her. 'I really do. My daughter will be thrilled. And any time you want to come and see him, or meet up on the beach to throw a stick or two, you just bang on my front door…'

Ryan took a deep breath. 'Jenna, perhaps you should think about this—'

'I've thought about it for about thirty years. I've wanted a dog since I was a child.'

But her mother had said no. Then Clive had said no.

The advantage of being her own woman, in charge of her own life, was that there was no one to say no. And even if someone did say no, she wasn't sure she'd listen any more. She'd been weak, she realised. She'd allowed her own needs to come second. Her life had been about what Clive wanted. What Clive needed. And she'd been so busy keeping him happy, determined to keep her marriage alive and prove her mother wrong, that she'd stopped asking herself what she wanted.

Jenna straightened her shoulders and stood a little taller. 'If you wouldn't mind holding on to Black for one more day. I need to buy a book, check on the internet—make sure I know what I'm doing. A patient I saw last week breeds Labradors—I'd like to give her a ring and chat to her before I take Black.' Suddenly she felt strong, and the feeling was good—almost as if happiness was pouring through her veins.

Elaine gave a delighted laugh, relief lighting her face. 'If you're sure?'

'I'm completely sure.' And she had no need to ask Lexi what she thought. Lexi had wanted a dog all her life. 'I can take him with me on my visits—tie him to my bicycle while I go indoors. When I'm in clinic he can either play with Evanna's dog, or just stay in our garden. I'll find someone to build a fence.'

Elaine looked worried. 'Black rarely does what people want him to do.'

'That's fine by me.' Jenna stroked her hand over the dog's head, thinking of how often she'd disappointed her own mother. 'Maybe he and I have something in common. Welcome to rebellion.'

'That would be a good name,' Elaine laughed. 'Rebel. You should call him Rebel.'

'Just hope he doesn't live up to his name,' Ryan said dryly, closing his bag. 'There's a dog-training session every Thursday night in the church hall. You might want to book him in.'

'He ate your favourite shoes?' Laughing, Evanna leaned across the table and helped herself to more lasagne. 'You must have been mad.'

'With myself, for leaving them out.' Jenna was smiling too, and Ryan found it impossible not to watch her because the smile lit her face. He loved the dimple that appeared at the corner of her mouth, and the way her eyes shone when she was amused.

She was smiling regularly now, and the black circles had gone from under her eyes.

Extraordinary, he thought, how Glenmore could change people. 'What does Lexi think of him?'

'She adores him. She's the only teenager on Glenmore up at dawn during the summer holidays, and that's because she can't wait to walk him.'

Evanna cleared her plate and looked longingly at the food. 'Why am I so hungry? Do you think I could be pregnant again, Logan?'

It was only because he was looking at Jenna that Ryan saw her smile dim for a fraction of a second. Then she pulled herself together and joined in the conversation, her expression warm and excited.

'Do you think you could be? Charlie is two, isn't he? What a lovely age gap.'

Evanna agreed. 'I always wanted at least four kids.'

Ryan wondered if he was the only one who had noticed that Jenna had put her fork down quietly and was no longer eating.

Perhaps it was just that she found the whole happy family scene playing out in front of her emotionally painful. Or perhaps it was something else.

She'd been happy enough until Evanna had mentioned having more children.

Evanna lost the battle with her will-power and helped herself to more food. 'Weren't you tempted to have more children, Jenna?'

Sensing Jenna's tension, Ryan shifted the focus of the conversation away from her. 'If you're planning more children, you're going to have to build an extension on this house, Logan.'

'They can share a room,' Evanna said. 'If it's a girl, she can share with my Kirsty. If it's a boy, with Charlie.'

She and Logan spun plans while Jenna relocated her food from one side of her plate to the other.

It was the question about children that had chased away her appetite, Ryan thought grimly, reaching for his wine. And now he found himself wondering the same as Evanna. Why hadn't she had more children? She clearly loved being a mother.

Evanna heaped seconds onto everyone's plate except Jenna's. 'Aren't you enjoying it, Jenna?'

Jenna looked up and met Ryan's gaze.

They stared at each other for a moment, and then she gave a faltering smile and picked up her fork. 'It's delicious.' With a determined effort she ate, but Ryan knew she was doing it not because she was hungry, but because she didn't want to hurt Evanna's feelings. She was that sort of person, wasn't she? She thought about other people. Usually to the exclusion of her own needs.

He'd never actually met anyone as unselfish as her.

He felt something punch deep in his gut.

'Ryan—you have to fill those legs and wide shoulders with something.' Evanna pushed the dish towards Ryan but he held up a hand.

'Preferably not adipose tissue. I couldn't eat another thing, but it was delicious, thanks. I ought to be on my way.' Sitting here watching Jenna was doing nothing for his equilibrium.

Why had he accepted Evanna's invitation to dinner?

Over the past weeks he'd made sure he'd avoided being in a social situation with Jenna, and he had a feeling she'd been doing the same. And yet both of them had said yes to Evanna's impromptu invitation to join them for a casual supper.

'You can't go yet.' Evanna's eyes flickered to Jenna. 'Finish telling us about dog-training.'

It occurred to Ryan that the supper invitation probably hadn't been impromptu. Watching Evanna draw the two of them together, he had a sense that she'd planned the evening very carefully.

'The dog-training is a failure.' Jenna finished her wine. 'I really ought to go. Lexi was invited out to a friend's house, and she's taken Rebel, but she'll be back soon. I want to be there when they drop her home. I don't like her coming back to an empty house.'

Ryan poured himself a glass of water. 'I saw her eating fish and chips on the quay with the Harrington twins last week. She's obviously made friends.'

'Yes.' This time Jenna's smile wasn't forced. 'People have been very welcoming. There's hardly an evening when she's in.'

Which must mean that Jenna was often alone.

Ryan frowned, wondering how she spent her evenings.

Was she lonely?

He realised suddenly just how hard this move must have been for Jenna. Her relationship with her mother was clearly strained and her husband had left her. She'd moved to an area of the country where she knew no one, taken a new job and started a new life. And her only support was a teenager who seemed to blame her for everything that had gone wrong. And yet she carried on with quiet dignity and determination.

Unsettled by just how much he admired her, he stood up. 'I need to get back. I have things to do.'

Like reminding himself that the worst thing you could do after a relationship went wrong was dive into another relationship. That was the last thing Jenna needed right now. As for him—he had no idea what he needed.

'You can't possibly leave now! I made dessert—' Evanna glanced between him and Jenna and then cast a frantic look at Logan, who appeared oblivious to his wife's efforts to keep the two of them at her table.

'If Ryan has things to do, he has things to do.'

'Well, obviously, but—I was hoping he'd give Jenna a lift.'

'I'll give Jenna a lift if she wants one,' Logan said, and Evanna glared at her husband.

'No! You can't do it, you have that—thing—you know…' she waved a hand vaguely '…to fix for me. It needs doing—urgently.'

'Thing?' Logan looked confused, and Ryan gave a half-smile and strolled to the door, scooping up his jacket on the way. If Evanna had hoped for help in her matchmaking attempts then she was going to be disappointed.

'I don't need a lift,' Jenna said quickly. 'I brought my bike. I'll cycle.'

She was keeping her distance, just as he was. Which suited him.

Unfortunately it didn't suit Evanna.

'You can't cycle! It's late. You could be mugged, or you might fall into a ditch.'

'It isn't that late, and if I don't cycle I won't be able to get to work tomorrow. My bike won't fit into Ryan's car.' Ever practical, Jenna stood up. 'I hadn't realised how late it was. Supper was delicious, Evanna. Are you sure I can't wash up?'

'No—the dishwasher does that bit…' Evanna looked crestfallen, but Jenna appeared not to notice as she dropped to her knees to hand a toy to Charlie, the couple's two-year-old son.

Catching the wistful look on her face, Ryan felt something tug inside him. He found her kindness as appealing as the length of her legs and the curve of her lips.

As she walked past him to the door he caught her eye and she blushed slightly, said another thank-you to Evanna and Logan and walked out of the house, leaving the scent of her hair trailing over his senses.

By the time Ryan had said his farewells and followed her out of the house Jenna was fiddling with her bike, head down. Something about the conversation had upset her, he knew that. He also knew that if he delved into the reason he'd probably upset her more. He strolled across to her, his feet crunching on the gravel. 'Are you sure you don't want a lift home?'

'Positive. I'll be fine, but thanks.' She hooked her bag over the handlebars and Ryan noticed that her movements were always graceful, fluid. Like a dancer.

'Mrs Parker was singing your praises this week.'

'That's good to hear.' Smiling, she pushed a cycle helmet onto her head and settled onto the bike. 'Under that fierce exterior she's a sweet lady. Interesting past. Did you know she drove an ambulance during the war?'

'No. Did she tell you that during one of your afternoon tea sessions?'

'She told you about that?' Jenna fastened the chin strap. 'I call in sometimes, on my way home. I pass her front door.'

And he had a feeling she would have called in even if it hadn't been on her way home. The fact that she had time for everyone hadn't gone unnoticed among the islanders. 'Her leg is looking better than it has for ages. I suspect it's because you're nagging her to wear her stockings.'

'It isn't easy when the weather is warm. She needs a little encouragement.'

'So you've been stopping by several times a week, encouraging her?'

'I like her.'

They were making conversation, but he knew she was as aware of him as he was of her.

Looking at her rose-pink mouth, he wondered if she'd had a relationship since her husband.

'Evanna upset you this evening.'

Her gaze flew to his. Guarded. 'Not at all. I was a little tired, that's all. Rebel sometimes wakes me up at night, walking round the kitchen. I'm a light sleeper.'

Ryan didn't push it. 'I walk on the beach most mornings. If you want help with the dog-training, you could join me.'

'I'll remember that. Thanks.' She dipped her head so that her face was in shadow, her expression unreadable. 'I'll see you tomorrow, Ryan.'

He was a breath away from stopping her. A heartbeat away from doing something about the chemistry they were both so carefully ignoring.

What would she do if he knocked her off her bike and tumbled her into the heather that bordered Evanna's garden?

'Goodnight.' He spoke the word firmly and then watched as she cycled away, the bike wobbling slightly as she found her balance.

He was still watching as she vanished over the brow of the hill into the dusk.

CHAPTER FIVE

'TWO salmon fillets, please.' Jenna stood in the fishmonger's, trying to remember a time when she'd bought food that wasn't shrink-wrapped and stamped with a date. And she'd never bought fish. Clive had hated fish.

Was that why she now ate fish three times a week?

Was she being contrary?

Eyeing the alternatives spread out in front of her, she gave a faint shrug. So what if she was? The advantage of being single was that you could live life the way you wanted to live it.

She had a dog and a garden, and now she was eating fish.

'Just you and the bairn eating tonight, then?' Hamish selected two plump fillets, wrapped the fish and dropped it into a bag.

'That's right.' How did anyone have a secret life on Glenmore? After only a month on the island, everyone knew who she was. And what she ate. And who she ate it with. Strangely enough, she didn't mind.

'How was your dinner with Dr McKinley?'

All right, maybe she minded.

Wondering if the entire island was involved in the matchmaking attempt, Jenna struggled for an answer. 'Dinner was casual. With Evanna and Logan. Just supper—nothing personal.' She cringed, knowing she sounded as though she had something to hide. 'How's Alice doing?' Changing the subject quickly, she tried to look relaxed.

'Still rushing around. I say to her, "Rest, for goodness' sake." But does she listen?' Hamish added a bunch of fresh parsley to the bag. 'No, she doesn't. That's women for you. Stubborn. Alice would die if it meant proving a point.'

'Well, I saw her in clinic yesterday and the wound was healing nicely, so I'm sure she isn't going to die any time soon.' Jenna dug her purse out of her bag. 'How much do I owe you?'

'Nothing.' His weathered brow crinkled into a frown as he handed over the bag. 'As if I'd take money after what you did for my Alice. I said to her, "It's a good job you fell outside Nurse Jenna's house, otherwise it would have been a different story." You sorted her out, fed her, had a lovely chat.' He glanced up as the door opened behind her and a bell rang. 'Morning, Dr McKinley. Surf's up for you today. They had the lifeboat out this morning—two kids in trouble on the rocks round at the Devil's Jaws. Place is roped off, but they climbed over.'

Jenna froze. He was behind her? She'd thought about him all night—thought about the way he'd watched her across the table. He'd made her so nervous she hadn't been able to eat. And he'd noticed that she wasn't eating.

Adopting her most casual expression, she turned and looked.

He was standing in the doorway, a sleek black wetsuit moulding itself to every muscular dip and curve of his powerful shoulders.

The bag of salmon slipped from her fingers and landed with a plop on the tiled floor.

Hamish cleared his throat pointedly and Jenna stooped to retrieve her bag, her face as red as a bonfire. 'Good morning, Dr McKinley.' She turned back to the fish counter and developed a sudden interest in the dressed crab that Hamish had on display as she tried to compose herself. Over the past few weeks she'd had plenty of practice. In fact she was proud of how controlled she was around him.

They worked together every day, but so far she'd managed not to repeat any of the embarrassing sins she'd committed on her first day, like staring at his mouth. Even during dinner last night she'd managed to barely look at him.

And if she occasionally thought about how his hands had felt on her shoulders that day in her kitchen—well, that was her secret. A girl could dream, and she knew better than anyone that there was a world of difference between dreams and reality.

Jenna continued to stare at the crab. It was a shock to discover that, having thought she'd never trust a man again, she could actually find one attractive. But even if she could trust a man, the one thing she couldn't trust was her feelings. She knew she was hurt. She knew she was angry. And she knew that she was lonely for adult company.

This would be a bad, bad time to have a relationship even if one was on offer. Which it clearly wasn't—because, as Lexi was always telling her, she was past it. Why would Ryan want a relationship with someone like her?

'Thought I'd save you a journey and drop off that prescription.' Ryan handed it to Hamish. 'Did you know that crab personally, Jenna? You've been staring at him for the past five minutes.'

Jenna looked up, her inappropriate thoughts bringing the colour rushing to her cheeks. 'He has the same complexion as my first cousin.'

The corners of his mouth flickered. 'Yes? I can recommend a cream for that condition.'

She felt the breath catch in her throat because his smile was so sexy, and there was that unmistakable flash of chemistry that always occurred when they were together.

Imagining what it would be like to kiss a man like him, Jenna stared at him for a moment and then turned back to the crab, telling herself that even if things had been different she'd never have been sophisticated enough to hold a man like him. Ryan McKinley might be working on Glenmore, but she recognised a high-flier when she saw one. He was like one of those remote, intimidating consultants who strode the corridors of the hospital where she'd trained. Out of her league.

Hamish exchanged a look with Ryan and raised his eyebrows. 'You want to take a closer look at that crab?'

'No.' Flustered, Jenna pushed her hair out of her eyes. 'No, thanks— I— But it does look delicious.' Oh, for goodness' sake. What was the matter with her? Lexi was right—she was desperate. And she needed to leave this shop before she dropped her salmon a second time. Smiling at Hamish, she walked towards the door.

'Wait a minute, Nurse Jenna.' Hamish called after her. 'Has Dr McKinley asked you to the beach barbecue? Because if he hasn't, he's certainly been meaning to.'

Did everyone on Glenmore interfere with everyone else's lives?

Jenna looked at Ryan, who looked straight back at her, his expression unreadable.

Realising that Hamish had put them both in an impossible position, Jenna was about to formulate a response when Ryan straightened.

'It's on Saturday. In aid of the lifeboat. You should come.'

Knowing he'd only invited her because Hamish had pushed him, Jenna shook her head. 'I'm busy on Saturday.'

Hamish tutted. 'How can you be busy? Everything shuts early. Everyone on the island will be there. There's nothing else to do. Young thing like you needs a night out. You've done nothing but work since the day you stepped off that ferry.'

A night out?

When she finally felt ready for a night out it wouldn't be with a man like Ryan McKinley. When and if she did date a man again, she'd date someone safe and ordinary. Someone who didn't make her tongue knot and her insides turn to jelly. And preferably someone who didn't put her off her food.

He was watching her now, with that steady gaze that unsettled her so much. 'The islanders hold it every year, to raise funds for the lifeboat and the air ambulance. You're supposed to bring a dish that will feed four people. And wear a swimming costume.'

'Well, that's the end of that, then.' Somehow she kept it light. 'I can bring a dish to feed four people, but I don't own a swimming costume.'

'Swim naked,' Hamish said. 'Been done before.'

'And the culprits spent the night sobering up in one of Nick's four-star cells,' Ryan drawled, a sardonic gleam in his eyes. 'It's a family event. You can buy a costume from the Beach Hut, four doors down from here.'

Jenna had been into the Beach Hut twice, to buy clothes for Lexi. She hadn't bought anything for herself. 'Well—I'll think about it, thanks.'

Hamish scowled. 'You *have* to go. Isn't that right, Dr McKinley?'

Ryan was silent for a moment. 'I think Jenna will make her own decision about that.'

Jenna flushed. He wasn't going to coerce her. He wasn't going to tell her whether she should, or shouldn't go. He was leaving the choice up to her.

And that was what she did now, wasn't it? She made her own choices.

She decided whether she owned a dog and whether she was going to eat fish.

She shivered slightly, barely aware of the other customers who had entered the shop. She was only aware of Ryan, and the multitude of confusing feelings inside her. If she had to make a decision, what would it be?

She wanted to ask him whether he wanted her to go. She wanted to apologise for the fact that the islanders were match-making. She wanted him to know it had nothing to do with her.

Hideously embarrassed, she muttered that she'd think about it and walked out of the shop, her cheeks flushed.

It was crazy to feel this way about him, Jenna thought faintly. A man like him wasn't going to be interested in a divorced woman with a teenage daughter. And anyway, for all she knew he could be involved with someone. She couldn't imagine that a man like him could possibly be single.

Frustrated with herself, she hurried to her bike. She had to stop thinking about him. Even if he were interested in her, she wouldn't follow it through. For a start being with him would make her so nervous she wouldn't be able to eat a morsel, and to top it off Lexi was only just starting to settle into her new life. She could just imagine her daughter's reaction if her mother started seeing a man.

Thinking about Ryan occupied her mind for the cycle home, and she was still thinking about him as she propped her bike against the wall of the cottage and picked some flowers from the garden.

She walked into the kitchen to find Lexi sprawled on the kitchen floor, playing with Rebel.

Jenna put the flowers in a vase. 'How was the archaeology dig today?' Despite her complaints, it had taken Lexi only a matter of days to settle in and start enjoying herself. 'Did you have fun?'

'Yeah. Fraser found a piece of pot—everyone was really excited. I'm going to meet him for a walk on the beach later. I'll take Rebel. What time are we eating? I'm starving.'

Fraser? Lexi wanted to go for a walk on the beach with a boy?

'We're eating in about twenty minutes. So…' Retrieving the salmon fillets from her bag, Jenna tried to keep her voice casual. 'You haven't mentioned Fraser before. Is he nice?'

'He has a nose ring, five tattoos, long hair and swears all the time.' Lexi rubbed Rebel's glossy fur with her hands. 'You're going to love him—isn't she, Reb?'

With a wry smile, Jenna put the salmon under the grill. 'Lexi, you wait until you're a worried mother—'

'I'm not going to be like you. I'm going to trust my kids.'

Jenna sensed this was one of those moments when it was imperative to say the right thing. 'I trust you, Lexi,' she said quietly. 'You're a bright, caring, funny girl. But you're still a child—'

'I'm nearly sixteen—you're so over-protective.'

'I care about you. And you *are* still a child. Child going on woman, but still… I know all this has been hard on you. And being a teenager isn't easy.'

'What? You remember that far back?' But Lexi was smiling as she picked up Rebel's bowl. 'We're having fish again? I'm going to start swapping meals with the dog.'

'I thought you liked fish.'

'I do. But you never used to cook it in London. Now we have it almost every meal!'

'I didn't cook it in London because Dad hated it.' But Clive wasn't here now, and she was cooking what she wanted. And loving it, Jenna mused, mixing a teriyaki sauce to add to the salmon.

'Given that you're into all this healthy lifestyle stuff, I assume I *can* go for a walk on the beach with Fraser later?'

Jenna felt as though she was treading over broken glass. If she said no, she'd be accused of not trusting, and that could trigger a rebellious response. If she said yes, she'd worry all evening. 'Yes,' she croaked, washing a handful of tomatoes and adding them to the salad. 'All I ask is that you're home before dark.'

'Why? I can have sex in daylight just as easily as in the dark.'

Jenna closed her eyes. 'Lexi—'

'But I'm not going to. Credit me with some sense, Mum. You know I'm not going to do that. You've given me the sex, love, marriage talk often enough.'

'You've got it in the wrong order,' Jenna said weakly. 'And you've missed out contraception.' It was impossible not to be aware that Lexi was only a couple of years younger than she had been when she'd become pregnant.

Lexi rolled her eyes and then walked over and hugged her. 'Just chill, Mum.'

Astonished by the unexpected show of affection, Jenna felt a lump in her throat. 'That's nice. A hug.'

'Yeah—well, I'm sorry I was difficult about moving here. It's a pretty cool place. I didn't mean to be a nightmare.'

Jenna felt a rush of relief. 'You're not a nightmare, baby. I'm glad you're settling in.'

'It would be great if you could worry less.'

'It would be great if you could give me less to worry about.'

'OK. If I'm going to do something really bad, I'll warn you.'

'Lexi—about Fraser…'

'If you're going to talk to me about boys, Mum, don't waste your time. I probably know more than you anyway.'

Jenna blinked. That was probably true. She'd only ever had one boyfriend, and she'd married him at eighteen.

And he'd left her at thirty-two.

Lexi stole a tomato from the salad. 'We're just friends, OK? Mates. He's really easy to talk to. He really *gets* stuff. His dad—' She broke off and then shrugged. 'His dad walked out, too. When he was nine. That's why his mum came here.'

'Oh…'

What had happened to her had happened to millions of women around the world. She wasn't the only one in this situation. Lives shattered and were mended again, and she was mending, wasn't she? Slowly. She stared at the dog lying on her kitchen floor, and the bunch of flowers on her kitchen table. Life was different, but that didn't mean it wasn't good.

'You can go for a walk on the beach, Lexi.'

Lexi visibly relaxed. 'Thanks. We're just going to hang out, that's all. Fraser says there's really cool stuff on the beach once the tide goes out. He knows the names of everything. I feel like a real townie.'

'You'll have to teach me. Have they dug up anything else interesting at the castle yet?'

'Bits of stuff. They found these Viking combs—weird to think of Vikings combing their hair.'

'Perhaps their mothers nagged them,' Jenna said dryly, hugely relieved that Lexi appeared to be more like her old self. 'What's the castle like? I must go up there.'

'It's awesome. Fraser showed me this steep shaft into the dungeons. He fell down it a few years ago and had to have his head stitched up.'

'It sounds dangerous.'

'Only to you. You see danger everywhere.'

'I'm a mother. Worrying goes with the territory.'

'Fraser's mother doesn't fuss over him all the time. She just lets him live his life.'

Jenna bit her lip, trying not to be hurt, well used to being told what other mothers did. 'I'm letting you live your life. I'd just rather you didn't do it in a hospital or an antenatal clinic. Wash your hands, Lex—dinner is nearly ready.'

'Do you want me to lay the table or do drinks or something?'

Hiding her surprise, Jenna smiled at her. 'That would be a great help. There's lemonade in the fridge—Evanna gave it to us as a gift.'

'It's delicious. I had some at her house.' Lexi opened the fridge door again and pulled out the bottle. 'She makes it by the bucketload, all fresh lemons and stuff. She's a good cook. I told her you were, too. Are we going to the barbecue on Saturday, Mum?'

Still reeling from the compliment, Jenna turned the salmon. 'How do you know about the barbecue?'

'Fraser mentioned it.'

Fraser, Fraser, Fraser—

Still, at least Lexi seemed happy. Relieved, Jenna put the salmon on the plates. 'Do you want to go?'

'Why not? Might be a laugh.' Her eyes narrowed. 'How did *you* hear about the barbecue?'

'In the fishmonger's.' Jenna omitted to say who she'd bumped into there. 'It's amazing to be able to buy such fresh fish.'

'It's amazing what old people find exciting.' Lexi suppressed a yawn as she picked up her plate. 'Let's eat in the garden. So how many lives did you save today? Did you see Dr Hot?'

'Dr who?'

'Dr Hot. Ryan McKinley. I bet women who are perfectly well make appointments just to spend five minutes with him. Fraser says he's brilliant.'

Even at home there was no escape, Jenna thought weakly, taking her plate and following her daughter out into the sunshine.

She wasn't going to think of him as Dr Hot.
She really wasn't.

'She was playing on the deck with a water pistol and she slipped and crashed into the fence—the bruise is horrendous. I'm worried she's fractured her eye socket or something.' The woman's face was white. 'I tried to get an appointment with one of the doctors, but Dr McNeil is out on a call and Dr McKinley has a full list.'

Jenna gave her shoulder a squeeze. 'Let me take a look at it. If I think she needs to be seen by one of the doctors, then I'll arrange it. Hello, Lily.' She crouched down so that she was at the same level as the child. 'What have you been doing to yourself?'

She studied the livid bruise across the child's cheekbone and the swelling distorting the face. 'Was she knocked out?'

'No.' The woman hovered. 'I put an ice pack on it straight away, but it doesn't seem to have made a difference.'

'I'm sure it helped.' Jenna examined the child's cheek, tested her vision and felt the orbit. 'Can you open your mouth for me, Lily? Good girl—now, close—brilliant. Does that hurt?' Confident that there was no fracture, she turned to Lily's mother. 'I think it's just badly bruised, Mrs Parsons.'

'But she could have fractured it. Sorry—it isn't that I don't trust you.' The woman closed her eyes briefly. 'And I know I'm being anxious, but—'

'I know all about anxious. You don't have to apologise.' Seeing how distressed the mother was, and sympathising, Jenna made a decision. 'I'll ask Dr McKinley to check her for you. Then you won't be going home, worrying.'

'Would you?'

'I'll go and see if he's free—just wait one moment.' Giving Lily a toy to play with, Jenna left her room and walked across to Ryan just as the door to his consulting room opened and a patient walked out.

She paused for a moment, conscious that she hadn't seen him since Hamish had embarrassed them both the day before.

'Ryan?' Putting that out of her mind, Jenna put her head round the door. 'I'm sorry, I know you're busy…' And tired, she thought, looking at the shadows under his eyes. He worked harder than any doctor she'd ever met.

Or were the shadows caused by something else?

'I'm not busy—what can I do for you?' The moment he looked at her, Jenna felt her insides flip over.

'I have a patient in my room—I wondered if you could give me your opinion. The little girl is six—she's slipped and banged her face. The bruising is bad, but I don't think there's a fracture—there's no flattening of the cheek.'

Work always helped, she thought. After Clive had left, work had been her healing potion. It had stopped her thinking, analysing, asking 'what if?' And she'd discovered that if you worked hard enough, you fell into bed dog-tired and slept, instead of lying awake, thinking all the same things you'd been thinking during the day.

'Flattening of the cheek can be obscured by swelling—'

'It isn't that swollen yet. It only happened half an hour ago, and her mum put an ice pack on it immediately. I can't feel any defect to the orbit, and she can open and close her mouth without difficulty.'

'It sounds as though you're confident with your assessment.' His long fingers toyed with the pen on his desk. 'Why do you need me?'

'Because the mother is so, so worried. I thought some reassurance from you might help. I know what it's like to be a panicking mother.'

'Who is the patient?'

'Parsons?'

Ryan stood up. 'Lily Parsons? That explains why you have a worried mother in your room. Little Lily had a nasty accident a couple of years ago—almost died. She fell in deep water in the quay and a boat propeller caught her artery.'

'Oh, no—' Jenna lifted her hand to her throat, horrified by the image his words created. 'How did she survive that?'

'My predecessor, Connor McNeil—Logan's cousin—was ex-army. Trauma was his speciality, otherwise I doubt Lily would be with us today. She went into respiratory arrest, lost so much blood—'

'Were you here?'

'No. It was just before I arrived, but Connor's rescue has gone down in island folklore. Apparently Jayne totally flipped. She witnessed the whole thing—blamed herself for the fact that Lily had fallen in. The child was watching the fish, and a crowd of tourists queuing for the ferry bumped into her and she lost her balance.'

'Poor Jayne!' To stop herself looking at his mouth, Jenna walked back towards the door. 'All the more reason why you should reassure her.'

Without arguing, Ryan followed her into the room, charmed Jayne, made Lily laugh, and then checked the child's eye with a thoroughness that would have satisfied the most hyper-anxious mother.

Jenna watched, wondering why someone with his own trauma skills would give up a glittering career to bury himself on Glenmore.

Something must have happened.

Life, she thought, had a way of doling out grim surprises.

'You're right that there is no flattening of the cheek.' He addressed the remark to Jenna, gave the little girl a wink and strolled across the room to wash his hands. 'Jayne, I'm happy with her, but that bruising is going to get worse before it gets better, and so is the swelling. I'm guessing your worrying is going to get worse before it gets better, too. I'll have a word with Janet on Reception so that she knows to slot you in if you feel worried and want me to take another look.'

'You don't want to X-ray her?'

'No. I don't think it's necessary.' Ryan dried his hands and dropped the paper towel in the bin. 'Look, why don't you bring her back to my surgery tomorrow morning anyway? That will stop you having to look at her every five minutes and decide whether you need to bring her back.'

Jayne Parsons gave a weak smile. 'You must think I'm a total idiot.'

'On the contrary, I think you're a worried mum and that's understandable.' Ryan scribbled a number on a scrap of paper. 'This is my mobile number. I drive past your house on the way to and from the surgery—just give me a call if you're worried and I can drop in. Take care, Lily.'

Mother and child left the room, more relaxed, and Jenna stared at the door. 'Do you give your mobile number to every anxious patient?'

'If I think they need the reassurance, yes. Glenmore is an isolated island. It makes people more reliant on each other. They're in and out of each other's lives.' He gave a faint smile. 'As I'm sure you've noticed.'

She swallowed. 'I'm sorry about Evanna and Hamish—'

'Why are you sorry? None of it is your fault.' Ryan sat down at her desk and brought Lily's notes up on the computer screen. 'They just can't help themselves. Matchmaking is like eating and breathing to the people of Glenmore.'

'It happens a lot?'

'All the time—although I've pretty much escaped it up until now. That's one of the advantages of being a doctor. There are a limited number of people on this island who technically aren't my patients.'

'I expect they'll back off soon.'

'I wouldn't count on it.' Ryan typed the notes with one finger. 'Do you want a lift to the beach barbecue? I could pick you up on my way past.'

'I haven't even decided if we're going.'

'If you don't go, they'll come and get you. Come. Lexi would enjoy it. All the teenagers go. She seems to have made friends. Whenever I see her, she's smiling.'

'Yes.' Jenna was starting to wonder whether there was something more to her daughter's sudden change of attitude. 'What do you know about a boy called Fraser?'

'Fraser Price?' Ryan stood up. 'He lives near you. Just along the beach. His mum is called Ailsa—she's a single parent. Diabetic. Why are you asking?'

Jenna chewed her lip. 'Lexi seems to like him—'

'And you're worrying that he has unsavoury habits?'

'I'm just worrying generally. In London, Lexi started mixing with the wrong crowd. She made a point of doing all the things she thought would upset me…'

'Why would she want to upset you?'

Jenna hesitated. 'She blames me for not trying to fix my marriage.'

'Did you want to fix it?'

Jenna thought about Clive and the scene in his office that day. *Thought about what she'd learned about her marriage.* 'No. Some things can't be fixed.' She had an urge to qualify that with an explanation, but realised that there was no way she could elaborate without revealing that her husband hadn't found her sexy. Somehow that was too humiliating. She turned away and put a box of dressings back into the cupboard. 'There's nothing to talk about. My marriage ended. It happens to thousands of people every day.'

And thousands of people got on with their lives, as she had done. Picking up the pieces, patching them together again into something different.

'Did you think about buying him out so that you could stay in the house?'

It was a practical question, typically male. 'I'm a nurse, Ryan, not a millionaire. London is expensive. And anyway, I didn't want to stay in that house. It was full of memories I didn't want. I knew if I'd stayed there I'd always be looking back. I wanted to move forward. He offered me a sum of money and I took it.'

'I'm guessing it wasn't a generous sum.' His eyes darkened, and she wondered why he'd be angry about something that wasn't his problem.

'He completely ripped me off.' Only now, after almost a year, could she say it without starting to shake with emotion. 'I was really stupid and naïve, but in my own defence I was in a bit of a state at the time. I was more wrapped up in the emotional than the practical. I shouldn't really have been negotiating a divorce settlement so soon after he'd walked out. There were some mornings when I couldn't bear to drag myself from under the duvet. If it hadn't been for Lexi I wouldn't have bothered. I left it to him to get the valuations. And he took advantage.' She lifted her chin. 'He used his friends—fiddled with the numbers and offered me a sum that was just about plausible. And I took it. So I'm to blame for being a push-over.'

'You weren't a push-over. You were in shock, and I'm guessing you just wanted it to end.'

'I didn't want it dragging on and hurting Lexi. The whole thing was very hard on her.' Jenna rubbed her hands up and down her arms. 'And she was so angry with me.'

He took a slow breath. 'You did a brave thing, coming here. Was it the right thing to do?'

She considered the question. 'Yes. Yes, it was. We're healing.' The discovery warmed her. 'The best thing I did was to get Rebel. Lexi adores him. So do I. And we love living in the cottage. Having the beach on our doorstep is like heaven. And I'm relieved Lexi is happy, although I'm worrying that has something to do with her new friend.'

'I don't think you have to worry about Fraser. He's pretty responsible.'

'Well, if he's the reason Lexi is happy, then I suppose he has my approval.'

Ryan strolled towards the door. His arm brushed against hers and Jenna felt the response shoot right through her body. Seeing the frown touch his forehead, she wondered if he did, too.

'Our receptionist Janet was saying how smoothly everything is running since you arrived. The islanders love you.'

'Everyone has been very kind.' She wondered why she felt compelled to look at him all the time. If he was in the room, she wanted to stare. Every bit of him fascinated her, from his darkened jaw to his thick, lustrous hair. But what really interested her was him. The man.

She wanted to ask why he'd chosen to come to Glenmore, but there was something about him that didn't invite personal questions.

Respecting his privacy, she smiled. 'We'll see you at the barbecue on Saturday.'

'Good.' He watched her for a long moment and she felt that look all the way down to her bones.

'Thanks for seeing Lily.'

He stirred. 'You're welcome.'

The sun was just breaking through the early-morning mist when she walked Rebel early the following day. The garden gate no longer creaked, thanks to a regular dose of oil, and Jenna paused for a moment to admire the pinks and purples in her garden before walking along the sandy path that led through the dunes to the beach. The stretch of sand was deserted and she slipped off her shoes and walked barefoot, loving the feel of the sand between her toes. Rebel bounded ahead, investigating pieces of seaweed and driftwood, tail wagging. Every now and then he raced back to her, sending water and sand flying.

Huge foaming breakers rolled in from the Atlantic, rising high and then exploding onto the beach with a crash and a hiss. Jenna watched as a lone surfer achieved apparently impossible feats in the deadly waves. Admiring his strength and the fluidity of his body, she gave herself a little shake and turned her attention to the beach. After twenty years of not noticing men, suddenly she seemed to do nothing else.

Seeing a pretty shell poking out of the sand, she stooped to pick it up. The pearly white surface peeped from beneath a layer of sand and she carefully brushed it and slipped it into her pocket, thinking of the chunky glass vase in her little bathroom, which was already almost full of her growing collection of shells.

She was pocketing her second shell when Rebel started to bark furiously. He sped across the sand towards the water just as the surfer emerged from the waves, his board under his arm.

Recognising Ryan, Jenna felt her heart bump hard against her chest and she forgot about shells. She should have known it was him from the visceral reaction deep in her stomach. It wasn't men in general she was noticing. It was just one man.

Without thinking, she dragged her fingers through her curls and then recognised the futility of the gesture. She was wearing an old pair of shorts and a cotton tee shirt. Running her fingers through her hair wasn't going to make her presentable. For a moment she regretted not spending a few moments in front of the mirror before leaving her cottage. Thinking of herself doing her morning walk in lipgloss and a pretty top made her smile, and she was still smiling when he ran up to her.

'What's funny?'

'Meeting someone else at this time of the morning.'

He put his surfboard down on the sand. 'It's the best time. I surf most mornings, but I've never seen you out before.' The wetsuit emphasised the width and power of his shoulders and she looked towards the waves, trying to centre herself.

'Normally I'm a little later than this but I couldn't sleep.' Because she'd been thinking about him. And then pushing away those thoughts with rational argument. But now those thoughts were back, swirling round her head, confusing her.

'You couldn't sleep?' His tone was amused. 'Maybe you were excited about the barbecue tomorrow.'

'That must have been it.' As Rebel bounded up to her, she sidestepped, dodging the soaking wet tail-wagging animal. 'Sit. *Sit!*' Ignoring her, Rebel shook himself hard and sprayed them both. 'Oh, you—! Rebel! I'm so sorry.'

'More of a problem for you than me. I'm wearing a wet-suit.' His eyes drifted to her damp tee shirt and lingered. 'Obviously the dog-training is progressing successfully.'

'It's a disaster. He obeyed me that day at Elaine's just to charm me into giving him a home. Since then he's been a nightmare.' Giggling and embarrassed, Jenna grabbed Rebel's collar and glared at him severely. 'Sit! Sit, Rebel. I said sit!'

The dog whimpered, his entire body wagging, and Ryan sighed.

'Sit!'

Rebel sat.

'OK—that's annoying.' Jenna put her hands on her hips. 'I've been working non-stop with him and you just say it once. What do you have that I don't?'

'An air of menace. You're kind and gentle. A dog can sense

you're soft-hearted. Especially a dog like Rebel, who has had his own way for far too long.'

'You think I'm a push-over?'

'I don't see you as tough and ruthless, that's true.'

Her heart was pounding as if she'd run the length of the beach. 'I'll have you know I'm stronger than I look!'

'I didn't say you weren't strong.' The pitch of his voice had changed. 'I know you're strong, Jenna. You've proved your strength over and over again in the last month. You've dragged up your roots and put them down somewhere new. That's never easy.'

His eyes were oceans of blue, waiting to draw her in and drown her.

The want inside her became a desperate craving, and when his arm curled around her waist and he drew her towards him she didn't resist. Her thinking went from clear to clouded, and she waited, deliciously trapped by the inevitability of what was to come. She watched, hypnotised, as he lowered his head to hers. His mouth was warm and skilled, his kiss sending an explosion of light through her brain and fire through her belly.

It should have felt wrong, kissing a man. But it felt right—standing here with his lips against hers and nothing around them but the sound and smell of the sea.

Jenna dug her fingers into the front of his wetsuit, felt the hardness of his body brush against her knuckles. The fire spread, licking its way through her limbs until she was unsteady on her feet, and his grip on her tightened, his mouth more demanding as they kissed hungrily, feasting, exploring, discovering.

Rebel barked.

Ryan lifted his mouth from hers, his reluctance evident in the time he took. Dazed and disorientated, Jenna stared up at him for a moment and then at his mouth.

Now she knew how it felt...

Rebel barked again and she turned her head, trying to focus on the dog.

'What's the matter with you?' Her voice was croaky and Ryan released her.

'People on the beach.' His voice was calm and steady. 'Clearly we're not the only early risers.'

'Obviously not.' She knew she sounded stilted but she had no idea what to say. Were they supposed to talk about it? Or pretend it had never happened? 'I should be getting home. Lexi will be waking up…' Feeling really strange, she lifted a shaking hand to her forehead. The kiss had changed everything. Her world had tilted.

'Jenna—'

'I'll see you tomorrow.'

His gaze was disturbingly acute. 'You'll see me at the surgery today.'

'Yes—yes, of course I will. That's what I meant.' Flustered, she called to Rebel, who was nosing something on the sand, apparently oblivious to the fact that his owner's life had just changed.

Ryan seemed about to say something, but the people on the beach were moving closer and he shook his head in exasperation. 'I've never seen anyone else on this beach at this hour.'

'It's a very pretty place.' Babbling, Jenna backed away. 'You'd better go and have a shower—warm up—you can't do a surgery in your wetsuit—I really ought to be going—' She would have tripped over Rebel if Ryan hadn't shot out a hand and steadied her. 'Thanks. I'll see you later.' Without looking at him, she turned and almost flew over the sand after Rebel, not pausing until she was inside the cottage with the door shut firmly behind her.

'Mum? What's the matter with you?' Yawning, Lexi stood there in tee shirt and knickers.

'I've been—' Kissed, Jenna thought hysterically. Thoroughly, properly, deliciously kissed. '—for a walk. On the beach. With Rebel.'

Lexi threw her an odd look. 'Well, of course with Rebel—who else?'

'No one else. Absolutely no one else.' She needed to shut up before she said something she regretted. 'You're up early.'

'I'm going over to Evanna's to give the children breakfast before I go to the dig. She has that appointment thing today on the mainland so she took the first ferry.'

'Yes, of course. I know. I remember.' Her lips felt warm and tingly, and if she really concentrated she could still conjure up the feel of his mouth against hers. 'I have to take a shower and get ready for work.'

'Are you all right? You look—different.'

She felt different.

Up until today she'd felt as though she was surviving. Now she felt as though she was living.

Everything was different.

CHAPTER SIX

Too dressy.

Too casual.

Too cold—

Jenna threw the contents of her wardrobe onto her bed and stared at it in despair. Was it really that hard to decide what to wear to a beach barbecue? It was so long since she'd been out socially she'd lost her confidence. But she knew that the real reason she couldn't decide what to wear was because Ryan would be there and she wanted to look her best. Without looking as though she'd tried too hard.

Infuriated with herself, she reached for the first skirt she'd tried on, slipped it over her head and picked a simple tee shirt to go with it. The skirt was pretty, but the tee shirt was plain—which meant that the top half of her was underdressed and the bottom half was overdressed.

Looking in the mirror, Jenna scooped up her hair and piled it on top of her head. Then she pulled a face and let it fall loose around her shoulders. She gave a hysterical giggle. Maybe she should wear half of it up and half of it down.

'Mum?'

Hearing Lexi's voice, Jenna jumped guiltily and scooped the discarded clothes from the bed. She was just closing the wardrobe door on the evidence of her indecision when Lexi sauntered into the room.

'Are you ready?'

'Nearly.' Jenna eyed the lipgloss that she'd bought. It was still in its packaging because she hadn't decided whether or not to wear it. 'I just need to do my hair.' Up or down?

'Can I go ahead? I'm meeting Fraser.'

'We'll go together,' Jenna said firmly. With no choice but to leave her hair down, she grabbed a cardigan and made for the stairs. 'I'd like to meet him.'

'We're just mates,' Lexi muttered, sliding her feet into a pair of pretty flip-flops. 'We're not quite at the "meet the parents" stage.'

Jenna picked up her keys and the bowl containing the strawberries. 'This is Glenmore. On an island this size you have no option but to meet the parents. Everyone meets everyone about five times a day.' She wished she hadn't left her hair down. It made her feel wild and unrestrained, and she wanted to feel restrained and together.

'Are you all right, Mum?'

'I'm fine. Why wouldn't I be?'

'I don't know…' Her phone in her hand, Lexi frowned. 'You just seem jumpy. Nervous. You've been acting really weird since yesterday.'

'Nervous? I have no reason to be nervous!'

'All right, calm down. I realise it's a big excitement for you, getting out for an evening. Don't be too embarrassing, will you?'

Jenna locked the door because she hadn't got out of the London habit. 'I'm meant to be the one saying that to you.'

'Going out with your mother would never happen in London. Just promise me that whatever happens you won't dance.'

* * *

Ryan watched her walk across the sand towards him.

She'd left her hair loose, the way she'd worn it on the day she'd arrived on the island.

Feeling the tension spread across his shoulders, he lifted the bottle of beer to his lips, thinking about the kiss. He hadn't intended to kiss her but the temptation had been too great, and now he couldn't get it out of his mind.

He wondered why this woman in particular should have such a powerful effect on him. Not for one moment did he think it was anything to do with her gorgeous curves—he'd met plenty of women with good bodies and none of them had tempted him past the superficial. But Jenna…

Maybe it was her generous smile. Or her air of vulnerability—the way she was so painfully honest about the things that had gone wrong in her life when most people just put up a front. Or the way she put herself last. Either way, she was sneaking under his skin in a way that should have set off warning bells.

If his aim was to protect himself, then lusting after a recently divorced single mother with a teenage daughter was probably the stupidest thing he'd ever done.

She was clearly desperately hurt after her divorce, and any relationship she entered into now would be on the rebound.

But his body wasn't listening to reason and he felt himself harden as he watched her approach. She'd dressed modestly, her summery skirt falling to her ankles, her tee shirt high at the neck. But the Glenmore breeze was designed to mock modesty and it flattened the skirt to her legs, found the slit and blew it gaily until the soft fabric flew into the air, revealing long slim legs and a hint of turquoise that looked like a swimming costume.

Ryan saw her clutch at the skirt and drag it back into position, her face pink as she pinned it down with her hand, defying the wind.

For a girl who was fresh out of the city, there was nothing city-slick about her. She was carrying a large flowery bag over one shoulder and she looked slightly uncertain—as if she wasn't used to large gatherings.

He was fully aware that she'd avoided him the day before at the surgery, going to great lengths to make sure they didn't bump into one another. Seeing her now, the emotion he felt was like a punch in the gut. He was attracted to her in a way he hadn't been attracted to a woman in years.

'She'd be perfect for you.' Evanna's voice came from behind him and he turned, keeping his expression neutral.

'You never give up, do you?'

'Not when I think something is worth the effort.' Evanna replied. 'Don't be angry with me.'

'Then don't interfere.'

'I'm helping.'

'Do you think I need help?'

'When you first came here, yes. You were so angry,' she said softly. 'I used to hear you sawing wood and banging nails. You swung that hammer as if you hoped someone's head was underneath it.'

Ryan breathed out slowly. 'I hadn't realised anyone witnessed that—'

'I came down to the lighthouse from time to time, trying to pluck up courage to ask you to join us for supper, but whenever I saw you your expression was so black and you were so dark and scary I lost my nerve.'

'I didn't know.' He'd been aware of nothing, he realised, but his own pain. 'So, have you become braver or am I less scary?'

Her smile was wise and gentle. 'You banged in a lot of nails.'

'I guess I did.' He respected the fact that she hadn't pushed him for the reason. She'd never pushed him. Just offered unconditional friendship. Humbled once again by the generosity of the islanders, he frowned. 'Evanna—'

'Just promise me that if I back off you won't let her slip through your fingers.'

'Life doesn't always come as neatly wrapped as you seem to think.'

'It takes work to wrap something neatly.' She stood on tiptoe and kissed his cheek. 'You've been here for two years. It's enough. Don't let the past mess up the future, Ryan.'

'Is that what I'm doing?'

'I don't know. Are you?'

Ryan thought about the kiss on the beach and the way he felt about Jenna. 'No,' he said. 'I'm not.'

He knew Jenna was nothing like Connie. And maybe that was one of the reasons he was so attracted to her.

'Is my wife sorting out your love-life?' Logan strolled over to them, Charlie on his shoulders.

'Who? Me?' Her expression innocent, Evanna picked up a bowl of green salad. 'Can you put this on the table, please? Next to the tomato salsa. I'm going to meet Jenna and make her feel welcome. She looks nervous. I'm sure she feels a bit daunted by the crowd.'

Ryan was willing to bet that her nerves had nothing to do with the crowd and everything to do with the kiss they'd shared. He'd flustered her.

He gave a faint smile. And he was looking forward to flustering her again.

'What does tomato salsa look like?' Logan's expression was comical as he steadied Charlie with one hand and took the salad from Evanna with the other. 'Is that the mushy red stuff?' Leaning forward, he kissed her swiftly on the mouth and Evanna sighed and kissed him back.

Watching them together, seeing the soft looks and the way

they touched, Ryan felt a stab of something sharp stab his gut and recognised it as envy.

Even in the early days, his relationship with Connie had never been like that. They'd never achieved that level of closeness. They'd been a disaster waiting to happen. If he hadn't been so absorbed by his career maybe he would have picked up on the signs. Or maybe not. Connie had played her part well.

Lifting the bottle to his lips again, he watched as Evanna sprinted across the sand to meet Jenna—watched as she gave her a spontaneous hug and gestured with her hands, clearly telling her some anecdote. He had no idea what she was saying, but it had Jenna laughing, and her laugh was so honest and genuine that Ryan felt every muscle in his body tighten. He doubted Jenna had ever manipulated a man in her life. She wouldn't know how—and anyway, such behaviour would go against her moral code.

As they approached he could hear Evanna admiring Jenna's skirt, the conversation light and distinctly female in tone and content. Jenna responded in kind, handing over a bowl of rosy-red strawberries and chatting with the group gathered around the food table as if she'd been born and raised on the island.

It took less than a few seconds for him to realise that she was looking at everyone but him. Talking to everyone but him.

Aware of Evanna's puzzled expression, Ryan sighed. If he didn't do something, the situation would be taken out of his hands.

He strolled over to Jenna, who was busily sorting food on the long trestle table, carefully ignoring him.

'Where's Rebel?' Ryan felt the ripple of tension pass through her body and she carefully put down the bowl she was holding.

'Lexi has him on a lead. I thought all those sausages and

steaks on the barbecue might prove too much of a temptation for a dog with a behavioural problem.'

'You could be right.' He noticed that her cheeks had turned a soft shade of pink and that she was making a point of not looking at his mouth.

No, he thought to himself. Jenna would never play games or manipulate. She was honest and genuine—surprisingly unsophisticated for a woman in her thirties.

Lexi strolled up to the table, earphones hanging from her ears, her iPod tucked into the back pocket of her jeans, her head bobbing to the rhythm. She was hanging on to Rebel, who was straining to run in the opposite direction. 'Hi, Ryan.'

Jenna looked embarrassed. 'Dr McKinley—'

'Ryan is fine.' He bent down to make a fuss of Rebel, who looked him in the eye and immediately sat.

'Mum, did you see that? He sat without even being told!' Lexi gaped at the dog. 'Given that he's behaving, you can hold him. I'm going to see my friends.' Without waiting for a reply, she pushed the lead into her mother's hand, took the cola Evanna was offering her with a smile of thanks and strolled across the sand to join a group of teenagers who were chatting together.

'I have a feeling it was a mistake to bring a dog—this particular dog, anyway—to a barbecue.' Gripping the lead until her knuckles were white, Jenna was still concentrating on Rebel. 'Hopefully your influence will prevail and he'll behave.'

'I think you may have an exaggerated idea of my power.'

'I hope not or I'm about to be seriously embarrassed.'

'I think you're already embarrassed.' Ryan spoke quietly, so that he couldn't be overheard by the people milling close to them. Keeping his eyes on her face, he watched her reaction. 'And there's no need to be. Just as there was no need to run off yesterday morning and avoid me all day in surgery.'

She took a deep breath, her gaze fixed on Rebel. Then she glanced sideways and checked no one was listening. Finally, she looked at him. 'I haven't kissed, or been kissed, for a long time.'

'I know.' He watched as the tension rippled down her spine.

'I wasn't sure how I felt about it— I mean—' Her colour deepened. 'Obviously I know how I felt, but I wasn't sure what it all meant. I hadn't expected—'

'Neither had I.' Suddenly he regretted starting this conversation in such a public place. He should have dragged her somewhere private where he could have matched actions with words.

'Everyone is trying to pair us up.'

'I know that, too.'

'Doesn't that put you off?'

'I didn't kiss you because it was what other people wanted, Jenna. I kissed you because it was what I wanted.' And he still wanted it, he realised. Badly. Maybe two years of self-imposed isolation had intensified his feelings, but he had a feeling that it was something more than that.

'Is everyone watching us now?'

'Ignore them. What can I get you to drink?'

'What are you drinking?'

'Ginger beer,' he said dryly, 'but I'm on call. How about a glass of wine?'

She hesitated for a moment, and then something sparked in her eyes. 'Actually, I'd like a beer,' she said firmly. 'From the bottle. Don't bother with a glass.'

Hiding his surprise, Ryan took a bottle of ice-cold beer from the cooler and handed it to her. Maybe he didn't know her as well as he thought. She certainly didn't strike him as a woman who drank beer from a bottle.

'Thanks. Cheers.' Her grin was that of a defiant child, and

she took a large mouthful and proceeded to spill half of it down her front. 'Oh, for goodness' sake!'

Struggling to keep a straight face, Ryan rescued her beer before she spilt the rest of it. 'You haven't done that before, have you?'

Pulling a face, she tugged her wet tee shirt away from her chest. 'What a mess! Everyone is going to think I'm an alcoholic.'

'Alcoholics generally manage to get the alcohol into their mouths, Jenna. I gather your husband was more of a wine in a glass sort of guy?' Ryan put their drinks down on the table and grabbed a handful of paper napkins.

'How do you know what my husband drank?'

'It's a wild guess, based on the fact you seem to be doing the opposite of everything you ever did with him.' He pressed the napkins against the damp patch, feeling the swell of her breasts under his fingers.

'Am I?'

'You got yourself a dog, you're drinking beer from the bottle for the first time in your life, you eat fish three times a week and you never used to eat fish—' He could have added that she'd kissed a man who wasn't her husband, but he decided it was better to leave that alone for now.

'How do you know how often I eat fish?'

'Hamish mentioned it.'

Her gasp was an astonished squeak. 'The islanders discuss my diet?'

'The islanders discuss everything. You should know that by now.'

'In that case you should probably let me mop up my own wet tee shirt.' She snatched the napkins from his hands, their fingers brushing. 'If we're trying to kill the gossip, I don't think you should be doing that.'

'Do you care about the gossip?'

'I care about Lexi hearing the gossip.'

'Ah—' He noticed the pulse beating in her throat and knew she felt the attraction as strongly as he did. He retrieved his bottle from the table. 'Can I get you something different to drink?'

'Absolutely not.' There was humour in her eyes. And determination. 'I'm not a quitter. If you can drink from the bottle without dribbling, then so can I.' She lifted the bottle carefully to her lips and this time didn't spill a drop.

His body throbbing, Ryan stood close to her. 'You were late. I thought you weren't coming.'

'I was working in the garden, and then Lexi had to change her outfit four times. And I wasn't sure if it was a good idea…' She paused, staring at the label on the bottle. 'This stuff is disgusting.'

'It's an acquired taste. And now?'

'I still don't know if it's a good idea. I've never been so confused in my life.'

Evanna was back at the table, rearranging salads and plates. Ryan saw the happy smile on her lips and ground his teeth. Suddenly he felt protective—Jenna ought to be able to get out and spread her wings socially without being made to feel that everything she did was being analysed and gossiped about.

He was about to intervene when Kirsty, Evanna's six-year-old daughter, sprinted across the sand and launched herself at Lexi. 'Lex—Lex, I want to show you my swimming.'

Ryan watched as the teenager stooped to pick the little girl up. 'Wow. Lucky me. I can't wait to see.' She was a million miles from the moody, sullen teenager who had dragged her feet off the ferry a month before.

The little girl's smile spread right across her face as she bounced in Lexi's arms. 'I can swim without armbands.'

'Really? That's cool.'

'Watch me.'

'Please would you watch me.' Evanna tipped dressing from a jug onto a bowl of salad leaves. 'Manners, Kirsty.'

'Pleeeease—'

Lexi grinned. 'Sure. But don't splash me. It took me ages to get my hair straight.' Her face suddenly turned scarlet, and Ryan glanced round and saw Fraser strolling across the sand towards them, a lopsided grin on his face.

'Hey, if it isn't the city girl.' He wore his board shorts low on his hips and carried a football under his arm. 'We were wondering when you were going to get here. You going to swim for us, Kirst?'

Ryan felt Jenna tense beside him and saw Lexi's shoulders stiffen.

'This is my mum—' She waved a hand awkwardly towards Jenna. 'This is Fraser.'

'Hi, Fraser.' Jenna's voice was friendly. 'Nice to meet you.'

'Hi, Mrs Richards.' With an easy smile Fraser pushed his sun-bleached hair out of his eyes and kicked the football towards his friends. 'Evanna, is it OK if we take Kirsty swimming?'

'You'd be doing me a favour.' Evanna didn't hesitate. 'Don't let her get her own way too often.'

With Kirsty still in her arms, Lexi slid off her shoes and walked barefoot across the sand with Fraser. Close, but not touching.

Watching Jenna sink her teeth into her lower lip, Ryan sighed. 'Relax.'

'Lexi isn't old enough to have responsibility for Kirsty. I'd better follow them.'

He wondered who she was worried about—Kirsty or her own daughter.

'She'll be fine,' Evanna said calmly. 'Fraser is very responsible. The beach here is pretty safe, and Ryan can keep an eye on them—he's the strongest swimmer round here.' Smiling, she gave Ryan a little push. 'Go on. You're on lifeguard duty.'

Ryan glanced at Logan, who was expertly flipping steaks on the barbecue.

'Your wife is a bully.'

'I know. I love a strong, forceful woman, don't you?'

It was a flippant remark, with no hidden meaning, but Ryan felt his jaw tighten as he considered the question. He liked a woman to be independent, yes. Strong? He had no problem with strong—he knew from experience that life dealt more blows than a boxer, so strong was probably good. But forceful? Was forceful a euphemism for selfish and single-minded? For doing absolutely what you wanted to do with no thought for anyone else? If so, then the answer was no—he didn't like forceful women.

The question killed his mood, and he was aware that Jenna was looking at him with concern in her eyes.

'I'll keep you company. You made me buy a swimming costume so I might as well use it.' She put her drink down. 'If you're really on lifeguard duty then you can come in the water with me. It's so long since I swam I'm probably going to need my own personal lifeguard.'

Wanting to escape his thoughts, Ryan put his drink down next to hers. 'All right.'

They walked across the sand and she quickened her pace to keep up with him.

'You seem upset.' She kept walking. 'Is something wrong?'

Startled by her insight, Ryan frowned, his eyes on the sea, where Lexi was dangling a shrieking Kirsty in the water. 'What could be wrong?'

'I don't know. I just thought—you seem very tense all of a sudden. I thought maybe you needed some space.' She took a deep breath. 'If you want to talk to someone, you can talk to me.'

Ryan turned his head in astonishment and she bit her lip, her smile faltering.

'I know, I know—men don't like to talk about their problems. But you've listened to me often enough over the past month—I just want you to know that the friendship works both ways.'

'Friendship?' He realised that he was looking at her mouth again, and the strange thing was he didn't need to look. He'd memorised everything about it, from the way her lips curved to the soft pink colour. 'Is that what we have?'

'Of course. I mean, I hope so. You've certainly been a friend to me since I arrived here.'

He stared down into her eyes and something shimmered between them. Something powerful. So powerful that if they hadn't been standing in the middle of a crowded beach with the entire population of Glenmore watching he would have kissed her again.

Unsettled by his own feelings, Ryan shifted his gaze back to the sea. 'I don't have any problems.' His tone was rougher than he'd intended and he heard her sigh.

'You've known me long enough to kiss me, Ryan,' she said quietly. 'Hopefully you've also known me long enough to trust me.'

He was about to say that it was nothing to do with trust, but he was too late. She was already walking ahead, her hair tumbling down her back, sand dusting her toes.

Wondering whether he'd hurt her feelings, Ryan followed her to the water's edge, relieved when she smiled at him.

Clearly Jenna Richards didn't sulk. Nor did she bear grudges.

Fraser and Lexi were either side of Kirsty, holding her hands and swinging her over the waves while she squealed with delight. All of them were laughing.

Ryan was about to speak when he caught the wistful expression on Jenna's face. Her eyes were on Kirsty, and she had that look on her face that women sometimes had when they stared into prams.

He wondered again why she'd only had one child when she was clearly a born mother. Patient, caring, and unfailingly loving.

Pain shafted through him like a lightning bolt and he watched as she lifted her skirt slightly and tentatively allowed the waves to lick her feet. With a soft gasp of shock she jumped back, her eyes shining with laughter as she looked at him.

'It's freezing! Forget swimming. I'll definitely turn to ice and drown if I go in there!'

Forcing aside his dark thoughts, Ryan strode into the waves. 'No way are you using that pathetic excuse.' He took her hand and pulled her deeper. 'You get used to it after a while.'

'After losing how many limbs to frostbite?' Still holding his hand, she lifted her skirt above her knees with her free hand. 'I'm not going to get used to this. I'm losing all sensation in my feet.'

'What are you complaining about?' He tightened his grip on her hand. 'This is a warm evening on Glenmore.'

'The evening may be warm, but someone has forgotten to tell the sea it's summer. My feet are aching they're so cold.' Her laughter was infectious, and Ryan found that he was laughing, too.

Laughing with a woman. That was something he hadn't done for a long time.

He intercepted Lexi's shocked stare and his laughter faded. She glanced between him and her mother, suspicion in her eyes.

Jenna was still laughing as she picked her way through the waves, apparently unaware of her daughter's frozen features.

'We wouldn't be doing this in London, would we, Lex?'

'Pull your skirt down, Mum,' Lexi hissed, and Ryan watched as Jenna suddenly went from being natural to self-conscious. The colour flooded into her cheeks and she released the skirt. Instantly the hem trailed in the water. Flustered, she lifted it again.

'Lexi, watch me, watch me—' Kirsty bounced in the water, but Lexi stepped closer to her mother and dumped the child in Jenna's arms.

'Here you are, Mum. You take her. You're good with kids. Probably because you're old and motherly.'

Ryan was about to laugh at the joke when he realised that no one was laughing.

Old and motherly?

Was that how Lexi saw her mother? Was that how Jenna saw herself?

How old was she? Thirty-two? Thirty-three? She could have passed for ten years younger than that. She had a fresh, natural appeal that he found incredibly sexy. And, yes, she was different from Connie.

His jaw hardened. Connie wouldn't have paddled in the sea—nor would she have appeared in public with a face free of make-up. And he couldn't remember a time when she'd giggled. But that might have been because Connie wasn't spontaneous. She was a woman with a plan and nothing was going to stand in her way. Certainly not their marriage.

'I can't believe you're brave enough to swim!' Jenna was beaming at Kirsty, as if the child had done something incredibly clever. 'I'm so cold I can barely stand in the water, let alone swim.' She sneaked a glance after her daughter, who was walking away from them, Fraser by her side.

'I swim with my daddy.' Keen to demonstrate her skills, Kirsty wriggled in Jenna's arms and plunged back into the water, thrashing her arms and kicking her legs.

Drenched and shivering, Jenna laughed. 'Kirsty, that's fantastic. I couldn't swim like that at your age. And never in sea this cold.' The water had glued the skirt to her legs and Logan looked away, forcing himself to concentrate on something other than the shape of her body.

A crowd of locals were playing volleyball, and he could see Evanna handing out plates of food. 'I smell barbecue,' he said mildly. 'We should probably go and eat something. Sausages, Kirsty?'

The child immediately held out her arms to Jenna, who scooped her out of the water and cuddled her, ignoring the damp limbs and soaking costume.

Ryan felt his body tighten as he watched her with the child.

It was such a painful moment that when the phone in his pocket buzzed he was grateful for the excuse to walk away.

'I'm on call. I'd better take this.' He strode out of the water and drew the phone from his pocket. Was he ever going to be able to look at a mother and child without feeling that degree of agony? He answered his phone with a violent stab of his finger. 'McKinley.' It took him less than five seconds to get the gist of the conversation. 'I'll be right there.' Even as he dropped the phone into this pocket, he was running.

Cuddling a soaking wet Kirsty, Jenna watched as Ryan took off across the beach. It was obvious that there was some sort of emergency. Knowing he'd probably need help, she waded out of the water as fast as her soaked skirt and the bouncing child would allow. Once on the sand, she put the little girl down and ran, holding the child's hand.

'Let's see how fast we can reach Mummy.' At least an emergency might stop her thinking about that kiss. Nothing else had worked so far.

They reached Evanna as she was handing Ryan a black bag.

'What's wrong?' Jenna handed Kirsty over to her mother. 'Is it an emergency?'

Ryan glanced at her briefly. 'Ben who runs the Stag's Head has a tourist who has collapsed. Logan—' He raised his voice. 'I'm going to the pub. Keep your phone switched on.'

'I'll come with you.' Jenna glanced across at Evanna. 'Lexi's walked off with Fraser—will you keep an eye on her for me?'

'Of course.' Looking worried, Evanna held toddler Charlie on her hip and a serving spoon in her other hand. 'I hope it turns out to be nothing. We'll hold the fort here, but if you need reinforcements call.'

Hampered by her wet skirt, Jenna sprinted after Logan and it was only when her feet touched tarmac that she realised she'd left her shoes back at the barbecue. 'Ouch!' Stupid, stupid. 'I left my shoes—'

The next minute she was scooped off the ground and Logan was carrying her across the road.

She gave a gasp of shock. 'Put me down! I weigh a ton!'

'You don't weigh anything, and it's good for my ego to carry a helpless woman occasionally.' He was still jogging, and she realised how fit he must be.

'I'm not helpless, just shoeless.'

'Cinderella.' With a brief smile, he lowered her to the pavement and strode into the pub.

Jenna followed, feeling ridiculous in a wet skirt and without shoes. But all self-consciousness faded as she saw the man lying on the floor. His lips and eyes were puffy, his breathing was laboured and noisy, and the woman next to him was shaking his shoulder and crying.

'Pete? Pete?'

'What happened?' Ryan was down on the floor beside the patient, checking his airway. His fingers moved swiftly and skilfully, checking, eliminating, searching for clues.

'One moment he was eating his supper,' the landlord said, 'and then he crashed down on the floor, holding his throat.'

'He said he felt funny,' his wife sobbed. 'He had a strange feeling in his throat. All of a sudden. I've no idea why. We've been on the beach all afternoon and he was fine. Never said a thing about feeling ill or anything.'

'Anaphylactic shock.' Ryan's mouth was grim and Jenna dropped to her knees beside him.

'Is he allergic to anything?' She glanced at the man's wife. 'Nuts? Could he have been stung? Wasp?'

The woman's eyes were wild with panic. 'I don't think he was stung and he's not allergic to anything. He's fine with nuts, all that sort of stuff—is he going to die?'

Ryan had his hand in his bag. 'He's not going to die. Ben, call the air ambulance and fetch me that oxygen you keep round the back.' Icy calm, he jabbed an injection of adrenaline into the man's thigh, working with astonishing speed. 'Pete? Can you hear me? I'm Dr McKinley.'

Catching a glimpse of the role he'd played in a previous life, Jenna switched her focus back to the man's wife. 'What were you eating?' She looked at the table. 'Fish pie?'

'Yes. But he'd only had a few mouthfuls.'

'Are there prawns in that fish pie?'

'Yes.' Ben was back with the oxygen. 'But they were fresh this morning.'

'I'm not suggesting food poisoning,' Jenna said quickly, 'but maybe shellfish allergy?'

Covering the man's mouth and nose with the oxygen mask, Ryan looked at her for a moment, his eyes narrowed. Then he nodded. 'Shellfish. That's possible. That would explain it.' He adjusted the flow of oxygen. 'I'll give him five minutes and then give him another shot of epinephrine. Can you find it?'

Jenna delved in his bag and found the other drugs they were likely to need.

'Shellfish allergy?' The wife looked at them in horror. 'But—this isn't the first time he's eaten shellfish—can you just develop an allergy like that? Out of nowhere?'

'Jenna, can you squeeze his arm for me? I want to get a line in.'

'Actually, yes.' Jenna spoke to the woman as she handed Ryan a sterile cannula and then watched as he searched for a vein. 'Some adults do develop an allergy to something that hasn't harmed them before.'

'The body just decides it doesn't like it?'

'The body sees it as an invader,' Jenna explained, blinking at the speed with which Ryan obtained IV access. Her fingers over his, she taped down the cannula so that it wouldn't be dislodged, the movements routine and familiar. 'It basically overreacts and produces chemicals and antibodies. Dr McKinley has just given an injection to counter that reaction.'

The woman's face was paper-white. 'Is it going to work?'

'I hope so. This is quite a severe reaction, so I'm giving him another dose.' Ryan took the syringe from Jenna. 'And I'm going to give him some antihistamine and hydrocortisone.'

'Air ambulance is on its way,' Ben said, and at that moment Jenna noticed something. Leaning forward, she lifted the man's tee shirt so that she could get a better look.

'He has a rash, Ryan.'

'I think it's safe to assume we're dealing with a shellfish allergy—when you get to the mainland they'll observe him overnight and then make an appointment for you to see an allergy consultant. Where do you live?'

'We're from London. We're just here for a holiday. We have another week to go.' The woman was staring at her husband's chest in disbelief. 'I've never seen a rash come on like that.'

'It's all part of the reaction,' Jenna said quietly. 'The drugs will help.'

'How long do you think they'll keep him in hospital?'

'With any luck they'll let you go tomorrow and you can get on with your holiday—avoiding shellfish.' Ryan examined the rash carefully. 'The hospital should refer you for allergy testing so you can be sure what you're dealing with. You may need to carry an Epipen.' He checked the man's pulse again. 'His breathing is improving. That last injection seems to have done the trick.'

'Thank goodness—' The woman slumped slightly and Jenna slipped her arm round her.

'You poor thing. Are you on your own here? Do you have any friends or family with you?' She tried to imagine what it must be like going through this on holiday, far from home, with no support.

'My sister and her husband, but they've gone to the beach barbecue.'

'I'll contact them for you,' Ben said immediately, taking the details and sending one of the locals down to the beach to locate the woman's family.

Once again the islanders impressed Jenna, working together to solve the problem in a way that would never really happen in a big city.

By the time the air ambulance arrived the man had regained consciousness and the woman had been reunited with her family. Jenna listened as Ryan exchanged information with the paramedics and masterminded the man's transfer. As the helicopter lifted off for the short trip to the mainland, she turned to him.

His face was tanned from the sun and the wind, his dark hair a surprising contrast to his ice-blue eyes.

Trapped by his gaze, Jenna stood still, inexplicably drawn to him. She forgot about the small stones pressing into her bare feet; she forgot that she was confused about her feelings.

She forgot everything except the astonishing bolt of chemistry that pulled her towards Ryan.

She wanted to kiss him again.

She wanted to kiss him now.

Feeling like a teenager on her first date, she leaned towards him, melting like chocolate on a hot day. His hands came down on her shoulders and she heard the harshness of his breathing.

Yes, now, she thought dreamily, feeling the strength of his fingers—

'Mum!'

The voice of a real teenager carried across the beach, and Jenna jumped as if she'd been shot as she recognised Lexi's appalled tones. For a moment she stared into Ryan's eyes, and then she turned her head and saw her daughter staring at her in undisguised horror.

'What are you doing?'

Her heart pounding and her mouth dry, Jenna was grateful for the distance, which ensured that at least her daughter couldn't see her scarlet cheeks.

What *was* she doing?

She was a divorced mother of thirty-three and she'd been on the verge of kissing a man with virtually all the islanders watching.

'We probably ought to get back to the barbecue…' Ryan's tone was level and she nodded, feeling numb.

'Yes. Absolutely.' If Lexi hadn't shouted she would have put her arms around his neck and kissed him.

And what would that have done for her relationship with her daughter, let alone her relationship with Ryan?

This was her new life and she'd almost blown it. If Lexi hadn't called out to her she would have risked everything. And all for what? A kiss?

'If they've eaten all the food, I'll kill someone.' Apparently suffering none of her torment, Ryan turned towards the steps that led down to the sand, as relaxed as if they'd been having a conversation about the weather. 'How are things, Jim?'

Jim?

It took Jenna a moment to realise that the ferryman was standing by the steps, chatting to another islander. Had he been that close all the time? There could have been a fire, a flood and a hurricane, and all she would have noticed was Ryan.

'Another life saved, Doc.' Grinning, Jim scratched the back of his neck and looked up at the sky, where the helicopter was now no more than a tiny dot. 'Another good holiday experience on Glenmore. They'll be coming back. I overheard someone saying on the ferry this morning that they'd booked a short break here just so that they could ask a doctor about a skin rash, because you lot always know what you're doing.'

Ryan rolled his eyes. 'I'll mention it to Logan. We obviously need to make more of an effort to be useless.'

Jenna produced a smile, pretending to listen, wondering whether she could just slink onto the ferry and take the first sailing back to the mainland in the morning. Maybe distance would make her forget the kiss, because nothing else was working—not even an emergency.

Lexi was waiting for them at the bottom of the steps. 'Mum? What were you doing?'

'She was debriefing with Dr McKinley,' Evanna said smoothly, and Jenna jumped with shock because she hadn't seen Evanna standing next to her daughter. Last time she'd looked Evanna had been serving sausages and salad. But somehow the other woman had materialised at the foot of the steps, Charlie in her arms. 'I gather everything went smoothly, Jenna? Rapid response from the air ambulance? Did things go according to plan?'

Grateful as she was for Evanna's focus on the professional, Jenna didn't manage to respond.

Fortunately Ryan took over. 'Things don't always go according to plan,' he said softly, 'but that's life, isn't it? Ideally I would have liked to lose the audience, but you can't choose where these things happen.'

Jenna couldn't work out whether he was talking about the medical emergency or the fact she'd almost kissed him. They'd had an audience for both. and she was painfully aware that she'd embarrassed him as much as herself. These were his friends. His colleagues. No doubt he'd be on the receiving end of suggestive remarks for the rest of the summer. Yes, he'd kissed her on the beach, but that had been early in the morning with no one watching.

Because Lexi was still looking at her suspiciously, Jenna forced herself to join in the discussion. 'I—it was a bit unexpected. I'm not used to dealing with emergencies.' And she wasn't used to being attracted to a man. She'd behaved like a crazed, desperate woman.

'From what I've heard you were fantastic—a real Glenmore nurse.' Evanna was generous with her praise. 'We're expected to be able to turn our hands to pretty much anything. People are already singing your praises all over the island.' She tucked her hand through Jenna's arm, leading her back across the beach as if they'd been friends for ever. 'Word travels fast in this place. How are your feet?'

Jenna glanced down and realised that she'd forgotten she wasn't wearing shoes. 'Sore. I need to find my sandals.' Her face was burning and she didn't dare look round to see where Ryan was. Hiding, probably—afraid of the desperate divorcee who had tried to attack him. As for Lexi, she still wasn't smiling, but the scowl had left her features. Which presumably meant that Evanna's explanation had satisfied her.

'Your Lexi is so brilliant with the children.' Evanna led her back to the food and heaped potato salad on a plate. 'Logan—find something delicious for Jenna. She's earned it.'

Jenna accepted the food, even though the last thing she felt like was eating. She just wanted to go home and work out what she was going to say to Ryan next time she saw him on his own.

She had to apologise. She had to explain that she had absolutely no idea what had happened to her. Yes, she'd got a dog, she ate fish three times a week and she'd drunk beer from a bottle, but kissing a man in public…

Lexi flicked her hair away from her face. 'I'm off to play volleyball.' With a final glance in her direction, her daughter sauntered off across the sand towards Fraser, who was laughing with a friend, a can of cola in his hand. 'See you later.'

Jenna wanted to leave, but she knew that would draw attention to herself, and she'd already attracted far too much attention for one evening. Even without turning her head she was painfully aware of Ryan talking to Logan, discussing the air ambulance.

She wondered whether she should request that the air ambulance come back for her when they'd finished. She felt as though she needed it.

'Have a drink.' Clearly reading her mind, Evanna pushed a large glass of wine into her hand. 'And don't look so worried. Everything is fine. You and Ryan were a great team.'

Jenna managed a smile, but all she could think was, *Why am I feeling like this?*

She had to forget him. She had to forget that kiss.

Thank goodness tomorrow was Sunday and she didn't have to work. She had a whole day to talk some sense into herself.

CHAPTER SEVEN

10 reasons why I shouldn't fall in love with Ryan:
I've been divorced less than a year
I am too old
I'm ordinary and he is a sex god
Being with him puts me off my food
I have Lexi to think of
I need to act my age
I have to work with the man
He'll hurt me
I'm not his type

'MUM?'

Jenna dropped the pen before number ten and flipped the envelope over. 'I'm in the kitchen. You're up early.' Too early. Deciding that she couldn't hide the envelope without looking suspicious, Jenna slammed her mug of tea on it and smiled brightly. 'I was expecting you to sleep in.'

'I was hungry, and anyway I'm meeting the gang.' Yawning, Lexi tipped cereal into a bowl and added milk. 'You're up early, too.'

'I had things to do.' Like making a list of reasons why she shouldn't be thinking of Ryan.

Her head throbbing and her eyelids burning from lack of sleep, Jenna stood up and filled the kettle, bracing herself for the awkward questions she'd been dreading all night. 'You normally want to lie in bed.'

'That's only during term time, when there's nothing to get up for except boring old school.' Lexi frowned at her and then eyed the mug on the envelope. 'Why are you making tea when you haven't drunk the last one?'

Jenna stared in horror at the mug on the table.

Because she wasn't concentrating.

She'd been thinking about the kiss again.

Exasperated with herself, she picked up the half-full mug and scrunched the envelope in her hand. 'This one is nearly cold. And anyway, I thought you might like one.'

Lexi gaped at her. 'I don't drink tea. And why are you hiding that envelope? Is it a letter from Dad or something?'

'It's nothing—I mean—' Jenna stammered. 'I wrote a phone number on it—for a plumber—that tap is still leaking—'

Lexi's eyes drifted to the tap, which stubbornly refused to emit even a drop of water. 'So if there's a number on it, why did you just scrunch it up?'

'I only remembered about the number after I scrunched it up.'

Lexi shrugged, as if her mother's strange behaviour was so unfathomable it didn't bear thinking about. 'I won't be back for lunch. I'm meeting Fraser and a bunch of his friends up at the castle ruins at nine. We're making a day of it.'

'It's Sunday. Archaeology club isn't until tomorrow.'

'Not officially, but the chief archaeologist guy is going to show us the dungeons and stuff. Really cool.'

'Oh.' Still clutching the envelope, Jenna sat back down at the table, relieved that there wasn't going to be an inquisition about the night before. 'I was going to suggest we made a picnic and went for a walk on the cliffs, but if you're meeting your friends—well, that's great.'

Lexi pushed her bowl away and stood up. 'Do I look OK?'

Jenna scanned the pretty strap top vacantly, thinking that the blue reminded her of Ryan's eyes in the seconds before he'd kissed her on the beach. Had she ever felt this way about Clive? Was it just that she'd forgotten? And how did Ryan feel about her?

'Mum? What do you think?'

'I think he's a grown man and he knows what he's doing.'

'What?' Lexi stared at her. 'He's fifteen. Same age as me.'

Jenna turned scarlet. 'That's what I mean. He's almost a man. And I'm sure he's responsible.'

'But I didn't ask you—' Lexi shook her head in frustration. 'What *is* wrong with you this morning? Mum, are you OK?'

No, Jenna thought weakly. She definitely wasn't. 'Of course I'm OK. Why wouldn't I be? I'm great. Fine. I'm good. Really happy. Looking forward to a day off.'

Lexi backed away, hands raised. 'All right, all right. No need to go overboard—I was just asking. You look like you're having a breakdown or something.'

'No. No breakdown.' Her voice high pitched, Jenna pinned a smile on her face. She was good at this bit. Feel one emotion, show another. She'd done it repeatedly after her marriage had fallen apart. Misery on the inside, smile on the outside. Only in this case it was crazy lust-filled woman on the inside, respectable mother on the outside. 'Have a really, really nice day, Lexi. I'm glad you've made friends so quickly.'

Lexi narrowed her eyes suspiciously. 'What? No lecture? No "Don't go too near the edge or speak to strangers"? No "Sex is for two people who love each other and are old enough to understand the commitment"? Are you sure you're OK?'

Back to thinking about Ryan, Jenna barely heard her. 'I thought you wanted me to worry less.'

'Yes, but I didn't exactly expect you to manage it!'

'Well, you can relax. I haven't actually stopped worrying—I've just stopped talking about it.' Still clutching the envelope, Jenna stood up and made herself another cup of tea. 'I've brought you up with the right values—it's time I trusted you. Time I gave you more independence and freedom to make your own mistakes.'

'Mum, are you feeling all right?'

No. No, she wasn't feeling all right.

She was feeling very confused. She was thinking about nothing but sex and that just wasn't her, was it? Had Clive's brutal betrayal left her so wounded and insecure that she needed affirmation that she was still an attractive woman? Or was it something to do with wanting what you couldn't have?

Lexi folded her arms. 'So you're perfectly OK if I just spend the day up at the castle, taking drugs and making out with Fraser?'

'That's fine.' Thinking of the way Ryan's body had felt against hers, Jenna stared blindly out of the kitchen window. 'Have a nice time.'

'OK, this is spooky. I just told you I'm going to use drugs and make out and you want me to have a *nice time*?'

Had she really said that? 'I know you wouldn't do that.' Jenna mindlessly tidied the kitchen. 'You're too sensible. You're always telling me you're going to have a career before children.'

'Sex doesn't have to end in children, Mum.' Lexi's voice was dry as she picked up her phone and her iPod and walked towards the door. 'One day, when you're old enough, I'll explain it all to you. In the meantime I'll leave you to your incoherent ramblings. Oh, and you might want to remove the teabags from the washing machine—you'll be looking for them later.'

She'd put the teabags in the washing machine?

Jenna extracted them, her cheeks pink, her brain too fuddled to form an appropriate response. 'Have fun. Don't forget your key.'

'You're acting so weird.' Lexi slipped it into her pocket, staring at her mother as if she were an alien. 'You know—last night, for a moment, I really thought—'

Jenna's breathing stopped. 'What did you think?'

'I thought that you—' Lexi broke off and shrugged. 'Never mind. Crazy idea, and anyway I was wrong. Thank goodness. What are you planning to do today?'

Chew over everything that had happened the night before; try not to spend the day thinking of Ryan; remind herself that she was too old to have crushes on men— 'Housework,' Jenna muttered, staring blindly at the pile of unwashed plates that were waiting to be stacked in the dishwasher. 'Catch up on a few things. The laundry basket is overflowing, and I need to weed the herbaceous border.' It all sounded like a boring day to her, but her answer seemed to satisfy Lexi.

Clearly Lexi had been reassured by Evanna's assertion that the two of them had been discussing the emergency they'd dealt with. Either that or she'd just decided that no man was ever going to be seriously interested in her mother.

'I'll see you later, then. Do you mind if I take Rebel?' Grabbing his lead, Lexi whistled to the dog and sauntered off to meet Fraser and his friends at the castle, leaving Jenna to face a day on her own with her thoughts.

And her thoughts didn't make good company.

Tormented by the memory of what had happened the night before, she pulled out one of the kitchen chairs and sat down with a thump. Then she smoothed the crumpled envelope she'd been clutching and stared at her list. She'd started with ten but there were probably a million reasons why it was a bad idea to kiss Ryan McKinley.

With a groan, she buried her face in her hands. She had to stop this nonsense. She had to pull herself together and act like an adult. She was a mother, for goodness' sake.

'You're obviously feeling as frustrated as I am.' His voice came from the doorway and Jenna flew to her feet, the chair crashing backwards onto the tiled floor, her heart pounding.

'Ryan!' The fact that she'd been thinking about him made the whole thing even more embarrassing—but not as humiliating as the fact that she was wearing nothing but her knickers and the old tee shirt of Lexi's that she'd worn to bed. Jenna tugged at the hem, until she realised that just exposed more of her breasts. 'What are you doing here?'

'Trying to have five minutes with you without the whole of Glenmore watching.' He strode across the kitchen, righting the chair that she'd tipped over. Then he gave her a wicked smile. 'Nice outfit.'

Too shocked to move, Jenna watched him walk towards her, dealing with the fact that a man was looking at her with undisguised sexual interest and he wasn't Clive. There was no mixing this man up with Clive. Her ex-husband was slight of build, with pale skin from spending most of his day in an office. Ryan was tall and broad-shouldered, his skin bronzed from the combination of wind and sun. When she'd looked at Clive she hadn't thought of sex and sin, but when she looked at Ryan—

He stopped in front of her. 'You have fantastic legs.'

A thrill of dangerous pleasure mingled with embarrassment. 'How did you get in?'

'The usual way—through the door.' Before she could say a word, he caught the front of her tee shirt in his hand, jerked her against him and brought his mouth down on hers. A thousand volts of pure sexual chemistry shot through her body and thoughts of sex and sin exploded into reality.

Jenna gripped his arms, feeling hard male muscle flex under her fingers. 'I've been thinking about you—'

'Good. I'd hate to be the only one suffering. You taste so good…' Groaning the words against her lips, Ryan sank his hands into her hair and devoured her mouth as if she were a feast and he was starving. His kiss was hot and hungry, and she felt her knees weaken and her heart pound. Flames licked through her veins and Jenna tightened her grip on his arms, grateful that she was leaning against the work surface.

Engulfed by an explosion of raw need Jenna wrapped her arms around his neck and pressed closer. His hands came round her back and he hauled her against him, leaving her in no doubt as to the effect she had on him. Feeling the hard ridge of his erection, Jenna felt excitement shoot through her body.

Dizzy and disorientated, she moaned against his mouth and he slid his hands under the tee shirt, his fingers warm against her flesh. She gasped as those same fingers dragged over her breasts, moaned as he toyed and teased. And still he kissed her. Mouth to mouth they stood, the skilled sweep of his tongue driving her wild, until she squirmed against him, the ache deep inside her almost intolerable.

Dimly, she heard him groan her name, and then he was lifting her tee shirt over her head and his mouth was on her bare breast. Jenna opened her mouth to tell him that it felt good, but the only sound that emerged was a faint moan, and her breathing became shallow as he drew the sensitive tip into his mouth. Her fingers sank into his thick dark hair as the excitement built, and suddenly she was aware of nothing but the heavy throb in her body and the desperate need for more. Every thought was driven from her mind, but one—

She wanted him. She wanted sex with him, and she didn't care about the consequences.

His mouth was back on hers, the slide of his tongue intimate and erotic.

Shaking now, Jenna reached for the waistband of his jeans and felt his abdomen clench against her fingers. She fumbled ineptly for a few moments, and then his hand closed around her wrist.

'Wait—God, I can't believe the way you make me feel.'

She moaned and pressed her mouth back to his, their breath mingling. 'I want to—'

With obvious difficulty he dragged his mouth from hers. 'I know you do, and so do I, but this time I really don't want to be disturbed—how long is Lexi out for? Is she going to be back in the next few hours?'

'Lexi?' Disorientated, Jenna stared at him for a moment, and then shook her head and rubbed her fingers over her forehead, trying to switch off the response of her body so that she could think clearly. 'Lexi.' She felt as though her personality had been split down the middle—mother and woman. 'She's out, but— What on earth am I doing?' Realising that she was virtually naked, Jenna quickly retrieved her tee shirt from the floor, but she was shaking so much that she couldn't turn it the right way round.

'I wish I hadn't said anything.' His tone rough, Ryan removed it gently from her hands, turned it the right way round and pulled it carefully over her head. 'I just didn't want her walking in on us.'

'No. And it's ridiculous. This whole thing is ridiculous—I'm— And you're—'

He raised an eyebrow. 'Is there any chance of you actually finishing a sentence, because I have no idea what you're thinking.'

'I'm thinking that this is crazy.' Jenna straightened the

tee shirt and flipped her hair free. 'I'm thinking that I don't do things like this.'

'That doesn't mean you can't. You hadn't owned a dog or eaten fish until a month ago.'

She gave a hysterical laugh. 'Having sex is slightly different to getting a dog or eating fish.'

'I should hope so. If a few hours in my bed is on a par with eating fish or getting a dog, I'll give up sex.'

'That would be a terrible waste, because you're obviously very good at it.' Jenna slammed her hand over her mouth and stared at him, appalled. 'I can't believe I just said that.'

But he was laughing, his blue eyes bright with humour. 'I love the way you say what you think.'

'What I think is that I don't know what you're doing here with me.' With an embarrassed laugh, she yanked the tee shirt down, covering herself. 'I'm not some nubile twenty-year-old. I'm a mother and I'm thirty-three…' The words died in her throat as he covered her mouth with his fingers.

'You're incredibly sexy.'

Staring up into his cool blue eyes, Jenna gulped, still coming to terms with the feelings he'd uncovered. He'd had his hands on her, and as for his mouth… An earthquake could have hit and she wouldn't have noticed. In fact, she felt as though an earthquake *had* hit.

Everything about her world had changed and it was hard to keep her balance.

But she had to. She couldn't afford the luxury of acting on impulse. She wasn't a teenager.

Thinking of teenagers made her groan and close her eyes.

'Ryan, what are you doing here?' She jabbed her fingers into her hair, horrified by what could have happened. 'We could have— Lexi might have—'

'I saw her leave. And before you panic, no, she didn't see me. I stayed out of the way until she'd disappeared over the horizon. Given the way she guards you, I thought it was wise. She obviously doesn't see her mother as a living, breathing sexual woman.'

'That's because I'm not. I'm not like this. This isn't me.'

'Maybe it *is* you.' His eyes lingered on her mouth. 'Do you want to find out?'

Her heart bumped hard. 'I can't. I have responsibilities.'

'Talking of which, did she give you a hard time about last night?'

'She started to say something and then decided that she'd imagined it all. Thanks to Evanna. But—I'm sorry about last night. I was going to apologise to you.'

'Don't.' His mouth was so close to hers that it was impossible to concentrate.

'You must be furious with me for embarrassing you in public—'

His hand was buried in her hair, his lips moving along her jaw. 'Do I seem furious?' His mouth was warm and clever, and Jenna felt her will-power strained to the limit.

She put a hand on his chest, trying to be sensible. Trying to ignore the way he made her feel.

Then he paused and stooped to retrieve something from the floor. It was her envelope. He would have discarded it had she not given an anguished squeak and reached for it.

'That's mine.'

'What is it?'

'It's nothing.' Jenna snatched at it but he held it out of reach, unfurling it with one hand.

'If it's nothing, why are you trying to stop me reading it?' He squinted at the crumpled paper. '"10 reasons why I shouldn't fall in love with Ryan—" Ah.'

With a groan, Jenna covered her face with her hands. 'Please, just ignore it—'

'No.' His voice was calm and steady. 'If you can make a

list of ten reasons not to fall in love with me, I have a right to know what they are.' He scanned the list and frowned. 'I put you off your food? That's why you don't eat?'

Mortified, Jenna just shook her head, and he sighed and tucked the mangled envelope into the back pocket of his jeans.

'If you want my opinion, I don't think it matters that you've been divorced for less than a year, nor do I think your age has any relevance. The fact that I put you off your food might be a problem in the long term, but we won't worry for now. As for Lexi—' He stroked his fingers through her hair. 'I can see that might be a problem. That's why I stopped when I did. I didn't want her to walk in.'

'So you're not just a sex god.' She made a joke of it. 'You're thoughtful, too.'

'For selfish reasons. I want you, and you come with a daughter.'

Did he mean he *wanted her* body or he wanted her? She was afraid to ask and she found it hard to believe that he wanted her at all. 'Why do I always meet you looking my worst?' Jenna couldn't believe the unfairness of it all. He looked like a living, breathing fantasy and she was wearing Lexi's cast off tee shirt.

'I think you look fantastic.' Ryan slid his hand into her hair, studying each tangled curl in detail. 'Does your hair curl naturally?'

'Yes, of course. Do you think I'd pay to make it look like this?' She snapped the words, embarrassed that she was looking her worst when he was looking his best, and really, really confused by the way he made her feel.

'I really like it.' His smile was slow and sexy. 'You look as though you've had a really crazy night in some very lucky man's bed.'

Jenna couldn't concentrate. His fingers were massaging

her scalp and she felt his touch right through her body. How did he know how to do that? Her eyes drifted shut and suddenly the impact on her other senses was magnified.

'As a matter of interest, what did you wear to bed when you were married?'

Jenna gulped. 'A long silky nightdress that Clive's mother bought me for Christmas. Why do you want to know?'

'Because I suspect this is another of your little rebellions. And now we've established that Lexi isn't coming back in the immediate future…' His voice husky, Ryan slid his hands under the offending tee shirt and she gasped because his hands were warm and strong and her nerve-endings were on fire.

'Ryan—'

His fingers slid down her back with a slow, deliberate movement that was unmistakably seductive. 'I hate to be the one to point this out, but I have a strong suspicion that neither Clive nor his mother would approve of your current choice of nightwear.'

'They'd be horrified—'

'Which is why you're wearing it.'

Jenna gave a choked laugh. 'Maybe. In which case I'm seriously disturbed and you should avoid me.'

Ryan lifted her chin so that she had no choice but to look at him. 'Is that what you want?'

All the pent-up emotion inside her exploded, as if the gates holding everything back had suddenly been opened. 'No, that isn't what I want! Of course it isn't. But I feel guilty, because I know I shouldn't be doing this, and confused because I've never lost control like that before. I'm angry with myself for being weak-willed, terrified that you'll hurt me—'

'Ah, yes—number eight on your list. Why do you assume I'll hurt you?'

Jenna thought about Clive. If Clive had found her boring,

how much more boring would this man find her? 'I'm not very exciting. I'm sure I'm all wrong for you.'

'In what way are you wrong for me?'

'For a start I've never had sex on a desk,' she blurted out, and then paled in disbelief. 'Oh, no—I can't believe I said that—'

'Neither can I. You're saying some really interesting things at the moment.' To give him his due, he didn't laugh. But he did close his hands around her wrists and drew her closer. 'I'm guessing that statement has some significance—am I right?'

Jenna stared at a point on his chest. 'I walked in on them,' she breathed. 'She was lying on his desk.'

'And you think that's what was wrong with your marriage?'

'No. The problems in our marriage went far deeper than that. I wouldn't have wanted to have sex on a desk with Clive, whereas—' She broke off, and he was silent for a moment.

Then he lifted his hand and slowly dragged his finger over her scarlet cheek. 'Whereas you do want to have sex on a desk with me?'

'Yes,' she whispered. 'Well, I don't mean a desk specifically—anywhere… But that's crazy, because I'm just not that sort of person and I know I'm really, really not your type.'

'Number nine on the list. So what *is* my type, Jenna?'

'I don't know. Someone stunning. Young. You're disgustingly handsome and you're sickeningly clever.' She mumbled the words, making a mental note never to commit her thoughts to paper again. 'I may be naive, but I'm not stupid. You could have any woman you want. You don't need to settle for a mess like me. And now you ought to leave, because all I ever do when you're around is embarrass myself. I need to get my head together and think about Lexi.'

'Why do you want to think about Lexi? She's out enjoying herself.'

Jenna felt her heart bump against her chest. 'I don't want to hurt her.'

'Is it going to hurt her if you spend the day with me?' His head was near hers, their mouths still close.

'No. But it might hurt me. I find this whole situation scary,' she confessed softly. 'What if I'm doing this for all the wrong reasons?' She looked up at him. 'What if I'm trying to prove something? What if I'm just using you to prove to myself that someone finds me attractive?'

'That objection wasn't on your list.' His mouth was against her neck, his tongue trailing across the base of her throat. 'You're not allowed to think up new ones.'

'I can't think properly when you do that—'

'Sorry.' But he didn't sound sorry, and he didn't stop what he was doing.

Jenna felt her insides melt but her brain refused to shut up. 'What if I'm just doing this because I'm angry with Clive?'

With a sigh, Ryan lifted his head. 'You're suggesting that kissing me is an act of revenge?'

'I don't know. I have no idea what's going on in my head. What I'm thinking is changing by the minute.'

There was a trace of humour in his eyes as he scanned her face. 'When you kissed me were you thinking of Clive?'

'No! But that doesn't mean it isn't a reasonable theory.'

'Answer me one question.' His mouth was against her neck again and Jenna closed her eyes.

'What?'

'If Lexi wasn't part of the equation—if it were just you and me—what would you like to do now?'

'Spend the day together, as you suggested. But somewhere private. Somewhere no one will see us.' She sighed. 'An impossible request on Glenmore, I know.'

'Maybe not.' Stroking her hair away from her face, Ryan gave a slow smile. 'In fact, I think I know just the place.'

The lighthouse was perched on a circle of grass, and the only approach was down a narrow path that curved out of sight of the road.

'It's the most secluded property on the island.' Ryan held out his hand as she negotiated the stony path. 'Even Mrs Parker has never been down here.'

Jenna shaded her eyes and stared up towards the top of the lighthouse. 'It's incredible. I can't believe it's a house.'

'It used to be fairly basic, but I made a few changes.' Ryan opened the door and she walked through, into a beautiful circular kitchen.

'Oh, my!' Stunned, she glanced around her. It was stylish and yet comfortable, with a huge range cooker, an American fridge and a central island for preparing food. By the window overlooking the sea the owner had placed a table, ensuring that anyone eating there could enjoy the fantastic view. 'A few changes?'

'Quite a few changes.' Ryan leaned against the doorframe, watching her reaction. 'Do you like it?'

'I love it. I had no idea—from the outside it looks…' Lost for words, she shook her head. 'It's idyllic.'

'Do you want breakfast now, or after you've looked round?'

'After…'

'Oh, yes—objection number four.' He gave a faint smile and urged her towards an arched doorway and a spiral staircase. 'I put you off your food. I don't suppose you'd like to tell me why? I don't think I've ever made a woman feel sick before.'

She giggled. 'You don't make me feel sick. You make me sort of churny in my stomach.'

'Sort of churny?' He lifted an eyebrow at her description. 'Is that good or bad?'

'Good, if you're trying to lose weight.'

'Don't. I like you the way you are.' He was right behind her on the stairs and it was impossible not to be aware that it was just the two of them in the house.

'So no one overlooks this?'

'It's a very inhospitable part of the coast of Glenmore—hence the reason they built a lighthouse here originally. This is the living room.'

Jenna emerged into another large, circular room, with high ceilings and glass walls. It had been decorated to reflect its coastal surroundings, with white wooden floors, seagrass matting and deep white sofas. Touches of blue added colour and elegant pieces of driftwood added style. A wood-burning stove stood in the centre of the room. 'This is the most beautiful room I've ever seen. I can't imagine what it must be like to actually live somewhere as special as this.'

'It was virtually a shell when I bought it from the original owner.' Ryan strolled over to the window, his back to her. 'It took me a year to make it properly habitable.'

'Where did you live while you were renovating it?'

'I lived here. Amidst the rubble.'

'You did most of it yourself?'

'All of it except the glazing. I used a lot of glass and it was too heavy for one person to manipulate.'

Stunned, she looked around her. 'You did the building—the plumbing, electricity?'

'I'm a doctor,' he drawled. 'I'm used to connecting pipes and electrical circuits. Building a wall isn't so different to realigning a broken bone—basically you need the thing straight.'

Jenna shook her head in silent admiration and carried on up the spiral staircase. She pushed open a door and discovered a luxurious bathroom, complete with drench shower. Another door revealed a small guest bedroom. Deciding that she'd never seen a more perfect property in her life, Jenna took the final turn in the staircase and found herself in paradise.

The master bedroom had been designed to take maximum advantage of the incredible view, with acres of glass giving a three-hundred-and-sixty-degree outlook on Glenmore.

Speechless, Jenna walked slowly around the perimeter of the breathtaking room. Out of the corner of her eye she was conscious of the enormous bed, but she was also acutely conscious of Ryan, watching her from the head of the spiral staircase. The intimacy was unfamiliar and exciting.

Hardly able to breathe, she stared out across the sparkling sea, watching as the view changed with every step. Far beneath her were vicious rocks that must have sent so many boats tumbling to the bottom of the ocean, but a few paces on and she had a perfect view of the coast path, winding like a ribbon along the grassy flanks of the island. A few more steps and she was looking inland, across wild moorland shaded purple with heather.

'It's like living outside.'

'That was the idea.'

'I can see everything,' she whispered, 'except people. No people.'

'Just beyond the headland is the Scott farm.' Ryan was directly behind her now, and he closed his hands over her shoulders, pointing her in the right direction. 'But everything here is protected land. No building. No people. Occasionally you see someone on the coast path in the distance, but they can't get down here because the rocks are too dangerous. The path we took is the only way down.'

'I've never been anywhere so perfect.' Acutely aware of his touch, Jenna could hardly breathe. He was standing close to her and she could feel the brush of his hard body against hers. Her heart racing, she stared up at the roof—and discovered more curving glass. 'It must be wild here when there's a storm. Is it scary?'

'It's tough glass. You'd be surprised how much sound it blocks out. Do you find storms scary?' He turned her gently, and suddenly she thought that what she was starting to feel for him was far scarier than any storm.

'I don't know.' Looking into his eyes, she felt as though everything in her life was changing. And not only did she not trust her feelings, she knew she couldn't have them. She had to think about Lexi. But Lexi wasn't here now, was she? Maybe there was no future, but there could be a present. She was a woman as well as a mother.

His mouth was close to hers but he didn't kiss her, and she wondered whether he was waiting for her to make the decision.

Jenna lifted her hand to his face, the breath trapped in her throat. His jaw was rough against her fingers and she felt him tense, but still he didn't kiss her. Still he waited.

Consumed by the thrill of anticipation, she wrapped her arms around his neck and lifted her mouth to his, feeling her stomach swoop. It was like jumping off a cliff. As decisions went, this was a big one, and deep down in her gut she knew there would be a price to pay, but right now she didn't care. If she had to pay, she'd pay.

As her lips touched his she felt the ripple of tension spread across his shoulders—felt the coiled power in his athletic frame.

'Be sure, Jenna…' He breathed the words against her mouth, his hand light on her back, still giving her the option of retreat.

But the last thing she had in mind was retreat. She kept her mouth on his and he slid his hands into her hair and held her face still, taking all that she offered and more, his kiss demanding and hungry.

Someone groaned—her or him?—and then his arms came around her and he held her hard against him. The feel of his body made her heart race, and Jenna felt her linen skirt slide to the floor, even though she hadn't actually felt him undo it. And suddenly she was acutely aware of him—of the strength of his hands, the roughness of his jeans against the softness of her skin, the hard ridge of his arousal—

'Jenna—I have to—' His hands were full of her, stripping off her skirt, peeling off underwear until she was naked and writhing against him. And her hands were on him, too, on his zip, which refused to co-operate until he covered her hands with his. This time instead of stopping her, he helped her.

Hearts pounding, mouths fused, they fell to the floor, feasting.

'The bed is a metre away—' Ryan had his mouth on her breast and pleasure stabbed hard, stealing her breath. 'We should probably—'

'No—too far.' Terrified he'd stop what he was doing, Jenna clutched at his hair, gasping as she felt his tongue graze her nipple. Sensation shot through her and he teased, nipped and sucked one rigid peak while using his fingers on the other. The burn inside her was almost intolerable. Her hips writhed against the soft rug and she arched in an instinctive attempt to get closer to him. But she wasn't in charge. He was. Maybe there was some pattern to what he was doing, some sequence, but for her it was all a blur of ecstasy.

The words in her head died as his hand slid between her legs.

It had been two years since a man had touched her intimately, and even before that it had never felt like this. Never before had she felt this restless, burning ache.

'Ryan—' The slow, leisurely stroke of his skilled fingers drove her wild. 'Now.'

'I haven't even started…' His voice was husky against her ear, and his fingers slid deeper. Heat flushed across her skin and her breathing grew shallow. Her hand slid down and circled him and she heard him catch his breath.

'On second thoughts—now seems like a good idea…' He slid his hand under her bottom and lifted her, the blunt head of his erection brushing against her thigh.

Trembling with expectation, Jenna curved one thigh over his back and then groaned when he hesitated. 'Please…'

'Forgot something—' His voice hoarse, he eased himself away from her, reached forward and grabbed something from the cupboard by his bed. 'Damn!' He struggled with the packet while he kissed her again.

Jenna was panting against his mouth. 'Just—can you please—?'

'Yeah, I definitely can.' He hauled her under him, dropping his forehead to hers. 'Are you sure?'

'Is that a serious question?' She was breathless—desperate—conscious of the press of his body against hers. 'If you stop now, Ryan McKinley, I swear, I'll punch you.'

His laugh was low and sexy, and her stomach flipped as she stared into those blue, blue eyes. And then she ceased to notice anything because the roughness of his thigh brushed against hers and then he was against her and inside her and Jenna decided that if sex had ever felt like this before then she must have lost her memory.

Heat spread through her body and she tried to tell him how good it felt, but the sleek thrust of his body drove thought from her brain. He kissed her mouth, then her neck, ran his hand down her side and under her bottom—lifted her—

She moaned his name and he brought his lips back to hers, taking her mouth even as he took her body, and the pleasure was so intense that she could hardly breathe. Her nails sank into his back and the excitement inside her roared forward like a train with no brakes—

'Oh— I—' Her orgasm consumed her in a flash of brilliant light and exquisite sensation and she heard him growl deep in his throat, surging deeper inside her as she pulsed around him. She sobbed his name, tightened her grip and felt him thrust hard for the last time. They clung, breathless, riding the wave, going where the pleasure took them.

With a harsh groan Ryan dropped his head onto her shoulder, his breathing dragging in his throat. 'Are you OK?'

'No, I don't think so.' Weak and shaky, Jenna stared up at the ceiling, shell shocked, stunned by the intensity of what they'd shared. 'It's never been like that before.'

'That's probably because you've never made love on a wooden floor.' Wincing slightly, Ryan eased his weight off her and rolled onto his back, his arms still round her. 'I need to buy a different floor covering. This was designed for walking on and aesthetic appearance, not for sex. Do you want to move to the bed?'

'I don't want to move at all.' She just wanted to lie here, with him, staring up at the blue sky and the clouds above them. It seemed a fitting view. 'It's perfect here.'

'Perfect, apart from the bruises.'

'I don't have bruises, and even if I do I don't care.' She turned and rested her cheek on his chest, revelling in the opportunity to touch him. 'This morning I was wondering whether I ought to kiss you again—'

'And what did you decide?'

'You interrupted me before I'd made my decision.'

'If you want my opinion, I think you should definitely kiss me again.' His eyes gleamed with humour and he lifted her chin with his fingers and kissed her lightly. 'And again.'

Jenna shifted until she lay on top of him. 'I've never done this before.'

He raised an eyebrow. 'You have a child.'

'I mean I've never been so desperate to have sex I couldn't make it as far as the bed—never lost control like that.' She kissed the corner of his mouth, unable to resist touching him. 'I've never wanted anyone the way I want you. Ever since I arrived on the island I've wanted you. I thought I was going crazy—'

'I was going crazy, too.' He sank his hands into her hair and kissed her. 'Believe me, you're not the only one who has been exercising will-power.'

'I wasn't sure this was what you wanted.' She was conscious that she still knew next to nothing about him, and suddenly a stab of anxiety pierced her happiness. 'Can I ask you something?' Through the open window she could hear the crash of the waves and the shriek of the seagulls, reminding her how isolated they were.

'Yes.'

'Are you married?'

He stilled. 'You think I'd be lying here with you like this if I were married?'

'I don't know. I hope not.'

'And I hope you know me better than that.'

'Now I've made you angry.' Suddenly she wished she hadn't ruined the mood by asking the question. 'I'm sorry—I shouldn't have—' She broke off and then frowned, knowing that her question was a valid one. 'You have to understand that I thought I knew Clive, and it turned out I didn't.'

'Jenna, I'm not angry. You don't have to talk about this.'

'Yes, I do. You thought it was an unjust question, but to me it wasn't unjust and I need you to understand that.' Her voice was firm. 'I lived with a man for sixteen years and I thought I knew him. I married him and had his child, I slept in his bed—we made a life together. And it turned out he had a whole other life going on that didn't involve me. He had three affairs over the course of our marriage, one of them with a friend of mine. I didn't find out until the third.'

Ryan pulled her back down into the circle of his arms. 'You have a right to ask me anything you want to ask me. And I'm not married. Not any more.'

'Oh.' Digesting that, she relaxed against him, trailing her fingers over his chest, lingering on dark hair and hard muscle. 'So it went wrong for you, too?'

'Yes.'

She waited for him to say something more but he didn't, and she lay for a moment, listening to his heartbeat, her fingers on his chest.

Obviously that was why he'd come here, she thought to herself. Like her, he'd found comfort in doing something, found a channel for his anger. He'd built something new.

Ryan sighed. 'I'm sure there are questions you want to ask me.'

But he didn't want to answer them; she knew that.

'Yes, I have a question.' She shifted on top of him, feeling his instant response. 'How comfortable is that bed of yours?'

'Fruit, rolls, coffee—' Ryan started loading a tray. 'How hungry are you?'

'Not very. You put me off my food, remember?' Having pulled on her linen skirt and tee shirt, Jenna sat on a stool watching him.

'You just used up about ten thousand calories. You need to eat.' Ryan warmed rolls in the oven, sliced melon and made a pot of coffee. 'This should be lunch rather than breakfast, but never mind.'

'Lunch? But we—' Her gaze slid to the clock on the wall and her eyes widened. 'Two o'clock?'

'Like I said—ten thousand calories.' And ten thousand volts to his system. He couldn't believe he wanted her again so quickly, but he could happily have taken her straight back to bed.

Ryan grabbed butter and a jar of thick golden honey and then handed her some plates and mugs. 'You can carry these. I'll bring the rest.'

She stood still, holding the plates and mugs, staring at him.

Removing the rolls from the oven, he glanced at her. 'What's wrong?'

'Nothing.' Her voice was husky, and he frowned as he tipped the warm bread into a basket.

'Honesty, Jenna, remember?'

'It feels strange,' she admitted, 'being here with you like this.'

'Strange in a good way or strange in a bad way?'

'In a scary way. I was with Clive for sixteen years and he was my only boyfriend.'

Thinking about it, he realised he'd probably known that all along, but hearing it was still a shock. 'Your only boyfriend?'

'I met him when I was sixteen. I had Lexi when I was eighteen.'

Ryan wondered whether her selfish ex-husband had taken advantage of her. 'Does that have anything to do with why you have a difficult relationship with your mother?'

'I've always disappointed her.'

He frowned. 'I can't imagine you disappointing anyone.' But he could imagine her trying to please everyone, and her next words confirmed it.

'My parents had plans for me—which didn't involve me getting pregnant as a teenager.' Her head dipped and she pulled a pair of sunglasses out of the bag on her lap. 'Are we eating outside? I'll probably need these. It's sunny.'

He remembered the conversation she'd had with her

mother. How distressed she'd been. 'So what did they want you to do?'

'Something respectable. I had a place lined up at Cambridge University to read English—my parents liked to boast about that. They were bitterly upset when I gave it up.'

'Did you have to give it up?'

'I chose to. Everyone thought I'd be a terrible mother because I was a teenager, and it made me even more determined to be the best mother I could be. I don't see why teenagers can't be good mothers—I'm not saying it's easy, but parenthood is never easy, whatever age you do it.' Tiny frown lines appeared on her forehead. 'I hate the assumption that just because you're young, you're going to be a dreadful parent. I know plenty of bad parents who waited until their thirties to have children.'

Ryan wondered if she was referring to her own. 'For what it's worth, I think you're an amazing mother.'

'Thank you.' Her voice was husky as she cleaned her sunglasses with the edge of her tee shirt. 'I don't think I'm amazing, but I love Lexi for who she is, not what she does. And I've always let her know that.'

'Who she is, not what she does…' Ryan repeated her words quietly, thinking that his own parents could have taken a few lessons from Jenna. In his home, praise had always revolved around achievement.

Jenna fiddled with her glasses. 'My parents were always more interested in what I did than who I was, and I was determined not to be like that. Clive worked—I stayed at home. Traditional, I know, but it was the way I wanted it.'

'Can I ask you something personal? Did you marry him because you loved him or because you were pregnant?'

She hesitated. 'I thought I loved him.'

'And now you're not sure?'

'How can you love someone you don't even know?' Her

voice cracked slightly and Ryan crossed the kitchen and dragged her into his arms.

'The guy is clearly deranged.' Dropping a kiss on her hair, he eased her away from him. 'So now I understand why you asked me that question. You must find it impossible to trust another man.'

'No.' She said the word fiercely. 'Clive lied to me, but I know all men aren't like that—just as not all teenage mothers are inept and not all boys wearing hoodies are carrying knives. I won't generalise. I don't trust him, that's true, but I don't want Lexi growing up thinking the whole male race is bad. I won't do that to her.'

Her answer surprised him. He'd met plenty of people with trust issues.

He had a few of his own.

'You're a surprising person, Jenna Richards.' Young in many ways, and yet in others more mature than many people older than her.

'I'm an ordinary person.'

He thought about the way she loved her child, the way she was determined to be as good a mother as she could be. He thought about the fact that she'd been with the same man since she was sixteen. 'There's nothing ordinary about you. I'm intrigued about something, though.' He stroked her hair away from her face, loving the feel of it. 'If you were at home with Lexi, when did you train as a nurse?'

'Once Lexi started school. I had a network of friends—many of them working mothers. We helped each other out. Sisterhood. They'd take Lexi for me when I was working, I'd take their children on my days off. Sometimes I had a house full of kids.'

He could imagine her with children everywhere. 'Can I ask you something else? Why didn't you ever have more children? You obviously love them.'

'Clive didn't want more. He decided Lexi was enough.'

'Like he decided that you weren't going to have a dog or eat fish?'

She gave a shaky smile. 'Are you suggesting my final act of rebellion should be to have a baby? I think that might be taking it a bit far. And anyway, I couldn't do that now.'

'Why not?'

'Well, for a start, I'm too old.'

'You're thirty-three. Plenty of women don't have their first child until that age.'

She looked at him, and he knew she was wondering why he was dwelling on the subject. 'And then there's Lexi. If I had a baby now, it would be difficult for her.'

'Why?'

'Because there have been enough changes in her life. I suspect that at some point, probably soon, her father is going to have another child. I don't want to add to the confusion. I want her relationship with me to be as stable as possible. Why are you asking?'

Why *was* he asking? Unsettled by his own thoughts, Ryan turned his attention back to his breakfast. 'I'm just saying you're not too old to have a child.' He kept his voice even. 'Put your sunglasses on. You're right about it being sunny outside.'

CHAPTER EIGHT

IT WAS an affair full of snatched moments and secret assignations, all tinged with the bittersweet knowledge that it couldn't possibly last.

At times Jenna felt guilty that she was keeping her relationship with Ryan from Lexi, but her daughter was finally settled and happy and she was afraid to do or say anything that might change that.

She just couldn't give Ryan up.

They'd meet at the lighthouse at lunchtime, make love until they were both exhausted, and then part company and arrive back at the surgery at different times.

And, despite the subterfuge, she'd never been happier in her life.

'I actually feel grateful to Clive,' she murmured one afternoon as they lay on his cliffs, staring at the sea. Her hand was wrapped in his and she felt his warm fingers tighten. 'If he hadn't done what he did, I wouldn't be here now. I wouldn't have known it was possible to feel like this. It's scary, isn't it? You're in a relationship, and you have nothing to compare it to, so you say to yourself this is it. This is how it's supposed to feel. But you always have a sense that something is missing.'

'Did you?'

'Yes, but I assumed it was something in me that was lacking, not in my relationship.'

'Life has a funny way of working itself out.' He turned his head to look at her. 'Have you told Lexi about us yet?'

A grey cloud rolled over her happiness. 'No,' she said. 'Not yet.'

'Are you going to tell her?'

'I don't know.'

'You're afraid of her reaction?'

'Yes. She was devastated when Clive left. Horrified that he was involved with another woman. Apart from the obvious issues, teenagers don't like to see their parents as living, breathing sexual beings.'

And she didn't know what to say. *I've taken a lover...*

What exactly was their relationship? What could there be?

Ryan rolled onto his side and propped himself up on his elbow so that he could see her. 'I want to be with you, Jenna. I want more than lunchtimes and the occasional Sunday afternoon when Lexi is with her friends. I want more.'

Looking into his blue eyes, she felt her heart spin and dance. 'How much more?'

'I love you.' Ryan touched her face gently, as if making a discovery. 'I've loved you since you stepped off that boat looking like someone who had walked away from an accident.'

'You love me?' Jenna was jolted by a burst of happiness and he smiled.

He looked more relaxed than she'd ever seen him. 'Is that a surprise?'

'I didn't dare hope. I thought it might be just—' She was whispering, afraid that she might disturb the dream. 'I love you, too. I've never felt this way about anyone before. I didn't know it was possible.'

'Neither did I.' He kissed her gently, stroked her hair protectively with a hand that wasn't quite steady. Then he gave a shake of his head. 'You've never asked me about my marriage or why I ended up here. I'm sure there are things you want to know about me.'

'I assumed that if there was anything you wanted me to know, you'd tell me when you were ready.'

'You're a very unusual woman, do you know that? You're able to love me, not knowing what went before?'

'It's not relevant to how I feel about you.'

He breathed in deeply, his eyes never shifting from hers. 'I was married—to Connie. She was a very ambitious woman. Connie was born knowing what she wanted in life and nothing was going to stand in her way. We met when we were medical students. We were together briefly, and then met up again when we were both consultants in the same hospital. Looking back on it, we were a disaster waiting to happen, but at the time I suppose it must have seemed right.'

Thinking of her own situation, Jenna nodded. 'That happens.'

His laugh was tight and humourless. 'I think the truth is I was too busy for a relationship and Connie understood that. I was fighting my way to the top and I didn't need a woman asking me what time I'd be home at night. Connie didn't care what time I came home because she was never there to see. She was fighting *her* way to the top, too.'

Jenna sat quietly, letting him speak. She had an image in her head. An image of a beautiful, successful woman. The sort of woman she'd always imagined a man like him would choose. The cream of the crop. Bright and brilliant, like him. They would have been a golden couple. 'Was she beautiful?'

'No.' His hand dropped from her face and he sat up. Stared out across the sea. 'Physically I suppose she would be considered beautiful,' he conceded finally. 'But to me beauty is so much more than sleek hair and well-arranged features. Connie was cold. Selfish. Beauty is who you are and the way you behave. We were both very wrapped up in our careers. We worked all day, wrote research papers in what little spare time we had—our house had two offices.' He frowned and shook his head. 'How could I ever have thought that what we had was a marriage?'

'Go on…'

'I wanted us to start a family.'

'Oh.' It hadn't occurred to her that he might have a child. That was one question she hadn't asked. 'You have—?'

'I brought the subject up one night, about a week after I'd made Consultant. I thought it would be the perfect time.'

'She didn't agree?'

He stared blindly across the ocean and into the far distance. 'She told me she'd been sterilised.'

Jenna sat up. 'She— Oh, my gosh—and you didn't know?' She licked her lips, digesting the enormity of it.

'At medical school she decided she didn't ever want to have a baby. She wanted a career and didn't want children. In her usual ruthlessly efficient way she decided to deal with the problem once and for all. Unfortunately she didn't share that fact with me.' The confession was rough and hoarse, and she knew for sure he hadn't spoken the words to anyone else. Just her. The knowledge that he'd trusted her with something so personal was like a gift, fragile and precious, and Jenna tried to understand how he must be feeling, unwilling to break the connection between them by saying something that might make him regret his show of trust.

In the end she just said what was in her heart. 'That was wrong. Very wrong.'

'Some of the blame was mine. I made assumptions—didn't ask—I suppose I could be accused of being chauvinistic. I presumed we'd do the traditional thing at some point. It came as a shock to discover she had no intention of ever having a family.'

Jenna reached out a hand and touched his shoulder. 'She should have told you.'

'That was my feeling. I suddenly realised I'd been living with a stranger. That I didn't know her at all.' He gave a wry smile. 'But you know how that feels, don't you?'

'Only too well. I was living in this imaginary world—thinking things were fine. But Clive was living a completely different life. A life I didn't even see.' She looped her arms around her legs and rested her chin on her knees. 'I suppose part of the problem was that we just didn't communicate. We fell into marriage because I was pregnant and because it was what my parents expected. I made assumptions about him. He made assumptions about me.' Jenna turned her head and looked at him. 'So you told Connie you wanted a divorce?'

'Yes. I discovered that although I'd achieved what could be considered huge success in my professional life, my personal life was a disaster. I hadn't even thought about what I wanted, and suddenly I realised that what I wanted was the thing I didn't have—someone alongside me who loved me, who wanted to share their life with me. I wanted to come home at night to someone who cared about what sort of day I'd had. I didn't want our only communication to be via voicemail. And I wanted children. Connie thought I was being ridiculous—her exact words were, "It's not as if you're ever going to change a nappy, Ryan, and I'm certainly not doing it, so why would we want children?"'

'She didn't want a divorce?'

'I was flying high in my career and she liked that. I looked good on her CV.' There was a bitter note to his voice and his eyes were flint-hard. 'Being with me opened doors for her.'

'Did she love you?'

'I have no idea. If she did then it was a very selfish kind

of a love. She wanted me for what I added to her, if that makes sense.'

'Yes, it makes sense. I don't know much about relationships…' Jenna thought about her own relationship with Clive '…but I do know that real love is about giving. It's about wanting someone else's happiness more than your own. If you care about someone, you want what's right for them.'

And that was the way she felt about Ryan, she realised. She wanted him to be happy.

Ryan put his arm around her shoulders and drew her against him. 'That's what you do with Lexi, all the time. You're lucky to have her. Lucky to have that bond.'

'Yes.' She melted as he kissed her, knowing that everything was changing. Once again life had taken her in a direction she hadn't anticipated, but this time the future wasn't terrifying. It was exciting. 'I'm going to talk to her. I've decided. I think maybe she's old enough to understand.' Strengthened by her feelings and his, she suddenly felt it was the right thing to do.

'You're going to talk to her about us?'

'Yes. This is what life is, isn't it? It's the happy and the sad and the unpredictable. It would be wrong to pretend anything different. Lexi needs to know that life is sometimes hard and that things can't always stay the same. She needs to know that change isn't always bad and that the unfamiliar can become familiar. And she needs to know that my love for her will never change, no matter what happens to the way we live.'

Ryan stroked his fingers over her cheek. 'You're the most selfless person I've ever met. When your husband walked out, who supported you? Not your mother, I assume. Your friends?'

'For a while. Then I discovered that they'd all known he was having the affair and that they'd known about his other affairs and hadn't told me.' Jenna pulled away from him. 'I found that hard. That and all the advice. "Turn a blind eye." "Dress like a pole dancer and seduce him back—"'

There was amusement in his eyes. 'Did you adopt that suggestion?'

'Of course—I went around wearing nothing but fishnets and a basque.' Pleased that she was able to make a joke about something she'd never thought would seem funny, she wound a strand of hair around her finger. 'To be honest, I didn't want him back. Not after I found out that he'd had a string of affairs throughout our marriage. But the worst thing of all was the way he behaved towards Lexi—it was as if he suddenly just washed his hands of her. His own daughter!' Humour faded and anger flooded through her, fresh as it had been on that first day. 'Whatever he felt about me, that was no excuse for cutting Lexi out of his life.'

'Forget him now.' His voice was rough as he pulled her back to him. 'He was your past. I'm your future.'

Jenna stared at him, silenced by the possibilities that extended in front of her. She wanted to ask what he meant. She wanted to ask whether the future meant a few weeks, or more than that, but she was terrified of voicing the question in case the answer was something she didn't want to hear.

He was watching her, absorbing her reaction. 'Jenna, I know this is soon, but—' There was a buzzing sound from his pocket, and Ryan swore fluently and dragged out his phone. 'Maybe there are some advantages to living in a city—at least someone else can carry the load when you want some time off.' He checked the number and frowned. 'It's Logan. I'd better take this—sorry.'

As he talked to the other doctor, Jenna gently extracted herself from his grip, wondering what he'd been about to say. It was obvious that she wasn't going to find out quickly, because Ryan was digging in his pocket for his car keys as he talked, the expression on his face enough for her to know that the phone call was serious.

He sprang to his feet. 'I'll get up there now.' His eyes flickered to hers. 'And I'll take Jenna with me—no, don't worry, we'll handle it together.'

Realising that she was supposed to help him with something, Jenna stood up and brushed the grass off her skirt.

Ryan was already striding towards the path that led up to his car. 'Have you done any emergency work?'

'Sorry?' Jenna jammed her feet into her shoes and sprinted after him, wondering how the tone of the afternoon could have shifted so quickly.

Glenmore, she thought, and its ever-changing moods.

Even the weather had changed. While they'd been talking the blue sky had turned an ominous grey and the sea a gunmetal-blue.

There was a storm coming.

'Did you ever work in an emergency department?' His mouth grim, Ryan was in the car and firing up the engine before she had time to answer the question.

'Yes. But it was quite a few years ago. What do you need me to do?' Her head smacked lightly against the headrest as he accelerated along the empty road, and Jenna felt the power of the car come to life around her. She felt a shimmer of nerves mingled with anticipation. What if she wasn't up to the job?

To give herself confidence she cast a glance at Ryan, looking at his broad shoulders and strong, capable hands. He shifted gears like a racing driver, pushing the car to its limits as he negotiated the tight turns and narrow roads that led from the lighthouse. Even after a comparatively short time she knew he would be able to handle anything he encountered, and that knowledge gave her courage. 'Tell me what's happened.'

'Group of teenagers tombstoning on the Devil's Jaws. It's close to here.'

'Tombstoning?' Jenna rummaged in her pocket and found something to tie back her hair. 'What's that?'

'It's when they stand on the top of a cliff and jump into the sea.' Ryan slowed to take a sharp bend. 'The problem is the depth of the water changes according to the tide. Even when the tide is on your side it's a dangerous activity. And the Devil's Jaws is the most dangerous place you could wish for. It's narrow there—the cliffs have formed a tight channel, so not only can you kill yourself when you hit the bottom, if you get really lucky you can kill yourself on the way down.'

'Kids are doing that? Can't they fence the cliffs off or something?'

'It *is* fenced off. The place is lethal. No one is meant to go within a hundred metres of it, but you know teenagers.' He swung the car into a space at the side of the road and killed the engine. 'We have to walk from here. Are you afraid of heights?'

'I don't know. I don't think so.'

'Watch your footing. To add to the fun, the rocks are crumbling.' Ryan opened his boot and Jenna blinked as she saw the contents.

'You carry ropes in your boot?'

'I climb sometimes.' Without elaborating, he selected several ropes and started piling equipment into a large rucksack. Then he opened his medical bag and added another series of items, including drugs he thought he was going to need. His movements were swift and economical, brutally efficient.

Jenna focused on the drugs. 'Ketamine?'

'I prefer it to morphine. It doesn't produce respiratory depression or hypotension, and in analgesic doses it produces a mild bronchodilator effect.'

'Translate that into English?' A voice came from behind

them and Jenna turned to see Nick Hillier, the island policeman. Only today he wasn't smiling.

'It means it controls the pain without affecting the breathing.' Ryan hoisted the bag out of the boot. 'Is it as bad as they say?'

'Worse. Two in the water—one trapped halfway down the cliff. They're right in the Jaws.'

'Of course they are—that's where they get the maximum adrenaline rush.'

'The one stuck on the cliff might be all right, as long as he doesn't let go, but he's getting tired. Coastguard helicopter has chosen today to have a technical problem—they're fixing it, but the cavalry isn't going to be arriving any time soon.' Nick sucked in a breath. 'I don't want anyone going near the edge. I don't want more casualties. We're going to wait and hope to hell they get that helicopter airborne in the next ten minutes. I think this is a rescue best carried out from the air or the sea.'

'I'll take a look at it. Then I'll decide.' Ryan lifted the rucksack onto his back and walked over the grass towards a gate. A sign warned the public that the area was dangerous. Dropping his rucksack onto the other side, Ryan vaulted the gate. Nick climbed over slightly more awkwardly, holding out a hand to Jenna.

She wondered who was going to have the last say on this one. The law or the doctor.

His mind clearly working in the same direction, Nick became visibly stressed. 'Ryan, you know how risky it is. A climber was killed abseiling from here earlier in the summer—the rocks sawed through his rope.'

'Then he didn't have his rope in the right place.' Ryan dropped his rucksack again, onto the grass a safe distance from the edge. 'There are injured kids, Nick. What do you expect me to do? Leave them?'

'My job is to make sure we rescue them with minimum further casualties—that doesn't involve you abseiling down a sheer, crumbling rock face.'

Listening to them, Jenna felt her heart race, and she wondered if she was going to be any use at all.

Yes, she'd worked in an emergency department for a short time, but working in a well-equipped department was quite different from giving pre-hospital care on a sheer cliff face.

She was so busy worrying about her own abilities that it was a few seconds before she noticed the teenager sitting on the grass. He was shivering and his face was white.

Focusing on his face, Jenna recognised Fraser and her stomach dropped. Suddenly everything seemed to happen in slow motion. She was aware of the guilt in Fraser's anguished glance, and of Ryan turning his head to look at her.

And those looks meant only one thing—

That it was Lexi who was lying in the grip of the Devil's Jaws.

Maternal instinct overwhelming everything else, Jenna gave a low moan of denial and stepped towards the edge, unthinking.

Ryan caught her arm in an iron grip.

'Don't take another step.' His hand was a steadying force and his voice was hard, forcing itself through the blind panic that clouded her thinking. 'Breathe. Up here, you don't run. You take small steps. You look where you're going and you make sure it's safe underfoot. I'll get her. I swear to you I'll get her. But I can't do it if I'm worrying about you going over the edge.'

Jenna stood still, held firm by the strength of his hand and the conviction in his voice.

Fraser struggled to his feet, his lips dry and cracked from the wind and the sun. 'You don't understand—she didn't jump. Lexi was trying to stop Matt doing it—we both were.

But he did it anyway—he jumped at the wrong moment. You have to get it exactly right or you hit the rocks.' His voice shook. He was a teenager on the cusp of manhood, but today he was definitely more boy than man. 'Lexi went down there to save Matt. We could see him slipping under the water. He was going to drown. Jamie tried first, but he lost his nerve halfway down and now he can't move. I dunno—he just freaked out or something. So Lexi did it. She insisted. She was dead scared about getting down there, but she said she'd done first aid so she should be the one.'

'She climbed down?' There was a strange note in Ryan's voice and already he had his hands in his rucksack. 'Fraser, take this rope for me.'

'You should have seen her—she was amazing. Just went down slowly, hand and foot, hand and foot, muttering "Three points of contact on the rock face..." or something.'

'She did a climbing course last summer,' Jenna said faintly. Last summer—just before everything had fallen apart. 'It was indoors on a climbing wall in London.'

Nowhere near greasy, slippery rocks or furious boiling sea.

Ryan's gaze met hers for a moment. 'I'd say that was money well spent.'

Fraser was sweating. 'I almost had a heart attack watching her. I'm not good with heights since I fell into that dungeon.' He looked at Jenna, shrinking. 'I'm really sorry. I tried to stop her...'

'It isn't your fault, Fraser.' Jenna's lips were stiff and her heart was pounding. 'Lexi is not your responsibility. She's old enough to make her own decisions.'

'She's as sure-footed as a goat.' There was awe in Fraser's voice. 'Matt was face-down in the water and she dragged him towards the rocks. She's been holding him, but he's too heavy for her to get him out by herself and the tide is coming in. The water level is rising. The ledge they're on will be underwater soon.'

That news made Jenna's knees weaken with panic, but Ryan was icy calm. When he spoke there was no doubt in anyone's mind who was in charge of the rescue.

'Fraser, I want you to stay here and act as runner. Is your mobile working?'

'Yes, the signal is good.'

'Keep it switched on. Dr McNeil is bringing equipment from the surgery. If the helicopter is delayed, then that will change the way we manage Matt's injuries.' Ryan stepped into a harness and adjusted it with hands that were steady and confident. 'Keep the phone line clear—if I need to talk to you, I'll call.'

Nick stepped forward and caught his arm. 'Ryan, for goodness' sake, man, I'm telling you we should wait for the helicopter.'

Jenna couldn't breathe. If Ryan agreed to wait for the helicopter then Lexi might drown. But if Ryan went down there—if he put himself at risk for her daughter and the two boys…

'You're wasting time, Nick.' His eyes flickered to hers and for a brief moment the connection was there. 'It will be all right. Trust me.'

And she did. Although why she should be so ready to trust a man she'd known for weeks when a man she'd known for years had let her down, she didn't understand. But life wasn't always easy to understand, was it? Some things happened without an explanation.

'What can I do?' Her mouth was so dry she could hardly form the words. 'How can I help?'

'You can stay there, away from the edge.'

Nick caught his arm. 'Ryan—'

'I'm going to abseil down, and I want you to lower the rest

of my pack.' He adjusted his harness for a final time and held out his hand. 'Do you have a radio for me?'

Nick gave up arguing, but his face was white and his eyes flickered between the rising tide and the sky, obviously looking for a helicopter. Hoping.

Jenna felt helpless. 'I want to do something. If the boy is badly injured you'll need help. I can abseil down, too—'

Ryan didn't spare her a glance. 'You'll stay here.'

'It's my daughter down there.'

'That's why you're staying up here. You'll be too busy worrying about her to be any use to me.'

'Don't patronise me.' Anger spurting through her veins, Jenna picked up a harness. 'You need me down there, Ryan. Two of them are in the water, one of them injured, and one of them is stuck on the rock face. He could fall at any moment. You can't do this by yourself, and Lexi is just a child.'

Ryan paused. Then he looked over his shoulder, down at the jagged rocks. 'All right. This is what we'll do. I'll go down there first and do an assessment. If I need you, Nick can get you down to me. But watch my route. Have you abseiled before?'

Jenna swallowed, wishing she could tell him she'd scaled Everest four times without oxygen. 'Once. On an adventure camp when I was fifteen.'

'I love the fact that you're so honest. Don't worry—Nick can get you down there if I need you. Hopefully I won't.'

He went over the edge like someone from an action movie and Jenna blinked. Clearly there was plenty she still had to learn about Ryan, and the more she knew, the more she liked and admired him.

'I should have stopped him,' Nick muttered, and Jenna lifted an eyebrow because the idea of stopping Ryan doing something he was determined to do seemed laughable to her.

'How?'

The policeman gave a short laugh. 'Good question. Still, what Ryan doesn't know about ropes and climbing isn't worth knowing. I'm going to get this on you Jenna.' He had a harness in his hands. 'Just in case. I have a feeling he's going to need you. I can't believe I'm doing this.'

'If he's going to need me, why didn't he just say so?'

'Honestly? I'm guessing he's being protective. Either that or he doesn't want any of us to know how easy it is.' With a weak grin, Nick adjusted the harness and glanced at her face. Jenna wondered if he knew that there was something going on between them or whether he was matchmaking like the others.

Ryan's voice crackled over the radio. 'Nick, do you read me? I need you to lower that rope to me, over.'

'What he really needs is a miracle,' Nick muttered, lowering one end of a rope down to Ryan and securing the other end to a rock. 'That should keep the boy steady while Ryan finds out what's going on. I hope he does it quickly. There's a storm coming. Great timing. Can today get any worse?'

Only an hour earlier she'd been lying on the grass on Ryan's cliffs, bathed in sunshine and happiness.

Eyeing the rolling black clouds, Jenna approached the edge cautiously. Peering over the side, she caught her breath. Here, the cliff face was vertical. The rocks plunged downwards, the edges ragged and sharp as sharks' teeth, ready to razor through the flesh of the unwary. Her stomach lurched, and the sheer terror of facing that drop almost swallowed her whole.

'I can't believe they thought they could jump down there,' she said faintly, biting her lip as she saw Ryan attaching the rope to a boy clinging halfway down. Then her gaze drifted lower and she saw Lexi's small figure, crouched on an exposed rock at the bottom. The girl had her arms around a boy's shoulders, holding him out of the water, straining with the effort as the sea boiled and foamed angrily around them, the level of the water rising with each incoming wave.

Watching the waves lick hungrily at her daughter, Jenna felt physically sick. 'That boy is going to be under the water in another few minutes. Lexi isn't strong enough to pull him out. And she isn't going to be strong enough to keep herself out.' Feeling completely helpless, she turned to Nick. 'Get me down there now. Don't wait for Ryan to talk to you. He has his hands full. I can help—I know I can.'

'I'm not risking another person unless I have to. It's bad enough Ryan going down there, but at least he knows what he's doing. You have no cliff rescue skills—'

'I'm her mother,' Jenna said icily. 'That counts for a great deal, believe me. Get me down there, Nick.'

He slid his fingers into the collar of his jacket, easing the pressure. 'If someone has to go it should probably be me.'

'You need to stay up here to co-ordinate with the coast-guard. I don't know anything about that—I wouldn't have a clue.' Jenna glanced down again and saw that Ryan had secured the boy and was now abseiling to the bottom of the cliff. He landed on shiny deadly rock just as another enormous wave rushed in and swamped both teenagers.

Instantly Ryan's voice crackled over the radio. 'Get Jenna down here, Nick. It's an easy abseil—'

Easy? Torn between relief and raw terror, Jenna switched off her brain. To think was to panic, and she couldn't afford to panic. Her daughter had climbed down there, she reminded herself as she leaned backwards and did as Nick instructed. All the same, there was a moment when her courage failed her and she thought she was going to freeze on the black forbidding rock.

'Just take it steady, Jen.' Ryan's voice came from below her, solid and secure. 'You're nearly there.'

To stop would be to disappoint him as well as risk lives,

so Jenna kept going, thinking to herself that if he genuinely thought this was easy she wouldn't want to do a difficult abseil. The cliff fell away sharply and she went down slowly, listening to Ryan's voice from below her, thinking of Lexi and not of the drop, or of the man who had died when his rope was severed. As her feet finally touched the rocks strong hands caught her. Ryan's hands.

He unclipped the rope and the sea immediately swamped her feet. If he hadn't clamped an arm around her waist she would have stumbled under the sudden pressure of the water. As it was, the cold made her gasp. Above her the cliff face towered, blocking out the last of the sunshine, revealing only ominous clouds in the chink of sky above. Here, in the slit of the rock, it was freezing.

She guessed that if the helicopter didn't manage to get to them soon, then it would be too late. The weather would close in and make flying impossible.

And then what?

'The tide is coming in—Ryan, I can't hold his head any longer—' Lexi's voice came from behind them and Jenna turned, her stomach lurching as she saw the blood on her daughter's tee shirt.

'It's not mine.' Lexi read her mind and gave a quick shake of her head. 'It's Matt's. His legs—both of them, I think. He jumped in and hit rock under the surface. I didn't know what to do—he's too heavy. Mummy, do something!'

Mummy. She hadn't heard 'Mummy' since Lexi was about six, and it sent strength pouring back through her rubbery legs.

'Just hold on, Lexi.' Her voice was firm and confident, and Ryan gave her a brief smile and released her, checking that she was steady on her feet before crossing the rocks to the two teenagers.

'You're a total star, Lexi. I just need you to hold on for

another minute. Can you do that?' He ripped equipment out of the rucksack as he spoke, and Jenna saw Lexi swallow as she stared up at him.

'Yes.'

'Good. We're going to get him out of the water now, and you're going to help.' Ryan had a rope in his hand. 'Just do everything I say.'

Jenna saw the fierce light of determination in her daughter's eyes—saw the faith and trust in her expression as she looked at Ryan.

Gone was the child who moaned when she couldn't get a mobile phone signal.

Jenna's flash of pride lasted only seconds as she saw another huge wave bearing down on them.

She saw Ryan glance at Lexi and then back towards her, trying to make a decision.

Jenna made the decision for him. 'Hold onto the children!' She slithered towards the rock face and managed to get a grip just as the wave rose in height and started to break. With a ferocious roar it crashed onto the rocks with an explosion of white froth, as if determined to claim its prize. Jenna clung, feeling the water pull at her and then retreat.

Wiping salt water from her face, she looked over her shoulder and saw that Ryan had his hands on Lexi's shoulders, holding her. As soon as the wave receded he turned his attention to Matt. The boy was moaning softly, his body half in and half out of the water.

'My legs—I can't put any weight—'

'Yeah—we're going to help you with that.' Ryan glanced around him, judging, coming up with a plan. 'If we can get him clear of the water and onto that rock higher up, that should give us at least another ten minutes before the tide hits us again. Enough time to check the damage and give him some pain relief.' He spoke into the radio, telling Nick what he was doing and listing the equipment he needed. 'While they're sorting that out, I'm going to get a rope on you, Matt.'

'Just leave me.' His face white with pain, the boy choked the words out. 'I don't want anyone to drown because of me.'

'No one is drowning today.' Ryan looped the rope under the boy's shoulders and secured it to a shaft of rock that jutted out of the cliff. Then he did the same to Lexi. 'The rope is going to hold both of you if another wave comes before we're done. We're going to get you out of the water, Matt. Then I'm going to give you something for the pain.' He questioned the boy about the way he'd landed, about his neck, about the movement in his limbs.

Jenna wondered why he didn't give the boy painkillers first, but then she saw another wave rushing down on them and realised that the boy was only minutes from drowning. Rope or no rope, if Ryan couldn't lift him clear of the water the boy was dead.

As the wave swamped all four of them Jenna held her breath and gripped the rock tightly. The tide was coming in. They didn't have much time.

'What can I do?'

'Do you see that narrow ledge just under the waterline? Stand on it. I need you to hold his body steady so that we move him as little as possible.' As a precaution, Ryan put a supportive collar around Matt's neck.

Jenna stepped into the water, gritting her teeth as the ice-cold sea turned her legs numb. If she felt this cold, how must the children be feeling? She steadied Matt's body, her hands firm. 'I'm ready.'

'I'm going to lift—try not to let his legs drag against the rocks.'

Using nothing but brute strength and hard muscle, Ryan hauled the boy out of the water. Matt's screams echoed around the narrow chasm, bouncing off the rocks and adding to the deadly feel of the place.

Her heart breaking for him, Jenna gritted her teeth, wanting to stop but knowing they couldn't. They had to get him clear of the water. He'd already been in there too long. Even as Ryan lifted him she saw the terrible gashes on the boy's legs and knew they were dealing with serious injuries. Blood mixed with the water, and as they laid him flat on the rock Matt was white-faced, his lips bloodless.

'Shaft of femur—both legs.' Now that he could see the damage, Ryan worked swiftly, checking for other injuries and then examining the wound. 'Jenna, we need to control the bleeding on his left leg and cover that wound. Get me pads and a broad bandage out of the rucksack. I'm going to give him some Ketamine. Matt, this will help with the pain.'

Matt groaned. 'I'm going to die. I know I am—'

'You're not going to die.' Seeing Lexi's horrified look, Jenna spoke firmly, and Ryan gave the boy's shoulder a quick squeeze.

'No one is dying on my shift,' he said easily, and Matt made a sound that was halfway between a sob and a moan.

'If the pain doesn't kill me, my mum will.'

Jenna closed her hand over his, checking that Lexi was safely out of the water. 'Your mum won't kill you,' she said huskily. 'She's just going to be relieved you're OK.'

Ryan's gaze flickered to hers and she read his mind.

Matt was far from OK. He had two fractured femurs and he was still losing blood. Knowing that she had to help, Jenna let go of the boy's hand and dug into the rucksack, finding what she needed. Thinking clearly now, she ripped open the sterile dressings and talked to her daughter. 'Lexi? Do you have your digital camera with you?'

'What?' Soaked through and shivering, Lexi stared at her

mother as though she were mad. 'Matt's bleeding half to death here and you want me to take a photo of the view?'

'He's not bleeding to death.' Taking her cue from Ryan, Jenna kept her voice calm. 'I don't want you to take the view. I want you to take a picture of Matt's legs. It will help the ER staff.'

'Good thinking.' Ryan injected the Ketamine. '*Do* you have your camera, Lex?'

'Yes—yes. But…' Baffled, Lexi cast a glance at Matt and rose to her feet, holding the rocks so that she didn't slip. She was wearing jeans, and the denim was dark with seawater. 'In my jacket pocket. What do you want me to do?'

'Take several pictures of the wounds. I'll do it, if you like.' Jenna was worried about her daughter seeing the extent of the injuries, but Lexi just gritted her teeth and pointed her digital camera. She took several photos and checked them quickly.

'OK. It's done.'

'Good.' Now that the pictures were taken, Jenna covered the wounds. 'It saves the receiving team in the hospital from removing the dressings from his legs to see what's going on.'

'Oh. I get it.' Several shades paler than she'd been a moment earlier, Lexi nodded. 'What else can I do?'

'Stay out of reach of the waves,' Ryan said immediately, his hands on Jenna's as they packed the wound, using a bandage to hold it in place. 'Any change—tell me. Jen, I'm going to splint both legs together.'

They worked as a team, Jenna following his instructions to the letter. It didn't matter that she'd never done anything like this before because his commands were clear and precise. Do this. Do that. Put your hands here—

Later, she'd look back on it and wonder how he could have been so sure about everything, but for now she just did as she was told.

Checking the pulse in both Matt's feet, she nodded to Ryan. 'His circulation is good in both legs.'

'Right. Lex, take this for me.' Ryan passed his radio to Lexi, freeing up his hands. Then he turned back to the boy. 'Matt, you've broken both your legs. I'm going to put a splint on them because that will reduce the bleeding and it will help the pain.' He looked towards Lexi. 'Logan should be up there by now. Make contact and tell Nick I need a towel.'

A towel? Glancing at the water around them, Jenna wondered if he'd gone mad, and then reminded himself that everything he'd done so far had been spot-on.

Worried that all this was too much for Lexi, Jenna was about to repeat the instructions but Lexi was already working the radio. Doing everything she'd been asked to do, she talked to Nick and relayed messages back and forth, copying the radio style she'd heard Ryan use.

'Dr McNeil is there. He wants to know what you need.'

'I'll have a Sager splint, if he has one, otherwise any traction splint. And oxygen. And ask Nick if we have an ETA on the helicopter.'

'Sager?' Jenna handed him a Venflon and Ryan slid the cannula into the vein in Matt's arm as smoothly as if he was working in a state-of-the-art emergency unit, not a chasm in the rocks.

'It's an American splint. I prefer it.'

'They're lowering it down now. I'll get it.' One eye on the waves, Lexi picked her way across the slippery rocks like a tightrope walker and reached for the rucksack that had been lowered on the end of a rope.

Watching the boiling cauldron of water lapping angrily at her daughter's ankles, Jenna prayed that she wouldn't slip. Pride swelled inside her and she blinked rapidly, forcing herself to concentrate on her part of the rescue. 'Is it possible to apply a splint in these conditions with just the two of us?'

'I can do it in two and a half minutes, and it will make it easier to evacuate him by helicopter.' Ryan took the rucksack Lexi handed him and opened it. Using the towel, he dried Matt's legs and then opened the bag containing the splint. In a few swift movements he'd removed, unfolded and assembled the splint. 'OK, that's ready.' He positioned it between Matt's legs, explaining what he was doing.

Hearing the sound of a helicopter overhead, Jenna looked up, relief providing a much-needed flood of warmth through her body. 'Oh, thank goodness—they're here.'

Ryan didn't look up. 'They can take Jamie off first. By the time they have him in the helicopter Matt will be ready.' He wrapped the harness around the boy's ankles. 'Lexi, tell Nick.' He was treating the girl like an adult, showing no doubt in her ability to perform the tasks he set.

Without faltering Lexi spoke into the radio again, obviously proud to have something useful to do.

Jenna helped Ryan with the splint. 'How much traction do you apply?'

'Generally ten per cent of the patient's body weight per fractured femur.' Eyeing Matt's frame, Ryan checked the amount of traction on the scale. 'I'm making an educated guess.'

The noise of the helicopter increased, and Jenna watched in awe as the winchman was lowered into the narrow gap between the cliffs. In no time he had a harness on Jamie and was lifting him towards the helicopter.

'At least there's no wind.' Ryan secured straps around Matt's thighs until both legs were well supported.

Staggered by the speed with which he'd applied the splint, Jenna took Matt's hand. 'How are you doing?'

'It feels a bit better,' Matt muttered, 'but I'm not looking forward to going up in that helicopter.'

'You're going to be fine. They're experts.' Ryan watched as

the winchman was lowered again, this time with a stretcher. 'We're going to get you on board, Matt, and then I'll give you oxygen and fluid on our way to hospital. Once we're on dry land, we can make you comfortable.'

Jenna looked at him, his words sinking home.

Ryan was leaving them.

She gave herself a mental shake. Of course he had to go with the casualty. What else? But she couldn't stop the shiver, and her palms dug a little harder into the grey slippery rock as she kept hold.

Ryan helped the winchman transfer Matt onto the stretcher. They had a conversation about the injury, the loss of blood—Jenna knew they were deciding whether it was best to have a doctor on board. The winchman was a paramedic, but still—

She watched as Matt was lifted slowly out of the narrow gap between the rocks, the winchman steadying the stretcher.

Once he was safely inside the helicopter, Ryan turned to Jenna.

Seeing the indecision on his face, she didn't hesitate.

'You should go! He might need you. You have to leave us here while you get him to hospital.'

Ryan's face was damp with seawater, his hair soaked, his jaw tense. 'I can't see any other way.' Already the winchman was being lowered for the final time.

Jenna lifted her chin. 'You're wasting time. We'll be fine, Ryan. We'll climb a little higher and the helicopter will be back for us soon. They're ready for you.' She watched, dry-mouthed, as the winchman landed on the rocks. 'Go.' To make it easier for both of them, she turned away and picked her way over the rocks to Lexi.

The girl was shivering, although whether it was from the cold or shock, Jenna didn't know.

She was shivering, too.

'They'll be back for us ever so quickly. You did so well,

Lexi. I was so proud of you.' She wrapped her arms around her daughter and rubbed the girl's back, trying to stop the shivering. 'Oh, you're soaked through, you poor thing. How long have you been in that water? You must be freezing.'

'Is Matt going to die, Mum?' Lexi's teeth were chattering and her long hair fell in wet ropes around her shoulders. 'There was so much blood—'

'That's because the seawater made it seem like more.' Jenna's protective instincts flooded to the surface as she heard the fear in Lexi's voice and decided this was one of those times when it was best to be economical with the truth. 'He isn't going to die. He is seriously injured, and he's going to be spending quite a bit of time in hospital, but he'll be all right, I'm sure. Largely thanks to you. How did you do it, Lexi? How did you climb down here?' Her stomach tightened at the thought.

'He was just lying there, Mum. I had to do something.'

Jenna hugged her tightly. 'You saved his life.'

'Not me. Ryan.' Lexi hugged her back. 'Did you see him come down that cliff face, Mum? It was like watching one of those special forces movies. Commandos or something.'

'Yes, I saw.' Jenna closed her eyes, trying to wipe out the image of her daughter negotiating those deadly, slippery rocks without a rope.

'And he knew exactly what to do—'

'Yes.'

Lexi gave a sniff and adjusted her position on the rock. 'He's so cool. And you were good, too, Mum. I've never seen you work before. I didn't know you were so—I dunno—so great.'

Jenna smiled weakly. 'It's amazing what you can do when the tide is coming in.'

'You and Ryan get on well together. You look like—a team.'

Jenna stilled. Had Lexi guessed that her relationship with Ryan had deepened into something more? 'We are a team. A professional team,' she said firmly, and Lexi lifted her head.

'Do you like him, Mum?'

Oh, no, not now. 'Of course I like him. I think he's an excellent doctor and—'

'That wasn't what I was asking!' Lexi's teeth were chattering. 'He was really worried about you. You should have seen the look on his face when he had to decide whether to hang onto me or you. He never took his eyes off you. If you'd been swept into the water he'd have been in there after you. What's going on?'

This was the perfect time to say something.

Jenna licked her lips. 'Do you like Ryan, sweetheart?'

'Oh, yes. And I like Evanna and the kids, and Fraser. Loads of people, actually. I never thought this place would be so cool.' Lexi clung tighter. 'I've got used to it here, Mum. I like Glenmore. And do you know the best thing?'

Ryan, Jenna thought. He was the best thing. 'Tell me the best thing for you.'

'The fact that it's just the two of us. I love that.'

Just the two of us.

Jenna swallowed down the words she'd been about to speak.

How could she say them now?

Lexi buried her face in Jenna's shoulder. 'Dad was awful to you. I see that now. He didn't even tell you stuff face to face. He just let you find out.'

'I expect he did what he thought was best.' Burying her own needs, Jenna watched as the sea level rose. 'Don't think about it now.' They needed to climb higher, she thought numbly, glancing upwards with a sinking feeling in her stomach. Now that the immediate crisis was over, the impossibility of it overwhelmed her.

'I want to talk about it, Mum!' Lexi seemed to have forgotten her surroundings. 'You're always protecting me, but I want the truth.'

Shivering, wet, chilled to the bone, Jenna tried to stop her teeth from chattering as she searched for the right thing to say. 'Dad— He— Actually, Lex, I don't know what happened with your dad. The truth is that sometimes the people we love disappoint us. But I'm not going to do that. I will always be here for you. Always. You'll have a home with me always.' She smoothed the girl's soaking hair. 'Even when you're off at university, or travelling the world, you'll still have a home with me.'

If they survived.

If they didn't both drown in this isolated, godforsaken gash in the cliff face.

'Dad just acted like he didn't have a family—' Lexi's voice jerked. 'I mean, he made you sell the house so that he could have the money, and he didn't even want me to go and stay with him this summer. That's why we came up here, isn't it? You made it impossible for me to get back there, so I wouldn't find out the truth. But when I rang him he told me it wasn't convenient for me to come—he didn't want me around, and that's why we came up here.'

Jenna stroked her daughter's soaking hair, smoothing it away from her face. 'I don't know what's going on in your dad's head right now, sweetheart, but I do know he loves you. You need to give him time to sort himself out.'

'He loves me as long as I don't mess up his new life.' Lexi scrubbed tears away with her hand. 'I'm sorry I was so difficult. I'm sorry I made it hard for you.'

'You didn't. It always would have been hard. Having you is what's kept me going. Having you is the best thing that ever happened in my life.' With a flash of relief, Jenna saw the helicopter and drew Lexi back against the rock face. 'Right. They're going to get us out of here. You go first.'

Lexi clung to her mother. 'I don't want to leave you here—'

'I'll be right behind you, I promise.'

As Lexi was clipped onto the rope and lifted into the helicopter Jenna had a few moments alone on the rock.

Looking at the swirling, greedy sea, she knew that she was facing the most difficult decision of her life. She thought back to the moment when Ryan had been forced to choose between holding her and holding her daughter and the injured boy. That was life, wasn't it? It was full of tough decisions. Things were rarely straightforward and every decision had a price.

If she told Lexi about her relationship with Ryan, she'd threaten her daughter's security and happiness. And what could she offer Ryan? He wanted a family. Babies. Even if she was able to have more children, how could she do that to Lexi?

There was no choice to make because it had already been made for her.

Clinging to the rock, Jenna watched Lexi pulled to safety inside the helicopter, the seawater mingling with her tears.

CHAPTER NINE

OVERNIGHT, Lexi became a heroine.

As word spread of her daring climb down the cliffs to save Matt, Jenna couldn't walk two steps along the bustling quay without being stopped and told how proud she must be feeling. Every time she opened her front door there was another gift lying there waiting for them. Fresh fruit. Cake. Chocolate. Hand-knitted socks for Lexi—

'What am I expected to do with these? They're basically disgusting!' Back to her insouciant teenage self, Lexi looked at them in abject horror. 'I wouldn't be seen dead in them. Who on earth thinks I'll look good in purple and green? Just shoot me now.'

'You'll wear them,' Jenna said calmly, and Lexi shuddered.

'How to kill off your love-life. If I'd known there was going to be this much fuss I would have let Matt drown.' She grabbed a baseball cap and pulled it onto her head, tipping the brim down. 'If this is how it feels to be a celebrity, I don't want any of it. Two people took photos of me yesterday, and I've got a spot on my chin!'

Jenna smiled at the normality of it. It helped. There was an ache and an emptiness inside her, far greater than she'd felt after Clive had left. One pain had been replaced by another. 'Ryan rang.' She kept her voice casual. 'He thought you'd want to know that Matt's surgery went well and he's definitely not in any danger. The surgeons said that if he'd lost any more blood he might have died, so you really are the hero of the hour.'

'It wasn't me, it was Ryan.' Obviously deciding that being a heroine had its drawbacks, Lexi stuffed her iPod into her pocket and strolled towards the door. 'I'm meeting Fraser on the beach. At least that way I might be able to walk five centimetres. And, no, I'm not wearing those socks.'

'You can wear them in the winter.'

'Any chance of us moving back to London before the weather is cold enough for socks?' But, despite the sarcasm, there was humour in her eyes and Lexi gave Jenna a swift hug and a kiss. 'What are you doing today?'

'Nothing much. Just pottering. I might go for a walk.' To the lighthouse, to tell Ryan that their relationship had to end.

Jenna watched as Lexi picked up her phone and strolled out of the house, hips swaying to the music which was so loud that Jenna could hear it even without the benefit of the earphones.

Her daughter was safe, she thought. That was all that mattered. Safe and settled. And as for the rest—well, she'd cope with it.

Ryan was standing on the cliffs, staring out over the sea, when he heard the light crunch of footsteps on the path. Even without turning he knew it was her. And he knew what she'd come to say.

Bracing himself, he turned. 'I didn't think you'd be coming over today. I assumed you'd be resting—that's why I rang instead of coming round.'

'We appreciated the call. We've both been thinking about Matt all night.' She was wearing jeans and her hair blew in the wind. She looked like a girl, not a mother. 'Lexi has gone for a walk and I wanted to talk to you.'

He wanted to stop her, as if not giving her the chance to say the words might change things. But what was the point of that? Where had denial ever got him? 'Are you all right after yesterday? No ill effects?'

'No. We were just cold. Nothing that a hot bath didn't cure. Ryan—'

'I know what you're going to say, Jenna.'

'You do?'

'Of course. You want to end it.'

She took so long to answer that he wondered if he'd got it wrong, and then she made a sound that was somewhere between a sigh and a sob. 'I have to. This just isn't a good time for me to have a new relationship. I have to think of Lexi. She's found out just how selfish her dad has been—she feels rejected and unimportant—if I put my happiness before hers, I'll be making her feel as though she matters to no one. I can't do that. She says she likes the fact that it's just the two of us. Our relationship is her anchor. It's the one thing that hasn't changed. I don't want to threaten that.'

'Of course you don't.' Ryan felt numb and strangely detached. 'I love you—you know that, don't you?'

'Yes.' Her feet made no sound in the soft grass as she walked towards him. 'And I love you. And that's the other reason I can't do this. You want children. You deserve children, Ryan. I'm thirty-three. I have no idea whether I can even have another child. And even if I could—and even if Lexi accepted our relationship in time—I couldn't do that to her. She'd feel really pushed out.' The hand she placed on his arm shook. 'What am I saying? I'm talking about children and a future and you haven't even said what you want—'

'I want you.' It was the one question he had no problem answering. In a mind clouded with thoughts and memories, it was the one thing that was shiny and clear. 'Have you talked to Lexi about it at all?'

'No. No, I haven't.'

'Maybe you should.' Refusing to give up without a fight, he slid his hands into her hair and brought his mouth down on hers. The kiss was hungry and desperate, and he wondered if by kissing her he was simply making it worse for them both. He tasted her tears and lifted her head. 'Sorry. That wasn't fair of me.'

'It isn't you. It isn't your fault.' She scrubbed her palm over her cheek. 'But we're grown-ups. She's a child. This whole situation is terrible for her, and I'd do anything to change it, but I can't. The one thing I can do is not make things worse.' Her voice broke. 'She is not ready for me to have another relationship.'

'Are you telling me that you're never going to have another relationship in case it upsets Lexi?'

'One day, maybe. But not yet. It's just too soon. I won't do anything that makes this whole thing worse for her. I suppose I could hide our relationship, but I don't want to. I don't want to sneak around and live a lie. We deserve better.' Jenna lifted her fingers to her temples and shook her head. 'This is ridiculous. I may be thirty-three but I feel seventeen. And I never should have started this. I never should have hurt you—'

'You've always been honest with me, and that's all I ask.' The hopelessness of it made the moment all the more intense, and their mouths fused, their hands impatient and demanding as they took from each other. Urgent, hungry, they made love on the grass, with the call of the seagulls and the crash of the sea for company.

Aferwards they lay on the grass in silence, because there was nothing more to say.

When Jenna stood up and walked away he didn't stop her.

* * *

The following day Jenna was half an hour late to surgery because everyone had kept stopping her to ask her for the details or give her another bit of gossip. Feeling numb inside, she'd responded on automatic, her thoughts on Ryan. 'Thank you—so kind—yes, we're both fine—no permanent damage—Matt's doing well—'

The effort of keeping up a front was so exhausting that she was relieved when she finally pushed open the glass doors to the Medical Centre. Hurrying through Reception, she was caught in an enormous hug by a woman she'd never met before.

'Nurse Jenna—how can I thank you?'

'I—' Taken aback, Jenna cast a questioning glance at Janet, the receptionist, who grinned.

'That's Pam. Matt's aunt. He has four aunts living on the island, so there's going to be more where that came from.' Janet handed a signed prescription to one lady and answered the phone with her other hand. 'There's a crowd waiting for you here, Jenna.'

Matt's aunt was still hugging her tightly. 'It's thanks to your lass that our boy's alive. I heard she climbed down—and then you went down that rope after her.'

'Lexi was brave, that's true—I'm very proud of her. And Ryan. But I didn't do anything.' Embarrassed by the fuss, desperate to be on her own, Jenna eased herself away from the woman, but people still crowded around her.

'Can't believe you went down that rope—'

'Lexi climbed down without any help—'

'Anyone who says today's teenagers are a waste of space has never met a Glenmore teenager—'

'Devil's Jaws—'

'Been more deaths there than any other part of Glenmore—'

Jenna lifted a hand to her throbbing head. 'Maybe I'd rather not hear that part,' she said weakly, remembering with horrifying clarity the moment when she'd stepped over the edge of the cliff. 'I'm just so pleased Matt's going to be all right. Dr McKinley rang yesterday and the hospital said surgery went well.' After a summer on Glenmore she knew better than to bother worrying about patient confidentiality. If she didn't tell them what was going on they'd find out another way, and the information would be less reliable. 'I'm just sorry I'm late this morning. If everyone could be patient…'

'Don't give it a thought.' Kate Green, who ran the gift shop on the quay, waved a hand. 'Won't kill any of us to wait. Anything we can do to help? We're sorting out a rota to make food for Matt's family when they're back from the mainland. They won't want to be fussing with things like that.'

Jenna looked at them all—looked at their kind faces, which shone with their eagerness to support each other in times of crisis. It was impossible not to compare it to the surgery she'd worked at in London, where patients had complained bitterly if they were kept waiting more than ten minutes. In London everyone led parallel lives, she thought numbly. Here, lives were tangled together. People looked left and right instead of straight ahead. They noticed if things weren't right with the person next to them. They helped.

Someone pushed something into her hand.

Jenna opened the bag and saw two freshly baked muffins.

'My mum thought you might not have had time for breakfast. We made you these.' The child was no more than seven years old, and for Jenna it was the final straw. Too emotionally fragile to cope with the volume of kindness, she burst into tears.

'Oh, now…' Clucking like a mother hen, Kate Green urged her towards the nearest chair.

'Shock—that's what it is. It was her lass who stayed with Matt. Saved him, she did. That's a worry for any mother.'

'Tired, I expect…'

'I'm so sorry.' Struggling desperately to control herself, Jenna rummaged in her pocket for a tissue. Someone pushed one into her hand. 'Just leave me for a minute—I'll be fine.' Oh, God, she was going to crack. Right here in public, with these kind people around her.

Evanna hurried out of her clinic, alerted by Janet. 'Jenna? Are you all right?'

Jenna blew her nose. 'Just being really stupid. And making my clinic even more behind than it is at the moment.'

'Then perhaps we can get on with it? I'm first.' Mrs Parker's crisp voice cut through the mumbling and the sympathy. 'And I've been standing on this leg for twenty minutes now. I'm too old to be kept waiting around. It isn't the first drama we've had on Glenmore and it won't be the last.'

Even the gentle Evanna gritted her teeth, but Jenna stood up, grateful to be forced into action.

'Of course, Mrs Parker. I'm so sorry. Come with me. The rest of you—' she glanced around the crowded waiting room '—I'll be as quick as I can.'

Following Mrs Parker down the corridor to her room, Jenna braced herself for a sharp rebuke and a lecture.

Instead she was given a hug. 'There, now…' Mrs Parker's voice shook slightly, and her thin fingers rubbed Jenna's back awkwardly. 'Those folks think they're helping, but they're overwhelming, aren't they? I've lived on this island all my life and there are times when I could kill the lot of them. You must feel like a crust of bread being fought over by a flock of seagulls.' With a sniff she pulled away, leaving Jenna with a lump in her throat.

'Oh, Mrs Parker—'

'Now, don't you get all sentimental on me, young lady.' Mrs Parker settled herself in the chair. 'Sentimental is all very well once in a while, but it doesn't solve problems. I'm guessing those tears have nothing to do with that foolhardy rescue or lack of sleep. Do you want to talk about it?'

Jenna blew her nose again. 'I'm supposed to be dressing your leg—'

'You're a woman. Are you telling me you can't talk and bandage a leg at the same time?'

Jenna gave a weak smile and turned her attention to work. Washing her hands, she prepared the equipment she needed. 'It's just reaction to yesterday, I'm sure. And I am a little tired. Really.'

'I'm old, not stupid. But not so old I don't remember how it feels to be confused about a man. You came here as a single mother. I'm guessing you're rethinking that now.'

Jenna's hands shook as she removed the bandage from the old lady's leg. 'No. No, I'm not rethinking that. Lexi and I are a team.'

'So you're going to let a strong, impressive man like Dr McKinley walk away from you?'

Jenna stilled. She thought about denying it and then realised it was useless. 'Does everyone know?'

Mrs Parker sighed. 'Of course. This is Glenmore. What we don't know is why you're not just booking the church. The Reverend King is quite happy to marry you, even though you've been divorced. I asked him.'

'You—?' Jenna gulped. 'Mrs Parker, you can't possibly—you shouldn't have—'

'You have a daughter. You need to keep it respectable. One bad marriage shouldn't put you off doing it again.' Mrs Parker glared at her. 'What? You think it's right, teaching that girl of yours it's all right to take up with whoever takes your fancy? You need to set an example. If you like him enough to roll around in his sheets with him, you like him enough to marry him. And he certainly likes you. There's a bet going on down at the pub that he's going to ask you to marry him. You'd better have your answer ready.'

'It would have to be no.'

Mrs Parker looked at her steadily, her customary frown absent. 'As we've been drinking tea together for almost two months now, perhaps you'd do me the courtesy of explaining why you'd say no to a man most women would kill to be with.'

Jenna didn't pause to wonder why she was talking to this woman. She needed to talk to someone, and Mrs Parker had proved to be a surprisingly good listener. 'Because of Lexi.'

She blurted it all out. Everything she was feeling. The only thing she didn't mention was Ryan's past. That wasn't hers to reveal.

Mrs Parker listened without interrupting. Only when Jenna had finished and was placing a fresh dressing on the wound did she finally speak. Her hands were folded carefully in her lap.

Age and wisdom, Jenna thought, wondering what secrets Mrs Parker had in her past. She was a girl once. A young woman. *We see them as patients, but they're people.*

'Tell me something.' The old lady looked at her in the eye. 'Do you plan to try and shield your daughter from everything that happens in life?'

Jenna swallowed. 'If I can.' Then she gave a sigh. 'No, of course not. Not everything, but—I love her. I want her to be happy.'

'Has it occurred to you that she might like a new man around the house?'

'I think it would unsettle her.' Jenna finished the bandage, concentrating on the job. 'Is that comfortable?'

Mrs Parker put her weight on her leg. 'It's perfect, as usual.' Her voice calm, she picked up her handbag. 'You're not the only one who can love, you know. And if love is wanting someone else's happiness, maybe Lexi should be thinking of yours. Maybe you should give her the chance to worry about you for a change. I want you to think about that.'

'Mrs Parker—'

'Just think about it. I'd hate to see you turning your back on something special. I'll send the next person in, shall I? Don't forget to drop in for tea when you're passing.' With a quiet smile, the dragon of Glenmore opened the door. 'I happen to know that Rev King has a date free in December. I always think a winter wedding is romantic. And I expect an invitation. I have a particularly nice coat that I haven't had reason to wear for at least two decades.'

'He rolled in a pile of something gross and now he stinks—Mum, are you listening to me? Basically, the dog is rank.' A frown on her face, Lexi helped herself to crisps from the cupboard and waved them under her mother's nose. 'Junk food alert! Time to nag!'

Her mind miles away, Jenna stared out of the window, trying to find the right way to say what needed to be said.

'On my fourth packet—' Lexi rustled the bag of crisps dramatically. 'Might add some more salt to them just to make them extra yummy—'

'Lexi…' Her strained voice caught her daughter's attention.

'What? What's wrong?'

'I—there's something I need to talk to you about. Something very adult.'

'Is it about the fact you're having sex with Ryan? Because honestly, Mum—' Lexi stuck her hand in the crisp packet '—I don't want to know the details. I mean, I love you, and I love that we talk about stuff, but I don't want to talk about that. It would feel too weird.'

Stunned, Jenna felt her face turn scarlet. 'You— I—'

'Don't get me wrong. I'm basically cool with it, Mum. I'm

pleased for you.' Grinning, Lexi nibbled a crisp. 'It's nice for someone of your age to have some excitement.'

Jenna moved her lips but no sound came out.

Lexi squinted out of the window. 'Better pull it together fast, Mum, lover-boy is strolling up the path. I'll go and let him in, shall I?' She sauntered towards the door, crisps in her hand. 'Hi, Ryan. I'm glad you're here, because Mum so needs a doctor. She's acting weird. I've waved, like, five packets of crisps under her nose and she hasn't even reacted. Normally she'd be freaking out and going on about too much salt, too much fat. Today—nothing. What's the matter with her?'

'Perhaps you'd better leave us for a moment.' Ryan dropped his car keys on the table, but Lexi shook her head and plopped onto a chair by the kitchen table.

'No way. I'm fed up with being the last person to know stuff around here. If you want to get rid of me you'll have to kick me out, and that will be child abuse.'

A smile flickered at the corners of Ryan's mouth. 'Presumably that wouldn't be a good start to our relationship.'

Lexi looked at him thoughtfully. 'You've got a thing for my mum, haven't you?'

Ryan winced, and Jenna came to her senses. 'Lexi!'

'It's too late for discipline. I'm already full of crisps.' Lexi folded her arms. 'It would be great if someone around here would give me a straight answer for once. I know you like my mum, so there's no point in denying it.'

'That isn't quite how I'd describe it,' Ryan said carefully, and Jenna felt the pulse beat in her throat.

Lexi didn't pause. 'What words would you use?'

'I love your mum.' Ryan spoke the words calmly, with no hint of apology or question. 'I love her very much. But I realise that the situation is complicated.'

'What's complicated about it? She's divorced, and you—' Lexi frowned. 'Are you married or something?'

'No. I was in the past.'

'So, basically, you're free and single?' Lexi grinned cheekily. 'I missed out the "young" bit, did you notice?'

'I noticed. Remind me to punish you later.' A sardonic smile on his face, Ryan sat down at the table. 'I'm not sure what order to do this in. If you want to be part of a family that already exists, do you propose to the woman or the daughter?'

'Don't waste your time proposing to me,' Lexi said casually. 'You may be hot, but you're way too old for me. How old *are* you?'

'Thirty-six.'

Lexi shuddered. 'You'd go and die, or something, while I was still in my prime. Mind you, that has its advantages. Are you rich?'

'Lexi!' Jenna finally found her voice. 'You can't—'

'Actually, I am pretty rich. Why does that matter?' Ryan's long fingers toyed with his keys. 'Are you open to bribery and corruption?'

'Of course. I'm a teenager. The art of negotiation is an important life skill.' Lexi grabbed a grape from the fruit bowl and popped it in her mouth. 'So how big a bribe are we talking about? If I let you marry my mum you'll buy me a pink Porsche?'

Ryan grimaced. 'Not pink. Please not pink.'

Glancing between the two of them in disbelief, Jenna shook her head. 'Can we have a proper conversation?'

'We are having a proper conversation.' Lexi looked at Ryan speculatively. 'What music do you like?'

'I have eclectic tastes.'

'In other words you'll pretend to like anything I like.'

'No. But I'm sure there would be some common ground.'

'If I let you marry my mum, will you teach me to abseil?'

Jenna felt faint. 'Lexi—Ryan—for goodness' sake—'

'I don't see why not.'

'And surf?'

'Your balance was pretty impressive on those rocks, and you don't seem to mind being swamped by seawater.' Ryan gave a casual shrug and a smile touched his mouth. 'Looks like I'm going to be busy.'

'And you promise not to tell me what time to go to bed or nag me about my diet?'

'You can eat what you like and go to bed when you like.'

Lexi fiddled with his car keys. 'Do I have to call you Dad?'

'You can call me whatever you like.'

'I never thought about having another father.'

There was a long silence, and then Ryan stirred. 'How about another friend? Have you thought about having another one of those?'

Lexi gave a slow smile and stood up. 'Yeah,' she drawled huskily, 'I could go with that. I'll leave you two alone now. The thought of watching a man kiss my mum is just a bit gross. I'm taking Rebel down on the beach to wash off whatever it is he's rolled in. I reckon it's going to take me at least two hours to get him clean, and I'm going to bang the front door really loudly when I come back.' Grinning wickedly, she scooped up the lead and then walked over to Jenna. 'Say yes, Mum. You know you want to.' She glanced over her shoulder to Ryan. 'And he's pretty cool—for an older person. We're going to do OK.'

Jenna couldn't find her voice. 'Lex—'

'You're almost too old to have another baby, so you'd better not waste any time,' Lexi advised, kissing Jenna on the cheek.

Sensing Ryan's eyes on her, Jenna swallowed. 'Lexi, we won't—'

'I hope you do. Think of all the money I'd earn babysitting.' Lexi grinned. 'How much would you pay me to change nappies? I'll think about a decent rate while I'm scrubbing

Rebel. See you later.' She sauntered out of the house, leaving the two of them alone.

Aware of Ryan still watching her, Jenna opened her mouth and closed it again.

He stood up and walked across to her. 'I had an unexpected visitor this morning.'

'You did?'

'The Reverend King.' There was a gleam of humour in his eyes. 'He wanted to know exactly what time we wanted the church on Christmas Eve. Apparently it's been reserved provisionally in our name. His suggestion was just before lunch, so that the entire island could then gather for food at our expense. I wondered what you thought.'

Jenna swallowed. Then she turned her head and stared into the garden, watching as Lexi put Rebel on his lead and led him through the little gate towards the beach. 'I think that life sometimes surprises you,' she said huskily. 'I think that just when you think everything is wrong, it suddenly turns out right. I think I'm lucky. What do you think?'

Ryan closed his hands over her shoulders and turned her to face him. 'I think we only have two hours before Lexi comes home.' His fingers were strong, and he held her as though he never intended to let her go. 'We should probably make the most of it. Especially if we want to make a baby before we're both too old.'

She made a sound that was somewhere between a laugh and a sob and flung her arms around his neck. 'What if I can't? What if I *am* too old? What if I can't give you a family?'

His hands gentle, he cupped her face and lowered his mouth to hers. 'Marry me and you will have given me all the family I need. You. Lexi.'

'But—'

'Sometimes we don't begin a journey knowing where it's

going to end,' he said softly, resting his forehead against hers as he looked down at her. 'Sometimes we don't have all the answers. We don't know what the future holds, but we do know that whatever it is we'll deal with it. Together. The three of us. And Rebel, of course.'

The three of us.

Holding those words against her like a warm blanket, Jenna lifted her head. 'The three of us,' she whispered softly. 'That sounds good to me.'

* * * * *

Turn the page for a sneak peek at Sarah Morgan's next book,
FIRST TIME IN FOREVER.

Windswept, isolated and ruggedly beautiful, Puffin Island is a haven for day trippers and daydreamers alike. But this charming community has a way of bringing people together in the most unexpected ways…

You won't want to miss Emily Donovan's story, the first in a fabulous new trilogy available in 2015!

CHAPTER ONE

It was the perfect place for someone who didn't want to be found. A dream destination for people who loved the sea.

Emily Donovan hated the sea.

She stopped the car at the top of the hill and turned off the headlights. Darkness wrapped itself around her, smothering her like a heavy blanket. She was used to the city, with its shimmering skyline and the dazzle of lights that turned night into day. Here, on this craggy island in coastal Maine, there was only the moon and the stars. No crowds, no car horns, no high-rise buildings. Nothing but wave-pounded cliffs, the shriek of gulls and the smell of the ocean.

She would have drugged herself on the short ferry crossing if it hadn't been for the child strapped into the seat in the back of the car.

The little girl's eyes were still closed, her head tilted

to one side and her arms locked in a stranglehold around a battered teddy bear. Emily retrieved her phone and opened the car door quietly.

Please don't wake up.

She walked a few steps away from the car and dialed. The call went to voicemail.

"Brittany? Hope you're having a good time in Greece. Just wanted to let you know I've arrived. Thanks again for letting me use the cottage, I'm really— I'm—" *Grateful*. That was the word she was looking for. Grateful.

She took a deep breath and closed her eyes.

"I'm panicking. What the hell am I doing here? There's water everywhere and I hate water. This is—well, it's hard." She glanced toward the sleeping child and lowered her voice. "She wanted to get out of the car on the ferry, but I kept her strapped in because there was *no way* I was doing that. That scary harbor guy with the big eyebrows probably thinks I'm insane, by the way, so you'd better pretend you don't know me next time you're home. I'll stay until tomorrow, because there's no choice, but I'm taking the first ferry out of here. I'm going somewhere else. Somewhere landlocked like—like—Wyoming or Nebraska."

As she ended the call the breeze lifted her hair and she could smell salt and sea in the air.

She dialed again, a different number this time, and felt a rush of relief as the call was answered and she heard Skylar's breathy voice.

"Skylar Tempest."

"Sky? It's me."

"Em? What's happening? This isn't your number."

"I changed my cellphone."

"You're worried someone might trace the call? Holy crap, this is exciting."

"It's not exciting. It's a nightmare."

"How are you feeling?"

"Like I want to throw up. But I know I won't because I haven't eaten for two days. The only thing in my stomach is a knot of nervous tension."

"Have the press tracked you down?"

"I don't think so. I paid cash for everything and drove from New York." She glanced back at the road but there was only the darkness. "How do people live like this? I feel like a criminal. I've never hidden from anyone in my life before."

"Have you been switching cars to confuse them? Did you dye your hair purple and buy a pair of glasses?"

"Of course not. Have you been drinking?"

"No, but I watch a lot of movies. You can't trust anyone. You need a disguise. Something that will help you blend."

"I will never blend in anywhere with a coastline. I'll be the one wearing a lifebelt in the middle of Main Street."

"You're going to be fine." Skylar's extra-firm tone suggested she wasn't at all convinced Emily was going to be fine.

"I'm leaving first thing tomorrow."

"You can't do that! We agreed the cottage would be the safest place to hide. No one is going to notice you on the island. It's full of tourists. It's a dream place for a vacation."

"It's not a dream place when the sight of water makes you hyperventilate."

"You're not going to do that. You're going to breathe in the sea air and relax."

"I don't need to be here. This whole thing is an overreaction. No one is looking for me."

"You're the half-sister of one of the biggest movie stars in Hollywood and you're guardian to her child. If that little fact gets out the whole press pack will be hunting you. You need somewhere to hide and Puffin Island is perfect."

Emily shivered under a cold drench of panic. "Why would they know about me? Lana spent her entire life pretending I don't exist."

And that had suited her perfectly. At no point had she aspired to be caught in the beam of Lana's spotlight. Emily was fiercely private. Lana, on the other hand, had demanded attention from the day she was born.

It occurred to Emily that her half-sister would have enjoyed the fact she was still making headlines even though it had been over a month since the plane crash that had killed her and her latest lover.

"Journalists can find out anything. This is like a plot for a movie."

"No, it isn't! It's my *life*. I don't want it ripped open and exposed for the world to see and I don't—" Emily broke off and then said the words aloud for the first time. "I don't want to be responsible for a child." Memories from the past drifted from the dark corners of her brain like smoke under a closed door. "I can't be."

It wasn't fair on the child.

And it wasn't fair on her.

Why had Lana done this to her? Was it malice? Lack of thought? Some twisted desire to seek revenge for a childhood where they'd shared nothing except living space?

"I know you think that, and I understand your reasons, but you can do this. You have to. Right now you're all she has."

"I shouldn't be all anyone has. That's a raw deal. I shouldn't be looking after a child for five minutes, let alone the whole summer."

No matter that in her old life people deferred to her, recognized her expertise and valued her judgment; in this she was incompetent. She had no qualifications that equipped her for this role. Her childhood had been about surviving. About learning to nurture herself and protect herself while she lived with a mother who was mostly absent—sometimes physically, always emotionally. And after she'd left home her life had been about studying and working long, punishing hours to silence men determined to prove she was less than they were.

And now here she was, thrown into a life where what she'd learned counted for nothing. A life that required the one set of skills she *knew* she didn't possess. She didn't know how to be this. She didn't know how to *do* this. And she'd never had ambitions to do it. It felt like an injustice to find herself in a situation she'd worked hard to avoid all her life.

Beads of sweat formed on her forehead and she heard Skylar's voice through a mist of anxiety.

"If having her stops you thinking that, this will turn out to be the best thing that ever happened to you. You weren't to blame for what happened when you were a child, Em."

"I don't want to talk about it."

"Doesn't change the fact you weren't to blame. And you don't need to talk about it, because the way you feel is evident in the way you've chosen to live your life."

Emily glanced back at the child sleeping in the car. "I can't take care of her. I can't be what she needs."

"You mean you don't want to be."

"My life is adult-focused. I work sixteen-hour days and have business lunches."

"Your life sucks. I've been telling you that for a long time."

"I liked my life! I want it back."

"That was the life where you were working like a machine and living with a man with the emotional compass of a rock?"

"I liked my job. I knew what I was doing. I was competent. And Neil and I may not have had a grand passion, but we shared a lot of interests."

"Name one."

"I—we liked eating out."

"That's not an interest. That's an indication that you were both too tired to cook."

"We both enjoyed reading."

"Wow, that must have made the bedroom an exciting place."

Emily struggled to come up with something else and failed. "Why are we talking about Neil? That's over.

My whole life now revolves around a six-year-old girl. There is a pair of fairy wings in her bag. I don't know anything about fairy wings."

Her childhood had been a barren desert, an exercise in survival rather than growth, with no room for anything as fragile and destructible as gossamer-thin fairy wings.

"I have a vivid memory of being six. I wanted to be a ballerina."

Emily stared straight ahead. At six, her life had fallen apart. She'd broken. Even after she'd stuck herself back together she'd been aware a piece was missing.

"I'm mad at Lana. I'm mad at her for dying and for putting me in this position. How screwed up is that?"

"It's not screwed up. It's human. What do you expect, Em? You haven't spoken to Lana in over a decade—"

Skylar broke off and Emily heard voices in the background.

"Do you have company? Did I catch you at a bad time?"

"Richard and I are off to a fundraiser at The Plaza, but he can wait."

From what she knew of Richard's ruthless political ambitions and impatient nature, Emily doubted he'd be prepared to wait. She could imagine Skylar, her blond hair secured in an elegant twist on top of her head, her narrow body sheathed in a breathtaking designer creation. She suspected Richard's attraction to Sky lay in her family's powerful connections rather than her sunny optimism or her beauty.

"I shouldn't have called you. I tried Brittany but she's

not answering. She's still on that archaeological dig in Crete. I guess it's the middle of the night over there."

"She seems to be having a good time. Did you see her Facebook update? She's up to her elbows in dirt and hot Greek men. She's working with that lovely ceramics expert—Lily—who gave me all those ideas for my Mediterranean Sky collection. And if you hadn't called me I would have called you. I've been so worried. First Neil dumped you, then you had to leave your job, and now this! They say trouble comes in threes."

Emily eyed the child, still sleeping in the car. "I wish the third thing had been a broken toaster."

"You're going through a bad time, but you have to remember that everything happens for a reason. For a start it has stopped you wallowing under the duvet, eating cereal from the packet. You needed a focus and now you have one."

"I didn't need a dependent six-year-old who dresses in pink and wears fairy wings."

"Wait a minute—" There was a pause and then the sound of a door clicking. "Richard is talking to his campaign manager and I don't want them listening. I'm hiding in the bathroom. The things I do in the name of friendship. You still there, Em?"

"Where would I go? I'm surrounded by water." She shuddered. "I'm trapped."

"Honey, people pay good money to be 'trapped' on Puffin Island."

"I'm not one of those. What if I can't keep her safe, Sky?"

There was a brief silence. "Are we talking about safe

from the press or safe from other stuff?"

Her mouth felt dry. "All of it. I don't want the responsibility. I don't want children."

"Because you're afraid to give anything of yourself."

There was no point in arguing with the truth.

"That's why Neil ended it. He said he was tired of living with a robot."

"I guess he used his own antennae to work that out. Bastard. Are you broken-hearted?"

"No. I'm not as emotional as you and Brittany. I don't feel deeply."

But she should feel *something*, shouldn't she? The truth was that after two years of living with a man she'd felt no closer to him than she had the day she'd moved in. Love wrecked people and she didn't want to be wrecked. And now she had a child.

"Why do you think Lana did it?"

"Made you guardian? God knows. But knowing Lana it was because there wasn't anyone else. She'd pissed off half of Hollywood and slept with the other half so I guess she didn't have any friends who would help. Just you."

"But she and I—"

"I know. Look, if you want my honest opinion it was probably because she knew you would put your life on hold and do the best for her child despite the way she treated you. Whatever you think about yourself, you have a deep sense of responsibility. She took advantage of the fact you're a good, decent person. Em, I am *so* sorry, but I have to go. The car is outside and Richard is pacing. Patience isn't one of his qualities and he has to watch his blood pressure."

"Of course."

Privately Emily thought if Richard worked harder at controlling his temper his blood pressure might follow, but she didn't say anything. She wasn't in a position to give relationship advice to anyone.

"Thanks for listening. Have fun tonight."

"I'll call you later. No, wait—I have a better idea. Richard is busy this weekend and I was going to escape to my studio, but why don't I come to you instead?"

"Here? To Puffin Island?"

"Why not? We can have some serious girl-time. Hang out in our pajamas and watch movies like the three of us did when Kathleen was alive. We can talk through everything and make a plan. I'll bring everything I can find that is pink. Get through to the weekend. Take this a day at a time."

"I am not qualified to take care of a child for five minutes, let alone five days."

But the thought of getting back on that ferry in the morning made her feel almost as sick as the thought of being responsible for another human being.

"Listen to me." Skylar lowered her voice. "I feel bad, speaking ill of the dead, but you know a lot more than Lana. She left the kid alone in a house the size of France and hardly ever saw her. Just *be* there. Seeing the same person for two consecutive days will be a novelty. How is she, anyway? Does she understand what has happened? Is she traumatized?"

Emily thought about the child, silent and solemn-eyed. Trauma, she knew, wore different faces. "She's quiet. Scared of anyone with a camera."

"Probably overwhelmed by the crowds of paparazzi outside the house."

"The psychologist said the most important thing is to show her she's secure."

"You need to cut off her hair and change her name or something. A six-year-old girl with long blond hair called Juliet is a giveaway. You might as well hang a sign on her saying 'Made in Hollywood.'"

"You think so?" Panic sank sharp claws into her flesh. "I thought coming out here to the middle of nowhere would be enough. The name isn't *that* unusual."

"Maybe not in isolation—but attached to a six-year-old everyone is talking about…? Trust me—you need to change it. Puffin Island may be remote geographically, but it has the internet. Now, go and hide out and I'll see you Friday night. Do you still have your key to the cottage?"

"Yes."

She'd felt the weight of it in her pocket all the way from New York. Brittany had presented them all with a key on their last day of college.

"And thanks."

"Hey…" Sky's voice softened. "We made a promise, remember? We are always here for each other. Speak to you later!"

In the moment before she hung up Emily heard a hard male voice in the background and wondered again what free-spirited Skylar saw in Richard Everson.

As she slid back into the car the child stirred. "Are we there yet?

Emily turned to look at her. The child had Lana's eyes—that beautiful rain-washed green. "Almost there." She tightened her grip on the wheel and felt the past rush at her like a rogue wave threatening to swamp a vulnerable boat.

She wasn't the right person for this. The right person would be soothing the child and producing endless supplies of age-appropriate entertainment, healthy drinks and nutritious food. Emily wanted to open the car door and bolt into that soupy darkness, but she could feel those eyes fixed on her.

Wounded. Lost. Trusting.

And she knew she wasn't worthy of that trust.

And Lana had known it too. So why had she done this?

"Have you always been my aunt?"

The sleepy voice dragged her back into the present and she remembered that *this* was her future. It didn't matter that she wasn't equipped for it, that she didn't have a clue, wasn't safe—she had to do it. There was no one else.

"Always."

"So why didn't I know?"

"I—your mom probably forgot to mention it. And we live on opposite sides of the country. You lived in LA and I lived in New York."

Somehow she formed the words, although she knew the tone wasn't right. Adults used different voices when they talked to children, didn't they? Soft, soothing voices. Emily didn't know how to soothe. She knew numbers. Shapes. Patterns. Numbers were controllable and logical—unlike emotions.

"We'll be able to see the cottage soon. Just one more bend in the road."

There was always one more bend in the road. Just when you thought life had hit a safe, straight section, and you could hit 'cruise', you ended up steering round a hairpin with a lethal tumble into a dark void as your reward for complacency.

The little girl shifted in her seat, craning her neck to see in the dark. "I don't see the sea. You said we'd be living in a cottage on a beach. You promised."

The sleepy voice wobbled and Emily felt her head throb.

Please don't cry.

Tears hadn't featured in her life for twenty years. She'd made sure she didn't care about anything enough to cry about it.

"You can't see it, but it's there. The sea is everywhere." Hands shaking, she fumbled with the buttons and the windows slid down with a soft purr. "Close your eyes and listen. Tell me what you hear."

The child screwed up her face and held her breath as the cool night air seeped into the car. "I hear crashing."

"The crashing is the sound of the waves on the rocks." She managed to subdue the urge to put her hands over her ears. "The sea has been pounding away at those rocks for centuries."

"Is the beach sandy?"

"I don't remember. It's a beach."

And she couldn't imagine herself going there. She hadn't set foot on a beach since she was six years old.

Nothing short of deep friendship would have brought her to this island in the first place, and even when she'd come she'd stayed indoors, curled up on Brittany's colorful patchwork bedcover with her friends, keeping her back to the ocean.

Kathleen, Brittany's grandmother, had known something was wrong, and when her friends had sprinted down the sandy path to the beach to swim she'd invited Emily to help her in the sunny country kitchen that overlooked the tumbling colors of the garden. There, with the gentle hiss of the kettle drowning out the sound of waves, it had been possible to pretend the sea wasn't almost lapping at the porch.

They'd made pancakes and cooked them on the skillet that had once belonged to Kathleen's mother. By the time her friends had returned, trailing sand and laughter, the pancakes had been piled on a plate in the center of the table—mounds of fluffy deliciousness with raggedy edges and golden warmth. They'd eaten them drizzled with maple syrup and fresh blueberries harvested from the bushes in Kathleen's pretty coastal garden.

Emily could still remember the tangy sweet flavor as they'd burst in her mouth.

"Will I have to hide indoors?"

The child's voice cut through the memories.

"I—no. I don't think so."

The questions were never-ending, feeding her own sense of inadequacy until, bloated with doubt, she could no longer find her confident self.

She wanted to run, but she couldn't.

There was no one else.

She fumbled in her bag for a bottle of water, but it made no difference. Her mouth was still dry. It had been dry since the moment the phone on her desk had rung with the news that had changed her life.

"We'll have to think about school."

"I've never been to school."

Emily reminded herself that this child's life had never been close to normal. The daughter of a movie star, conceived during an acclaimed Broadway production of *Romeo and Juliet*. There had been rumors that the father was Lana's co-star, but as he'd been married with two children at the time that had been vehemently denied by all concerned. Now he was dead too—killed in the same crash that had taken Lana, along with the director and members of the production team.

Juliet.

Emily closed her eyes. *Thanks, Lana*. Sky was right. She was going to have to do something about the name. "We're just going to take this a day at a time."

"Will he find us?"

"He?"

"The man with the camera. The tall one who follows me everywhere. I don't like him."

Cold oozed through the open windows and Emily closed them quickly, checking that the doors were locked.

"He won't find us here. None of them will."

"They climbed into my house."

Emily felt a rush of outrage. "That won't happen again. They don't know where you live."

"What if they find out?"

"I'll protect you."

"Do you promise?"

The childish request made her think of Skylar and Brittany.

Let's make a promise. When one of us is in trouble the others help, no questions.

Friendship.

For Emily, friendship had proved the one unbreakable bond in her life.

Panic was replaced by another emotion so powerful it shook her.

"I promise."

She might not know anything about being a mother, and she might not be able to love, but she could stand between this child and the rest of the world.

She'd keep that promise—even if it meant dying her hair purple.

"I saw lights in Castaway Cottage." Ryan pulled the bow line tight to prevent the boat moving backward in the slip. From up above the lights from the Ocean Club sent fingers of gold dancing across the surface of the water. Strains of laughter and music floated on the wind, mingling with the call of seagulls. "Know anything about that?"

"No, but I don't pay attention to my neighbors the way you do. I mind my own business. Did you try calling Brittany?"

"Voicemail. She's somewhere in Greece on an archaeological dig. I'm guessing the sun isn't even up there yet."

The sea slapped the sides of the boat as Alec set the inshore stern line. "Probably a summer rental."

"Brittany doesn't usually rent the cottage."

Together they finished securing the boat and Ryan winced as his shoulder protested.

Alec glanced at him. "Bad day?"

"No worse than usual." The pain reminded him he was alive and should make the most of every moment. A piece of his past that forced him to pay attention to the present. "I'll go over to the cottage in the morning and check it out."

"Or you could mind your own business."

Ryan shrugged. "Small island. I like to know what's going on."

"You can't help yourself, can you?"

"Just being friendly."

"You're like Brittany—always digging."

"Except she digs in the past and I dig in the present. Are you in a rush to get back to sanding planks of wood or do you want a beer?"

"I could force one down if you're paying."

"You should be the one paying. You're the rich Brit."

"That was before my divorce. And you're the one who owns a bar."

"I'm living the dream."

Ryan paused to greet one of the sailing club coaches, glanced at the times for high and low tides scrawled on the whiteboard by the dockside and then walked up the ramp that led from the marina to the bar and restaurant.

Despite the fact it was only early summer, it was alive

with activity. Ryan absorbed the lights and the crowds, remembering how the old disused boatyard had looked three years earlier.

"So how is the book going? It's unlike you to stay in one place this long. Those muscles will waste away if you spend too much time staring at computer screens and flicking through dusty books. You're looking puny."

"Puny?" Alec rolled powerful shoulders. "Do I need to remind you who stepped in to help you finish off the Ocean Club when your shoulder was bothering you? And I spent last summer building a replica Viking ship in Denmark and then sailing it to Scotland, which involved more rowing hours than I want to remember, so you can keep your judgmental comments about dusty books to yourself."

"You *do* know you're sounding defensive? Like I said. Puny."

Ryan's phone beeped and he pulled it out of his pocket and checked the text.

"Interesting..."

"If you're waiting for me to ask, you'll wait forever."

"It's Brittany. She's loaned Castaway Cottage to a friend in trouble. She wants me to watch over her."

"You?" Alec doubled up with soundless laughter. "That's like giving a lamb to a wolf and saying 'Don't eat this.'"

"Thank you. And who says she's a lamb? If the friend is anything like Brittany she might be a wolf too. I still have a scar where she shot me in the butt with one of her arrows two summers ago."

"I thought she had perfect aim. She missed her

target?"

"No. I *was* her target."

Ryan texted a reply.

"You're telling her you have better things to do than babysit the friend?"

"I'm telling her I'll do it. How hard can it be? I drop by, offer a shoulder to cry on, comfort her—"

"—take advantage of a vulnerable woman..."

"No—because I don't want to be shot in the butt a second time."

"Why don't you say no?"

"Because I owe Brit and this is payback." He thought about their history and felt a twinge of guilt. "She's calling it in."

Alec shook his head. "Again, I'm not asking."

"Good."

Pocketing the phone, Ryan took the steps to the club two at a time.

"So, again, how's your book going? Have you reached the exciting part? Anyone died yet?"

"I'm writing a naval history of the American Revolution. Plenty of people die."

"Any sex in it?"

"Of course. They regularly stopped in the middle of a battle to have sex with each other." Alec stepped to one side as a group of women approached, arm in arm. "I'm flying back to London next week, so you're going to have to find a new drinking partner."

"Business or pleasure?"

"Both. I need to pay a visit to the Caird Library in Greenwich."

"Why would anyone need to go *there*?"

"It has the most extensive maritime archive in the world."

One of the women glanced at Alec idly and then stopped, her eyes widening. "I know you." She gave a delighted smile. "You're the *Shipwreck Hunter.* I've watched every series you've made and I have the last one on pre-order. This is *so* cool. The crazy thing is, history was my least favorite subject in school—but you actually manage to make it sexy. Loads of us follow you on Twitter—not that you'd notice us, because I know you have, like, one hundred thousand followers."

Alec answered politely, and when they finally walked away Ryan slapped him on the shoulder.

"Hey, that should be your strapline. *'I make history sexy.'"*

"Do you want to end up in the water?"

"Do you seriously have a hundred thousand followers? I guess that's what happens when you kayak half-naked through the Amazon jungle. Someone saw your anaconda."

Alec rolled his eyes. "Remind me why I spend time with you?"

"I own a bar. And on top of that I keep you grounded and protect you from the droves of adoring females. So—you were telling me you're flying across the ocean to visit a library?" Ryan walked through the bar, exchanging greetings as he went. "What's the pleasure part of the trip?"

"The library is the pleasure. Business is my ex-wife."

"Ouch. I'm beginning to see why a library might look

like a party."

"It will happen to you one day."

"Never. To be divorced you have to be married, and I was inoculated against that at an early age. A white picket fence can look a lot like a prison when you're trapped behind it."

"You looked after your siblings. That's different."

"Trust me—there is no better lesson in contraception to a thirteen-year-old boy than looking after his two-year-old sister. They should give all thirteen-year-olds a baby to care for."

"If you've avoided all ties, why are you back home on the island where you grew up?"

Because he'd stared death in the face and crawled back home to heal.

"I'm here through choice, not obligation. And that choice was driven by lobster and the three and a half thousand miles of coastline. I can leave any time it suits me."

"I promise not to repeat that to your sister."

"Good. Because if there is one thing scarier than an ex-wife it's having a sister who teaches first grade. What is it about teachers? They perfect a look that can freeze bad behavior at a thousand paces."

Ryan picked a table that looked over the water. Even though it was dark, he liked knowing it was close by. He reached for a menu and raised his brows as Tom, the barman, walked past with two large cocktails complete with sparklers.

"Do you want one of those?"

"No, thanks. I prefer my drinks unadorned. Fireworks

remind me of my marriage and umbrellas remind me of the weather in London."

Alec braced himself as a young woman bounced across the bar, blond hair flying, but this time it was Ryan who was the focus of attention.

She kissed him soundly on both cheeks. "Good to see you. Today was amazing. We saw seals. Will you be at the lobster bake?"

They exchanged light banter until her friends at the bar called her over and she vanished in a cloud of fresh lemony-scented perfume.

Alec stirred. "Who was that?"

"Her name is Anna Gibson. When she isn't helping out as a deckhand on the *Alice Rose* she's working as an intern for the puffin conservation project. Why? Are you interested?" Ryan gestured to Tom behind the bar.

"I haven't finished paying off the last woman yet, and anyway I'm not the one she was smiling at. From the way she was looking at you I'd say she's setting her sat nav for the end of the rainbow. Never forget that the end of the rainbow leads to marriage—and marriage is the first step to divorce."

"We've established that I'm the last person who needs that lecture." Ryan slung his jacket over the back of the chair.

"So what's a girl like that doing so far from civilization?"

"Apart from the fact that the *Alice Rose* is one of the most beautiful schooners in the whole of Maine? She probably heard the rumor that only real men can survive here." Ryan stretched out his legs. "And do I need to remind you that my marina has full hook-ups, including phone, electricity, water, cable and WiFi? I'm introducing civilization to Puffin Island."

"Most people come to a place like this to avoid those things. Including me."

"You're wrong. They like the illusion of escaping, but not the reality. The commercial world being what it is, they need to be able to stay in touch. If they can't they'll go elsewhere, and this island doesn't need them going elsewhere. That's my business model. We get them here, we charm them, we give them WiFi."

"There is more to life than WiFi and there's a lot to be said for not being able to receive emails."

"Just because you receive them doesn't mean you have to reply. That's why spam filters were invented."

Ryan glanced up as Tom delivered a couple of beers. He pushed one across to the table to Alec. "Unless this is too civilized for you?"

"There are written records of beer being used by the Ancient Egyptians."

"Which proves man has always had his priorities right."

"And, talking of priorities, this place is busy." Alec reached for the beer. "You don't miss your old life? You're not bored, living in one place?"

Ryan's old life was something he tried not to think about.

The ache in his shoulder had faded to a dull throb, but other wounds, darker and deeper, would never heal. And perhaps that was a good thing. It reminded him to drag the most from every moment.

"I'm here to stay. It's my civic duty to bring civilization to Puffin Island."

"Mommy! Mommy!"

Devoured by the dream, Emily rolled over and buried her face in the pillow. The scent was unfamiliar, and through her half-open eyes she saw a strange pattern of tiny roses woven into white linen. This wasn't her bed. Her bedlinen was crisp, contemporary and plain. This was like falling asleep with her face in a garden.

Through the fog of slumber she could hear a child's voice calling, but she knew it wasn't calling her because she wasn't anyone's mommy. She would never be anyone's mommy. She'd made that decision a long time ago, when her heart had been ripped from her chest.

"Aunt Emily?"

The voice was closer this time. In the same room. And it was real.

"There's a man at the door."

Not a dream.

It was like being woken by a shower of icy water.

Emily was out of bed in a flash, heart pounding. It was only when she went to pull on a robe that she realized she'd fallen asleep on top of the bed in her clothes—something she'd never done in her life before. She'd been afraid to sleep. Too overwhelmed by the responsibility to take her eyes off the child even for a moment. She'd lain on top of the bed and kept both doors open so that she'd hear any sounds, but at some point exhaustion had defeated anxiety and she'd slept. As a result her pristine black pants were no longer pristine, her businesslike shirt was creased and her hair had escaped from the restraining clip.

But it wasn't her appearance that worried her.

"A man?" She slid her feet into her shoes—comfortable flats, purchased to negotiate street and subway. "Did he see you? Is he on his own or are there lots of them?"

"I saw him from my bedroom. It isn't the man with the camera."

The little girl's eyes were wide and frightened and Emily felt a flash of guilt. She was supposed to be sure and dependable. A parent figure, not a walking ball of hysteria.

She stared down at green eyes and innocence. At golden hair, tumbled and curling like a Disney princess's.

Get me out of here.

"It won't be him. He doesn't know we're here. Everything is going to be fine." She recited the words without feeling them and tried not to remember that if everything were fine they wouldn't be here. "Hide in the bedroom. I'll handle it."

"Why do I have to hide?"

"Because I need to see who it is."

They'd caught the last ferry from the mainland and arrived late at night, in the dark. The cottage was on the far side of the island, nestled on the edge of Shell Bay. A beach hideaway. A haven from the pressures of life. Except that in her case she'd brought the pressures with her.

No one should know they were here.

She contemplated peeping out the window, through those filmy romantic curtains that had no place in a life as practical as hers, but decided that would raise suspicions.

Grabbing her phone, and prepared to draw blood if necessary, Emily dragged open the heavy door of the cottage and immediately smelt the sea. The salty freshness of the air knocked her off balance—as did her first glimpse of their visitor.

To describe him as striking would have been an understatement. She recognized the type immediately. His masculinity was welded deep into his DNA, his strength and physical appeal part of nature's master plan to ensure the earth remained populated. The running shoes, black sweat pants and soft tee shirt proclaimed him as the outdoor type, capable of dealing with whatever physical challenge the elements presented, but she knew it wouldn't have made a difference if he were naked or dressed in a killer suit. The clothing didn't change the facts. And the facts were that he was the sort of man who could tempt a sensible woman to do stupid things.

His gaze swept over her in an unapologetically male appraisal and she found herself thinking about Neil, who believed strongly that men should cultivate their feminine side.

This man didn't have a feminine side.

He stood in the doorway, all pumped muscle and hard strength, dominating her with both his height and the width of his shoulders. His jaw was dark with stubble and his throat gleamed with the healthy sweat of physical exertion.

Not even under the threat of torture would Neil have presented himself in public without shaving.

A strange sensation spread over her skin and burrowed deep in her body.

"Is something wrong?"

She could have answered her own question.

There was plenty wrong—and that was without even beginning to interpret her physical reaction.

A stranger was standing at her door only a few hours after she'd arrived, which could surely only mean one thing.

They'd found her.

She'd been warned about the press. Journalists were like rain on a roof. They found every crack, every weakness. But how had they done it so quickly? The authorities and the lawyers handling Lana's affairs had assured her that no one knew of her existence. The plan had been to keep it quiet and hope the story died.

"I was about to ask you the same question." His voice was a low, deep drawl, perfectly matched to the man. "You have a look of panic on your face. Things are mostly slow around here. We don't see much panic on Puffin Island."

He was a local?

Not in a million years would she have expected a man like him to be satisfied with life on a rural island. Despite the casual clothes there was an air of sophistication about him that suggested a life experience that extended well beyond the Maine coast.

His hair was dark and ruffled by the wind, and his

eyes were sharply intelligent. He watched her for a moment, as if making up his mind about something, before his gaze shifted over her shoulder. Instinctively she closed the door slightly, blocking his view, hoping the child stayed out of sight.

If she hadn't felt so sick she would have laughed.

Was she *really* going to live like this?

She was the sober, sensible one. This was the sort of drama she would have expected from Lana.

"You live here?" she asked.

"Does that surprise you?"

It did, but she reminded herself that all that mattered was that he wasn't one of the media pack. He couldn't be. Apart from an island newsletter and a few closed Facebook groups there was no media on Puffin Island.

Emily decided she was so jumpy because of the briefing she'd had from Lana's lawyers. She was seeing journalists in her sleep. She was forgetting there were normal people out there. People whose job *wasn't* to delve into the business of others.

"I wasn't expecting visitors. But I appreciate you checking on us. Me. I mean me." She'd corrected herself quickly but knew from the faint narrowing of those eyes that her mistake hadn't gone unnoticed. "It's a lovely island."

"It is. Which makes me wonder why you're peeping at it round a half-closed door. Unless you're Red Riding Hood."

The amusement in his eyes was unsettling. Looking at that wide, sensual mouth, she had no doubt he could be a wolf when it suited him. In fact she was willing to bet that if you laid down the hearts he'd broken end-to-end across the bay you'd be able to walk the fourteen miles to the mainland without getting your feet wet.

"Tell me what's wrong."

His question confirmed that she didn't share Lana's acting ability.

His gaze lingered on hers and her heart-rate jumped another level. But then she reminded herself that a stressed-out ex-management consultant who could freeze water without the help of an electrical appliance was unlikely to be to his taste.

"There's nothing wrong."

"Are you sure? Because I can slay a dragon if that would help."

The warmth and the humor shook her more than the lazy, speculative look.

"This cottage is isolated and I wasn't expecting visitors, that's all. I have a cautious nature." Especially since she'd inherited her half-sister's child.

"Brittany asked me to check on you. She didn't tell you?"

"You know Brittany?"

That knowledge added intimacy to a situation that should have had none. Now, instead of being strangers, they were connected. She wondered why Brittany would have made that request, and then remembered the panicky message she'd left on her friend's voicemail the night before. She obviously hadn't wasted a moment before calling in help.

Her heart lurched and then settled, because she knew Brittany would never expose her secret. If she'd involved this man then it was because she trusted him, and his next answer confirmed that.

"Yeah, I know Brittany. We both grew up here. She was at school with my sister. They used to spend their summers at Camp Puffin—sailing, kayaking and roasting marshmallows."

It sounded both blissful and alien. She tried to imagine a childhood that had included summer camp.

"It was kind of you to drop by. I'll let Brittany know you called and fulfilled your duty."

His smile was slow and sexy. "Believe me, duty has never looked so good."

Something about the way he said it stirred her senses, as did his wholly appreciative glance. Brief, but thorough enough to give her the feeling he could have confirmed every one of her measurements if pressed to do so.

It surprised her.

Men usually found her unapproachable. Neil had once accused her of being like the polar ice cap without the global warming.

"If I married you I'd spend my whole life shivering and wearing thermal underwear."

He thought her problem lay in her inability to show emotion.

To Emily it wasn't a problem. It was an active decision. Love terrified her. It terrified her so much she'd decided at an early age that she'd rather live without it than put herself through the pain. She couldn't understand why people craved it. She lived a safe, protected life. A life in which she could exist safe in the knowledge that no one was going to explode a bomb inside her heart.

She didn't want the things most people wanted.

Flustered by the look in his eyes, she pushed her hair back from her face in a self-conscious gesture. "I'm sure you have a million things you could be doing with your day. I'm also sure babysitting isn't on your list of desirable activities."

"I'll have you know I'm an accomplished babysitter. Tell me how you know Brittany. College friend? You don't look like an archaeologist."

He had the innate self-confidence of someone who had never met a situation he couldn't handle and he was handling *her*, teasing out information she didn't want to give.

"Yes, we met in college."

"So how is she doing?"

"She didn't tell you that when she called to ask you to babysit?"

"It was a text and, no, she didn't tell me anything. Is she still digging in Corfu?"

"Crete." Emily's mouth felt dry. "She's in Western Crete." There was something about those hooded dark eyes that encouraged a woman to part with confidences. "So you've known Brittany all your life?"

"I rescued her from a fight when she was in first grade. She'd brought a piece of Kathleen's sea glass into school for Show and Tell and some kid stole it. She exploded like a human firework. I'm willing to bet they could see the sparks as far south as Port Elizabeth."

It sounded so much like Brittany she didn't bother

questioning the veracity of his story.

Relaxing slightly, she took a deep breath and saw his gaze drop fleetingly to her chest.

Brittany had once teased her that God had taken six inches off her height and added it to her breasts. Given the choice, Emily would have chosen height.

"You knew Kathleen?"

"Yeah, I knew Kathleen. Does that mean you're going to open the door to me?" His voice was husky and amused. "Puffin Island is a close community. Islanders don't just know each other—we rely on each other. Especially in winter after the summer tourists have gone. A place like this brings people together. Added to that, Kathleen was a close friend of my grandmother."

"You have a grandmother?" She tried to imagine him young and vulnerable and failed.

"I do. She's a fine woman who hasn't given up hope of curing me of my wicked ways. So, how long are you staying?"

His question caught her off guard. It made her realize how unprepared she was. She had no story. No explanation for her presence.

"I haven't decided. Look, Mr.—"

"Ryan Cooper."

He stepped forward and held out his hand, giving her no choice but to take it.

Warm, strong fingers closed around hers and she felt something shoot through her. The intense sexual charge was new to her, but that didn't mean she didn't recognize it for what it was. It shimmered in the air, spread along her skin and sank into her bones. She imagined those hands on her body and that mouth on hers. Unsettled, she snatched her hand away, but the low hum of awareness remained. It was as if touching him had triggered something she had no idea how to switch off.

Shaken by a connection she hadn't expected, she stepped back. "I'm sure Brittany will appreciate you dropping by to check on the cottage, but as you can see everything is fine, so—"

"I wasn't checking on the cottage. I was checking on you. I'm guessing Eleanor. Or maybe Alison." He stood without budging an inch, legs spread. It was obvious he wasn't going to move until he was ready. "Rebecca?"

"What?"

"Your name. Puffin Island is a friendly place. Round here the name is the first thing we learn about someone. Then we go deeper."

Her breath caught. Was that sexual innuendo? Something in that dark, velvety voice made her think it might have been—except that she didn't need to look in the mirror to know that a man like him was unlikely to waste time on someone like her. He was the type who liked his women thawed, not deep-frozen.

"I don't think I'll be seeing much of people."

"You won't be able to help it. It's a small island. You'll need to shop, eat and play, and doing those things will mean meeting people. Stay for a winter and you'll really learn the meaning of community. There's nothing like enduring hurricane-force winds and smothering fog to bring you close to your neighbors. If you're going to be living here you'll have to get used to it."

She couldn't get used to it. She was responsible for

the safety of a child and, no matter how much she doubted she was up to the task, she took that responsibility seriously. Brittany would have said she took *everything* seriously.

"Mr. Cooper—"

"Ryan. Maybe your mother ignored the traditional and went for something more exotic. Amber? Arabella?"

Should she give him a false name? But what was the point of that if he already knew Brittany so well? She was out of her depth. Her life was about order and suddenly all around her was chaos. Instead of being safe and predictable, the future suddenly seemed filled with deep holes just waiting to swallow her.

And now she didn't only have herself to worry about.

"Emily," she said finally. "I'm Emily."

"Emily."

He said it slowly and then gave a smile that seemed to elevate the temperature of the air by a couple of degrees.

"Welcome to Puffin Island."

If you enjoyed this book, try more from Sarah Morgan

Following the success of the Snow Crystal trilogy, Sarah Morgan returns with the sensational Puffin Island trilogy. Follow the lives and loves of Emily, Brittany and Skylar as they embark on new journeys and unexpected encounters.

Look out for these titles, coming soon in 2015!

Some Kind of Wonderful – July 2015

Christmas Ever After – October 2015

Find out more at www.millsandboon.co.uk/first-time-in-forever

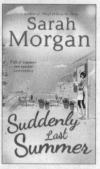

THE DISTANCE CURE

THE DISTANCE CURE

A History of Teletherapy

HANNAH ZEAVIN

The MIT Press
Cambridge, Massachusetts
London, England

The MIT Press would like to thank the anonymous peer reviewers who provided comments on drafts of this book. The generous work of academic experts is essential for establishing the authority and quality of our publications. We acknowledge with gratitude the contributions of these otherwise uncredited readers.

This book was set in Adobe Garamond Pro and Berthold Akzidenz Grotesk by Westchester Publishing Services. Printed and bound in the United States of America.

Library of Congress Cataloging-in-Publication Data

Names: Zeavin, Hannah, author.
Title: The distance cure : a history of teletherapy / Hannah Zeavin ; foreword by John Durham Peters.
Description: Cambridge, Massachusetts : The MIT Press, [2021] | Includes bibliographical references and index.
Identifiers: LCCN 2020041105 | ISBN 9780262045926 (hardcover)
Subjects: MESH: Distance Counseling--history | Psychotherapy--history | Professional-Patient Relations
Classification: LCC RC480.5 | NLM WM 11.1 | DDC 616.89/14--dc23
LC record available at https://lccn.loc.gov/2020041105

10 9 8 7 6 5 4 3 2 1

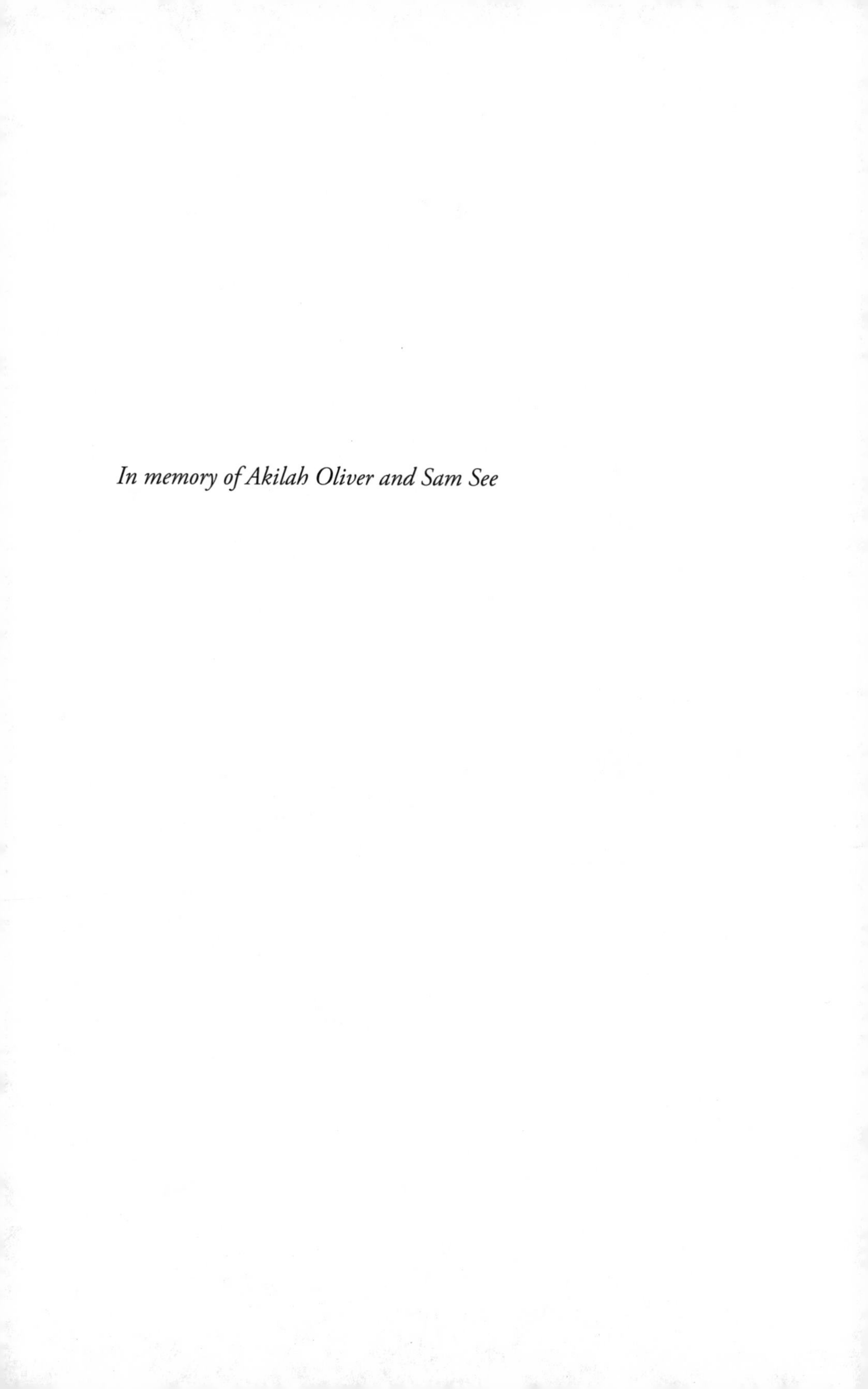

In memory of Akilah Oliver and Sam See

Contents

List of Figures

Foreword

How strange that Sigmund Freud seems to have sometimes wishfully pictured the encounter between analyst and analysand as direct and immediate (i.e., without media)!

Hannah Zeavin is not having it. Therapy, she brilliantly shows, is always a constellation of at least the therapist, the patient, and some mediating link; it is thus prone to interruption or expansion by third parties. The practice of therapy receives here a much-needed excavation of its own mediatic unconscious, one that goes beyond the oft-noted hieroglyphic, postal, and archaeological metaphors that abound in Freud's texts. Psychoanalysis and the many varieties of therapy that have cropped up since turn out in Zeavin's groundbreaking analysis to be lessons in the many forms that mediation can take. Freud himself hovered between telepathy and broadcasting as visions of the therapeutic encounter; Zeavin discerningly notes psychoanalysis's "tense and envious" relationship to media (indeed, like its relationship to many things).

Therapy, whatever its school or approach, was always to some degree teletherapy, the crossing of distances. In an observation that deserves engraving in stone, Zeavin reminds us that distance is not the opposite of presence; absence is. Presence may occur at any distance, and media pop up not only where the distances are great: nothing is more media-rich than two people talking to each other. In another granite-ready observation, Zeavin notes that all therapies are "rife with medium-specific contradictions." The media whose previously untold therapeutic histories she tells such as telephone, radio, tape, and screen only reveal and complicate structures already there in the face to face. This is especially so in a context framed by money, the clock, and the clinic, as psychotherapy classically is.

Twentieth-century teletherapy, we learn, is one long experiment with mediated variations of the dyadic frame. (I first mistyped *teletherapathy*, which might work as well!) Therapists, trying out media that span gulfs of space and time between people, richly employed their already highly developed symptom-reading skills, briefly becoming, perhaps in spite of themselves, media theorists—thus yielding a fresh archive of implicit media analysis, wonderfully curated by Zeavin. D. W. Winnicott experimented with radio as a means of batch-processing therapy for adults and children in Britain during and after World War II. Telephone suicide-prevention techniques were first pioneered as Christian pastoral outreach, a fact I wish I had known years ago when I was writing about Paul of Tarsus's media imagination of the church as an *ekklēsia*, literally, as a virtual assembly called out from the world. Online therapeutic chat takes us back to the self-fashioning of diary keeping, routing a written encounter with the self through a nonhuman other, whether paper or pixels. Auto-intimacy, audio-intimacy, auto-mation, other-intimacy: Zeavin shows us the rich tangle of the ways that people come to themselves by means of media, including human therapists. The history of therapy, once more, is also a history of media.

I do not want to dwell on the present in a work that will far outlast it, but I couldn't help but read this book partly as a genealogy of our Zoom-saturated moment. (In a few years, nobody may even know what Zoom is. What a lovely thought!) In the past six months I can count on two hands the number of face-to-face interactions I have had with people besides members of my immediate family. Never was the truth that the face to face is always mediated so perversely evidenced. Zoom's media particularities morph our mutual modes of appearance again: we show our faces and hide everything else; in public we mask our faces and show our bodies. (When was the last time any of us wore fancy shoes or uncomfortable trousers?) I know my new students as headshots in landscape format: I have no idea of their faces in profile or their stance, height, or gait. Plato's pedagogical dream was of mutual lovers of truth pulled to learn by the beauty of their bodies. Zoom fulfills half of his dream—the part about bodies not touching—but wrecks the other half, of actually seeing them. (That could also be a good thing.)

I recently broke my long self-imposed quarantine and six-foot shield from all other people—for the sake of therapy. Driven to frustration by back spasms, I finally went to see my physical therapist. She practiced laying on of hands on my back, diagnosed the trouble, and sent me home with new exercises. It helped—a lot: I can now sit long enough to write this foreword. The visit was mediated by many things, including the clock and clinic, and ended promptly after half an hour. But it was also glorious. A tele-visit wouldn't have done it. Maybe physical therapy is different, but maybe there is also some strange truth here about the peculiar intensity of the medium of the body for any kind of healing or discovery. And maybe there is also a lesson about the relation of mind and body: there is no mind without body, but the body follows mind through all the media through which it goes. Therapy at a distance is one more way our mind-body ensembles have expanded.

Hannah Zeavin has made us all smarter in thinking about some urgent and fascinating questions.

John Durham Peters
New Haven, Connecticut
September 21, 2020

Acknowledgments

I am deeply grateful to Gita Devi Manaktala and to the MIT Press for believing in this project. Thank you to everyone who had a hand in the making of this book, especially Erika Barrios, Jason Begy, Alison Britton, María Isela Garcia, Gregory Hyman, Jim Mitchell, and Molly Seamans. To three anonymous reviewers—thank you for your exquisite attention to the manuscript. Excerpts from this book appeared in *American Imago* (part of chapter 1) and *Slate* (part of the coda). I thank my editors there, Louis Rose and Susan Matthews, respectively. Parts of this project have been presented in various iterations at the Japanese Society of Transcultural Psychiatry, the American Psychoanalytic Association, New York University Center for the Humanities, the Department of Media, Culture, and Communication at New York University, Johns Hopkins School of Medicine, the Richardson History of Psychiatry Seminar at Weill Cornell Medical Center, and Sound Signatures Winter School at the University of Amsterdam—many thanks to the organizers of these events and to the audiences there.

This project simply wouldn't exist without the archives and archivists at the Freud Archive at the Library of Congress, the Wellcome Library, the British Psycho-Analytical Society, Hope College, KPFA, University of Tennessee Special Collections, Syracuse University, University of Virginia, the GLBT Archive in San Francisco, Stanford University, the Special Collections at UCLA, and the Internet Archive and its Wayback Machine, nor could it exist without the many practitioners, patients, CEOs, programmers, and engineers who let me interview them. Special thanks to Jackie

Wang for allowing me to use an image of her tele-analysis session, which so perfectly concludes the book. I am honored that John Durham Peters's words front this book. His work was constantly in my mind as I went about making mine.

The Distance Cure would be a very different project without my training in the Department of Media, Culture, and Communication at NYU. My heartfelt gratitude goes to Ben Kafka for mentoring me as a historian. His commitment to precise, slow reading and thinking in a world that too often values expedience remains deeply instructive. I thank Mara Mills for her tireless reading and thinking on my behalf, for modeling how to do media history, and for teaching me how to be a teacher. Elizabeth Wilson's writing had made me believe in the power of history and theory long before I was acquainted with her personally; she has my gratitude for her incisive, rigorous feedback throughout the whole process of writing the book. Erica Robles-Anderson performed a shockingly generous amount of labor on the manuscript, which informed this book on a cellular level. Finn Brunton's expertise in the history of the Internet was indispensable; he helped me resee the project—more than once—and I'm so grateful to have him as a friend and advocate. Lisa Cartwright, Jeremy A. Greene, A. B. Huber, Jessica Feldman, Nathan Kravis, Lana Lin, Kelli Moore, Susan Murray, Martin Scherzinger, Natasha Dow Schüll, Beth Semel, Lee Slome, Luke Stark, Nicole Starosielski, Marita Sturken, Bruce Weitzman, Laura Wexler, and Mitchell Wilson were each invaluable as interlocutors and supporters along the way. I feel deeply lucky to have started this project alongside four other dear friends engaged in the same task: Diana Kamin, Ella Klik, Ben Mendelsohn, and Dan Wiley. Tamara Kneese's companionship in early motherhood (and in academia) has been crucial. I'm very grateful to all my students and my colleagues at UC Berkeley, especially Charlie Altieri, Morgan Ames, Oliver Arnold, Eric Falci, Jacob Gaboury, Lyn Hejinian, Steven Justice, Grace Lavery, Steven Lee, David Marno, Massimo Mazzotti, and Elisa Tamarkin.

While living in Berkeley, I trained and volunteered to be a state-licensed rape crisis counselor. Most of my volunteer hours were performed over the telephone. I am very grateful for my training and the peer advocates who work the hotline. That work has no doubt informed my scholarship, and it remains an honor to be trusted by anonymous callers. In 2016–2017 I participated in the Northern California Society for Psychoanalytic Psychology's Intensive Study Group on "The Virtual Edge of Psychotherapy," which provided key insight into how contemporary psychologists and psychoanalysts *actually* think and feel the technological shifts in their practice and discipline—I remain indebted to that group. The NYU Humanities Center graciously supported my work in 2017–2018; our Tuesday meetings were a joy to participate in, and I'd especially like to thank Gabriela Basterra, Cécile Bishop, Joan Flores, Ayasha Guerin, M. C. Hyland, Mikiya Koyagi, Heather Lee, Gwynneth Malin, Christine Mladic, Wendy V. Muñiz, Wendi Muse, Kaitlin Noss, Simón Trujillo, and Gregory Vargo for their rigorous thinking. In 2018–2019, I was a Fellow of the American Psychoanalytic Association, which allowed me to meet with and receive mentorship from Francisco González, whose vital work in psychoanalysis, community mental health, and group dynamics is deeply informative.

I couldn't have written this book without my families, especially my many parents, given that this project's ancient germination was, in some preconscious way, an attempt to better understand what they each do at work. I also want to thank my friends, both old and new, who help make thinking possible: Daniel Baker, Jessica Benner, Brandon Brown, Jeff Clark, Joshua Clover, Cheryl Finley, Callie Garnett, Jean Garnett, Jane Gregory, Ben Lerner, Eric Linsker, Eliza Martin, Jeff Nagy, Aaron Reiss, Margaret Ross, Connie Scozzaro, Stephen Smith, Julianna Spahr, Julia Ward, Alli Warren, Carlin Wing, and Stephanie Young.

Geoffrey G. O'Brien: when I imagine a reader, it has always been you. Thank you for your tireless reading and rereading of this book. Malachai, you reorganized my life and have retaught me everything just in time.

Lastly, this book is dedicated to the memory of two friends who passed away far too soon: Akilah Oliver (2011) and Sam See (2013). In brief: Akilah Oliver taught me via experience a new kind of friendship and relationship to the world as a lasting instruction in how to be. My encounters with Sam's mind, his teaching, his kindness, and his joy, are the reason I pursued graduate study in the first place. I endeavor to carry their clarity with me always. I miss you both daily.

distance avails not

—WALT WHITMAN, 1860

And as soon as our call has rung out, in the darkness filled with apparitions to which our ears alone are unsealed, a tiny sound, an abstract sound—the sound of distance overcome—and the voice of the dear one speaks to us.

—MARCEL PROUST, 1920

At the end of the evening, not hearing the Voice, the listener would sometimes leave the needle on a jammed wave-length, or one that simply produced static, and would announce that the voice of the combatants was here.

—FRANTZ FANON, 1965

Very often people don't listen to you when you speak to them. It's only when you talk to yourself that they prick up their ears.

—JOHN ASHBERY, 1984

when i went into cyberspace i went into it thinking that it was a place like any other place and that it would be a human interaction like any other human interaction. i was wrong when i thought that. it was a terrible mistake.

—CARMEN HERMOSILLO A.K.A. HUMDOG, 1994

INTRODUCTION: DISTANCED INTIMACIES

In the twenty-four-hour period after Donald Trump was elected to the presidency in 2016, the San Francisco-based hotline Trans Life reported that it received its most calls ever in a day; the National Suicide Prevention Lifeline received more than double the calls it normally does in the hours after the election results were announced. After Hurricane Maria, calls spiked to Puerto Rico's sole suicide hotline and the service remained in high demand long after. In the wake of COVID-19, new hotline services have debuted with astounding speed to provide mental health care to nurses and other emergency, essential workers.

In a moment of personal and national crisis, people seeking help still turn to a form of teletherapy pioneered in the 1950s: the suicide hotline. At the same time, users who previously might not have used a traditional suicide hotline have turned to platforms still based on the crisis telephone line, such as the Crisis Text Line, a non-profit, SMS-based crisis line (whose board of directors includes danah boyd of Microsoft Research, Elizabeth Cutler, the founder of SoulCycle, and Jeff Lawson of Twilio).[1] This service received over two thousand text messages from its users on election night in 2016 and was flooded with an increase in users as the shelter-in-place orders went out in March and April 2020 in response to the COVID-19 pandemic. Even in daily moments of media consumption—the reading of articles or watching of television shows that deal with suicide—media now refer their consumers to hotlines. How has picking up the phone and speaking or typing to a trained, nonprofessional stranger come to seem like a favorable way to seek help and a crucial service to offer?

Hotlines specialize in making callers comfortable enough to do the work of talking about what's happening to and for them in the moment. For some, this state of intimate communication is much more easily achieved over the phone than in person, given the sheltering effect anonymity can have and that the treatment's access and duration are by and large user determined. Sometimes, being in crisis precludes the possibility of leaving the home. Beyond the conducive distance they offer, hotlines and other forms of teletherapy work because they are available when and where no one else is: any time, on demand, wherever the caller is with their phone; if contacting crisis support doesn't help, or doesn't feel right, the caller can simply hang up. The phone, in both its calling and text functions, contains an enabling distance and an ease of access that allow helpful communications to take place. This form of help is not entirely defined by how good or how bad the particular hotline center and its volunteers are—although those things matter too. It's also a question of offering the right combination of presence, distance, intimacy, and control.

Therapy has long understood itself as necessarily taking place in a room, with two (and sometimes more) people engaged in in-person conversation. What kind of productive communication happens when a patient and therapist aren't in the room together for fifty minutes at a time weekly, let alone four, five, or even six times a week (as was instructed by Freud)? Can a once-a-week, or once-a-month, or on-demand treatment suffice? Can it help a person to be in therapy when that therapy is conducted by letter, over the radio, the telephone, the personal computer, or an app on a cellphone, either anonymously or not, with a person or with an algorithm? In short, yes. These forms of networked, broadcast, tele- and computational therapies may not accomplish what long-term embodied psychotherapeutic or cognitive behavioral therapies do or aim to provide; they are understood to be different than traditional ongoing, in-person therapies. That difference, namely the dislocation of patient and therapist from the office and the inclusion and use of explicit communication technologies, can make practitioners as well as patients anxious. Nonetheless, users call on distance therapies to intervene in their own crises, to acquire tools for future self-intervention in suicidal feelings, to obtain crucial support after traumatic experience, and to receive help with handling microaggressions or upsetting interactions at school, at home, or in the workplace. These spontaneous patients also enjoy the secondary benefit of having witnessed their own decision to seek help; users perform self-directed care in the moment of seeking care from another.

It isn't always easy to find conventional therapeutic help or even teleforms in the moment of need, let alone make use of that help. Beyond the barriers that exist to finding a therapist and being in therapy, communicating itself is a difficult task—John Durham Peters calls this paradox the "dualism of communication—at once a bridge and a chasm."[2] The work of therapy is to make communicating possible enough for long enough that the "magic" of talk therapy can do its work, the bridge momentarily spanning the chasm. More specifically, psychotherapy offers both a model of mind and a communicative practice that understands that communication is at once the goal and the cure, yet also often nearly impossible.

This is a book about the history of these helping relationships and the forms of communication on which they depend: with a human known to us, a stranger, a person we know only by voice, and with ourselves. It's about how we generate, maintain, and practice those relationships across time and across distance. It is about the transformations of human (and human/nonhuman) intimacy in the long twentieth century. To study these kinds of relationships accurately, I have had to reconceive them: they are not dyads but triads, composed of patients, therapists (broadly defined), and communication technology—the means by which they connect (and disconnect). Mental health and care delivery thus form an aperture onto communication as such: how we do it, when, where, over what medium, and how that affects us, makes us anxious, rewards us, allows us to "talk" with others we otherwise wouldn't, in ways that otherwise might not be available. The actors transmitting and receiving the "talk" are those in need of help and the mental health care workers who "listen," the psychotherapists, social workers, clergy, volunteers, phones, and computers that help them.

The Distance Cure is structured as a study in a single genre of communication: therapies performed via various kinds of distance, including mediated, tele-, and automated therapies. Although there is a millennia-long

Western tradition of speech as cure—from Socrates' idea that the cure of the soul is "fair words,"[3] and Aristotle's notion of catharsis in *Poetics*, to the ongoing use of the Catholic confessional—this study begins in 1890, when psychoanalysis becomes codified as a formal, institutional discipline. As the book moves into the twentieth century, distance therapy is conducted under the sign of many subgenres and theories of practice including psychoanalytic, psychodynamic, and cognitive behavioral therapy (CBT), as well as lay forms of help and care such as pastoral counseling, peer-to-peer help, self-help, and self-improvement. All these different forms of mental health care have at least one thing in common: the belief that some kind of communication helps if not cures, regardless of its medium.[4]

Despite the word "cure" being in its title, this book doesn't assess teletherapy's general curative function nor does it make *direct* recommendations for clinicians about how to practice teletherapy.[5] Instead, *The Distance Cure* focuses on the helping interaction itself: whether patients seek it, how they seek it, how they are and are not helped, and what may be able to help them. And at what cost? As the function of the clinician declines and the serial, weekly face-to-face appointment gives way to broadcast models, volunteer labor, peer-to-peer aid, and self-tracking therapies, access to treatments that were historically prohibitively expensive for the many becomes more thinkable. Parallel to this, free therapies decrease, as patients become understood as clients and then as customers. Often, teletherapy projects prioritize "help" being made more easily available via the tele-delivery of therapy over attention to how much help is on offer, what that help is, who provides it, what it instructs, and for whom it actually feels usable.

The Distance Cure shows that teletherapy, far from being a recent invention, is at least as old as psychoanalysis itself. Beginning in the 1890s with a reading of Freud's treatments by mail and his moment's epistolary conventions, I offer a new history of the conventional therapeutic scenario, one that cannot be told in isolation from its shadow form, teletherapy. Subsequent chapters demonstrate that psychotherapy has always operated through multiple communication technologies and media, including advice columns, radio broadcasts, crisis hotlines, the earliest mainframe networks, home computing, the Internet, and mobile phones. To protect the supposed "purity" of the dyadic model of therapy, practitioners since Freud have almost completely resisted reflecting on these channels; my aim has been to do just the opposite. This study restores to the therapeutic past a history of the discipline's robust real and metaphorical use of communication technology.

Retelling the history of therapy as teletherapy allows us to examine contemporary fantasies, concerns, and panics about the impact of media on social and clinical relationships. Engaging with mental health care over distance is often framed as the abandonment of proper human connection. Both the popular press and critical media theorists take for granted that teletechnologies undermine conversation, empathy, and "real" connection—all of which are the basis for in-person psychodynamic therapy (see coda).

The Distance Cure argues that the therapist-patient dyad, reconceived as a triad, provides a unique site for examining these current concerns about what media add to human relationships and what they subtract. This book contends that media technologies have always played a central and sometimes alarming role in our intimate social relationships, producing medium-specific forms of relating that allow for unexpected and new kinds of human-to-human communication. This book considers what happens when an explicit third communication technology again and again enters into the extraordinary relationship between patient and therapist.

THE SETTING

At first glance, the modes of connection proper to teletherapies may seem as if they radically depart from those used during in-person talk therapy. Subtract two-way conversation, spoken exchanges, and the room, and what is left over from the traditional therapeutic scene? In fact, many of the conventions of the traditional scenario reappear in tele-treatment. The logics of therapy, as a model of communication, are present and portable across a variety of media over which therapeutic contact occurs, even if handwritten letters or email carry that contact rather than the air.

Calling these embodied and disembodied practices "talk therapy" elides another foundational element of that communicative work: the scene in which it takes place. At its most basic, for a therapy to function, you need a patient expressing content within a relationship with a receptive other and what is called the "setting" or "frame."[6] The frame is part of how therapeutic intimacy is constructed, contained, and maintained. It allows a patient and clinician to have a close working relationship that is not *too* close. In the conventional therapeutic scenario, the ethical, temporal, and financial boundaries of the relationship and the physical space in which it occurs together comprise the frame: the office, the fixed appointments for the session or sessions, the session hours (especially their beginning and end), the fixed fee for this bounded time, the greeting at the door, the chairs or couch utilized by clinician and patient, and the clinician's particular form of attention and capacity to listen. The traditional therapeutic relationship is understood as one that is necessarily elaborated across time—and specific times at that, in a stable location. I would add that the very aspects of psychodynamic therapy that constitute the frame and its varying durability—the referral, the office, the fee, the hour of the appointment, and cancellations on part of clinician or patient—are on one level neutral and material but immediately become infused with the psychic contents of that particular therapeutic relationship. For example, the regimented clinical hour and schedule of appointments may be unconsciously reminiscent of early regimens, such as the fee(d)ing schedule of an infant, or of the custody arrangement imposed on a child of divorce. Those reminiscences will be brought up in the therapeutic relationship in those moments where the therapeutic frame is maintained (including keeping appointments and billing) and interrupted (the therapist asking to change an hour, raise the fee, and so on). Described this way, therapy and the frame that undergirds it can have the quality of enacted, ongoing ritual—as long as the patient is able to perform it with their therapist.

The site of that ritual in the traditional therapeutic scheme—the office, the consulting room—presents the embodied environmental conditions of the relationship between patient and clinician. The materiality of this room is important: a room is not always a secure container for speech, either actually or fantastically. Soundproofing is often referred to as one of the many parameters that provide quality assurance in therapy.[7] It falls into the same category as the conditions for patients outside the office: offering a separate toilet for patients, having a waiting room, and for some, maintaining a library.[8] Inside the office waits a pair of chairs or, for analytic patients, a couch and its accompanying chair.[9] The furniture, beyond what type is selected—its size, the choice of color and fabric, a decision as to what might be the optimal *distance* between clinician and patient—is not explicitly legislated even though clinicians also understand these features to be important and impactful.

While I reconceive the original therapeutic dyad as the triad of patient, clinician, and mediating frame, it must be acknowledged that the frame, far from being a rigid, static set of rules and regulations even in the most traditional therapeutic relationships and schools, has always been theoretically flexible and constantly shifts in practice. Immediately following its theorization and establishment,[10] the psychoanalytic frame was repeatedly broken, challenged, revised, and moved by both patients and clinicians, including Freud himself. The frame is responsive to revision, whether the concrete shift from the six days a week analytic schedule of late nineteenth-century Vienna to the five days a week schedule of the UK and US in the twentieth century (both based on the length of the work week in those nations), to theories of how and when the patient can be involved in generating the frame, and to the inclusion of technologies in the treatment.[11] The frame or the setting is an open enough concept that it is now being called a "device" by some therapists, in keeping with the move toward technologically mediated therapy.[12] Both the rigidity of the frame and its capacity for alteration may be part of how new forms of therapy emerge, both in person and over distance. Mediated, networked, and teletherapies do not quite rescind traditional framing. Instead, these forms require the elaboration of new frames that are similarly rigid and moveable in their new contexts; the therapeutic scene takes new, media-specific forms that are in turn invested with meaning on the part of both users and providers. The ritual of therapy is flexible enough to absorb new conventions and decorum from the communication technologies it makes use of and to modify them for therapeutic aims; this moving, shifting, rupturable frame is also where some therapists locate their anxieties about bringing telecommunications into the therapeutic triad, or about the suddenly palpable triadic nature of traditional therapy itself. These clinicians think that a roomless frame changes what a therapy is or whether it can happen at all. Put another way, if the frame is too mobile, too responsive, the status of the treatment comes into question. The rupture of the traditional frame as laid out above supposedly wrecks the purity of a therapeutic treatment; the fatal impurity is often associated with the dislocation of therapist from patient and the inclusion of media (the phone, the Zoom session).

Yet it is possible to experience transference without bodies, or to generate productive speech without lying down, or miss appointments digitally. The British psychoanalyst D. W. Winnicott's World War II radio broadcasts occurred at the same time every week and home radios were in the same location—just not the same location as Winnicott's BBC recording booth. Hotline users call when they need to but the frame is reaffirmed via the greeting and structure of the call; some hotline users only call in during particular volunteers' schedules in order to reach the same voice at the same time week to week. Self-tracking therapies reconfigure a frame via push notifications to their users to say, "You haven't interacted with me yet today." In these ways, teletherapies preserve the ritual and framing inherent in the therapeutic relationship via the conventions, affordances, and materiality of their own new triadic configuration.

ON MONEY

There is yet another medium present whenever and wherever therapists and their patients relate to one another: money. It can also keep therapists and patients from relating at all. Money as medium needs distinct and particular attention in a history of teletherapy because its effects on therapeutic communication vary with the medium grounding that therapeutic speech. Money is notoriously difficult for (some) people to talk about. Freud acknowledged that, in general, analysts "can point out that money matters are treated by civilized people in the same way as sexual matters—with the same inconsistency, prudishness and hypocrisy."[13] Brenda Berger and Stephanie Newman argue in their book *Money Talks* that the American financial crisis of 2008 finally made money a broachable topic of conversation both on the couch and between analysts: it merely took the financial landscape collapsing all around the consulting room. It is in just such moments of material and national crisis, where psychotherapists are unsure of their future, that the frame of the frame shifts.

Many therapists, including psychoanalysts and psychotherapists, understand money to be its concrete function (an exchange rate for time spent in a professional setting) and to have symbolic function. For my purposes, money will be considered as a generally undermentioned element in therapeutic technique and theory and as a medium where patients and therapists can (and do) freely create meaning together. While this inextricably includes money as a site of fantasy, I am going to leave to the side the ways psychoanalysts from Freud forward have thought about money as a symbol in the clinical treatment of patients in order to think about the historical, material, and relational function of money in the teletherapeutic context.

The economic conditions of traditional therapy are those from which teletherapy arises and on which it depends. Despite the fact that this project tracks the decline of traditional, face-to-face, serial psychotherapy and the emergence of more contingent, para-psychotherapeutic, and experimental modes of doing therapy at a distance, it needs to be said that teletherapy is most frequently a free or low-fee modality for providing mental health care (except where it's the *only* means of mental health care, as in the COVID-19 pandemic). Freud's letters, psychotherapeutic broadcasts, crisis hotlines, online clinics, and many chat services were fee-less. Instead, patients paid and pay for utilities: the post, the radio, telephone, and Internet. Teletherapy is not incidentally low-cost: its users are largely excluded from the traditional full-fee session, in-person and with a degreed expert. There are differences between "paid attention" (traditional, hourly, billed) and "free attention" (gifted attention, volunteer attention, or algorithmic attention). This project elaborates the many ways that teletherapies keep their costs down (by using volunteer labor, by offering asynchronic help, by being informal, and through automation) and access patients that in-person therapy cannot.

The problems of cost and access (of which cost is one element) are as old as psycho- and teletherapies. While elaborating the nascent practice of psychoanalysis, Freud prepared "On Beginning the Treatment (Further Recommendations on the Technique of Psychoanalysis I)" (1913). Freud mentions money directly eight times and includes it in the frame: "Points of importance at the beginning of the analysis are arrangements about *time* and *money*."[14] Here, Freud elaborates a scheme for time and money at once. First, he recommends the "leasing of a definite hour" by patients and that patients will pay regardless of whether or not they come—much like "teachers of music or languages in good society."[15] Along with the definite leasing of hours, the fee is also deployed and seen here as a definitional and relational boundary: the labor of the analyst is purchased, not freely given. Economically, it is not a confessing relationship like that provided by the Catholic Church (when confession is more directly the form therapy remediates, as is the case with a peer-to-peer hotline, the help is usually offered for free; for more on this see chapter 3). Instead, Freud compared analysis to the labor and hourly wage of a private teacher or a doctor. Freud's argument is that patients will find conscious and unconscious reasons not to come to treatment and that even the "occasional non-attendances" ruin the livelihood of psychoanalysts.[16] In-person treatment is incredibly difficult work and hard for a patient to sustain (which is why it is so surprising that *enjoying* treatment and finding pleasure in it figure so heavily in automated therapies—see chapter 4).[17]

Next, Freud deals with the fee and urges analysts to speak openly and directly with new patients in setting the fee:

> An analyst does not dispute that money is to be regarded in the first instance as a *medium* for self-preservation and for obtaining power; but he maintains that, besides this, powerful sexual factors are involved in the value set upon it. . . . He shows them that he himself has cast off false shame on these topics, by voluntarily telling them the price at which he values his time. . . . (It is a familiar fact that the value of the treatment is not enhanced in the patient's eyes if a very low fee is asked.)[18]

Freud here seems to acknowledge money as medium, or means (*Mittel*), directly. But he restricts that notion to a one-time, one-way communication from analyst to analysand that occurs only in the moment of the therapeutic frame's establishment. Here, the fee is considered to be as much a communication as literal money. It at once communicates the analyst's own value economically and in terms of their own self-worth and the value of the treatment as cure. In turn, this sets the value of the treatment as well as the analyst in the patient's estimation. Freud conveniently suggests that the higher the fee, the better for *both patient and analyst.* If you make analysis cost a goodly amount, the treatment will be understood as highly valuable, where value moves between economic worth and cultural capital and curative element. An analyst is to set the price at which the return to health is to be valued. Freud writes, "The absence of the regulating effect offered by the payment of a fee to the doctor makes itself very painfully felt; the whole relationship is removed from the real world, and the patient is deprived of a strong motive for endeavoring to bring the treatment to an end."[19] Money functions like a reality principle: treatment cannot go on forever.[20]

The establishment of the fee is therefore the beginning of a treatment whose aim is to restore health to the patient-participant. Health is inextricably linked with work for Freud—his adage that health means the ability to work and love puts those two activities on equal footing. The fee then offers both a quantitative and a qualitative measure of health as something to be gained—to be purchased—through psychoanalysis. In return the clinician provides expert "paid attention" to the patient. This restricts the category of eligible and worthy patients to those who can afford to seek and to undertake such a treatment (even for a little while). Freud, by his own admission, is talking about the upper and middle classes, whose illness and its cure cannot be thought apart from their socioeconomic condition. He writes, "As far as the middle classes are concerned, the expense involved in psycho-analysis is excessive only in appearance. Quite apart from the fact that no comparison is possible between restored health and efficiency on the one hand and a moderate financial outlay on the other, when we add up the unceasing costs of nursing-homes and medical treatment and contrast them with the increase of efficiency and earning capacity which results from a successfully completed analysis, we are entitled to say that the patients have made a good bargain."[21] Psychoanalysis is figured here as *efficient, effective and, ultimately, low cost.* But only for the right patient. Freud argues that the working class and working poor, who have no means to purchase their own psychic health, are paradoxically protected by that class status from the illnesses Freud attributes to the bourgeoisie. Instead, the working poor are constantly exposed to an illness that has no therapeutic cure: poverty. It is doubly irremediable: capital requires of the working class perpetual immiseration and thus precludes the very fee Freud has just established as intrinsic to the therapeutic frame.

This schema wasn't Freud's last word on which classes or which patients could make use of his technique. Just five years later in 1918, right before the close of the Great War and at the start of the Spanish Flu pandemic (to which he would lose his daughter Sophie), Freud had a different proposal: to use free clinics and institutions to provide mass mental health care. Freud argued in a speech, at the first gathering of international psychoanalysts since the start of that war, that there would first have to be a large increase in practicing psychoanalysts and that initially private charities would have to provide economic backing for such new institutions; but that if these material conditions were met, "the poor man [would] have just as much right to assistance for his mind as he now has to the life-saving help offered by surgery; and that the neuroses threaten public health no less than tuberculosis, and can be left as little as the latter to the impotent care of individual members of the community. . . . Such treatments will be free."[22] Here, from the middle of an international crisis, Freud flexibly imagines a *future* in which treatment will be had by all. He continues, "We shall then be faced by the task of adapting our technique to the new conditions. . . . It is very probable, too, that the large-scale application of our therapy will compel us to alloy the pure gold of analysis freely with the copper of direct suggestion. . . ."[23] Using specie (gold and copper) as a metaphor, Freud argues that in breaking one aspect of the frame—money—the rest of therapeutic technique is also called into question.

Despite the conditional mood of this talk, "Lines of Advance in Psychoanalysis" was not merely a one-off speech in favor of a psychoanalysis for all. The "activist generation" of psychoanalysis (1920–1938) founded free clinics in seven countries.[24] Psychoanalysis was made available to the working class and unemployed. What determined the technique of those treatments was up for grabs: Freud thought that in order to make a therapy that would work for the masses, "pure" psychoanalysis could not be imposed. Here, moving away from purity refers both to a set of techniques (Freud mused that direct suggestion and hypnotic influence might again be used) and to the class of patients to whom those techniques could be offered. In practice, this meant that psychoanalysis occurred in "plain offices, case by case, on couches where theory hovered invisibly over clinical encounters. . . . Psychoanalysis was neither impractical for working people, nor rigidly structured, nor luxurious in length."[25] With the fee removed, the kinds of patients Freud thought could make use of therapy changed significantly; so did his dogma around strict psychoanalytic technique as concerns the actual treatment, the frame, and money.[26] The elements of the therapeutic triad (patient, analyst, and medium), or tetrad if you include money as a distinct medium, are not parallel forms of a clinical relationality but intersecting features of relationality and technique that can destabilize one another. If you remove the fee, why does the session have to last fifty minutes? Or for that matter, why does it have to be in an office? Or in person?

The presence (and absence) of money is keenly tied up in that other undertheorized therapeutic object: the medium. A constellation of material forces instructs and shapes the conditions of possibility for traditional therapy to take place, both socially and on an individual level: how the government funds mental health care, how much insurance costs and reimburses for mental health care, how many experts/clinicians there are, where they are, how much their services cost, how many people demand care, and who can and cannot access care (economically, linguistically, culturally, and because of dis/abilities). When these forces clearly make themselves known via a visible breakdown in social conditions (The Great Depression, World Wars I and II, the financial crisis of 2008, Trump's election, the aftermath of Hurricane Maria in Puerto Rico, pandemics), with the result that there are patients demanding care and an in-person version of care is not available or accessible enough, teletherapy proposes itself as a real alternative. To put it bluntly, alongside the therapeutic usefulness of a distance between clinician and patient, teletherapy exists largely because in-person therapy is excruciatingly expensive for almost all people, including many people who still manage to undertake it.

Yet teletherapy also necessarily presumes fluent access to whatever technology a treatment deploys. *The Distance Cure* covers cases where teletherapy seemingly makes good on this democratizing function, such as suicide hotlines, which were and are available to anyone who has access (however momentarily) to the nearly ubiquitous telephone line. The book also contends with teletherapies that are less readily accessible without expensive equipment or particular social standings; some teletherapies incorrectly assume universal access to connectivity where others work to offer a form of universalized health care. This necessarily means that while this book chronicles marginal forms of mental health care, it isn't always able to tell the story of marginal groups being invited into such forms or gaining access to them. Additionally, I focus on the lineage of mental health care that begins with Freud, even as it turns deeply against him (see chapter 4), and therefore the book predominantly deals with Europe and the United States (although not exclusively). Whereas traditional psychotherapy tries to convert patients in crisis to subjects who can make use of palliative and ongoing treatment (even though the word *palliation* is a misnomer—systemic and personal crisis touch everyone, however unevenly), teletherapy can be sought in the moment when the crisis arises and thus frames itself as contingent, convenient, accessible: dial in, download, and you're connected to help.

Teletherapy is therefore often the emergency room of mental health care. To stick with this metaphor: if all could afford to go to a primary care physician with regularity and receive ongoing primary care, there would likely be a decline in the number of ER visits. The ER is generally not the first or best choice for a patient but medical crisis sends one to seek treatment there for a variety of reasons; sometimes heading to the ER is best. The ER can also collapse the difference between crisis intervention and palliative treatment if you use it only when you need it, but regularly—care we might call "palliative intervention." Teletherapy, whether delivered via the letter, radio, hotline, IRC, or app, has often been sought for crisis care and crisis management, as an adjunct to in-person treatment, or as a stopgap when traditional therapy is too difficult or expensive.

To stop the metaphor: at the end of an ER visit, one is presented with a bill, often horrifically high even for the insured. Teletherapists, across time, most frequently do not bill. While this has in part changed with the appification of mental health care, as well as the ubiquity of teletherapy across modalities during the COVID-19 pandemic, nonetheless teletherapies traditionally address themselves to those who can afford traditional therapy out of pocket, or are insured, but also to those whom our (mental) health care system has economically excluded. The history of teletherapy charts the decline of a kind of reified expert care, or the removal of one element of the original clinical triad; this gradual attenuation of the expert unsurprisingly co-varies with another element, money, which frequently gets subtracted from the scenario altogether: it is understood that normal long distance or local phone charges may apply when you call a hotline, or that one pays for the electricity and Internet connection that allow for an e-therapy but no check is made out directly to any given provider or service. When therapy is performed for free, money is still a medium in its own absence: the lack of money exchanging hands between patient (or insurance company) and therapist has effects on and within the treatment. One such correlation is that tele-crisis care is often free whereas tele-palliative care is more commonly not. The fee and the bill are the index of the presence of an expert, and of a therapist performing ongoing, open-ended care as we've traditionally understood it. When money and the expert are subtracted, some version of therapy can be had by most, if still not all.

AS-IF THERAPY

Even when the fee is operant, both patient and clinician often find it convenient to operate as though money were not a structuring medium of the scenario. This is only one example of how fantasy organizes both the most traditional version of embodied psychoanalytic therapy and teletherapy. The patient's entire relationship to their therapist can be understood to be "as-if" (for more on this construction, see chapter 4). This quality of fantasy and hypotheticality is at play in all relationships. It is what is meant by Freud's adage, "The finding of an object is in fact a refinding of it."[27] It is understood that if the therapy (especially psychoanalytically oriented treatment) is working, the patient will experience the clinician as part of a complex revivification of their early relationships. Neither therapist nor patient is supposed to literally mistake the therapist for, say, the patient's parent, yet for the duration of the treatment it may be "as-if" the therapist is the neglectful parent, the depressed parent, or any other fantasized object. These fantasies manifest through what psychoanalysts call the transference/countertransference relationship, or the projection of feelings for a primary historical object onto and from the analyst, which the analyst and patient then engage in a lived repetition (and hopefully a working through). Given that one of the concerns about a mediated therapy is its dissolution of a concrete relationship because of the disruption of the traditional physical setting, a place of fantasy is important to elaborate. Elizabeth Wilson calls this one of the central paradoxes of psychotherapy—that the analytic relationship is an "artificial encounter: it is a model relationship."[28] Wilson attaches this artificiality to the therapeutic frame, stating that the "intensely affecting business" of psychotherapy is contrasted and underpinned by those aspects that are rule-based, that make it a *business* as well as a model verbal and affective encounter and "distinguish, in ways that are crucial to good therapeutic outcomes, the difference between this encounter and those more organically constituted relations. . . ."[29] These frame elements help to bind and determine the relationship. The disruption of some of those frame elements (embodiment, the room, a fixed calendar of sessions) might also disrupt some of the material supports for fantasy and transference but those dissolves also promote new forms of wish and fantasy—it is neither easier nor harder to project onto a physically absent other, only different. I will add that the therapeutic relationship itself is uniquely limited (in its rules) and paradoxically therefore full of potential; it is both a model relationship and an extraordinary one, in which deep psychical forces are represented through an other. It is therefore a laboratory for thinking relation at a distance, its limits and opportunities.

It is through the inevitable transference that another central paradox of psychodynamic therapy emerges for Wilson: via this engagement with another in a ruled relationship, theoretically, one can become more autonomous; working together with the clinical other of treatment (the analyst) allows the patient to separate from a primary historical other. Autonomy is a fraught construct across different schools of psychoanalysis and outside that discipline has a clear politic. Autonomy is an expression of omnipotence; where it means self-sufficiency it devalues the other and constitutes a rebuke to normal human interdependence. To be autonomous is to be—by definition—disengaged from relationship, free to act out one's own will. I therefore prefer separation as a term for this psychotherapeutic goal; instead of generating brute autonomy, it might be that an aim of psychodynamic treatment is the gradual creation of a separation over time that then enables real relationship with an actual and contemporary other, ostensibly first in an extraordinary instance (with a therapist) and then in more ordinary conditions (family of origin, partners, friends, children). It is this separation that promotes growth, intra- and inter-psychically. Another major aim of psychodynamic therapy is both compromised and reinvigorated by doing therapy over distance: to help the patient tolerate others (and in this retraining, the first other is the therapist) and negotiate frustration. One frustration can be separateness itself.

Mediated, networked, and teletherapeutic relationships physically literalize this separation, even as they work to diminish it. They also literalize a quality of as-ifness present in other therapeutic relationships: teletherapies are often predicated on the fantasy of togetherness while apart. This means, too, that relationships can acquire the same qualities and depth over distance they do in person—even if those as-if qualities, intimacies, and communications are structured and conducted differently. Depending on the medium and the historical moment, therapists and patients try to enact a frictionless importation of the feeling of presence—no matter how great the distance. That fantasy of togetherness, of being in the same "place," can occur no matter how brief the contact and seems to occur via every imaginable medium. The telephone, for instance, can bring together a counselor in London with a client in New York. If this is not an ongoing phone therapy relationship, it is likely they have never, and will never, meet face to face. It is possible they will never even speak via phone again. And yet, for the duration of the call, they have a relationship. During this call, the phone paradoxically brings the voice of the counselor or therapist even closer to the ear than that of in-person speech (for more on therapeutic contacts like these, see chapter 3).

DISTANCED INTIMACY

The as-if qualities of teletherapeutic communication and the conventions that presence the teletherapeutic relationship are of course present in all distance communication and in communication as such. Retelling the history of therapy as teletherapy allows us to examine our current fantasies, concerns, and panics about the impact of media on social and clinical relationships. While engaging with mental health care over distance is often framed as the abandoning of proper human connection, I argue that distance is not the opposite of presence; absence is. *The Distance Cure* contends that media technologies have always played a central role in therapeutic relationships, and indeed within all interactions, producing medium-specific forms of what I call "distanced intimacy." These intimate configurations—of patients, therapists, and technologies—allow for the regulation of cathexis and unexpected kinds of relation, interaction, care, and help; they also permit new forms of user-exploit while posing threats to traditional modes of clinical labor, security, privacy, confidentiality, and self-understanding. Moving away from the traditional conception of the therapeutic encounter (and its multiple actors) as a private, singular undertaking, this book tracks that phenomenon across shifting social, clinical, technical, and theoretical conventions at the personal, relational, and collective levels.

The major spoken fear around the inclusion of media in the extraordinary relationship between therapist and patient is, in essence, what I've just described: the diminishment of relationships because of their distanced nature and because they are no longer "pure," but "newly" mediated or technologized. As I argue above, these anxieties also circulate around more ordinary relationships (the kinds that obtain between friends, kin, partners, colleagues). There is an unstated worry that parallels this expressed one: the fear of not knowing what has been put into you and how. That media are doing something and doing it within the bounds of human-to-human interactions and relationality, we grant—but we don't quite agree on what that something is or if it's cognitively, psychically, and ethically good or bad. Further, we can't distinguish between us (two people or more) and what we're doing relationally, and the medium that allows us to communicate and determines our communications (see coda). These unknowns and problems of distinction attend all new communication technologies. Therapy is perhaps the only tool that explicitly promises, through the gradual work of separation, to describe what the self is and distinguish that being from what has been put into it (by parents or others).

The addition of media is thus often figured as a loss. Public intellectuals talk about the loss of closeness, the loss of affective textures in the shift from, say, the telephone to email (for more on this, see chapter 5). As Sherry Turkle has recently argued in her book *Alone Together*, "Our networked life allows us to hide from each other, even as we are tethered to each other. We'd rather text than talk."[30] I would argue that this has been true since well before our digital moment even if the digital amplifies and inflects the phenomenon; an anxiety at the prospect of excessive intimacy, *too much* presence, has always informed choices about how to communicate. On June 28, 1945, Dorothy Parker sent a Western Union telegram to her editor that opens, "This is instead of telephoning because I can't look you in the voice."[31] In it, she apologizes for being late with a manuscript (one not published in her lifetime). Here, Parker confesses that she could not bring herself to communicate this disappointment to her editor by voice, either over the telephone or in person (looking her editor in the eye). What she does feel able to do is look him in the text. Therapists worry over the loss of intimacy when dislocated and, with it, the ability to elicit the productive speech and working through crucial to the practice. But what if some patients, or all patients sometimes, need that "loss" in order to secure an intimacy they can actually use?

Another way to describe the feeling of loss attendant on new technologies is to claim their addition estranges: in the supersession of one medium after another, some users experience a loss of the form of mediation they have just gotten used to and had gradually imbued with an authentic, "pure" feeling of non-mediation. The telephone, as much as in-person voiced speech, can be back-formed as the last place of natural authentic communication. Temporarily it becomes understood as the appropriate, close medium compared with the supposedly cold, flat medium of, say, a text message. We are supposed to offer our therapeutic interpretations in person, not over text.

Or, in the case of ordinary human relationships, our congratulations and condolences should be given over the phone; over text, we're seen as violating a social contract and decorum around what kinds of technologies get used for what kinds of communicative activities.

These narratives of loss depend on the idea that media are disorienting new elements in a human relationship as old as language—but mediation is as old as language. Therapy is always open to mediation. Therapy is always conducted at a distance. Despite my claim that these are inescapable facts of the practice, therapy has usually also produced a functional intimacy. I call the general human relationality encouraged, created, and maintained by persons in tele-contact with one another *distanced intimacy*. Distanced intimacy is, in a way, self-explanatory: it names the intimacy elaborated between two or more persons over distance via communication technology. This is different from tele-presence, which can be defined as the feeling of being *present* at another location via telecommunication networks or, as Jonathan Steuer argues, the mediated perception of presence at another location *over* being present in the immediate location.[32] While some distance therapies reestablish their frames by projecting and fantasizing a togetherness—especially when those networked therapies do not occur via telecommunications—most do not rely on tele-presence to produce connectedness and shared frameworks. Instead, most teletherapeutic frames allow for a self-protection via an acknowledgment of distance, while generating a feeling of intimacy in the work of helping and being helped. Put another way, distanced intimacy operates dialectically: on the one hand, it stipulates a distance it must then cross, while on the other it maintains that distance as a shield enabling safe disclosure. The process of becoming intimate occurs over this distance and on both sides of it, whether or not the two (or more) intimate persons have ever met face to face. Distanced intimacies vary with the particular affordances of the medium by which they are built and maintained, and the ways that that medium structures relationality. An intimate relationship elaborated via the letter is different from one established over the phone. It is different still when the other is computational or one is interacting with an other via a beloved device only an arm's length away.

John Durham Peters calls communication "a registry of modern longings"; it is also an index of modern need.[33] The concept of distanced intimacy requires that we consider not only the way people fantasize, generate, and receive intimacy via a medium and presence (the handwriting of the beloved, or the timbre of a stranger's voice, the abbreviations in a text) but also the ways in which a medium provides a technological regulation of cathexis: the unopened or unanswered letter; turning the dial; hanging up; closing out; deleting; "ghosting." As I argue, even the traditional face-to-face scenario can provide moments of distanced intimacy, including the regulation of clinical attachment via the boundedness of the frame. These moments are also enacted bodily: not appearing for sessions, silence, and so forth. That kind of distancing, or bounding of one individual in the intimacy shared with another, or acting out, as the case may be, also regulates emotional nearness in distanced intimacy. Distanced intimacy can promote greater intimacy, being more willing to "speak" both because of a kind of protection (privacy) attributed to a medium and because one can halt speech and intimacy by terminating tele-contact more quickly and easily than by physically exiting a room, especially if that contact is asynchronous. Like embodied therapies, distanced intimacy involves at once both presence and absence; it can communicate them and communicate *by* them.

A NOTE ON METHOD

This book is a history of teletherapy and its precursors (such as epistolary therapy). It is structured as a study in a single task performed by many practitioners via various communication technologies across a hundred and thirty years. That may give the sense that this is a supersession narrative in which the speech of talk therapy yields to the letter, which in turn makes way for the radio, to be replaced by the phone, e-therapy, and then automated and algorithmic mental health care. Instead, there is substantial historical overlap between chapters: the rise of the hotline (chapter 3) and early experiments with automating a therapist (chapter 4) largely unfold within the same time frame and in an attempt to address the same problem: the lack of sufficient trained mental health care professionals in the

1950s and 1960s. Chapters 4 and 5 both examine online therapies and share the history of early and contemporary personal computing, convergence media, and the Internet. Although some of the media discussed in the project are less prevalent than others in our moment, *The Distance Cure* in no way argues that therapists have, for example, abandoned speaking in person (except during the COVID-19 pandemic, see coda).

The Distance Cure investigates the therapeutic work done under the auspices of religious organizations, individual psychoanalysts, clinics, social service agencies, and artificial intelligence labs, moving from the late nineteenth century across the twentieth century and into the present. The project is also transnational, as is the reach of the therapeutic media considered in it. Each of my case studies required slight shifts in a set of approaches for collecting and analyzing data. While this narrative by its nature will focus somewhat on the actors who might belong to the category of inventor, theorist, and clinician, the history is also sensitive to the quieter stories of those who fall on the other side of treatment: adopter, user, volunteer, and patient. In this latter group of actors, collected papers in a traditional archival context often do not exist to substantiate these narratives. I could not merely make use of archival research but had to employ strategies from the traditions of oral history and autoethnography in order to investigate these experiential aspects of the history of teletherapy. Similarly, this book not only seeks to illuminate the ways in which therapy technologies come into being but how they are adopted, exploited, and made part of everyday life.

The Distance Cure examines the therapeutic intervention and work conducted in clinical encounters, social service agencies, church programs, and media/technological labs. Therefore, the research methods necessary for acquiring and processing data are transdisciplinary and move between those used in the history of medicine/mind sciences and in cultural and media history. Generally, the documents used here fall into the following categories: clinical texts, primary documents of treatment by distance (training documents, phone counseling scripts, accounts of treatment, accounts of developing clinics, personal papers), software, newspaper clippings, and radio shows. I visited both processed, well-organized national and university archives as well as those archives that are smaller and rarely visited—medical, social agency, and scientific archives—including those that have hardly been studied.

Because of the nature of these archives, these materials are often sensitive in a variety of different ways: they contain patient and clinician histories; the technologies used to implement technological experiments are obsolete; papers have just become available for research after a time-based restriction has been lifted. As Cait McKinney has said of her archival work on feminist hotlines, it focuses on a "telephone hotline that none of us can ever call. It's . . . about how we study the sound of silence, of breathing, on the other end of a phone. Of how we use archives full of documents to understand past feminist media practices when the organizations doing that work, and their actual phone calls, are long gone."[34] This was often the case in doing a history of teletherapy. Materially, there are very few direct recordings of mental health patient histories as produced by the patients themselves. Similarly, there are few recordings of teletherapies actually transpiring, and for good reason: these conversations are confidential. Instead they are implied by private records, interviews, or recorded oral testimony after the fact. What exists is a recollection of the interaction from either the perspective of the patient or, much more likely, that of the therapist, in the form of published case studies. This dearth of documentation in a traditional archival mode required me to conduct original oral history interviews with those participating in crisis intervention or mediated therapeutic technologies. In regard to one of the earliest cases of distance therapy I will discuss, that of Freud's "Little Hans" (1909), oral testimony and the recollection of Herbert Graf ("Hans") exist and are maintained in the Freud Archive in the Library of Congress. Moving forward through my subsequent cases, all that might remain as a trace of any given user of a teletherapy is a phone record, a transcript of a crisis call, or a receipt for downloading an app. Because of the anonymity of much of teletherapy, I use the pronouns they/them throughout for any person whose gender is not knowable, both in the therapist and patient positions. The materials that remain are sensitive, if they are even available. It may be that the most troubling work I did in this project was wading through the call logs of a suicide hotline in which the names, addresses, and phone numbers of those contemplating suicide and undergoing other kinds of crisis evaluation were plainly written. I doubt very much that anyone calling a suicide hotline in the 1970s thought that in giving their information to a counselor, it would end up in an archive that was publicly accessible within their lifetime, if ever. Sometimes, I was presented with papers at archives when it was quite clear I should not have been; part of doing this work involved seeing documents and then working to unsee them.

STUDIES IN DISTANCE

The Distance Cure consists of five subsequent chapters and a coda that track teletherapy as it exchanges a model of cure for one of contingent help, moving from its initial use in ongoing care to its ever-enlarging role in crisis intervention and symptom management, only to then reacquire a routinized function in the contemporary. Teletherapy, like telemedicine, is a catch-all term to describe a therapeutic interaction over distance, now most frequently accessed over the computer and mobile phone in order to go where traditional therapy can't: to locations where no specialists are available, to the institutionalized or homebound, to vulnerable or at-risk populations, to patients with different linguistic needs. I take teletherapy as a genre to mean those therapies facilitated by a class of techniques and tools that allow patients to communicate with clinicians (or volunteers, or machines) not in their physical proximity at the time of communication.[35]

Chapter 1: The Written Hour explores a precursor to teletherapy: mediated, networked, epistolary treatment. It is well known that Sigmund Freud routinely used media metaphorically in his theories of the psychic apparatus; this chapter recovers the early history of Freud's real use of media in therapies over distance. The chapter reads epistolary and postal conventions in Freud's moment, intertwined with Freud's own epistolary self-analysis (in correspondence with Wilhelm Fliess) and the unconventional treatment by correspondence of his only child patient, the agoraphobic "Little Hans," in order to rethink the coincidental origins of psychoanalysis and teletherapy.

Chapter 2: Mass Intimacy considers new disseminative and broadcast forms of mental health care delivery. I start with the psychoanalytic advice column of Susan Isaacs and British psychoanalytic wartime radio shows before moving on to more radical reinvestments in the radio by Frantz Fanon and Félix Guattari. I then turn to the United States context of women's call-in radio shows, hosted by psychologists, offering romantic and familial advice. Through Ester Perel's podcast *Where Should We Begin?*, I consider the kinds of relating advanced by each of these subgenres, both in relation to therapeutic frames and to traditions of broadcasting including the modes of identification and distance transference.

Chapter 3: The Far Voice discusses the rise of mass telecommunication therapies, focusing on the suicide crisis hotline (originated by Protestant clergy) in England and the United States in the 1950s and 1960s and investigates how this service first became thinkable, and then widely adopted and used. The chapter redescribes the hotline as psycho-religious in origin and intent, rather than as the secular service it has usually been assumed to be. I argue that these services, in their use of the peer-to-peer modality, radically upset former regimes of pastoral care and counseling, as well as those of psychodynamic therapy. Hotlines generate a new, hyper-transient frame for the helping encounter, removing nearly all the traditional aspects of the therapeutic setting except for speech and listening. At the same time, these hotlines devalue the need for expertise and rescind the fee associated with that expertise. They challenge every clinical concept associated with the structure and dynamic of the analytic encounter. It is contingent, it is not in person, and requires (or permits) a distanced intimacy with no guarantee of repeating; and it makes use of the phone—an appliance paradoxically thought of as capable of bringing people together and as responsible for their greater alienation.

Chapter 4: Auto-Intimacy engages with therapeutic and psychiatric treatment by algorithm, or automated therapy, and interrogates what therapy becomes when the therapist is a computational actor. These applications are often grouped with teletherapy and telemedicine but definitionally and practically fall outside that genre. Building on scholarship on the early chatter bots ELIZA and PARRY, this chapter begins with a brief, situating discussion of those and other very early attempts to write a responsive algorithm that models a therapeutic relationship. I argue that computerized therapy is a form of "auto-intimacy" in which the human user produces a kind of self-knowing through an engagement with the natural language processing and therapeutic vocabulary of a computer program.

Chapter 5: Written Speech examines the shifts in relationality, intimacy, and liability in therapeutic culture and practice when counseling relationships leave the consulting room to move onto the Internet. From university networks in the 1980s to private practice cyber-clinics in the 1990s, the first decade of e-therapy saw a series of efforts to produce viable therapeutic counseling across time and place. This new platform for clinical intimacy relies on a system of novel communication techniques and conventions proper to its digital moment that I describe as "written speech."

The Distance Cure takes the teletherapeutic relationship as a model for thinking communication and as a mode of communication. The coda, "When Distance is Everywhere," examines how we're doing therapy online during the COVID-19 pandemic. I argue that this crisis reveals the feeling structures associated with the extraordinary relationship between therapist and patient, which functions as a litmus test for the possibilities of relating over distance. I also revisit the critiques of teletherapy from this unique vantage point.

Instead of investigating whether or not teletherapy is "the same as" or "as good as" live, in-person therapy, this book and its conclusion seek to disrupt the notion that contacts occurring by distance are automatically lesser, hopelessly troublesome, or useless to the person seeking a form of therapeutic treatment or connection. Yet teletherapy is not merely a site for working on the general capacity to be with the other via time with a disembodied other; it is also a tool for developing the ability to tolerate being alone. As Sherry Turkle has demonstrated, one can be problematically "alone, together" via media, a state that results in increased loneliness. Loneliness in turn produces a need for connection—which has often occurred via these distant communications. *The Distance Cure* instead examines what happens when we're together, alone.

1 THE WRITTEN HOUR

In addition to being the father of psychoanalysis, Sigmund Freud was also a furtive parapsychologist and a card-carrying member of both the British and American Associations of Psychical Research.[1] For Freud and his moment, these two theories of mind posed no obvious contradiction. Freud was intimately involved in theorizing the workings of telepathy, and his first student, Wilhelm Stekel, wrote an entire monograph on telepathic dreams; two of his closest confidants—Sándor Ferenczi and Carl Jung—wrote their dissertations on telepathy as "thought transference" and worked to substantiate empirical evidence for the occult. Freud went so far as to host a medium, who conducted a séance in his own home.[2] Freud wrote to Hereward Carrington, the director of the American Psychical Institute, "If I were at the beginning of a scientific career, instead of, as now, at its end I would perhaps choose no other field of work, in spite of all its difficulties."[3] Séances, mind reading, and telepathy all insisted that thoughts could be communicated immediately and without speech, including through objects, and that such communication could occur not only between the living but also between the living and the dead. For the nascent science of psychoanalysis and its founder, the immediacy and reach of this type of communication presented both a tantalizing ideal and a mortal threat. If in his living room Freud privately showed interest in the possible existence and actual nature of occult phenomena, in public forums he defended his new science by performing a responsible skepticism about mediums and their unproven communication practices. Psychoanalysts

Figure 1.1
Photograph of the Austrian psychologist Sigmund Freud (1856–1939) and the German biologist and physician Wilhelm Fliess (1858–1928).

and, subsequently, scholars of Freud and his circle addressed themselves to the difficult and slightly more palpable work of recovering and understanding the inaccessible dimensions of the subject through another kind of "thought transference," while telepathy and séances promised to put practitioners in instantaneous touch with subjects who should not be accessible at all.[4]

Whereas Freud's interest in telepathy has been connected to his understandings of transference, I argue that we can also look to Freud's ambivalence toward telepathy in relation to his theories of communication: communication in the consulting room, understandings of communication technology, what constitutes psychoanalytic treatment, what comprises the analytic frame or analytic relationship and, therefore, what an analytic communication might be. Freud's public negation of telepathy and of its pure, unmediated transfer of communication would prove entirely continuous with his discipline's anxiety surrounding another supposed impurity: mediated communication in the psychoanalytic scenario. To ignore the means by which communication occurs (if not via telepathy) may seem paradoxical because psychoanalysis is understood as the "talking cure." The "talking cure" refers to a verbal therapy that works to address somatoform disorders and other symptoms through speaking about them. This form of treatment relies on a specific kind of relationship (clinician–patient) and communication technique (speech, utterances, and their interpretation) for its clinical impact. And yet, when this relational communication is discussed in theory—and it often is, to elucidate specific claims, notions, and theories in psychoanalysis—mediation consistently appears as a metaphor, as a virtual phenomenon rather than as an intrinsic feature. It is *as if* some expression is mediated; it is never actually understood to be so.

Freud was keenly aware that psychoanalysis and mediation had something to do with one another. Although early psychoanalysis did not foster wide discussion of literal mediation or communication technology, Freud specifically emphasized media in his theory of the functioning of the psychic apparatus and in his transformation of clinical method. Freud's conception of psychoanalysis is, at its core, a theory of spoken communication on the scale of person-to-person exchange. The one-to-one relationship of analyst and patient is fundamental; through the process of unconscious transference and countertransference, the analyst facilitates, or mediates, the patient's access to his or her own unconscious. This access is premised on the passing back and forth of freely associated speech and interpretation, underpinned by the conditions of the relationship, and the relationship entailed in transference. Presented this way, transference is a medium that can be harnessed, not just a psychic effect.

Freud thus saw his science as mediated and situated between two additional tantalizing mediums—the voiceless spirit of telepathy and the spirit voice of broadcast and peer-to-peer media—while unable to afford being mistaken for either. His moment was even capable of seeing the one *as* the other. Telepathy and séances were often described in terms of emerging communicative media, as though the mental processes of one subject were transferred to another along channels, in the mode of a "mental radio" or along a dematerialized telephone wire.[5] Freud's strategy for establishing his science had therefore to deal with this dual threat of the supernaturally media-less and the mundanely over-mediatized, as well as his own fascination with both methods of communication. His solution would be to deny or defer the occult form while displacing the role of communicative media to an only metaphorical role in therapeutic speech (i.e., analysis *is like* using the telephone, phonograph, and radio). Put another way, psychoanalysis needed to appear as free of mediation as telepathy but avoid being identified with the occult.[6]

In the fall of 1921, Freud gathered a small group of his most loyal followers for a private meeting in the Harz Mountains.[7] There, Freud delivered a paper, never published in his lifetime, on "Psycho-analysis and Telepathy."[8] Freud warns this cohort in the strongest language of the "peril" of an "occult phenomenon" being attached to the work of psychoanalysis. Freud wants no analyst to give credence to phenomena such as telepathy while his new discipline is still under attack by established science and thus vulnerable to charges of charlatanism and quackery. He stresses that if occultism were to rise above science, psychoanalysis—depending as it does on the "mysterious unconscious"—would not be able to escape such a "collapse in values as this."[9]

In 1925, Freud published direct remarks on thought transference for the first time in his talk "Dreams and Telepathy," wherein he continues to safeguard psychoanalytic practice and its objects from telepathy by arguing that these two experiences "have little to do with each other, and that if the existence of telepathic dreams were to be established there would be no need to alter our conception of dreams in any way."[10] By 1932, with psychoanalysis better established as a discipline, Freud has grown more calm about the proximity of its method to a supernatural form of thought transference, which he describes as "mental processes in one person—ideas, emotional states, conative impulses— . . . transferred to another person through empty space without employing the familiar methods of communication by means of words and signs."[11] Freud's description of thought transference (*Gedankenübertragung*) sounds quite a bit like his own concepts of transference (*Übertragung*) and countertransference (*Gegenübertragung*). Just as it is in English, in German Freud has removed *Gedanken*, or thought, from his conception of *Übertragung*, or transference. Freud presents his transference as a less immediate, two-way exchange, a broad conception of the same process. While Freud's transference goes beyond the projection of contemporary thoughts to a deeper history of feeling, thought transference is still the more efficient version, presented as occurring instantaneously and without mediation over distance. Freud's former antipathy has been replaced with a quiet wonder at an ideal form of his own praxis, though one still understood as fantasy:

> The telepathic process is supposed to consist in a mental act in one person instigating the same mental act in another person. What lies between these two mental acts may easily be a physical process into which the mental one is transformed at one end and which is transformed back once more into the same mental one at the other end. The analogy with other transformations, such as occur in speaking and hearing by telephone, would then be unmistakable.[12]

Think something and the other immediately thinks it too. A medium is an open channel and, unlike a psychoanalyst, has no liability to error, no self to disrupt the reception of the other. This is also the way science was, and is, typically misunderstood as objective: it is supposed to be unimpacted by the unconscious and culture and is never mediated; it follows logical unfolding inquiry. While Freud was previously suspicious of telepathy and all that it could do to damage or discredit his fledgling science, he now waxes almost envious or reverent of its immediacy. That passage from fear to admiration marks the beginning of a descriptive tactic in psychoanalytic literature: like the scientist and like the telepath or the fortune-teller/medium, the work of the analyst is suddenly figured as free of mediation, despite a literal use of mediated communication and a simultaneous and constant metaphoric recourse to media (the telephone and the like). This tense (and envious) relationship to media did not disappear with Freud. In the intervening course of its century-long history, psychoanalysis has codified into a clinical practice that frequently brackets mediation, is made anxious by it, or treats it with suspicion by excluding mediated therapy from the category of proper analysis.

FREEING ASSOCIATION

Telepathy was one, but not by any means the only, investigation Freud conducted into communication. In instances of theorization, Freud deploys figuration to name and contain the connection between media, technology, and his schema of psychic processes. He attempts to better understand psychic and clinical relations as mediated operations: memory is like a mystic writing pad; psychoanalytic listening is like a telephone call; dreaming is censored like the post. In other moments and in Freud's actual practice, media appear twinned with concerns about who can be analyzed, and where: Freud extended the spatial and temporal boundaries of conventional analysis through cases where the patient is Freud himself, close to him psychically (his daughter), those he never met (Schreber), those long dead (Da Vinci), and patients far away (Herbert Graf, a.k.a. "Little Hans"). Freud, ever experimenting, used letters to access psychoanalysis's first two distance therapy patients—himself and the child of his colleague and friend, Herbert Graf (whose treatment became the case study referred to as "Little Hans"). Freud's correspondence with Wilhelm Fliess is usually heralded as the "origins of psychoanalysis," where he first drafted his theories for key texts: *The Interpretation of Dreams* (1899), *The Psychopathology of Everyday Life* (1901), and the "Oedipus Complex" (coined in 1910). That set of letters is generally understood to be the record of Freud's own self-analysis reported to his friend. I argue that what transpires for Freud in that communicative mode is not a self-analysis at all. Instead, the correspondence functions as the site of a conventional, relational analysis conducted through the mail—and thus alters what conventional analysis looks like to the point of unrecognizability: it is a long, sustained, treatment over distance. The "Little Hans" case is special in its own right as it was Freud's only known analysis of a child and was also conducted via epistolary contact, with an infrequent in-person component.

These efforts were not merely exceptional circumstances where Freud's treatment schema departed the room. While psychoanalysis has always been anxious about the kinds of intimacy and distance present in clinical interactions and invested in bounding that scene, it has from the outset also adjusted and shifted the bounds of its ideal scenario. Neither Freud's self-analysis nor his work with Little Hans transpired in sessions that had progressed according to the logic of a *spoken* free association. In the analytic mode of free association, the patient is asked to say whatever is on their mind, followed only by whatever comes to mind next; there is no directed, goal-oriented path that the thinking and discussion must follow. Through such a conversation, in which various defensive or pathological impediments to free association are illuminated and their possible determinants exposed, a treatment can ensue. Put another way, the inability to speak of specific things is undone by the patient's speech and the analyst's listening. Speech is at once the marker of the unconscious and of pathology (blocked or inhibited speech) and what allows for a working through. In his two distance treatments, Freud ventured to see if his technique could withstand a total shift in frame: he would have psychoanalysis transpire as writings sent and exchanged through the mail. This is not so radical as it might seem. Freud's biographer and colleague Ernest Jones writes that Freud's notion of free association was influenced by Ludwig Börne, who wrote, "Write down, without any falsification or hypocrisy, everything that comes into your head."[13] The original medium for free association was that of automatic writing. Yet these two analytic treatments are never grouped or considered as a trial in therapy via distance. In the case of Freud's so-called self-analysis, it is widely understood that Freud *reports* his analysis in his letters, not that the analysis *happens* there as a correspondence between two persons, conducted through an epistolary relationship with the analyst's best friend. In the case of Hans, the treatment's import has been historically codified as the first instance in which a child was seen in analysis—already a shift in the boundaries of analysis—not as the extension of Freud's method beyond the consulting room. In both cases, the letter serves as the mobile container for the practice of analysis.

In Freud's own analysis with Fliess and that of his work with Hans, the "talking cure" is written. The thoughts of one are "transferred to another person through empty space without employing the familiar methods of communication" of psychoanalysis: speech and the embodied and enacted frame. This chapter will look at these key early moments in the history of psychodynamic treatment conducted via letter writing—efforts to expand treatment beyond the initial couch-based, in-person psychodynamic framework with patients—that altered the structure of psychodynamic relationality, intimacy, and care, and revealed a subsequent openness to many forms of mediation that had always already been there.

THE OPEN LETTER

The letter, letter writing, and correspondence constituted a quotidian communication network in Freud's sphere. As a medium, the letter was pervasive in Freud's daily intimacies and work practice. Freud made extensive, regular use of the postal service to keep up with his family and social circle near and far, as well as to stay connected while in a long-distance relationship (whether with his fiancé, her sister, or his best friend). Freud moved easily between using the letter for casual social communication and as an instrument in the service of scientific and clinical labor; he deployed letter writing especially for working out and working through the early development of psychoanalysis. Freud did not keep a diary; instead, his

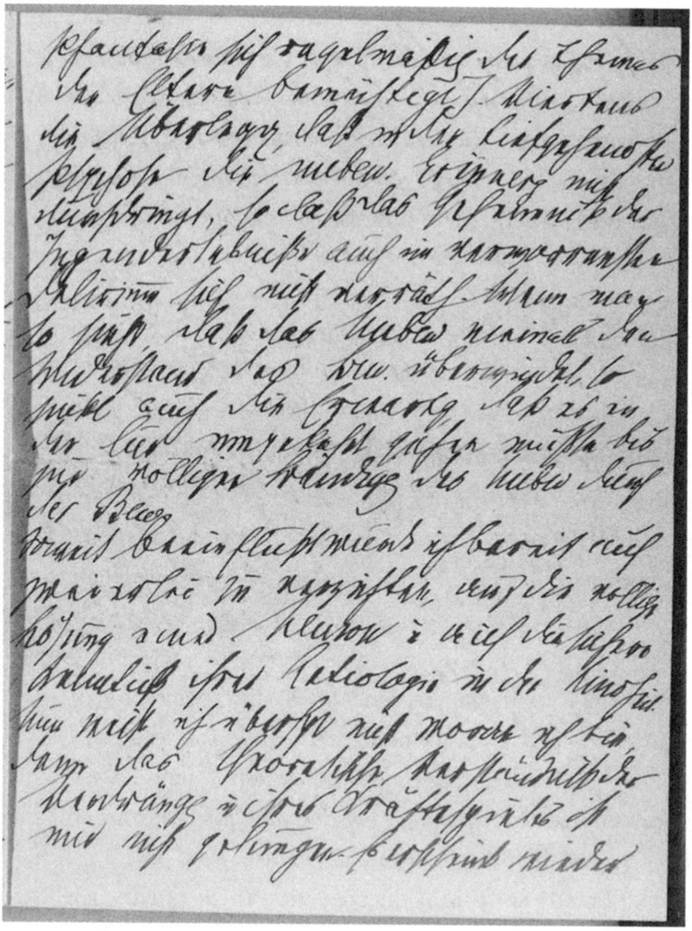

Figure 1.2
Freud to Fliess. Holograph letter, September 21, 1897, Library of Congress.

correspondences provide both the function of connection with the other and a cathartic connection with the self. Or Freud did keep a diary—it was just hidden within epistolary address and the form of the letter. Beyond the social and personal functions of his letters, Freud's prolific correspondences contain key dreams, drafts of papers, developing theories, and, as I will argue, not only the record of his analysis with Fliess but the medium by which it occurred.

Freud's epistolary relationships have been treated as an important window into his life and work by biographers and theorists alike.[14] While his letters are understood as foundational, no "standard edition" of his correspondence exists. Though access to his letters is restricted, an ever-increasing ability to read sets of his correspondence, beginning in the 1950s, has helped perpetuate popular investigations into Freud-the-man via biographical workups in Anglo-America.[15] One correspondence in particular expresses Freud's versatile use of the medium to transact a crucial friendship while developing psychoanalytic theory: the archive of 284 intimate letters[16] sent by Freud to Wilhelm Fliess between 1887 and 1904.[17]

Freud and Fliess' friendship, as cataloged throughout the one-sided exchange, is one of serious intellectual admiration and collaboration.[18] The two advise one another on their theories and practices and share and refer patients up until (and even after) the very bitter end of their relationship. It has been noted that Freud was completely devoted to Fliess and tried to protect him when their collaborations went very poorly, as in the case of their joint patient, Emma Eckstein.[19] Freud, who was notoriously tight-fisted with drafts of his papers, sent serially numbered efforts to Fliess for comment. Fliess had great influence on Freud's thinking, including those works of his published during their long correspondence, *The Interpretation of Dreams* and *The Psychopathology of Everyday Life*. Dreams and anecdotes that later appear in print first appear handwritten to Fliess. The letters also catalog Freud's shift from the seduction theory (namely, all hysterical symptoms arise from sexual trauma) to the theory of infantile sexuality (which puts a primacy on fantasy life).

Mediating the distance between Vienna and Berlin was paramount. Meetings, when they infrequently did take place, were done at a remove from family and friends. Freud referred to these sessions as "private congresses," including the final "congress" which served as a "termination" of their friendship in 1900—termination being the word used by psychoanalysts to describe the conclusion of the *analytic* relationship.[20] The relationship is therefore keenly aware of its near-total reliance on letter writing for contact and intimacy and also its relation to the as-if quality of the analytic relationship despite the actuality of friendship. Though there is much to say about this friendship and its body of correspondence, the inquiry here will focus on the ways in which the particularities and affordances of letter writing mediate scientific inquiry and analysis conducted via correspondence. As a communication network, as a technology, and as a culture, letter writing and its attendant conventions contain much of what Freud deems proper to the analytic scenario. The letter is seen as an envelope, a container—the setting—that allows a writer to pour out the contents of the mind; correspondence records conversation such that letters can grow self-referential, establishing an archive of shared material to be kept, reviewed, and brought back to life; the letter contains chatter as well as information; it's a productive site of written parapraxes of both the mind and the hand; and it's an ostensibly closed form that in actuality is perforated by internal and external censorship and monitoring of several kinds. The letter as a medium has its own conventions that have resonances within, and impacts upon, notions of psychoanalytic techniques. The letter can be metaphorized as recorded speech; it allows for an asynchronous, disembodied presence through several rhetorical tactics and material significations.[21] Some of these conventions and affordances proper to letter writing even allow it to work as a psychodynamic medium, both in Freud's analysis with Fliess and in Freud's treatment of Little Hans.

In its progressive, unfolding, serial frame, letter writing contains much of what allows analytic relationships to form. The correspondence is at its core a reciprocal, participatory, one-to-one model; one addresses oneself to the other and reads the other in turn in an ongoing interchange. The structure of correspondence is conversational in the full etymological sense: to discuss, to keep company with, and to be familiar with. Familiarity is negotiated throughout a letter's content, salutations, and repetitions; keeping company is asserted through metaphors of bodily proximity and quotidian minutiae; discussion is alluded to in metaphors of time and speech. The feelings of presence and intimacy that occur in letter writing, despite bodily absence, are connected to its asynchronicity as a medium. As Freud puts it in *Civilization and Its Discontents*, "Writing was in its origin the voice of an absent person."[22] One is present while the other is absent and is not immediately (if ever) granted a reply.

In psychoanalysis, interpretation should not come directly on the heels of speech either. Freud is very careful to say that one must first hear a full account before speaking in turn. Unlike the temporality of embodied analysis, letter writing does not unfold at the same pace for both correspondents. Letter writers of the late nineteenth century rely on metaphors that simultaneously acknowledge and disavow this asynchronicity and distance inherent in the practice of correspondence; figurations of time, delay, and waiting are pervasive. Epistolary time exists on both the macro and micro level, cycling daily, weekly, and annually. Letter-writing etiquette suggests that specific letters for specific calendric events must be managed (the New Year, the birth, the anniversary);[23] the post is delivered several times daily but not on the Sabbath;[24] one must devote time to keeping up a correspondence and therefore have access to leisure time;[25] letters may not arrive;[26] and one must wait for a reply and excuse delay in making one. Letters are stopped and restarted and correspondents indicate this as compositional rhythm, writing and demarcating different sections of different thoughts as written on different days.[27] Where this is acknowledged in a letter, it is often a means to seek absolution for not writing quickly enough or to correct information above that no longer proves to be true or has required elaboration, given the collapse of time between sitting down to write yesterday and this next present moment. William Decker writes, "Represented in the text of the letter . . . [is] something of the addresser's 'here' to the addressee's 'there.' Exchange of letter sheet thus articulates and substantiates the central paradox of epistolary discourse: that the exchange of personally inscribed texts confirms even as it would mitigate separation."[28] One strategy for mitigation is to recast writing (an asynchronous communication) as speech (a dialogic, synchronous medium). When Freud writes to Fliess that they are chatting, he asserts a fantasized physical intimacy and presence and, with it, a different mode of communication: one that allows for the ability to exchange simultaneously.

This is not to say that Freud is merely just another correspondent, nor is it to make his exchange with Fliess exceptional. The features and limitations of letter writing, and the rhetorical strategies they inspire, allow Freud to inhabit his correspondence with his peer both typically and radically. In and among all the conjurations of presence and intimate chattiness proper to the medium of letter writing, Freud is able to transmit a discontinuous and necessarily disembodied analytic experiment, the first conventional treatment at distance in which he carries the analytic scenario beyond the consulting room and into a correspondence and transference with Fliess, far away in Berlin.

Yet distance avails not. Communicating intimately via written correspondence relies on a wide variety of stratagems for reiterating closeness in spite of distance, establishing thereby a *distanced intimacy*. The paradox of distanced intimacy is that the dislocation and removal of the other's body is precisely what allows for a feeling of connectedness. The communication is a response to a felt absence that aims to mitigate that absence and thereby close the gap in affirming it. Nineteenth-century correspondents are tethered to a series of conventions for bringing the body back into the letter. Epistolary relationships are staked on references made to the embodied scene of writing, to recounting bodily actions taken while letters are composed, and through declarations that the writer feels *as if* they were next to their reader.[29] To generate presence and intimacy in letters—oneself to the other, and the other to the self—is an accomplishment of pretense, where the simulation of proximity is made to suffice.

One of the overall effects of this presence-via-absence paradox is that the other with whom one is intimately in touch becomes a palimpsest. Their real qualities become overlaid with fantastical, unconscious feeling. This is also true in psychoanalytic treatment conducted via the couch. Instead of distance or absence being negative, or negating intimacy, it can provide the necessary space for fantastical engagement. As Esther Milne notes, "For many correspondents, 'absence' is creative; it opens a discursive space in which desires and subjectivities that might not otherwise be articulated can be explored. . . . Paradoxically, then, references to the real, lived, situated, physical body of the epistolary exchange can produce a 'fantasized body.'"[30] The inherent failure to reach the real body allows presencing to bridge the gap. The real body is exchanged for its imaginary counterpart, much like the analysand, once lying on the couch and visually removed from their clinician, begins to fantasize the analyst via transference. The analyst, too, eventually participates in this new kind of relationality through countertransference. The removal of the body allows unconscious work to occur on both sides of a communication. Epistolary relationships and the analytic relationship between patient and clinician do not merely have equivalency here. Instead one can read these two sites of relating as drawing on some of the same mechanisms and techniques to invite such a relationship—it is nearly inevitable. Erik Erikson, the American psychologist, analogizes epistolary friendship to analytic relationality in describing the work between Freud and Fliess. He writes:

> A correspondence of long standing is a *ritual á deux*. It develops and cultivates particular levels of mood, selected confessions, and habitual admissions; it is apt to indulge in expressions of admiration and even plaintive comparison with the unseen recipient's person or fate, and, of course, in fervent hopes for a reunion; in other words, it invites some kind of mutual correspondence transference.[31]

Letter writing is described here as a frequent undertaking, a practiced habit whose duration allows for mutual transference. This kind of fantastical relating to the other relies on collaboration between letter writers, as between analyst and patient. The writing of oneself relies on more than oneself, becoming a collaborative project dependent on the other and one's particular relationship to that other audience over time.[32] Claudio Guillén writes that the space opened up in correspondence has a particular status in relationality: "There is hardly an act in our daily experience, rooted in life itself, that is as likely as the writing of a letter to propel us toward inventiveness and interpretation. . . . The 'I' who writes may not only be pretending to act upon a friend . . . but acting also upon himself, upon his evolving mirror image. . . . To compose a letter . . . is to become better conscious of ourselves."[33] Namely, the letter writer is able to perform a kind of self-talk by acting on and through the other; in doing so they are able to act (out) on themselves. This kind of dialectical dance between consciousnesses is deeply important not only for Freud's particular experimental distance analysis but for Freudian psychoanalysis more generally. Much like what Guillén observes in the letter writer, this kind of acting out and working through allows for a fuller understanding of the self in the analytic scenario. The parallel relationalities of psychoanalysis and letter writing can coincide—psychoanalysis can occur via letter. When Freud participates in his analysis by writing to Fliess (as he must so that the analysis can be mediated through another), he is adhering to this notion laid out by Guillén—that across time one develops a greater intimacy with oneself as a byproduct of engagement with the other.

It is no secret that the period of time during which Freud worked with Fliess was highly generative for the making of Freudian psychoanalytic theory. This was partially achieved through Freud's deep investment in his analysis. The term "self-analysis" assumes that Freud analyzed the contents of his mind alone. Classifying Freud's analysis as such would suggest he was autonomously poring over the contents of his mind, serving as both patient and clinician. And while Freud did massive labor on his psychic content, the analysis was still mediated through a consciousness, an unconscious, and a medium that was not solely Freud's. Even Freud admits that he doubts the possibility of a *self*-analysis. He writes to Fliess in the very letter in which he first refers to the undertaking of his own analysis, "My self-analysis is still interrupted. I have now seen why. I can only analyze myself with objectively acquired knowledge (as if I were a stranger); self-analysis is really impossible, otherwise there would be no illness."[34] However, this didn't theoretically preclude a successful "self-analysis." Instead, Freud had to acquire knowledge of himself as if he were not himself. In order to do so, Freud required a transference figure. Masud Khan writes in *The Privacy of the Self* that "I do not think it too much to claim for this friendship that it alone made Freud's self-analysis possible and helped him to discover his analytic method, the essence of which is that a person can observe himself as-if the other through the presence of and instrumentality of an actual other. Fliess had been this 'actual other.'"[35] Or in Freud's own words to Fliess, "I am so immensely glad that you are giving me the gift of the Other."[36] If Fliess is the transference figure, we must not limit the analysis to those topical aspects of their letters directly pertaining to the so-called "self-analysis" or even dream content as scholars have previously. Taking the term "self-analysis" for a distance treatment represses the medium by which it occurs (it is cast as occurring in the self) and therefore disavows the relationality of the treatment altogether. Instead, the entirety of the correspondence must be seen as shot through with the relationship of transference and countertransference proper to the in-room analytic scenario; the body of correspondence and the analysis of Freud with Fliess (if not "by" him in the traditional sense) are indistinct and coextensive.

Ernst Kris writes in the first introduction to the Freud–Fliess correspondence that reading the letters is analogous to overhearing a telephone call.[37] Others, perhaps more accurately, compare it to overhearing an analysis taking place from the couch[38]—Freud the patient "chatters on" and, because Fliess's letters have been burnt, he inadvertently assumes the role of the silent analyst. But one can do away with analogy—reading the letters *is* reading an analysis, while the rhetoric of letter writing and the one-sided archive allow the flow of information to feel like monodirectional associative speech. The self-analysis is properly then an ordinary analysis by letter, which is to say that Fliess mediates it, offering the key relational figure of transference (and implied capacity for countertransference). The epistolary relationality takes the place of the in-room scenario as the correspondent takes on the character of fantasized transference (or countertransference from Fliess' unavailable perspective). The two are not identical but can be used to achieve similar aims.

A similar slippage occurs between spoken words and written notation. Acknowledging the particularity of the written form at hand, whether received or authored (this is a letter, not a book), allows for a shift in relation to literacy; handwriting indicates private speech intended for a single party while print implies dissemination. Letter writing to and between familiars can function as spoken exchange, reading as listening, and a site of secondary orality under Walter Ong's formulation.[39] Epistolary guides on the art of letter writing, ever more popular in the nineteenth century,[40] insist that letters should be formed as "oration written."[41] In her work on nineteenth-century letter-writing manuals, Cecile Dauphin claims that the widespread definition of a letter is "a conversation between people who are absent from one another. . . . To succeed at it, imagine you are in the presence of whomever you are addressing, that they can hear the sound of your voice."[42] The letter is one half of a magic trick, organized to produce mutual illusion. Not only is each letter supposed to conjure a body far away; it also brings a voice into the mind. Though writing is read and interpreted through eye knowledge as opposed to that of the ear, the personal letter is made to feel conversational by transfiguring the act of writing into one of speaking. One is supposed to write to their familiar whatever it is that one would (wish to) say.[43] The formal construction of the letter invites a kind of open and free associative "speech" that contains reportage, chatter, and information (for more on this phenomenon in digital writing, see chapter 5). Yet in order to say "it" one had to be indoctrinated into this particular art of letter writing. Manuals from Freud's moment contain advice on how to produce various genres of the letter: for business, best wishes, announcements of births, weddings, and deaths.[44] Each set of advice contains informatics, conventional language, and instruction in spontaneity.[45] Spontaneity—or how to appear unstudied in written communication and produce the presencing of speech—had to be learned, and learned so as to appear unlearned.[46]

The convention of writing as speech is realized by correspondents of the late nineteenth century in their reliance on metaphors that redescribe letter writing as chatting,[47] speaking face to face.[48] This is not to say that the scene of writing, or the frustration of putting words to page, does not appear in letter writing.[49] Instead, it is to suggest that there is a tactical slippage between media. When Freud writes to Fliess, his letters often switch between familiar and scientific matters in keeping with a kind of written free-associative communication. Freud writes about his illness, his deep love for Fliess, his own analytic work, and the comings and goings of his family and friends. These writings are often related as "talking" or "telling";[50] sometimes Freud still writes to Fliess even when he would rather be "silent" or is resistant to the act of telling in writing. He writes, "To describe it in writing is more difficult than anything else,"[51] before proceeding to describe it (in this case a dream) or "I have nothing to write really; this happens only during an hour when one could use dialogue and encouragement" before proceeding to write a full letter.[52] The letter, which in a way is made only to contain communication, is here configured as holding both productive "telling" and its resistance, and its content presents to its participants as a conversation—a fantasy of two-way communication covering the reality of turn-based monologue.

In order to mitigate and manage the emotionality of distance, conventions of speaking (which imply presence) supersede those of writing (which announce separation). In one such letter, Freud writes: "Today I shall allow myself a good hour and chat only about science with you. It is obviously no special favor of fate that I have approximately five hours a year to exchange ideas with you, when I can barely do without the other—and you are the only other, the *alter*."[53] Here, Freud collapses his writing to Fliess—which he states is the result of a "good hour to chat"—with the two intimates' very infrequent face-to-face visits. Freud terms Fliess his only other while in other places in the correspondence Freud singles Fliess out as his only audience; Freud assigns his friend the role of being the single destination for both his scientific and self-analytic revelations, rendering them somewhat indistinct on the plane of therapeutic "content."[54] It is also important to note that the predominantly "scientific" letter is stated to have the duration of a "good hour." Freud is making his temporality and its constraints known to his reader by asserting a grounding "frame," one already at work both in therapeutic and epistolary convention. The letter itself mimics the time scale (the "Freudian hour") and subject positions intrinsic to those psychoanalytic sessions conducted by Freud (and his subsequent followers).

If the letter mimics orality, it is also speech made visible: handwriting contributes to presencing and authenticity in epistolary communication as much as metaphor and asynchronicity do. Each script is the peculiar somatic trace of a particular intimate. Not only does lettering convey the writer's class, gender, and education level, it also marks a sentimentalizable body. Handwriting functions as a proxy for both the body and bodily connectedness, thus the trope of nineteenth-century readers of love letters kissing the missive instead of the lover.[55] Freud writes to Fliess shortly after the birth of his daughter Anna, "When I see your handwriting again, those are moments of great joy, which allow me to forget much of my loneliness and privation."[56] Handwriting serves as an indexical mark of the other and gives the feeling of company; it is itself communicated content. The preserved appearance of a particular hand serves as a sign that a particular body interacted with the materiality of the missive, obscuring the distance and network through which the communication has subsequently traveled. Letter writers rely on the medium's unique and identifiable qualities to conjure intimacy, much like the timbre of voice. When Marie Bonaparte finds the cache of Freud's letters to Fliess, she is able to authenticate *her* intimate Freud (who was her teacher and correspondent), writing that she "would of course recognize [his] hand!"[57] She does not rely on content recognition or his turns of phrase and cadences—instead the indicator is the graphological made dear.

Handwriting is susceptible to error as well as fantasy. Both components of epistolary communication—reading and writing—are liable to be loci for motivated misprision. Freud provides a dedicated theory for understanding this kind of mistake as it appears in both speech and writing. Letter writing and all of its conventions figure as evidence throughout many of the sections of Freud's *The Psychopathology of Everyday Life*.[58] The text is filled with references to Fliess and their observations exchanged via letter.[59] Though the book is a general survey of motivated parapraxis, Freud argues that these errors are more likely to come through in (letter) writing than in speech, relying on Wilhelm Wundt, who, according to Freud, has given

> an explanation which deserves notice for the fact . . . that we make slips of the pen more readily than slips of the tongue. "In the course of normal speaking the inhibitory function of the will is continuously directed to bringing the course of ideas and the articulatory movements into harmony with each other. If the expressive movement which follows the ideas is retarded through mechanical causes, as is the case in writing . . . such anticipations make their appearance with particular ease."[60]

The act of writing by hand—wherein mental thoughts formulate more quickly than can be recorded—leads to a more transparent transcript of unconscious communication or parapraxis. Writing is a mechanism for recording that registers something different from speech and, for both Wundt and Freud, is more accurate due to the legibly expressive nature of its inaccuracies. Moreover, letters, unlike live speech, can be reread before they are sent; if self-censorship does not catch the error twice (and blot it out), its presence becomes even more expressive and illuminating. While the consulting room is a privileged location for performing the kind of hermeneutic labor involved in making and catching slips and gaining a better understanding of the root of symptoms generally (parapraxes are classically symptomatic), it need not be the only containing site for this deep "telling" and reading of productive speech.[61] Correspondences, with their generative conventions that invite fantasized relationality and register unconscious trace, are yet another scene for this kind of work.[62] Symptomatic slips can appear in statements that differ from intended meaning, in miswriting, in misreading, and in simply omitting to post a missive. The only failure inherent in these scenarios is the failure of the ego to screen out unconscious motivation.[63] Instead of apprehending these parapraxes as errors, they can be understood better as expressing a therapeutically available ratio of failure and success in self-censorship.

Letter writers imagine the correspondence, with all of its components (the envelope, the stamp, the address) and all of its contents (intentional and inadvertent), to be a closed form (as opposed to the postcard). The letter is understood to be a contained container: written on one end, sealed, securely sent, received at the other, read, and put away or burned. In reality, it can be assumed to be open and opened during each of these steps. Various kinds of routinized external intervention prevent the fantasy of direct and secure one-to-one communication from being perfectly realized. This includes state censorship's pre-reading of a letter before the intended recipient receives its contents, as well as the immediate or eventual recirculation of a letter beyond its intended audience by its recipient or their community.[64] This liability to openness generates two intertwined myths about letter writing: epistolary privacy[65] and epistolary security—both in terms of individual leaks in exchanges strategically (mis)understood to be exclusive and peer-to-peer and repressible notions of systemic surveillance and censorship. Instead of these questions only being raised when teletherapy migrates to the digital, the problem of maintaining a secure connection has always been present in the history of teletherapy.

Epistolary security depends similarly on a repression of material conditions and system, the enabling fantasy that a letter is inviolate from the moment of its being sealed to the instant of its being opened by its intended addressee. The letter writer understands the letter to be for the other's eyes only, and yet it is known that along the route from mailbox to address, postal workers and government officials acting as censors were able to, and did, open letters.[66] In Freud's moment there were both protections and propaganda aimed at preserving the notion that the post was secure. At the end of the eighteenth century in Prussia, violating the sanctity of a letter became a legal violation of privacy as opposed to an instance of fraudulent conduct.[67] A nineteenth-century German cabinet official stated, "What is locked up most carefully in the heart, in one's living room, is entrusted without hesitation to the postal service. . . . The symbol of discretion is none other than that of the postal service."[68] Yet there was widespread awareness that the material post was not as locked up as the abstract contents of the two intimate chambers of heart and home. In fact, it was not locked up at all: Vienna was home to some 3,000 censors in Freud's moment.[69] Letter writing was understood to be "as if" one-to-one while being decidedly a nonprivate form of communicating over distance.

Everyday media systems shaped Freud's understanding of mental life. Freud was well acquainted with the risk of censorship and it became integral to his work on the psyche; he assumes censorship in correspondences and underscores it when attending to his personal correspondence. He then brings this awareness with him into his clinical work metaphorically, where he becomes invested in thinking through notions of censorship in his models of mind and analytic practice. Well before Freud offered his metaphor of the telephone call as already being subject to self-censorship, as Peter Galison shows, Freud modeled the unconscious processes inherent in dreaming on his frustrations with the post.[70]

In his experience as a correspondent, Freud experienced his own self-censorship and endured that of the state. In letters, he bemoaned the role of censors in the post then marked his envelopes *offen* ("open") and in turn censors marked his envelopes with the sign of inspection.[71] These unsealed, open letters continued to house and transmit Freud's most intimate written relations, both clinical and casual.[72]

The fantasy that a letter is written by one hand and seen by one pair of eyes exclusively and the notion that one is "speaking" directly to an epistolary confidant are both underpinned by an ideological investment in "speech" being private. Routinely, both sides of a correspondence were kept together by copying the letters one authored, and these full correspondences were often preserved and thereby turned into a record for future generations.[73] Letter writers of the nineteenth century were fully aware of these common practices of duplication and archiving, undermining the important fallacy that correspondence was an absolutely confidential one-to-one form. Letters were shown before they were sealed, addressed to more than one person, and handed around after being received.[74] The writing typically treats its channel as secure while knowing that it is not. Or the channel is fantasized as secure so long as the relationship it sustains feels as though it is. The last sentence of the last letter from Freud to Fliess, after the termination of their relationship, simply reads, "Please keep the contents of this one to yourself."[75] Fliess is no longer to be trusted implicitly (and implicitly was never trusted previously either); it is a sign of the correspondence's end that privacy must become an explicit demand. Fliess did and didn't obey this wish.

While the Freud–Fliess correspondence is greatly celebrated and made use of for research into the theory and history of psychoanalysis, as is the "self-analysis" Freud claimed to report there, the two are not thought of together, or, more importantly, *as* each other. Freud can always make the whole of the letter serve the analysis and the analysis therefore is the whole of the letter. They disguise one another as categories by being indistinct. The missive—unconscious and conscious, in every inkblot and misspelling and missing word, and in every passage from casual sociality to rigorous theorization and back again—is the medium.

Though we only have one side of the equation to draw on (the most successful censorship of all), Freud's epistolary analysis is the earliest example of a therapeutic treatment attempted beyond the in-room scenario and without voiced exchanges of free association. Freud shows us that it is possible to analyze a psyche without spoken dialogue and with the visible vocabulary of the patient's body reduced to the peculiarities of its handwritten script.

THE SECOND EPISTOLARY PATIENT

Another analysis conducted by letter, the case of "Little Hans," further complicates these questions by displacing that treatment to an epistolary exchange between two doctors—Freud and Max Graf—on behalf of a patient, Graf's young son. While the Freud–Fliess correspondence is heavily safeguarded and only partially extant, the Freud–Graf correspondence, which contains the record of Hans Graf's treatment, has never even been made available. Instead, it is highly curated (censored) in the form of Freud's case study of Hans, *Analysis of a Phobia in a Five-Year-Old Boy*. If Freud's analysis by post was a site for determining the Oedipal Complex (along with dream interpretation technique), then *Analysis of a Phobia in a Five-Year-Old Boy* is the case study that was to prove the universality of that claim (and the claims in *Three Essays on Sexuality*) as scientific. Whereas Freud's own analysis with Fliess led to texts considered foundational in psychoanalysis, Freud's work with Hans is not much discussed, and where it is, it is somewhat discounted or forgotten and its material mediation neglected. *Analysis of a Phobia in a Five-Year-Old Boy* is an unusual case study, beyond its epistolary dimension, for several reasons. It is the first analysis of a child and it is Freud's sole analysis of a child. Freud only saw his patient in his office once while treating him, and the analysis is conducted almost exclusively via letter writing.[76] Given that Hans is five years of age, his father, Max Graf, further mediates the treatment, collecting and reporting Hans's remarks and behaviors for Freud to read. In this relationship, Freud serves as a supervisor (to Max Graf) more than, or as well as, the treating doctor to Hans.

Psychoanalyst critics of the case find it lacking, citing many weaknesses: Freud's desire to produce evidence for his theories in *Three Essays* is so strong that he himself censors important material related in Graf's letters;[77] Freud is criticized for his overidentification with both Max Graf and Herbert (Hans) and his previously completed analysis with Olga Graf (Herbert's mother); as a result of all these interfering connections, Freud does not interpret wide swaths of the presented material and flatters both the mother and father of "Hans."[78] Skeptics further object that Max Graf serves as the first listener-interpreter of his own child, determining and censoring what is and is not important to the case. Freud then combs the written material, selecting portions for publication. Beyond these criticisms, I will add that it is not simply that Freud comes to the case with his own biographical and clinical motivations and fetters. In addition, the case has multiple transferences and countertransferences running through its conduct. These transferences and countertransferences are already strange in their multiplicity but are rendered even more so by the fact of their circulation outside the consulting room and through the mail.

The atypical nature of the patient and the strength of Freud's investments are enough to leave the case open to suspicion, but the Hans case can also be read as unusual primarily because it is heavily mediated, both materially and theoretically, through Hans's parents. While the latter interference has attracted significant suspicion and inquiry, the former remains unthought. In engaging the series of interpretations that occur in Hans, one must mark and hold in mind three levels of mediation: we encounter Freud's analysis of the case simultaneously with the work done by the original physician-father Max Graf, all of which is possible only because the treatment is conducted outside of the consulting room, on the page, where speech has become correspondence, reportage, and symptom.

Analysis of a Phobia in a Five-Year-Old Boy is comprised of excerpted letters sent from Max Graf to Freud, sutured together by commentary from Freud. At first, Graf sent Freud these letters to assist the doctor in his general research into infant fantasy and sexuality. It is only after quite some time that Freud begins working with Hans as a patient, with Graf reporting on Hans and Freud replacing a formal reply by clarifications, theoretical extension and, eventually, interpretation. Freud does not specifically call attention to the material fact that the case is conducted by letter, nor to his censorship of its materials via selective excerpting. Instead the form everywhere quietly announces this to be so: all of the material is drawn from recorded, written reports delivered to Freud in the post.

These observations begin when Hans is nearly three years old and quickly increase in frequency upon the arrival of Hans's baby sister ("Hanna") some six months later.[79] Freud writes, "I shall now proceed to reproduce his father's records of little Hans just as I received them; and I shall of course refrain from any attempt at spoiling the *naïveté* and directness of the nursery by making any conventional emendations."[80] Freud makes an initial promise of completeness and transparency, yet this promise degrades immediately into a rhetorical and tactical excerpting of Graf's reports. This censorship in the form of curation and argumentation constitutes yet another trace of unacknowledged mediation of the "directness" of patient speech.

The first twenty pages of the case are carried on in this way: Max Graf writes to Freud, Freud extensively quotes the letters and offers interpretation as well as normalization and validation of Hans's sexual urges, preoccupations, and distinctions. After this initial and cursory consideration, Freud is brought in to treat Hans formally in collaboration with Max Graf, who is "most uneasy" at the appearance of a "nervous disorder" in his son. Though Graf will "call upon [Freud] tomorrow" in person, he first wishes to write via letter all the available material at once.[81] The disorder at hand presents as Hans's sudden agoraphobia and fear that a horse will bite him. Graf asserts that this must be traceable to Hans's knowledge of horses' large "widdlers" (penises). It is in this phase that Freud begins to act as remote supervisor on a "case history," writing:

> We will not follow Hans's father [to his conclusions] . . . we will begin by examining the material before us. It is not in the least our business to "understand" a case at once: this is only possible at a later stage, when we have received enough impressions of it. For the present we will suspend our judgment and give our impartial attention to everything that there is to observe.[82]

While Freud celebrates and makes note of the particularities of working with the patient's father, he does not distinguish this case study from his other psychoanalytic treatments because of its being conducted via a written exchange. Hans is being treated at a double remove: he is the first tele-patient, other than Freud himself, and his father reports his content to his analyst. Though Freud writes that everything must receive "impartial attention," he is once more transitioning his interpretive ear to the graphological eye.

This treatment at a distance is unlike the Freud–Fliess analytic relationship, conducted via letter in part because the two doctors lived in different countries; Hans and Max Graf lived in Vienna, not too far from Freud—epistolary treatment in this case would seem to be spatiotemporally optional but was in fact derived from a different necessity. Hans's onset of neurosis—or his self-described "nonsense"—involved agoraphobia—he refused to leave the safety of his home. The Freud–Graf treatment was supposed to accommodate, understand, and reverse this phobia by recourse to the medium of the letter. In the meantime, Hans shied away from outdoor activity. Max Graf wrote to Freud (which Freud quotes verbatim in the case study), "After an attack of influenza, which kept him in bed for two weeks, his phobia increased again so much that he could not be induced to go out, or at any rate no more than on to the balcony. . . . As soon as he gets to the street door he hurriedly turns round."[83] Not being able to leave the house, whether because one is suffering from agoraphobia or depression, is disabled, must perform childcare, or cannot take the additional time to travel, impedes access to psychodynamic treatment if treatment is understood to be restricted to the in-room scenario. As with subsequent forms of teletherapy, Freud's epistolary analysis dissolves the walls of the consulting room to allow access to help that one does not have to leave the confines of the home in order to receive.

Hans, even at five years old, is just such a patient. He benefits from having another way to contact an analyst for treatment (beyond the father he has at home). In other words, he is a patient rather than a nonconsenting subject, despite his age, his unwillingness to visit Freud, his father's surveillance of him, and the third-party reports to Freud it generates. In a "weekly report from Hans's Father," Freud quotes:

> My dear Professor, I enclose the continuation of Hans's story—quite an interesting installment. I shall perhaps take the liberty of calling upon you during your consulting hours on Monday and if possible of bringing Hans with me—assuming that he will come. I said to him to-day: "Will you come with me on Monday to see the Professor, who can take away your nonsense for you?"
>
> *He*: "No."

Hans rejects the notion of *going in* to treatment, while in other moments he demonstrates consent to *being in* treatment—provided it is written and he can stay at home.[84] Elsewhere, Hans is reported as asking Graf if he would write down little speeches and send them off to the "Professor" and goes so far as to say he is "always so glad when I can write to the Professor."[85] Eventually, Hans is persuaded to go Freud's office for an in-person visit—the only visit during the whole of the case. In his office, Freud tells Hans that his "nonsense" derives from his repressed love of his mother and his fear that his father will punish him for this love. After the consultation, Freud continues to receive "almost daily reports of the alterations in the little patient's condition."[86] Hans in return receives a written cure from the Professor: "From that time forward [Hans] carried out a programme which I was able to announce to his father in advance."[87] The frequency of analytic exchange is not undermined by distance—instead, the illness that precludes in-person visits can be treated through the post. It is this mediated, but not medium-specific, formulation—where a distance therapy goes to the ill instead of the ill to the therapy—that will be constantly asserted and reconfigured across every available medium over the next century.

MEDIATING METAPHORS

In order to gain standing as a medical science, Freud and his followers felt the need to protect the theory against any number of external threats: a confusion with the occult, the unorthodoxy of analysts who broke away from Freud's teachings, misuse of its archive, and degradation into lay analysis. The discipline has also had to deal with an internal interference, that thing in the room with clinician and patient, between them, which we can call materiality and which remains even when the room fades away and is replaced by another medium for conducting voice such as correspondence—speech made handwriting. Freud dealt with the internal threat of telepathy by foreclosing all inquiry into it; the external threat of mediation was neutralized by metaphorization and incuriosity, despite the actual use of media for treatment detailed here. Some of these safeguarding measures are still in place today: contemporary practitioners remain loyal to the tradition in their anxieties and suspicions about extending the analytic scenario beyond the room, even in the age of phone, FaceTime, and Zoom sessions, especially in the COVID-19 pandemic (see coda).

Freud repeatedly enriched his thought about therapeutic communication by turning, metaphorically, to the technical media of his day. First and foremost, these were postal and print technologies, with which he was intimately familiar from his experiences as a correspondent and from publishing. Secondarily, he would analogize to technologies like telephones, photographs, and gramophones, with which he seems to have had at least some personal experience, as recounted in *Civilization and Its Discontents*.[88] We can see this in one of his most famous analogies, in which he compares analytic listening to telephony.

After adopting the "talking cure" for his free associative practice, Freud continued to extend his oral emphasis figuratively. In his *Recommendations to Physicians Practicing Psycho-Analysis*, Freud famously insists that the relationship between the analyst and the patient is like that of two persons communicating by telephone. The telephone here is deployed metaphorically, though the telephone itself as a media technology has its own developmental history that intersects with identity politics and pathology of another order.[89] Freud writes:

> To put it in a formula: he must turn his own unconscious like a receptive organ towards the transmitting unconscious of the patient. He must adjust himself to the patient as a telephone receiver is adjusted to the transmitting microphone. Just as the receiver converts back into sound waves the electric oscillations in the telephone line which were set up by sound waves, so the doctor's unconscious is able, from the derivatives of the unconscious which are communicated to him, to reconstruct his unconscious, which has determined the patient's free associations.[90]

Freud's attention is squarely on the inevitable censorship conducted by the patient before they even begin to speak. What Freud listens to on the metaphorical telephone is a talking that has limits; self-censorship is the loophole in the "fundamental rule" of free association. Transference, at least, makes this *feel* impossible. The analyst, too, has their own limitations that must be managed.[91] Everything is never everything; it is only ever what can be spoken at a given time. While Freud opens with a discussion of censorship that calls to mind his worries about epistolary communication, he then shies away from the medium he makes actual use of in his work. Instead, he repairs to the fantastic, near-magical modern medium of the telephone to comment on the transference at work in the analytic encounter. Yet the telephone is not magical, and neither is psychoanalysis or any other form of psychotherapy. Psychoanalysis—occurring as in-person, in-room, one-to-one communication—is filled with its own perforations or opacities, just like the self-censorship required in letter writing or what the telephone user might experience during a call.[92] The therapeutic conversation is buffeted by multiple intrusions and censoring bodies. In the in-room scenario, clinicians and patients alike fail to hear or hear "correctly," whether due to ambient noise, intrusion, or transference/countertransference.

Freud then continues to elaborate the import of a particular listening in psychoanalysis, stating that proper analytic attention requires an "evenly hovering" or "evenly suspended" attention—not just listening. Attention is not medium specific. To insist on the analyst's attention as evenly hovering or suspended is to describe disembodied exchange—so far attached either to the telephone metaphor or to epistolary analysis.[93] If the analyst is floating or in flight, they do not have to be stationed anywhere in particular (for instance, behind a couch) or have a copresent body at all. Instead, the analyst's attention can be "transferred to another person through empty space." Freud's use of the telephone metaphor insists on a kind of practice that can travel.[94] The attention Freud describes here is a flexible one, not specific to therapy conducted in the bounded setting of an in-person analytic work site. If analysis can be conceived of metaphorically as a telephone call, one imagines it might be actually possible via telephone or at least under other disembodied arrangements.

Though Freud here describes this technique in conjunction with the telephone, he first advocated this listening practice in relation to his earlier—and silent—work in "Little Hans" (1909).[95] Listening there was equally metaphorical; Freud was not *listening* to Hans but reading reports of him and his speech. Freud seems to be comfortable lending the spoken utterance a wide range of manifestations for psychoanalytic attention and interpretation. In collapsing listening (to speech) with reading (words), the text is made to speak.[96] Freud can at once metaphorize the role of media in psychoanalysis and create a fungible logic by which new forms of mediation accommodate psychoanalysis and its clinical encounters. The "talking cure" is in actuality accomplishable by any medium that can support a form of speech; psychoanalysis as a technique is not premised on any of the single media and spaces in which it is practiced or was first conceived, even as the shift in medium necessarily changes the work.

Freud's use of the telephone metaphor also accommodates the in-room norm of the analyst's body, positioned out of view of the patient; the voice of the doctor *seems* disembodied even when the body is present. However, in his use of the telephone, Freud does not take into consideration the embodiment of either patient or doctor while describing them as caller and receiver. As a metaphor (as opposed to a differentiated therapy practice), the telephone occludes the specific therapeutic frame proper to the in-room scenario as well as the decorum of the phone call (after all, it may be difficult to refrain from reflexively asking your analyst how they are when communicating via phone, while this is somewhat easy to avoid from the couch). The metaphor captures the analytic voice and ear but not other aspects of the in-room scenario or the specificities of telephonic etiquette. In-room, the patient may not see their analyst, yet they are aware of their proximity to the body of the clinician. The patient greets the clinician, performs patterned gestures, hears the movements of the clinician along with their voice, says goodbye. Further, the telephone metaphor doesn't account for the clinician's potential field of vision and how that may play into apprehending the patient. Freud is assuming an analytic treatment. From their position behind the couch, the clinician may see some if not all of the patient's face and gestures while listening to vocal content, whereas the patient is turned away from the clinician so that the clinician takes on a more fantastic character. The telephone metaphor brackets the reception performed by all of our sense organs except our ears; it cordons off all interactions save for those spoken, in favor of re-describing a singular and uncontaminated or pure therapeutic technique for apprehending symptomatic speech.

Because Freud is already attentive to analysis occurring beyond the in-room scenario and insists that the listening performed from the couch is already akin to the kind of listening available via the telephone, he alerts us to the mediation (tele)present in the original analytic scenario. The telephone is not only a sonic, one-to-one technology allowing Freud to remove the body in favor of the content of exchange; it is also a medium that allows for communication over distance. Latent questions of technology and intimacy are at work in the selection of the telephone as a metaphor for psychoanalytic conversation. The ability to practice analysis through distanced intimacy—a close voice without a present body—conditions even embodied psychoanalysis in that, although it is only assumed as a possibility, this form of analysis is in fact already present in couch-bound treatment. Then there is the question of what that distance and dislocation do to transmission (of the unconscious). Instead of only seeing the deployment of the telephone metaphor as incoherent, we can value Freud's intuition that the intimacy and success of this mediated work is not dependent on the presence or absence of a room filled with bodies.

Deploying the hypotheticality of analogy, Freud evokes mediation as external and different to the therapeutic scenario when in fact it is internal and proper. Analytic listening—or for that matter, telepathy—relies on the metaphor of the telephone call. Mediation must be phrased through another figurative body in order to hide itself in plain sight. In undertaking the history of media at the core of psychoanalysis, one must narrate the presence of media as a peripheral yet persistent metaphorics—traces left behind that both disguise and allow access to the actual multiple mediations of the "talking cure" and to its practitioners' fascination and discomfort with the distances at work within the intimacy of analysis.

Freud, ever shifting in his own thinking, did not merely come out against his training in hypnosis and the power and fallibility of suggestion: he tried to remove the obtrusive, obvious mediating object between clinician and patient. There is a logical reason for not wanting to signal additional apparatuses of communication where they are present: one is already too much and is one more than telepathy hypothetically contains. To admit that the letter does something to the analytic scenario, or even supports it, requires us to think constantly of a third thing in the analytic scenario: clinician, patient, and medium. In psychoanalytic theory and practice, Freud tried to drop the *tele-* and keep the *-pathy.*

With this disconnect in place—psychoanalysis is open to mediation but not understood to be so despite its obsessive recourse to media analogies—those attempts to work with mediation, whether analog or digital, have been historically open to derision even though primary in the development of Freudian psychoanalysis. At the same time, Freud constantly experimented with expanding the analytic scenario and the medium of its cure. He smuggled the dream of telepathy back in. The result is that there is no stable notion of how and by what medium a patient *must* be treated (even as Freud lays out best practices for the psychoanalytic technique, to be pursued across any media environment that can support it). It turns out that psychoanalysis is not the "talking cure" after all. It is a *communication cure*, even or especially over distance. Analysis relies on a particular kind of constructed and open communication, not speech. Speaking and writing each allow for psychoanalysis to do its job, but the difference between the two and the levels of access, privacy, and security each permits have been left unexamined by Freud and his followers. Media, far from getting in the way of treatment, first facilitate it and then are put out of mind.

SIGNING OFF

After Freud was forced by the Nazi regime to move to England, he delivered his first and last radio address in the winter of 1938.[97] In it, Freud's voice is made nearly unintelligible, not only due to broadcast static but also because his jaw cancer was quite advanced and audibly affected his pronunciation. Nine months before the cancer would take his life, Freud used this single address to discuss the history of psychoanalysis at a deeply precarious moment in world history:

> I started my professional activity as a neurologist trying to bring relief to my neurotic patients. Under the influence of an older friend and by my own efforts, I discovered some important new facts about the unconscious in psychic life, the role of instinctual urges, and so on. Out of these findings grew a new science, psychoanalysis, a part of psychology, and a new method of treatment of the neuroses. I had to pay heavily for this bit of good luck. People did not believe in my facts and thought my theories unsavory. Resistance was

> strong and unrelenting. In the end I succeeded in acquiring pupils and building up an International Psychoanalytic Association. But the struggle is not yet over. Sigmund Freud.[98]

Freud concludes his radio address by "signing" his name—the secondary orality of the letter-writing form returned truly to the spoken and the spoken broadcast out to the public; the only known audio recording of the doctor ends in the conventions of the epistolary.

Figure 2.1

Drawings (airplanes), by "Richard," 1941, Wellcome Library, London. Wellcome Images, Drawings (airplanes) and manuscript by child patient. Recto pencil drawing, June 30, 1941.

2 MASS INTIMACY

Just over a year after Sigmund Freud and some of his family (including his wife Martha, and psychoanalyst daughter Anna) fled Nazi-controlled Austria for London in the wake of the recent *Anschluss*, Freud's jaw cancer had progressed to the point where it was "nothing but torture" and, on September 23, 1939, he took doses of morphine to end his life.[1] By the late summer of 1940, the British Psycho-Analytical Society (BPAS) had been doubly unsettled. Inside the society, Sigmund Freud's recent death had left a vacuum; he could no longer serve as a stabilizing force between the disparate factions already formed in which Melanie Klein and Anna Freud fought over the future of technical practice within the BPAS. Outside, London—as well as much of England—was under nightly siege from the skies.

Where World War I had sparked an interest in the crowd and mass psychology, World War II and its aftermath necessitated group therapy and mass therapeutic services, especially for children and veterans. This was a radical departure in how psychoanalytic therapy had been used in the mainstream: treatment of the group and children were only just emerging forms of therapeutic work in this moment. In order to reach those in need of help, psychoanalysis therefore underwent a series of revisions, delivered by multiple analysts with various technical approaches. Psychoanalysis during the war demanded at the very least a rethinking of these basic tenets of treatment: privacy, the economics of mental health, who and how many can be analyzed and from what distance, what constitutes a session, and where and how sessions can be conducted. Analysts experimented heavily with new techniques that relied on services subscribed to en masse, including the use of quotidian media and technology already highly depended upon because they brought news of the war to the home. Psychoanalysis underwent a series of strategic adaptations that made psychodynamic help increasingly available to children, veterans, and groups via letters, columns, and broadcasts—suddenly the discipline was thriving in the very conditions that had threatened its practice. The crisis of place and patient in wartime became the catalyst for producing new modes of psychodynamic help that cut across methodological lines in order to transform pressures into new forms of access. Mental health care workers in this period sustained the therapeutic frame by reformulating it and the forms, labors, and logistics of care. This was not a phenomenon unique to World War II; over the course of the twentieth century, therapists across the political spectrum would harness new media—from the radio to the newly ubiquitous telephone and television—to extend the reach of therapy beyond the one-to-one meeting of the consulting room, to follow the patient-in-waiting wherever they might be.

PUBLIC ANALYSIS

Transmission on a mass scale, especially making use of newspapers, magazines, and the national broadcasting service, greatly figured in these attempts to expand the analytic scenario beyond the consulting room and from a peer-to-peer model to a group as large as the nation. Freud's work with Little Hans is an important ancestor to this work in two ways (see chapter 1). The case demonstrates, before famous child analysts Anna Freud and Melanie Klein turn their attention to the treatment of children, that children can make use of therapy and be successfully helped by it—an expansion of the category of who can become a patient of this particular treatment.

"Little Hans" is also a secret manual for using mediation to reach patients wherever they may be. Hans was unable to leave his home and seek in-person treatment for individual reasons, and Freud dissolved the bounds of the consulting room by selecting additional media as the conduit for analysis, making teletherapy and tele-patients legitimate in part because he never dispels the point-to-point, one-to-one relationship between doctor and patient; even when, as in his work with Hans, two analysts jointly serve a single patient. During the War, when many were unable to meet and gather in consulting rooms for *national* reasons, psychoanalysis regathered the many who needed access to its treatment but were simultaneously unable to access its "pure" or embodied version.

In the interwar period through World War II, British-based psychoanalysis experimented with psychoanalysis for more patients via quotidian media and with new ways of treating children and their mothers. Even as the media these psychoanalysts necessarily selected to reach more patients shifted away from the one-to-one letter, letter writing and writing as such were maintained as part of the treatments in question. During the interwar period, there was a rise in the writing and publication of parenting books by behaviorists, feminists, mothers, and psychoanalysts. Hugh Crichton Miller, serving as the director of the Tavistock Clinic in London, contributed the celebrated book, *The New Psychology and the Parent* (1922), and Susan Isaacs, the child psychoanalyst and educator, wrote a parenting book specifically about early childhood, *The Nursery Years*, followed by a series of advice columns or "problem pages," sometimes penned under the pseudonym Ursula Wise.[2] Ursula Wise gave advice both scientifically psychoanalytic and empathetic to mothers—a decided contrast to her contemporaries. Her columns ran in "The Nursery World" and "The New Era in Home and School" from 1929 to 1939, at which point Isaacs became deeply involved in working with and surveying war-evacuated children.

Isaacs ran her column through two parallel channels: one public and one private.[3] Isaacs' writers were encouraged to send letters under a chosen pseudonym alongside their full biographical markers—replied to in order of arrival—with the promise that their identities would be kept confidential. The status of confidentiality is a mixed one—the writer agrees to have her situation revealed (even as her actual identity is kept safe) so it may serve as an exemplary site of education for many readers, while also receiving support for her particular problem. This allowed parents to write in about issues at home that could not be "spoken" in person without confidentiality, if at all. Run more like a mini-consultation over correspondence than a standard advice column, Isaacs used her column to become more involved with those that wrote to her than just the published letters would suggest.[4] Only the first querying letter (on having smacked a child, for instance) and the resulting advice (never to hit a child) appeared together in public—like a brief case study. However, Isaacs carried on backchannel correspondences with mothers in at least a few instances, replying to letters she received regardless of whether the letter was going to be featured—especially if the situation was quite dire and Isaacs was worried that her publication schedule would prevent her from being of use in time. In one case, she urged her anonymous correspondent to seek out in-person treatment for their child. Preserving the analytic convention of the referral, Isaacs sent a patient to Dr. D. W. Winnicott via this correspondence.[5] These rapid treatments thus occurred at the convergence of a disseminative medium, the epistolary mode it could present, and sometimes even an actual consulting room, all while producing a new therapeutic instrument: the semipublic letter. Isaacs treated her foray into the newspaper form as an extension of the analytic scenario despite all the media changes to the frame and the communication it could host. Backchannel correspondence and referral show Isaacs' commitment to care which in turn suggests she saw her readers not as an undifferentiated audience but as anonymous individual patients in need. In turn, each individual patient could be used educationally by any other anonymous reader (for more on this, see the second half of this chapter and chapter 5).

During the War, when batch processing veterans to return them to active duty, the question of new forms of analysis that could multiply their user number from one to many was at a premium. Psychiatrists were invited to pioneer new forms of therapy with an explicit, stated aim: to return as many neurotic soldiers to active duty as quickly as possible. This replaced the previous goal of accomplishing discharges of former soldiers and returning them to civilian life.[6] Wilfred Bion, a psychoanalyst, was one such military psychiatrist who participated in group therapy experiments for the British Army in these settings across a number of hospitals.[7] In 1942 at the Northfield Military Hospital, Bion began the first of these experiments in group therapy using protocols for those still within the military that were suffering from war neurosis. Bion defined group therapy in two ways: "[group therapy] can refer to the treatment of a number of individuals assembled for special therapeutic sessions, or it can refer to a planned endeavor to develop in a group the forces that lead to smoothly running co-operative activity."[8] This strategic definition can be applied to either crisis or palliative care within a group and contains flexibility in terms of scale, aim or activity. Here, it is meant to apply to Bion's wartime experiments during which he variously treated four hundred or sixteen men at a time in different hospital wards.

As he recounts in *Experiences in Groups*, Bion from the start formulated this particular kind of therapy in order to address several critiques he had made of institutionalized military psychiatry: that the whole process (the very buildings, the use of drugs, the individual and occupational therapies) seemed to "sedate" and "screen off" both clinician and patient from the putative aim of the therapy: to rehabilitate soldiers for either civilian life or a return to service.[9] Bion instead felt that it "seemed necessary to bring the atmosphere of the psychiatric hospital into closer relationship with the functions it ought to fulfill."[10] Bion described his running of this ward as a conscious recapitulation of the Army environment in which a common aim would unite the homosocial group under the command of a single leader.[11] Bion's role as a psychiatrist was twofold. He was an Army officer, in charge of his men and their unit, as well as a psychiatrist "consulting with these same men in assessing their condition and deciding with them their future in a nation at war."[12] Bion's secondary role as psychoanalyst is described in language that simultaneously addresses veterans and psychoanalysis's self-consideration and tactical adaptations. And yet, the role of the leader was to be minimalized; Bion swiftly decided that individual neuroses had to be displayed to the group so that it could "tackle neurotic disability as a communal problem."[13] Individual neurosis was also group neurosis, shared as a fact and worked on together. This shift marks a doubly radical undoing of the traditional frame of psychiatry and psychoanalysis. Gone is the one-to-one model of treatment; also banished is the foregrounding of expertise and therefore power. Therapy here is configured as a kind of group labor, group intimacy, and as seeking horizontality over and against its traditional understanding as dyadic intimacy with explicit power differentials.

Bion worked to extend the implications of his successes and failures in the ward to other potential populations, envisioning a paradigm shift in society that would make psychological treatment publicly available at scale:

> Society, like the individual, may not want to deal with its distresses by psychological means until driven to do so by a realization that some at least of these distresses are psychological in origin. The community represented by the training wing had to learn this fact before the full force of its energy could be released in self-cure. What applied to the small community of the training wing may well apply to the community at large.[14]

In his conclusions, Bion sounds much like Freud at the end of World War I (see introduction). Both understood that it was necessary to scale the psychoanalytic treatment of individuals to the level of the nation and both felt limited in any attempt to do so. Bion states that society too often uses discipline and punishment to stamp out neurosis instead of seeking to cure "psychological disorders by psychological means."[15] Society does not yet understand that "communal distress" is often psychological in nature.[16] Bion's experiment in the training wing demonstrates that "self-cure," or psychological help without explicit intervention from a particular clinician is possible—it is just not yet viable in that not even the "small community" was allowed to continue its work.

Group therapy is not particularly proposed as a pertinent way forward. Despite his interest in making psychological means available on a societal level, Bion does not confuse group therapy (the meeting of a particular group of people in conjunction with a clinician) with public analysis (an open form in which, Bion imagines, confidentiality and privacy would be nullified) and warns practitioners of the former not to mistake it for the latter. He writes that it "is important to realize that the psychoanalyst can easily make a blunder in a group that he would never make in a psycho-analysis, by treating the group as if the procedure were psycho-analysis in public."[17] Bion carefully notes that while individuals arrive to group treatment, once in the group they must no longer be treated as singular patients; group therapy is not to be either a series of public confessionals or an individual treatment conducted in front of an audience.[18] Though group therapy is concretely discounted as a form of public analysis given that it's not a viable example of the same, the scale of the group is one at which both neurosis and its cure present as systemic rather than individual. It is precisely this kind of thinking that expands the category of who can receive treatment, how, and by what means. While Bion's experiments are not technologically mediated, the therapy is mediated—by the group itself—and presages other efforts in peer-to-peer mental healthcare delivery (see chapter 3). When psychological problems can be held together and shared by many, a whole nation warrants and merits treatment. Here, and in Bion's later experiments, he had to extrapolate that largest group from a circle of veterans. For other socially engaged psychoanalysts who were his contemporaries, the treatable population was a wider segment of the public also experiencing the effects of war firsthand, though not on the battlefield—namely, mothers and their children.

THE RIGHT KIND OF PEACE

Even when patients were seen in their own, ongoing therapeutic treatments, public psychoanalysis could enter the frame. One of the most famous child patients of the World War II moment was a ten-year-old boy, Richard, whose treatment Melanie Klein recounts in great detail in *Narrative of a Child Analysis*. The analysis was comprised of ninety-three sessions conducted between late April and August of 1941—a very short treatment by her standard.[19] Klein had evacuated to Pitlochry, Scotland; Richard, who had also been evacuated after a bomb hit his home, was brought to Pitlochry by his mother specifically in order to enter a treatment with Klein.[20]

In Melanie Klein's last session with Richard, his ongoing feelings about their termination—by turns both loving and hateful—continued to come up in play, through the last minutes of the session. Richard was fixated on the clock:

> He caressed it, handled it, opened and closed it, wound it, and was deeply engrossed in these activities. When he set the alarm, he said: "Mrs. K. is broadcasting to the world. She is saying, 'I shall give the right kind of peace to everybody.'" Then he added a little shyly, "And Richard is a very nice boy, I like him."[21]

Richard, keenly aware of the number of minutes he has left with Klein, acts out a fantasy: he could continue to *hear* Klein after termination and others would hear her too—and of course she would explicitly refer to caring for him. His transferential fantasy is not about a continuation of therapy in the traditional sense (he can hear her, yes, but she doesn't speak to him but *of* him). The fantasy is that Mrs. Klein loves him and cares for him even when she is separated from him and off the clock, of which her public assertion over the channel Richard listened to daily would be the proof. Richard fantasizes that media will provide impossible, enduring access to his psychoanalyst when the traditional frame of care disappears. Wartime anxiety and its solution would both be broadcast and heard in the home, illness and cure coming in over the same channel. Klein would provide peace, not just psychically, but as an end to war. Richard replaces this anxious-making broadcast of the war with the comforting voice of his analyst speaking an ideal content and working to undo the war outside. Richard could count the RAF raids while also receiving—no matter where Klein was—"the right kind of peace": psychoanalysis.

The specifics of Richard's fantasy are his alone and interpretable within the confines of his already existing (and ending) treatment but the media setting for that fantasy, the national broadcast, was already happening in reality: psychoanalytic broadcasting had begun to occur with some frequency. While many of these broadcasts were quite well received, other appearances caused great controversy, particularly within the psychoanalytic profession. Such was the case when Dr. Edward Glover gave a radio address attacking war psychiatrists' efforts at the front.[22] Some radio shows were one-off, meant to address a specific topic (children and war anxiety or military psychiatry), while others appeared more than once. Even Richard's own Mrs. Klein appeared on a radio broadcast, urging parents not to forget that their children needed play in wartime.[23] Most regularly, Winnicott addressed the nation over the wireless in a series of discussions on mothering beginning in 1939 that were so successful they continued until 1962—a wartime necessity become a peacetime indispensability.[24] The psychoanalyst, using the ubiquity of private radio ownership and consumption in the home, was, in performing a kind of house call with some consistency, proving reliable in a moment of extended uncertainty and mobile in a time of restricted movement. Winnicott's radio show imagined a new kind of therapeutic help and advice that was at once psychoanalysis for the public and reliant on cohesive themes of communal distress at the level of the nation while simultaneously mimicking an individual treatment conducted *in* public. Winnicott operated with the nation's mothers as composite case in mind, moving Isaacs' advice column to the airwaves while drawing on Bion's theory of a public analysis.[25]

THE ORDINARY LISTENER

Winnicott began conducting frequent BBC addresses focused on mothering and children during the war crisis in 1939. In this moment, the BBC radio was also adapting to its new, homebound audience, an emerging "ordinary listening population," namely, the housewife. Sian Nicholas writes of the BBC's imagination of this listener:

> notably working-class housewives, whose existence as a significant component of the daily audience was one of the BBC's more striking wartime discoveries. . . . A policy document . . . circulated in August 1940 illuminated the BBC's changing perceptions of its audience. It began with a remarkable portrait of the "average listener": provincial rather than suburban, blue- rather than white-collar, elementary-school educated, a reader of the Sunday papers but not much else, resigned to periods of unemployment, likely to be conscripted but unlikely to contemplate a commission, morale "all right, he has no doubts about the necessity of beating Hitler, but he hasn't much faith in politicians and prefers not to think about the future." Indeed, he was more often than not a she: a housewife who "lost her looks when she was twenty-five," who went to the pictures at least once a week and "uses the 'wireless' even more than [her husband] does."[26]

Using the radio, Winnicott took the psychoanalytic advice column further into the public, delivering mass therapeutic advice specifically for this average listener—the precarious wartime mother and her child—over the same channel as entertainment forms and war updates. Psychoanalysis did not simply adapt itself to war conditions by experimenting with new media, new spaces, new patients and modalities; in so doing analysts also acted as ambassadors for their own practice, sharing its methods and therapeutic values with the largest audience it had ever had.

This hybrid genre—the radio show meets therapeutic communication—was comprised of the formal constraints of both. Put another way, radio broadcast as therapeutic method expanded greatly and diminished what could be accomplished in a "session" or "show." Early on in his broadcasts, Winnicott discussed the boundaries and limits for this kind of therapeutic communication over the wireless. The first order of business for Winnicott's serial addresses was to produce what Winnicott calls a "holding environment" for the listener that would allow for some form of productive relationality. The radio extends and stretches that which is already present in the traditional analytic scenario: an acousmatic voice.[27] The acousmatic sound of the analyst's speech—a voice heard without seeing the body that produces it—occurs as a one-sided phenomenon in the in-room, couch-reclining scenario; clinicians can see part of their patient's body while patients cannot see their analysts. The radio creates an environment in which the clinician's voice is bodiless yet present but dissolves the consulting room, removing the possibility of two-way conversation with the patient. Aspects of the therapeutic frame that rely on visuality (expressive motion, greeting the patient face-to-face) could not be literally translated to the radio.[28] Instead, much of the analytic environment is established (by both clinician and patient) in the constant "voice" that creates a space for holding.

Winnicott makes a one-sided attempt to establish some of the other conventions of psychoanalysis on the air. As a doctor, Winnicott presumes a patient. As a psychoanalyst broadcasting a talk, he is invested in imagining that patient and the ways in which she will encounter her analyst, despite the fact that they are unable to meet. Winnicott directly addresses an ordinary devoted mother, far away, in her home—or more rarely a father, away at war—tuning in to his broadcast. He often employs the second person, addressing an abstracted or multiplied single mother, her baby fussing nearby. The second person is supremely flexible in its indistinction between a single person and multiple persons. "You" thus works perfectly to admit and deny the one-to-many nature of the broadcasts (or insist that a one-to-one relationship was possible *inside* the one-to-many). As the only adult "you" usually in each household—especially with so many fathers away—the second person allows each maternal audient to feel intimately addressed despite the other embodied audients in the home and the many other audients, in their homes, also "listening in" to this fiction of peer-to-peer speech over an open channel.

Winnicott creates a one-to-one relationship with each of his "patients" while knowing that unintended audients (children or nonmothers) may be listening in as well, either alongside them or in other locations. His putative dedication to a single kind of person signals which listener is the intended one (the mother) and which is not (the nonmother, the child), producing an intimacy with each mother despite the open channel and open home or public space in which the listener most likely was; however, the broadcast's tight rhetorical beam also renders those intended listeners fungible in their demographics and concerns, creating a presumed normalcy and commutable set of cares among British mothers.

The enabling fiction of a therapeutic frame does not keep Winnicott from addressing other persons on other subjects. Instead of pretending that only his ideal listener is present, Winnicott tackles the common occurrence of children listening to his broadcast specifically, and war news more generally. As Klein saw with Richard, the daily consumption of news produced its own form of wartime anxiety. Winnicott recommended that parents "allow children to do other things—read or play dominoes—or to wander off altogether whilst the B.B.C. war news is being given."[29] Children would thereby self-regulate their engagement with the news, their internal censors protecting them from undue harm and their nearby and educable parents would be present to help them better apprehend what was taking place.[30] Winnicott also discussed specific situations in which many of his listeners, though by no means all, might be too pained by his broadcast to listen (whether the day's topic was the reintegration of a child who had been in foster care during the war or the ongoing separation of families). In his broadcast "Where Does Dad Come In?," which, as historian Michal Shapira notes, was partially censored by his producer Janet Quigley, Winnicott suggested that some of his listeners "may be hurt by this war in just this special way, your husband being unavailable, and if this is so I think you may not want to listen to me today, or perhaps father will hear me as he hangs around the canteen between jobs and I shouldn't think he'd like to hear what I have to say either . . . many people who want to be home can't get home."[31] In a self-referential act of imagining the impact of listening to the radio broadcast itself, Winnicott recalls Richard's fantasy. Winnicott notes the ways in which his new chosen medium can both induce pain and relieve it, that illness and its cure come over the same channel, indiscriminately broadcast into the home to its many kinds of subjects.

Winnicott also retained and dramatized the serial form of his psychoanalytic practice in his broadcasts. Much like a psychoanalyst would before seeing the patient in a consulting room, he sets the time and date for appointments: "Here we are right at the beginning . . . at this time on Wednesday you and I can meet, if we can together find we are sufficiently interested in each other."[32] Here Winnicott deploys the first person plural over distance; like the second person's obscured oscillation between singular and plural discussed above, this "we" also tactically occludes its quantity (a we of two or of many) and thus further works to create intimacy inside mass address. It also establishes the fiction of a two-way channel and its particular dynamics of agency, in which both must "find" and be "sufficiently interested"; if not, a mother could terminate the wireless session merely by turning the dial. Though the broadcasts were prewritten to fill exactly the length of his time slot, Winnicott ends several of his talks by announcing, "Our time is up."[33] While he simulates some of those room-based conventions an analytic patient (or analyst) might recognize, he goes beyond mimicking them in his addresses; he does not cover over the limits and affordances of broadcasting nor does he elide the dislocation of clinician and patient. The broadcasting booth is decidedly not the consulting room; Winnicott jokingly notes the pristine quiet of his new work conditions in contrast to the noise of seeing children in his consulting room as a way of indicating this from the very start. As Lisa Farley puts it: "Winnicott broadcast the failure of communication as the very grounds of thought."[34] Winnicott makes clear that he is not simply performing a consultation with his listener—or his tele-patients. While problematizing what it means to be "meeting" over the radio, Winnicott also makes plain his intention to protect his broadcasts from being reduced to non-psychoanalytic advice-giving—and throughout his broadcasts Winnicott reminds his listeners that if they want advice they should seek out welfare clinics.[35] Instead, Winnicott was clear that as a psychoanalyst, radio or no, he was not going to give instructions but instead *talk with* mothers, however monologically, about what various things in childhood mean and provide a larger understanding of what mothers do instinctively.[36]

Despite the deployment of the first-person plural on the radio, Winnicott discusses the problematic fact of separation and the one-sided limit of this oral communication. In the analytic scenario, the patient does most of the associative talking and the analyst comments and makes interpretation. One way of describing what Winnicott provides over the radio is a therapeutic monologue or soliloquy; the analyst *chattering on* instead of the patient. Winnicott asks, "What is there for me to do then, over the wireless, if I am not going to give instructions? Unfortunately we can't talk to each other, and I do indeed wish we could."[37] He then manages a solution that serves as an invitation: "Perhaps we can get round this difficulty . . . you can write [about your baby] . . . try and remember what made you feel pretty sure at that exciting moment that you were two people communicating with each other."[38] Here, Winnicott strategically foregrounds another common experience of one-way speech that yields two-way communication. He encourages the tele-patient to make of the unidirectional broadcast a two-way exchange by adding another medium, the letter; he further draws a metaphoric comparison between this epistolary contact and what the mother feels when she believes her infant to be communicating with her, before the child can speak. Winnicott's invitation to write was often acted upon; he received a great deal of "fan mail" throughout the course of his broadcasting career. The logic was extended yet again when on one of his broadcasts Winnicott's producers selected a number of such letters and recorded Winnicott reading the letters on the air—like Isaacs's advice column come to life—before answering specific questions, agreeing with some statements from his audience, and correcting misunderstandings.[39]

AFTER THE WAR

Despite having made efforts to attenuate these problems on his own radio broadcast (by speaking directly to a particular kind of listener, by inviting her to write and create a dialogue, by discussing a range of possible circumstances and reactions), Winnicott finds that his "good-enough"[40] treatment is not to be recommended, perhaps even during wartime, let alone in the peace presumed to follow. In critiquing his longstanding experiment, he idealizes a "pure" psychoanalysis located in a two-way analytic relationship that is either on demand or five times weekly, comprised of the ideal attention of the singular analysand—not a for-any-patient-as-some-patient structure—and therefore not offered in mass form. While Winnicott discusses the need to be flexible with patients in terms of how they are seen (given that one can't "know the distant future" of their treatment) and consistently experimented with the framing and boundaries of "seeing" patients, he renaturalizes a good analysis as one understood to be unmediated. Analytic treatment may be flexible—but it's not productive for it to be *that* flexible. In hindsight, Winnicott redescribed his broadcasts as emergency measures but only after having allowed this form of treatment to propagate among millions and despite the broadcasts continuing for seventeen years after the war's end. That continuance marks the shift from national crisis to the ongoing crisis that mothering is.

And yet, there remained a limited quantity of persons who could experiment with and wanted to provide new types of public therapy, let alone therapies that relied on media. On July 21, 1943, Ernest Jones chaired the Annual Meeting of the BPAS at which this problem of too few mental health care workers was discussed. A resolution was presented and brought up for vote: "that a committee should be appointed to consider the part which the Institute can take in the future in the training and education of various classes of workers."[41] Jones made the familiar argument that the Institute, its members, and the profession of psychoanalysis were "extremely precarious" due to the war conditions. He then argued for something surprising: the only way forward was to "ignore the red tape" of medical bureaucracy in order to mobilize more trainees to take part in the labor of helping the public. Jones continued, "If we do not do this in a few years' time we shall get no medical men or women applying for training unless they are seriously incapacitated themselves and it is probable that our younger medical members will tend to drift away."[42] This threat was echoed by Ms. Sharpe: "It would be lamentable if the knowledge and experience this society represents in its members were not made available and used for the benefit of the post-war world."[43] Contained within Sharpe's statement is an implicit plea to relax the training structure in the postwar moment such that more and more lay analysts—namely women analysts—could continue to participate in providing therapy as they had during the war. The crisis of the war had revealed the intrinsic flexibility of the discipline; as to the communicative media by which it practiced, the crisis was conducive rather than causal. Even as psychoanalysis met the present crisis of war and tended to the affected, it concentrated on a future in which palliative care would be more universally accessible to those with ordinary crises and symptoms, if only it had the practitioners to provide it.

RADICAL RADIO

World War II provided a litmus test for moving therapy away from the traditional intimacies of embodiment and the patient-clinician dyad. Allowing for the mediation collectivity requires, in the newspaper, in large groups, or on the radio, was a reformulating gesture of the very practice itself. Group therapy remained. Lay analysis increased. Therapeutic institutions for children and for veterans were founded and funded. Winnicott and others kept broadcasting therapeutic education that aimed to open up the strictures of therapy, even while the ends of this opening can be read, justifiably, as securing the domestic home front and nation-building (as Michal Shapira diagnoses much of the work of this moment in British psychoanalysis in her book *The War Inside: Psychoanalysis, Total War, and the Making of the Democratic Self in Postwar Britain*). The radio especially served as a way of providing help (as opposed to specific therapeutic treatment) to the many who needed it, precisely because it figured the problems of those on lockdown in their homes as a composite case. The listener could find themselves in some if not all facets of the broadcast. Help could be achieved, if not a proper conventional therapy.

The radio and its intertwined history with psychoanalysis had many afterlives, from practical uses of broadcast for therapeutic and pseudo-therapeutic treatment en masse, to the radio call-in show, to psychoanalytic theories of radio and the political significance of the medium.[44] If, as Shapira argues, Winnicott was helping keep the nation together at the level of the reproductive couple (both husband and wife and mother and child), ultra-left practitioners were also drawn to the radio as a tool for thinking of the system through the individual, instead of the individual through the system. The composite case imagined by Winnicott is one in which "mass intimacy" still means intimacy with a plurality of discrete subjects, all of whom contribute to the stability of the nation, rather than the attempt to form and care for a collective in order to generate a revolutionary cure for the system. Two other psychoanalysts, Frantz Fanon and Félix Guattari, who were both deeply invested in radical and new forms of group therapy, made use of the radio to describe and harness the collective for other purposes; namely, revolution and producing revolutionary subjects.

In the postwar moment, Frantz Fanon blended psychoanalysis with radical liberatory politics in his theorization of the role of radio in psychical nation-building. In *A Dying Colonialism*, Fanon describes the radio as a political and psychical medium; it isn't used to transmit therapeutic advice directly but to reach out to groups, to define and unify them. This unity has two historical aspects: the unification of European Algerians (colonialists) and the unification of the Algerian Front De Liberation Nationale (FLN). In the chapter, "This is the Voice of Algeria," Fanon argues that the radio, before the revolution in Algeria, played a psychical role as much as it functioned as a colonial information system. He writes that the radio market in Algeria was nearly entirely European Algerians; the use of the radio "reminds the settler of the reality of colonial power and, by its very existence dispenses safety, serenity. Radio-Alger is a confirmation of the settler's right."[45] When the FLN began broadcasting from Cairo in 1956, "The Voice of Fighting Algeria" was added to the chorus and Algerians began to buy radios at an ever-increasing rate to tune in. The radio quickly added to its previously comforting function a rallying capacity, becoming at once the hearth of the colonial family and the heart of the revolutionary family. The French began to jam the signal to prevent the FLN broadcast from reaching its audience; the operator of the home radio would then have to switch to new frequencies, chasing the voice. Fanon writes, "Often, only the operator, his ear glued to the apparatus, would have the unanticipated chance to hear the Voice. The other Algerians present in the room received the echo of this voice through the device of the privileged interpreter, who at the end of the broadcast was literally besieged. Precise questions were then posed to this incarnated voice. . . . At the end of the evening, not hearing the Voice, the listener would sometimes leave the needle on a jammed wave-length, or one that simply produced static, and would announce that the voice of the combatants was here."[46] Fanon is marking two radical modes of listening. One is participatory—which elsewhere he calls the "true lie" of the colonized—because the literal broadcast was difficult to hear, an interpreter had to fill in the opacities of the message, participating and becoming the broadcast.[47] Instead of the composite case implied in Winnicott's psychoanalytic broadcasts, Fanon describes a collective speaking through the individual, as an individual speaks the collective. Everyone felt the Voice, "welling up from within" and could access it, relay it.[48] Secondly, even in this absence, or especially in and via absence, the voice of the FLN was present.[49]

Félix Guattari, the radical French psychiatrist and collaborator of Gilles Deleuze, both theorized the use of media and was deeply involved with the Free Radio movement in France and Italy.[50] Guattari, like Bion before him, worked on questions of the group and group therapy (with veterans and not). His clinic outside Paris, La Borde, worked to rethink the traditional psychiatric and psychoanalytic relationship of clinician to patient by destroying the verticality and hierarchy explicit in traditional psychoanalysis. Like Fanon, Guattari saw the radio as a participatory form that could reconfigure the relationship of the one to the multiple, of the expert to the group. Guattari was committed to the use of free radio to disrupt hegemonic forces, considering the Free Radio a key site for revolutionary deterritorialization. In the late 1970s, he participated in and wrote about Radio Alice, the Italian free radio station founded by Franco "Bifo" Beradi.[51] At the same time, in Paris, Guattari participated in Free Radio on both an infrastructural and content level, securing transmitters from Italy for use in Paris and founding the twenty-four-hour broadcast Radio Libre Paris (later Radio Tomato), which initially broadcast from his kitchen. Until 1981, any use of a private radio station in France was a felony, met with steep fines and imprisonment.[52] This law only served to prove the import of such experiments. Guattari saw the Free Radio as an "immense, permanent meeting place" where "anyone, even the most hesitant, even those with the weakest voices, suddenly has the possibility of expressing themselves whenever they wanted. In these conditions, one can expect certain truths to find a new matter of expression."[53] Radio Tomato didn't become an immense gathering space precisely because of its technical limitations: it attributed its small audience to the poor quality of the broadcast (compared with what Fanon observed in Algeria, where signal jamming paradoxically became productive for spreading the Voice).[54]

These psychopolitical experiments in Algeria and in France attracted psychoanalysts precisely because they allow treatment of the "composite case," allow for anyone to become the speaker, deterritorialize, and allow the political aspects of subjecthood to be asserted and treated. Guattari and Fanon join with Winnicott in thinking of the radio as a therapeutic medium but seek a very different outcome: theirs is a theory of therapy as revolution and revolution as therapy; available, if not jammed or shut down, over the air.

DISTANCE TRANSFERENCE

Whereas Fanon and Guattari theorized that radio was essential to producing revolutionary subjects at distance, in the United States, psychological radio and its listeners would become a major market. By the mid-1970s, radio psychology had moved away from its historically educational format toward the participatory and interactive (far from the revolutionary modes of participation Fanon and Guattari imagine).[55] The shows still focus on a couple form, as Winnicott had, but not that of mother and baby. Instead, these shows are primarily concerned with marital and dating relationships, inflected by a variety of ideological commitments (religious right, anti-feminist, soft second-wave feminist) and by shifting conceptions of womanhood, femininity, and marriage. These shows spanned the late 1970s to the mid-1990s and indirectly addressed these phenomena. In brief, the fervor of second-wave feminism and the women's movement were still ongoing into the 1970s and early 1980s (before the culture wars markedly began in the early to mid-1980s). Women's talk radio addressed how to be a wife, partner, and mother in light of the women's movement, either directly or obliquely, either positively or reactionarily (see more below). Certainly, the hosts of these call-in shows were routinely asked to take a stand on the question of feminism (even as it is rather obvious where they fall on that political spectrum given the routine advice dispensed on marital issues). Secondly, and in parallel, in the 1970s to 1990s, divorce rates were ever increasing, peaking in 1981 and essentially leveling off at around 50 percent for the next fifteen years.[56] Where the BBC imagined a housebound housewife whose husband was ostensibly at war, the new average listener was just as likely to be a woman going through a divorce. Marital strife and marital maintenance were dominant themes across these shows (and the many books, television appearances, lectures, and other multimedia spin offs that followed).

The para-therapeutic call-in radio show of the 1970s and 1980s convened a new form of intimacy on air, syndicated nationally and led by charismatic hosts—the likes of Toni Grant, Barbara De Angelis, Laura Schlessinger, and Marilyn Kagan—with degrees in psychology (some licensed and some not), who eventually transitioned from careers in broadcast to careers in television.[57] As with earlier radio psychology, the target audience was reached, like Winnicott's broadcast or even Susan Isaacs' advice column, via a multiplicity and convergence of media forms, in this case the radio and the phone. Unlike Winnicott and Isaacs, who experimented and played with analysis in mediated forms, these radio shows trafficked in the life experience of their hosts even as they traded off their psychology credentials. The shows ran under the signifier of therapy while protesting, perhaps too loudly, that the shows were not meant to be therapeutic, just friendly. Such broadcasts rebrand the distance therapist, no longer an expert in public who offers education to a group, as an expert-friend (for more on the role of the "friend" in peer-to-peer counseling, see chapter 3) or confidante. This rebranding is also a concealment of authority, especially when gendered feminine—where the lay analyst (woman) becomes a sympathetic ear rather than an expert oracle. These disseminative media require this fantasy of mass intimacy, which also means hedging both against and in favor of the claim of expertise on offer, while keeping the mood personal. The mass intimacy convened here is deeply tied to profit motive: the service, like with Isaacs and Winnicott, is free (except for the cost of a newspaper, a radio license). The freeness of corporate radio is tied to ad revenue, so all the media affordances are also run through these substantial financial considerations for the station and its parent company.

Toni Grant is one of the most celebrated, if not controversial, women's radio psychologists. Her broadcasting career, like that of many who would follow her, began out of Los Angeles, the seat of American car culture, where she first appeared as a psychologist consultant on Bill Balance's *Feminine Forum* daytime talk show. Grant subsequently was given her own show, running nightly from midnight to 5 am in 1975. This show was the "prototype" all relationship advice call-in shows have followed; the format and success of call-in radio therapy is often attributed to Grant—the *New York Times* termed her the "true mother of all radio shrinks."[58] Her show concentrated on relationship and parenting advice, though not exclusively. In advising on marriage and in contrast to the tenets of the burgeoning women's movement, Grant's advice was "antifeminist" (advising women not to nag, to keep their husbands happy by tending to their masculinity). Prior to her radio career, Grant had worked with those suffering acutely—groups of Vietnam War veterans (making the slide from group therapy to public analysis that Bion had described in World War II) and patients with nonneurotic diagnoses (autism and schizophrenia)—but Grant saw the radio as a vehicle for reaching and helping the "mentally well."[59] The turn to focusing on the well of course greatly expanded her audience (a position both incommensurate and continuous with Freud's contentions about which classes could be helped—see introduction). When callers weren't well or were locked in an intractable pattern of behavior, Grant referred them out, advising them to seek normative, face-to-face therapy. In describing her show in an interview to the *Los Angeles Times* in 1977, Grant demonstrated the difficulty of categorizing exactly *what* kind of work was taking place via radio and what its limits were, saying, "I don't pretend its psychotherapeutic. . . . I deliver psychological information. Hopefully the show is . . . therapeutic."[60] In dropping the psycho- but reaffirming the therapeutic, Grant hedged whether some kind of overhearing can be a blend of the cathartic and educational—and not just prurient—for her listeners. At once a recognition of the limits of the form, a business decision that gathers the most listeners without alienating them via overtly psychodynamic theories or language, and a likely example of anti-Freudianism (see chapter 4), Grant wants it both ways. She needs to be an expert, in order to have the radio show to begin with, and to establish trust, but inside that frame performs the role of a friend.

As Grant's ratings began to wane in the 1980s, in part because of competition from those looking to improve upon and compete with her model, Barbara De Angelis,[61] a regular substitute for Grant, took over the show in 1989. De Angelis too broadcast daily via KFI, through the rest of 1989 and the 1990s, dispensing advice over the course of her two-hour noon time slot, again aimed at women in the home or in their cars. Where Grant had become more negative, direct, and admonishing of callers, De Angelis was "folksy" and considered herself a "love teacher."[62] Again, this coinage is a gendered surrender of explicit expertise of a certain kind in favor of another. Like Grant, De Angelis is trying primarily to avoid the stigma of illness in order to reach everyone without offense. De Angelis, a self-avowed feminist and child of the 1960s, was thirty-eight at the time and supposed to appeal to a younger audience, in part via her politics and laid-back nature.[63] In the toggle between Grant and De Angelis (both week-to-week where one filled in for the other and eventually in the full replacement), the call-in show is a flexible format, driven by its audience more than by its host; a feminist can be subbed in for an antifeminist in the same market.

In contrast to De Angelis's pseudo-hippie and feminist advice, Laura Schlessinger broadcast conservative family values as advice, "upbraiding" and "browbeating" her callers. She is known for in-person lectures, television guest spots, books, and, of course, her radio work (for more on this type of multimedia self-help culture, see chapter 3). Ironically, Schlessinger got her radio break as a caller herself. Her first experience with talk radio was phoning in to Balance's show in 1975, where Balance surveyed his audience with the question: "Would you rather be a widow or divorced?" Instead of the call lasting a minute or so (as is generally the temporal rhythm of call-ins), Balance let Schlessinger pontificate for a full twenty minutes. By 1976, she had her own late-night show in Los Angeles and was filling in for De Angelis and other broadcast daytime talk show hosts—again, diametrically opposed hosts are easily fungible. Schlessinger's work continued for more than ten years and, in 1990, she got her own nationally syndicated radio show on KFI, called *The Dr. Laura Program*. The show's title again contains the double bind of feminine expertise: Dr. is foregrounded—but it's the Laura program, her casualizing, approachable first name instead of the last. At its height, it was the second-most listened-to radio show in the United States, just behind Rush Limbaugh's, circulating daily via five hundred stations with eight million listeners.[64] Like De Angelis, Schlessinger too addresses the same stock set of relationship problems across media.

The most common situations that drove callers to seek Dr. Laura's advice were, "The custody of children after divorce and visitation rights, the pregnant teenager who though incompetent wants to keep the baby rather than providing a two-parent family for the child through adoption, invitation to a family gathering of in-laws, step-relatives, and blood relatives, and what to do after cheating on one's spouse."[65] Dr. Laura's responses to these situations were highly moralistic and self-avowedly antifeminist. Across the 1990s, she moved further and further right, as did her advice, becoming a lecturer on morality and conservatism and converting to Orthodox Judaism. The slippage from advice on marital relationships—the cornerstone of reproduction—to right-wing radio talking points is not a shocking one. The flexibility of mediated therapy allows for a tumble from the psychotherapeutic to the merely therapeutic, and from advice to ideological propaganda.

Last in the KFI-lineage of radio therapists is Marilyn Kagan, a licensed psychotherapist as well as an actress, who branded her KFI call-in show as a para-therapy, describing her daily 9 pm-midnight slot as "more psychologically stimulating talk radio" (adding "psychologically" to KFI's tagline "more stimulating talk radio"). Fielding calls from listeners using their car phones who, ostensibly, hopefully, pulled off the freeway, or those "lucky" enough to have a cellphone in 1992, Kagan would open her segment with a discussion on a psychological or educational topic such as empathy or community service.[66] The calls between therapist and user followed a script guided by the therapist–talk show host that allows for a quick understanding of the situation, a triage of the main concerns of the caller, and then some kind of advising intervention that the caller (and audience, in the case of the radio show) can take away. In brief, after cutting to traffic and commercial, during which the producer of a show would triage callers and get their basic narrative and data set[67]—Kagan would come back with a pre-vetted caller who would start to present a situation from their life—mostly about relationships in family (partners, children), introducing the caller by first name, location, sometimes how the caller was connecting (let's go to a payphone), and, most frequently, "first-time caller." No matter the subject, Kagan first allows the caller to give a small encapsulation of their situation. Quickly, she moves to ask a number of questions, affirming the problem, interrupting to say, "you bet" or "that's right." Kagan also helps the caller to narrativize for the audience, folksily reiterates the content of the caller's situation to recap before redirecting the caller back to the crux of the problem if they have gone astray or when the caller takes too long to unfold the narrative.[68] The need for pacing and a kind of enjoyable speed is a radio phenomenon (whose analogue for Isaacs would be column space) that Winnicott (because he was the solo broadcaster) and Guattari (because that was antithetical to Free Radio) didn't have to address. These rhythms diverge somewhat from the traditional psychodynamic session pace, where there are repeat standing appointments but time in any given meeting is finite (and distributed across patients in other group and mass therapies).

In all of these shows, segments could last as long as ten minutes on an undermotivated child, or aggressive son, a rough patch in a marriage, difficult expectations between siblings, work-life balance, and so on. Sometimes, a caller with a problem in one of these categories would spark another caller with a related problem to call in. On Kagan's show, she directs this second caller to act as if the other caller hadn't ever called in to keep the problem "fresh." This serves a dual purpose: it resets the case for new listeners joining as they hop in their cars across the three-hour timespan who have missed the earlier call; secondly, it bolsters the fantasy of intimacy and individuality in the encounter, making the interaction both personal and exemplary.

This is another way in which the call-in differs from Winnicott's public form of analysis. Winnicott treats, in both his radio show and his theory, an archetypal mother or several archetypal mothers that generate a spectrum he describes. Put another way, he recognizes that there are a range of experiences for mothers and seeks to speak into that range so that no matter what, if one is of the right category, one feels addressed, more or less (and if one is not the right category, one most likely would flick the dial to another broadcast). Whereas the logics of the Winnicott show relied on the composite case and partial identification with and within that composite, these shows relied on the logics of diffuse, ongoing, multiple identifications with callers as well as a deep-seated attachment to the host—even, or especially, if that host was negative and harsh (in the case of Grant and Schlessinger).

The mass intimacy of the radio call-in show is a form of magical thinking, precisely because it doesn't feel mass. As Paddy Scannell has argued, radio has moved toward replicating person-to person interaction; he terms this a "for-anyone-as-someone" structure.[69] Even though broadcasts (both radio and television) address the collective, an intimate coupling of two—the addresser and addressee—is deeply felt on the part of each audience member. This is predicated on two psychological experiences: identification and transference. All the radio shows on the left and the right and in between license and make use of these intersecting relationships, however different the texture and timbre of each.

Briefly, identification is the process through which any given individual takes on (internally) an aspect of the other and "is transformed" by that aspect. The classic first set of identifications one experiences is with one's parents and later friends, but also with social structures, political figures, and popular icons. The logic of the call-in show, which uses the rotating cast of the audience, is premised on this identification. Someone else's difficult marriage becomes one's own, however briefly, and so the advice given to a stranger becomes taken up as somehow pertinent to the self. This works precisely because the advice is situational—a "workaholic spouse," "the impact of an ex-wife on a new marriage," "helping a friend out of an abusive relationship," "how to accept a child's partner," "what to do if a partner says all the problems in the relationship stem from you."[70] Even though these are real individuals with specific problems, their exemplarity makes them useful outside of their intimate contexts. The shows depend on individual women who aren't in therapy and don't have access to other forms of mental health care. They are attracted to the expertise on offer (or attracted enough to get over becoming a public case study) and can make use of the space for free, quick, brief advice-driven consultations that could be had via broadcast phone call—toll free. Although economically free, a serious cost of being paid attention to in this forum is the risk of being overheard by the wrong person: that known others would overhear, and listen in on, their problems. Anonymity is a feature not just for the user but for the audience member who must find something in the underfeatured yet detailed situation of the caller seeking advice to hold on to, to relate to, or else these shows are reduced to prurient overhearing—a major element and attraction but not the only one. The hotline call is particularly apt for thinking through the radio call-in show, in that each time a caller makes use of the therapist they do so for a short duration, for a crisis—something important enough that they actually pick up the phone and dial the show's number and speak into a public forum—and may do it repeatedly; but more frequently, users only call in once. Unlike with problem pages and advice columns, anonymity is doubly in question, both because life situations are necessarily described and because voices can be recognized. This partial anonymity provides just enough to particularize callers, while still allowing them to remain underfeatured enough that the audience can identify with them, allowing them to be a mediating conduit for closeness to the host. Put another way, these minute-long case studies are exemplary but not only because they are examples; they may become personal via this process. And the hosts of radio shows were keenly aware of this phenomenon. Grant stated it was the aim of the show altogether: "The one thing I . . . hope for is identification, to have a call go out to someone in the listening audience and have them recognize their own symptom and say, 'Hey, that's me.'"[71]

A form of transference unfolds at the same time and is the central quality of relating important to psychoanalysis. Transference is difficult to define and some argue should only be used in the context of psychoanalysis proper. Most loosely, however, transference is thought of as a redirection of early, primal emotionality, wish, and association onto a stand-in—whether or not that transfer occurs inside a therapeutic context. In therapy, the stand-in is the therapist; in the pseudo-therapy provided by the call-in show, that transfer occurs onto the host at a distance. Under this sign, a pseudo-form of transference emerges, which we might call *distance transference*; transference that is begotten via identification with the treatment of another. The scenario recalls Richard's fantasy about hearing Klein on the radio, in which he is able to acknowledge that the "right kind of peace" is for "everyone"—he would not be alone in hearing the broadcast—while holding to the fact that he himself would be spoken to explicitly and directly. This is a kind of secondary transference, doubly mediated by technology and by an external human other. Though these hosts are famous, in their radio incarnation they are also reduced to a voice speaking with another voice, which allows fantasy to gain traction. This is the trick of radio, which Paddy Scannell sees as a unique form of mediated relating, a one-to-someone structure:

> For-anyone–as-someone structures show up mostly in the field of culture. . . . To understand this structure we must constantly keep in mind its double character that operates at two levels simultaneously: it is always, at one and the same time, for me *and* for anyone. This is an intermediary structure that mediates between the impersonal for-anyone structure and the personal for-someone structure. As such the for-anyone-as-someone structure expresses and embodies that which is between the impersonal third person and the

personal first person, namely the second person (the me-and-you). The for-anyone-as-someone structure expresses "we-ness."[72]

As John Durham Peters summarizes Scannell, "Radio separated the context of speaking and the context of listening."[73] I would add that the call-in show also separates the context of speaking, listening, *and* participating from each other even as they are sent back out to the audience over a single medium. Peters continues, "Radio was a set of sound-protocols designed for eavesdroppers."[74] This is nowhere more literal than in the call-in show, which invites listeners to overhear the speech and lives of callers and do so for free. We have an obvious desire to overhear the fight next door and a voyeuristic wish to know what's happening in the bedrooms and consulting rooms of others—but the logics of the call-in show go beyond peeking behind closed doors.

Peters, in writing about the pathological slippage between *feeling* this pseudo, distant transference and mistaking that relationship for something *actual*, argues that the error occurs in ignoring, "the contradiction between broadcasting's address (interpersonal) and distribution (mass). Though celebrities talk in personal styles apparently addressed to one or a few, their performances generate revenue according to statistical algorithms aimed at populations, not individuals."[75] Peters is writing about daytime TV hosts and their audience members who latch onto those hosts and pathologically are convinced that a *direct* form of communication is taking place, meant specifically for them—a phenomenon called "para-social interaction." He elaborates, too, that some level of fantasy always exists in the interpersonal. But "tele-advising" and its related forms depend on this slippage via not only the special relationship of pseudo-transference but also identification, so that every caller is every audience member and therefore, in fantasy, the host is always addressing, on some level, the individual.

CASTING THERAPY

There are now nearly endless iterations of therapy podcasting: those that speak to a wide range of mental health topics for a specific target audience, such as *Therapy for Black Girls* with Dr. Joy Harden Bradford, or focus on a specific diagnosis, like Eric Tivers's *ADHD Rewired*, or continue in the lineage of the call-in, tele-advice show, like Dan Savage's *Savage Love*. Perhaps most famous of all is Esther Perel's *Where Should We Begin?*, a psychodynamic podcast focused on marital relationships, which presents a return to Winnicott's public therapy efforts but also grows out of the recent history of radio-based therapeutic entertainment. Perel moved away from quasi- and para-therapies to direct, broadcast, actual therapy. Nonetheless, having those intimate moments displayed has psychical effects for both clinician and patient, as well as the users of the broadcast—the audience.

Where Should We Begin? features real couples in therapy and gives the audience complete access to real, serial therapies, allowing listeners distance identification and distance transference despite the sustained focus on particular clients. Perel is a public authority on married romance and sexuality and is now a celebrity therapist; she follows in the tradition of public psychologists building out a multimedia platform, first rising to prominence via TedTalks with millions of views on intimacy in long-term couples; she is also the author of best-selling self-help books like *Mating in Captivity: Unlocking Erotic Intelligence* and *The State of Affairs: Rethinking Infidelity* and a regular contributing writer for the *New York Times* and the *New Yorker*. *Where Should We Begin?* follows the same format weekly: a 45-minute-long condensed version of a one-off (as in, not repeated), three-hour long couples' session—combining the one-off call that earlier forms of radio psychology used with an extension of the in-person visit. Importantly, the podcast truly isn't radio and certainly not a radio call-in show—it isn't live. The effects of identification are increasingly curated: we get all the rawness of emotion without any of the deanonymizing factors. Transference, too, is heightened, as Perel specifically interweaves sections where she addresses "us"—not the couple in the office. Nonetheless, like therapy radio shows, *Where Should We Begin?* is about publicizing private problems and their treatment, fictive in how it presents the nonfictive as unmediated when our very access to it is the sign of a mediation that conforms and deforms its willing subjects.

The actual session is free in exchange for its use (the taped session is accessible for a small fee on iTunes and audible). These are not Perel's regular clients; couples apply online to work with Perel in this specific mode, first filling out a rather detailed Google Form, which functions as intake. As with Winnicott, who wrote his composites, or the producers of earlier radio-call in shows who selected their callers, Perel is curating, and curating for type. Perel asks a prospective couple basic biographical information, along with questions like, "What is the nature of the relationship you'd like to address with Esther?"; "What are the main stressors on your relationship?"; and "What would you like to accomplish? What is the outcome you hope for?" These are accompanied by more medicalized questions about preexisting relationships with mental health professionals, phobias, anxieties, overwhelming grief or depression, and sociopolitical questions such as "Has your relationship been affected by social factors like race, ethnicity, nationality, linguistic differences, or differences in socioeconomic background? If so, what has your experience been?"[76] After a preliminary screening, Perel's producer Jesse Baker gets on the phone for an hour-long interview with each member of the couple separately.[77] For the first season alone, 1,500 couples applied for six spots and were specifically chosen for their story's ability to translate both in the medium and in the time constraint; in subsequent seasons, novelty of the central problem is also a factor for selection.[78] The taping is done all in one session, in Perel's actual office, with her producer listening down the hall. The episode is then edited carefully for anonymity and condensation, with Perel providing some extra-diegetic remarks and commentary throughout. Lastly, in addition to allowing their session to be broadcast, there is at least one other catch: the couple must write to update Perel afterwards. This final communication is absolutely private and withheld from the podcasting audience. This requirement ramifies multiply: it's proof of expertise, of cure enacted if not begun, and an example of media convergence in therapeutic communication, the epistolary piggybacked onto the digital broadcast.

The finished episode is then broadcast. The show takes as its conceit that the audience, listening to Perel in their earbuds or in the car, is just a fly on the wall of a real but anonymous couple's session. Perel views the work of the couple's therapist as narrational. Of her approach she says, "People come in with a story. At the end of the first session, I want them to leave with a different story because a different story is what breeds hope."[79] Those stories, and their narrative adjustments, function on two levels for those listening at home. The first is the entertainment value of voyeurism. The second, again, is a kind of nexus of identification with the anonymous patients and distance transference with the celebrity therapist. Perel works with a wide range of couples—those in the aftermath of affairs, struggling with infertility, those who feel neglected, or who are overcoming a religious, sex-negative upbringing—and hopes that the audience identifies with the first edition of their story, so they can learn about rewriting their own narratives in their own partnered lives. In witnessing their shifts, the audience is supposed to shift privately as well. The podcast seeks to treat a real couple and have that real treatment be productively overheard. That productivity takes the form of learning general skills taught to couples about how to manage their particularities (which may be shared), alongside a more prurient drive to overhear and listen in on what occurs behind closed doors (on both sides of the dyad). The show is therefore as much about how and what we choose to publicize from the private life as it is about privacy as such.

Mimi White, writing about tele-advising shows, argues, "These programs can be seen as attempts to (re)instate the heterosexual couple as a stable social referent even as they endlessly rehearse the couple as a body constituted in unstable mobility. . . . The couple is naturalized in social relations as the linchpin between public and private identity. . . . Thus the couple is never strictly a personal affair."[80] This extends into our present as well, even as what constitutes the crisis of the particular couple has shifted. Perel says, "The couple today is treated as the central unit of the family. And the only reason the family survives is if the couple is remotely content. Families are not held together by kids, by female oppression, by economic dependence, by legalities that prevent divorce. . . . And never has this one unit of two had to fill so many expectations. Because, today, we have to give one person what an entire village used to provide."[81] For Perel, the couple is even more under threat as a form and even more essential to the functioning of the family.

Whether addressing a family gathered around the radio-as-hearth, a sole listener in their car, or both members of a couple at once, therapeutic uses of disseminative media have addressed themselves to the crisis of the family (whether mother and child or husband and wife) as well as geopolitical crisis (war, nation re-formation, liberation politics, or ascending fascism) or, frequently, both at once. At its base, the work of any of these shows (and the work of many, though by no means all, consulting rooms) is to use media to batch process at a distance the problem of the family and its breakages, whether caused by bomb or by divorce.

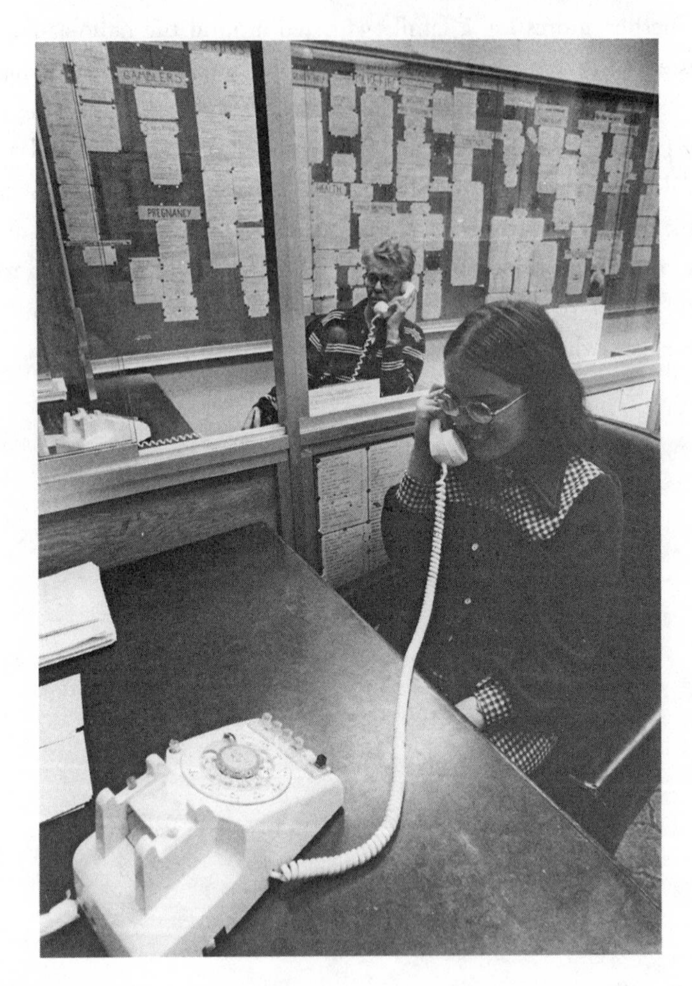

Figure 3.1

Hotline volunteers at Garden Grove Community Church, Robert H. Schuller, Crystal Cathedral Ministries (H93–1188). Courtesy of Joint Archives of Holland.

3 THE FAR VOICE

Chad Varah, a British Anglican vicar with experience in sex education and counseling, established the first known crisis hotline in the world in 1953.[1] Varah had been preoccupied by how to prevent suicide since 1935, when he began his ministry in the Church of England by presiding over the funeral of a fourteen-year-old girl. The young woman had taken her life, thinking she had contracted syphilis; in fact, she had begun to menstruate, mistaking her period for an STI. Though he describes this funeral as the start of his lifelong commitment to helping the suicidal, it was only some eighteen years later in 1953 that Varah turned to thinking systematically about suicide intervention. He was particularly disturbed by the lack of social services available to those in crisis and wanted to make a form of help that could be accessed by all, at any time. Varah recalls reading:

> Somewhere there were three suicides a day in Greater London. . . . How would they get in touch at the moment of crisis? In an emergency the citizen turns to the telephone and dials 999. I looked at mine: FIRE it said. But if you were on a ledge about to jump and needed a ladder, there'd be very few phones on the ledge with you. POLICE it said. But at that time suicide was a felony.[2]

Understanding the limits of current social services for crisis intervention, Varah proceeded to think a series of questions together: how could one help the suicidal at the crucial moment when intervention could prevent self-harm, who could provide this kind of help, and how could a population access it? In his own work as a vicar, Varah had often counseled those who were suicidal (he estimated 13 percent of those seeking pastoral counseling were there for that reason), but *none* followed his suggestion to consult a psychiatrist.[3] While psychiatrists seemed to be unimaginable to the suicidal or too late to be of help, Varah deemed emergency services no better; he questioned the efficacy of a phone line that dials out only to the fire station or to the police, neither of which he thinks will be of much help to the suicidal for different reasons, one material and one juridical; besides, the despairing would have to be at the point of action to make use of such a service. Yet being suicidal was an *emergency* like any other, and in emergencies people "reach for the telephone."[4]

Beyond its linkage to help in an emergency, Varah imagined the telephone to have two additional benefits for suicide counseling. One, the telephone could confer and protect anonymity, which Varah thought essential to his form of treatment given that suicide was taboo; two, suicidal feelings and depression didn't adhere to a schedule, so any service would need to be available at all times, including when transportation was materially or emotionally impossible.[5] Varah decided that the religious counselor was a particularly good candidate to *listen* to the problems of the suicidal and that mere listening could stand as a new, unofficial emergency service option available to people in the midst of their internal crises by yoking pastoral counseling and telephony: call an Anglican priest for support.[6]

Varah accepted an invitation to occupy the rectory of Saint Stephen's Walbrook—a church bombed during the Blitz and demolished during World War II that had recently been rebuilt.[7] He moved his practice there precisely because it was a rectory that lacked a priest and any congregation at all; he could not keep up with his normal pastoral activities *and* counsel the suicidal full time.[8] Instead, Varah established a telephonic church to serve an ever-shifting and scattered congregation, one that invited new participants who were also to be patients. St. Stephen's didn't add a media wing to its forms of pastoral counseling—the medium of the phone comprised the entirety of the church, its community, its activities, and its infrastructure. Varah turned the church's phone line into a dedicated hotline placed in the crypt and, together with Vivian Prosser (employed as Varah's secretary), began to gather and tend a new kind of flock inside a new kind of clinic: one tethered by telephone wire and crisis. It gathered souls in mortal danger via an instantaneously available connection over a common household appliance, the telephone.

Varah offered an on-demand therapeutic confessional that promised to provide nonjudgmental and noncriminalizing moral and emotional counsel. Varah termed his service "listening therapy," asserting his intervention was indeed a therapy—which deemphasized its paraprofessional status as a lay person's treatment—and that the therapy's method would be to provide a space for the caller's speech, following in the Freudian tradition of the "talking cure," which minimized Christianity in favor of a secular tradition of psychoanalysis.[9]

The service was immediately popular—and well-staffed—due to its immense publicity in the popular press and radio as a human-interest story (in 1965, roughly 12 press clippings featuring the hotline were sent in daily).[10] Varah quickly realized that, even with Prosser triaging the importance and urgency of calls, he alone could not serve as the hotline's only qualified counselor. In order to meet the increased demand for help over the phone, he trained fifty volunteers interested in mental welfare to join the staff and perform "befriendings" (an ancient Christian name for a new person-to-person mediated relationship) in order to provide simple, consoling interaction over the phone. The service was so popular that in 1971 Varah was invited to co-write "The Befrienders," an eleven-episode television show based on the activities of the hotline for the BBC. Varah's ever-expanding group would eventually become known as the Samaritans, who run the world's most-used suicide hotline, still active to date.

Suicide counseling is therefore not, as is generally held, secular in origin; it is Christian, and particularly Protestant. Its earliest forms began in the 1950s as services run by ministers, priests, and vicars selectively adopting and practicing psycho-religious pastoral counseling techniques. In the early 1960s, the *Christian Science Monitor* could report, "The practice of dialing by telephone for religious messages is spreading rapidly throughout the whole Western world."[11] By 1960, this form of pastoral care was already widely spread: 140 ministers participated in pastoral counseling by phone and forty-one unique Christian telephone counseling services had been launched in ten countries.[12] The telephone counseling centers in New York reported 20,000 calls, Los Angeles 10,000, and San Francisco 3,500 annually. This is both mediated therapy *and* a "mediated congregation"[13]—a second flock of believers reconfigured through a one-to-one, individual relationship to the church, maintained by crisis intervention over the phone. These communities—both congregational and therapeutic—don't necessarily meet as a body but instead receive disseminated messages and can call in for help. The phone served to further dissolve the physical bounds of the church, the consulting room, and the clinic, so that confession and therapy could merge in an emergency, whenever and wherever it occurred.

This service, in its use of the peer-to-peer modality, radically upsets the regimes of pastoral care and counseling, as well as psychodynamic therapy. The sin that can't be pardoned by a priest—suicide—breaches the church hierarchy and allows peers to step in and counsel each other. The new treatment modality circumvents both the need for expertise and the fee associated with expertise. It challenges every clinical concept associated with the frame, structure, and dynamic of a therapeutic encounter. It is contingent, not in person, and requires elaborating an intimacy with unknown voices and ears with no guarantee of repeating the connection; and it makes use of the phone—an appliance paradoxically thought of as capable of bringing people together and as partly responsible for suburban alienation. The appliance's deployment as a tool for therapy is rife with medium-specific contradictions, including a faith in it as a private medium when in fact lines were shared infrastructurally across homes (the party line) and by family members inside a single home. And yet, a therapeutic triad of phone, volunteer, and user became not only thinkable but also widely adopted and used to help the suicidal in crisis.

CALLING THE CALLED

Despite usually being thought of as both a Jewish and secular science, the idea that psychoanalysis had also remediated the confessional was around long before Foucault; Freud himself had directly named the Catholic Father the direct ancestor of the psychoanalyst and wondered why a Christian hadn't discovered his theory of the mind first. Freud was not being flippant: Christianity has its own theory of care of the mentally unwell and has been concretely providing lay mental health services since as early as the fourteenth century. The notion that psychoanalysis is the legitimization and rationalization of Catholic confession and that we are "an extraordinarily confessing society" was a mainstay in Freud's correspondence with his friend, the Swiss lay analyst Reverend Oskar Pfister, a Lutheran minister who practiced psychoanalytically oriented counseling within his congregation. Early in his thirty-year correspondence with Pfister, Freud wrote, "In itself psycho-analysis is neither religious nor non-religious, but an impartial tool which both priest and layman can use in the service of the sufferer."[14] In his letters with Pfister, Freud attempts to extend the uses of his new mind science by expanding its reach into the church, while Pfister in turn tries to leverage psychoanalytic practice to extend the reach of church care to all. Freud figures the "impartial tool" of psychoanalysis as being available to appropriation—it can be enlisted by any service provider for any person in need.

Varah's hotline, and others like it, emerges from this practice of pastoral counseling, itself a fusion of the centuries-long tradition of pastoral care on the one hand and the new mind science of psychoanalysis on the other. American Protestants were particularly attracted to this new form in the long aftermath of World War II, when the United States experienced a great shortage of available mental health resources and workers in relation to the psychic war injuries of returning veterans and their families. The US Army and Congress responded by increasing funding for nonmedical psychoanalysts and clinical psychologists beginning in 1945, while Protestant-led counseling services worked to close the gap between the number of traumatized persons and available clinicians by harnessing psychoanalytic theory and training the clergy and volunteers to do peer counseling. These psycho-religious services flourished in the very moment when psychoanalysis began to be taken seriously socially and politically in the United States.

While more patients than ever were participating in the original Freudian analytic scene and being secularly "converted" from sitting upright to lying down on the couch multiple times a week, elsewhere other attempts at conversions were taking place.[15] Outside the consulting room, these scenes of therapeutic conversion were happening where one might most expect them but not always how: in the church, often by pamphlet, radio, television, or phone. Given that the crisis facing Anglo-Americans in the post-War moment was understood to be not only mental but moral, pastoral counseling presented itself on both sides of the Atlantic as a way to combat the mental health crisis of the 1950s, as it had during the mental health crisis of the Great Depression. The lay analyst and the volunteer counselor emerge at the same time to the same end: to increase access to mental health care services. However, training a single clinical psychologist or psychoanalyst is a huge temporal and economic cost, whereas training a group of volunteers to follow scripts and staff a phone line takes thirty to fifty hours.[16]

Not only could Christians train huge numbers of volunteers quickly, churches could "send" those volunteers to meet people where they were: at home. By training volunteers instead of clinicians and by shifting from the in-person appointment to the phone, the psycho-religious hotline not only addressed the shortage nearly instantaneously but also ensured that the service would actually be used. The move from in-person therapy to phone counseling creates a remediation of the earliest form of pastoral care: the confessional—but improved, with the increased safeguard of true anonymity. Under both psychodynamic and Protestant rationale, the phone is a usable, if not initially thinkable, tool for care.

Suicide counseling and its adoption of the telephone are thus neither sacred nor secular exactly. The history of the suicide prevention hotline is one of collaborations across that false divide, the priest and the counselor coming together to remediate the "impartial tool" of therapy, through the medium of the telephone, such that any layperson can use it in the service of the sufferer. The remediation of the Catholic confessional into a Protestant crisis intervention hotline allows for the extension of care beyond the physical plant of the clinical office and the church. On the user end, more clients can call in to a hotline than would be able to be seen in traditional therapy for many reasons: the duration of such calls can be much shorter than the traditional analytic hour; callers are not limited to any particular set of business hours; they don't need a referral or appointment, and they don't have to be proximate to a trained psychiatrist or analyst or even to leave their home, and the help is free. The phone, and the way it signals a more conversational encounter, is a workable medium for connecting the lay volunteer to the hypothetical object of care or salvation. Tele-anonymity implies the dislocation of helper from helped, as does home access to help. Bracketing the embodied encounter between clinician and patient or minister and petitioner generates a new kind of protected agency through the removal of a whole register of expressivity (even though voice is physical). It's a mutation away from both the confessional screen and bracketed vision on the analyst's couch.

The phone also allows the user unbounded access to a service that contains within it a rotating staff of providers, suspending or at least distributing transference among volunteers, or reattaching it to the institution of the hotline. The phone further allows for an intimate anonymity between peers, where the historical power dynamic and relationship of clinician-patient and priest-parishioner can be left behind for new roles: that of the empowered user and the lay volunteer who can provide something a trained professional can't: a spontaneous "anonymous ear."[17] This allows the user to self-diagnose, determining when care is needed and prescribe both the kind of care required and its duration simply by dialing, speaking, and hanging up. The hotline service contains within it an interpretive flexibility because the phone permits a range of interactions. A user can place a single call, if that is all they want or can manage, or they can have several ongoing relationships with various volunteers or a specific relation with a single volunteer (managed by calling in exclusively at a particular time for a particular shift, just like going to treatment at the appointed hour). Further, the user is not responsible to a volunteer; one never need call the service but one always can.

DESPAIR

The traditional pastoral care of souls, including those in despair, or Durkheim's late nineteenth-century notion of anomie—"the malady of the infinite"—or the twentieth and twenty-first century equivalents—"loneliness" and suicidality—occurred in many forms and scenes: chaplaincy confession, sermons, and the conversion of the unchurched (either nonpracticing Christians or non-Christians).[18] The particularized attention to the suicidal is dependent on Christian belief in which these forms of care are indistinct from salvation. Despite the absence of any discussion of suicide in the Bible, St. Augustine institutionalized it as a sin in the fifth century (to address the problem of zealots who were killing themselves as martyrs)[19] and the Sixth Commandment, "Thou shall not kill,"[20] is taken to forbid murder generally, including self-murder; the punishment for suicide is the same as for murder, eternal damnation; historically it has also been an earthly felony.[21] Suicide is then a crisis of both body and soul. However, the suicided, unlike murderers, have no moment to repent after committing their crime against God, and therein lies the premium on saving these particular souls: they must be saved, in real time, before they act and are irremediably lost. In the words of Calvin: while the "spirit of repentance and faith is not given to all," still "all are called to repentance and faith."[22] Pastoral care must try to save the unsavable and tend their earthly concerns as much as it must minister to the predestined saved soul. By the 1950s, with participation in church life soaring in the United States,[23] these sacred imperatives also indicate a strategy for handling secular crisis and secular persons in order to build the church, providing ongoing care as though it were a matter of eternal salvation (and thus crisis intervention rather than palliation). The slippage between nonurgent and crisis care is tactical and a useful consequence of not knowing decisively whether or not someone is saved; one is always in need of saving and therefore always in danger—regularized care can be figured as ongoing crisis intervention from a church perspective, for the individual and for the health of the church itself. By treating this kind of palliation as critical and the crisis as doctrinal, the church expands its reach along a new therapeutic vector: the telephone. Because one can never be sure of a steady relation to God's grace, pastoral care is theoretically applicable to all persons at all times and thus a useful tool in accumulating souls and enlarging the congregation—whether through conversion of individuals or increased participation within church life for those already within the church—all while specifically addressing suicide prevention.

Pastoral counseling yokes mind science to the long tradition of pastoral care but still must be understood as a distinct phenomenon. Pastoral care has a greater scope of activities than twentieth century pastoral counseling and therapy, and the process of being in pastoral counseling, even if in therapy with one's own minister, is separate from being ministered to through confession and the like. While the minister is acting as a therapist, he cannot be involved in the forgiving of sins. The minister might try to understand why the parishioner has fallen prey to the devil, while the same person, in his role as pastoral counselor, may exchange the devil for the unconscious and "find that what seemed like a religious problem is really a psychological one."[24] The particular mode of interacting with a parishioner through a *therapeutic* relationship became thinkable at the turn of the twentieth century; it was not codified after psychoanalysis, but alongside it. While different schools of pastoral counseling exist (and include those which use only the Bible as a text) and provide different trainings in psychology, psychiatry, or psychoanalysis, the first pastoral *counselors* were not only Protestant but also explicitly Freudian.

The friendship and collaboration between the American analyst Smiley Blanton and the minister Norman Vincent Peale solidified the relationship between Freudian psychoanalysis and pastoral care. In 1932 during the Great Depression, Peale agreed to take up residence as the minister to Marble Collegiate Church in Manhattan, which provoked his colleague to say, "You'd better hurry up and take [that] job. At the rate people are jumping out of windows in New York, there won't be anyone left to hear you preach."[25] The colleague was right: when Peale arrived in New York, he found a congregation whose population was decimated by "despair" relating to the Great Depression; only two hundred parishioners regularly attended church services in an auditorium that could hold 1,600.[26] In this climate, the project of the accumulation of souls was under great threat and in need of new forms of outreach and intake.

Peale's message was straightforward: Christianity was a psychic regimen. Faith and prayer could lift a Christian out of despair and allow anyone to succeed in life by restoring a belief in God and a reconnection to grace, ensuring salvation both on Earth and in the afterlife. As early as

1934, Peale counseled depressed parishioners in person and by broadcasting his enthusiastic sermons on the radio (he would go on to make his own dedicated radio show, "The Art of Living," in 1935) in order to bring more souls into the flock—and particularly Marble Collegiate. Despite these therapeutic interventions, church membership did not significantly increase immediately and, after two years of preaching, Peale was exhausted and demoralized, especially when it came to his involvement with the personal counseling of parishioners. There were too many individuals calling on him to help with their personal problems and he realized that "his limitations were becoming more apparent all the time. His training had been too academic . . . for him to cope with some of the problems that were presented to him."[27] Like Varah after him, Peale alone was not enough, nor correctly trained, to deal with the demand of his congregants' mental health problems. When demand outstrips supply, care seeks out new methods of delivery (from free clinics to mediated therapy) and new providers. Peale sought out a referral for a psychiatrist to supervise him; his single requirement, reminiscent of the Protestant notion that one must only be a reasonable interpreter of God, was that the clinician be a "sound Christian."[28]

The referral was for Smiley Blanton, a Methodist and practicing psychiatrist who had trained in psychoanalysis under Freud beginning in 1929[29] and had also been his patient in analysis on and off, as Freud's health permitted.[30] In 1935, Peale and Blanton's arrangement was informal—Peale would prepare case notes on his more difficult congregants' problems and Blanton would provide supervision over lunch. Peale and Blanton's collaboration was welcomed enthusiastically on both sides; Blanton told Peale it was "as if" his prayers were answered: finally psychoanalysis and religion could come together to help Christians rid themselves of guilt and fully self-actualize.[31] In 1937, the collaboration was formalized when Blanton cofounded the Religio-Psychiatric Clinic with Dr. Clarence Leib and Dr. Blanton was brought in to take charge of the clinical work.[32]

The clinic was attached to Marble Collegiate Church and located in its basement, where it offered counseling services, free of charge, to those congregants suffering from anxiety and depression, those with difficulty in their social and marital relationships, and those with other mental health problems.[33] A "truly interfaith and interdisciplinary" team of psychologists, psychiatrists, and social workers provided the clinical help.[34] Although the clinic saw patients who were not members of Peale's church or religious in any way, Blanton understood the success of the clinic to lie at the intersection of clinical psychiatric care and a church setting, not only because some users' religiosity might have previously precluded them from seeking out psychiatric care, but also because "for many people the church is the home of love, a place where there will be found compassion for the unfortunate, help for the needy and forgiveness for those who have a deep feeling of guilt."[35] The religious setting of the clinic allowed those who would normally *want* religious help to *access* psychiatric help: being backed by a church undid the stigma of seeking formal psychiatric care as well as the feeling of being judged by one's attending clinician. The waitlists for this kind of help grew so long—roughly 3,500 patients sought treatment annually—Peale and Blanton needed to bring in young trainee psychologists and psychiatrists, volunteers, and ministers to supplement the staff and also began offering group therapy so that the clinic could "take care" of its ever-expanding set of patients.[36] The waitlists would only get longer at the end of World War II as veterans returned home with war trauma that had no ongoing, available, organized program for treatment. While economic policy provisions were made to aid their reintegration into civil society (such as the Servicemen's Readjustment Act of 1944, popularly known as the GI Bill of Rights), care for widespread mental problems in the veteran population was not sufficiently addressed.

The success of Peale and Blanton's Great Depression–era project carried forward into World War II and the post-war moment; it produced an army of lay counselors and newly mediated forms of outreach and intervention. By 1940, Peale and Blanton were no longer content to treat only their own congregants in person and coauthored *Faith Is the Answer: A Pastor and a Psychiatrist Discuss Your Problems* in order to reach despairing souls nationwide—an overheard "dialogue" functioning as proto-tele-help. Blanton wrote, "At least 80 per cent of the people in this country who look for help with personal problems first try to get it from their clergymen . . . and a clergyman usually needs a psychotherapist's knowledge of behavior to help remove them."[37]

The Religio-Psychiatric Clinic attempted to solve the problem: train clergymen to *be* Christian psychiatrists. In 1951, the clinic was renamed the American Foundation of Religion and Psychiatry and began offering a three-year, full-time pastoral counseling residency-training program heavily inflected by Freudian psychoanalytic theory. Clergy learned how to create their own mental health care apparatuses in order to tend to despair within their flocks, using the success of the Religio-Psychiatric Clinic as a model.

Paired with in-person service to the community, Peale—and to a certain extent Blanton—continued to extend the reach of the church by harnessing additional communication technologies. Peale worked across media, disseminating his sermons through the mail to 750,000 subscribers a month, while moving his radio broadcast, "The Art of Living," to television. In addition to *Faith is the Answer*, the two coauthored another self-help text, *The Art of Happiness*, informed by their religio-psychological perspective, with each going on to author his own titles (including Peale's best seller, *The Power of Positive Thinking* in 1952, which was widely critiqued and repudiated by psychologists and psychiatrists as "autohypnotism"). In 1954, the two again expanded the scope of their clinical project by introducing The Academy of Religion and Mental Health as an academic wing, while their patient caseload jumped from 3,500 in the late 1940s to 25,000 persons annually in the late 1950s.[38] Peale increased his congregation—at a distance through his broadcast pulpit and more immediately by drawing the despairing to his physical church through the mental health clinic—from some 200 members to over 5,000. This was estimated at the time to be the largest weekly in-person audience ever gathered by an American cleric.[39]

Perhaps because of this success, other famous preachers began to imitate Peale's efforts and took up the urgent message that religious groups must harness mental health care knowledge to improve the mental well-being of congregants and increase church attendance—two separate goals made achievable by merging them. On March 13, 1955, Rev. James A. Pike, dean of New York Cathedral at Saint John of the Divine, admonished in his sermon "Religion and Psychiatry Today" that psychoanalysis and depth psychology "are increasingly successful in taking people apart, but these sciences alone cannot put a man together again. . . . Self-understanding only brings distress if there is no way out through grace."[40] The sermon referred to a recent study by the internationally renowned psychiatrist Dr. Francis Braceland that cautioned that if the "present trend continued, one out of twelve children born in the United States would spend some time in a mental institution."[41] Reverend Pike declared that the only hope to combat that trend was for ministers and psychiatrists to share their skills; a minister must know his limits and a psychiatrist must make use of theology. He celebrated the conference recently held at the Menninger Foundation where ten psychiatrists and ten clergymen presented cases to one another. The final take-away was that frequent church attendance would make psychoanalysis unnecessary.[42] The church again was figured as the ultimate palliative care for the soul while psychiatric intervention (combined with ministering) was for those in the grips of crisis.[43]

Given that certain Christians are supposed to look continually to save souls, it is an aspect of pastoral care to find souls in need of saving. One way to do this is to tend to the congregation already filling pews (in the case of the minister) or in community (in the case of volunteering parishioners participating in this form of care). Another way is by growing the congregation—such that there are more souls in the flock and more people hearing God's word, which some, like Rev. James A. Pike, hoped would obviate particularized pastoral counseling. A third way to proceed is by broadcasting the church service to make it available anywhere and a fourth is to make the church mobile, callable, and unconditionally reachable by anyone—this is the church-run suicide hotline, which reciprocates the need for mental health care with church growth and outreach. No longer is the church sermon only a disseminative communication, coming from on high to be received by the congregation. On the hotline, any congregant can instigate a salvation: the church literally becomes peer-to-peer.

THE TELEPHONIC CHURCH

Given that Varah himself knew that "there'd be very few phones on the ledge with you," why did he—and the founders of all the other early psycho-religious hotlines—choose the phone as the medium through which pastoral help would be accessed and delivered? The hotline form, along with its contemporaries, the radio and television church service, were all configured as an uncomplicated and efficient *transfer* or *transmission* of faith rather than its site of mediation or ritual, bringing faith to the faithful and faithless, even over the phone.[44] For psychoanalytic therapy on the other hand, the phone call is at once problematic (as it does away with the standard in-person meeting) and the perfect setting for Freud's notion of listening being like a phone call to be taken to its logical conclusion. For twentieth-century Protestants in England, America, and Australia, the hotline becomes an acceptable remediation and restructuring of the lost confessional, informed by secular therapeutic conventions. Staffed by peers instead of priests, the hotline observes the Protestant allergy to intercessors and is thus revivable within the innovative culture of pastoral counseling and as part of a permanent commitment to tending and growing the flock. In keeping with Foucault's argument that psychoanalysis is itself a remediation of the confessional, the Protestant hotline draws doubly on the confessional scene in its sensibilities, reaccessing its own Catholic past through that past's transformation within the therapeutic scenario.

This relationship forged in the confessional, between seeing and knowing (and not knowing) with whom one is speaking, transfers easily to the hotline. The confessional booth contains compartments to separate the penitent from the priest, who whisper to each other through a lattice. In more contemporary face-to-face confession, the priest never sees the penitent, even if the priest is revealed. Of course, they may or may not recognize one another's voices, as the voice is often the single knowable index of the person on the other side. On hotlines like Varah's, it is highly unlikely that the caller and the counselor would ever interact in person—the bounds of his church are these phone calls and the church was without standard parishioners. In others, especially those set up in smaller communities, it is likely. Further, the multiple extensions of the home phone line, which gains prevalence in the 1950s and allows for individuation within a shared familial line, provides a feeling of privacy without securing it—these calls were placed over the party line and crosstalk, overhearing, or a family member deliberately eavesdropping on a call from another room were all real possibilities.[45] This illusory privacy is an importation of the regulations and decorum of the confessional or the psychoanalytic encounter, where anonymity is also only a feeling, available to one side or the other (the penitent or analyst) as opposed to a stable fact. What is (supposed to be) a fact is the confidentiality and privacy of the interaction. Given that the person on the other end of the line is likely to vary and is not acting in any other capacity in the church *during the entirety of the call*, the caller may feel more free to speak about those topics that otherwise would feel taboo, including suicidal ideation or what has triggered it. The encounter between disembodied anonymous voices coming in over the telephone wire allows for a less judgmental engagement, one free of punitive spiritual or juridical consequences. Depending on the particular procedures and ethics of a hotline, either side or both sides of the call could be anonymous or both sides could be named (some hotlines ask for the name, phone number, and home address of the caller, others do not, while some services name their volunteers and others do not).

Counterintuitively, anonymity does not arrest connectivity and relationality in the para-therapeutic encounter. Hidenori Tomita calls this new relationship that of the "intimate stranger" and it is "made possible by new media."[46] The intimate stranger is "a new category of social relationship where anonymity is the very condition for intimacy."[47] Tomita writes that while traditionally we have social contacts with strangers (anonymous and not intimate), acquaintances (known but not intimate), friends/lovers (known and intimate), we now can have a kind of relationship with someone unknown but intimate. I wish to extend Tomita's notion of the intimate stranger to earlier moments of mediated connection, particularly the relationships sought out and produced by the therapeutic encounter and the hotline as its medium. The therapeutic relationship, most generally, is an older form of intimate strangeness. From the patient's perspective, the clinician and patient meet in a room (or via letter, over radio, on the telephone), and *only* meet there. Although both participants know the other's name, the patient often knows little or nothing else of the person providing the treatment. The therapist occupies the position of the non-anonymous intimate stranger.

The new kind of therapeutic relationship forged by using a hotline has more conditions than that of Tomita's intimate stranger. One does not only experience the feeling of being unnamed. Beyond the intimacy with a stranger, security for a user on a hotline requires being at a distance, working with a *peer*-counselor, interacting in real time, and controlling duration. Further, the intimate stranger becomes multiplied across all the different interactions possible at a hotline; such an intimate interaction with a stranger becomes a form of relationality more than it is a concrete one-to-one relationship. I call this mode of interacting *distanced intimacy*—which focuses on relationality built across two or more persons. The way hotlines are used is directed as much by the callers' sense of what they want and need as by how the founders of hotlines believe they will be used. That the hotline observes confidentiality (legally, ethically, and socially) allows it to host, for some, a more open-ended and accommodating kind of protected speech than can occur with either a confessor or clinician. And while the volunteer may have their sense of community abstractly extended,[48] particular relationships are also formed, between caller and service, and sometimes even with particular volunteers; volunteers staffing hotlines often have regular schedules that allow callers to avoid a particular person, or a particular voice, counseling style, and attitude, by not calling during a certain shift or, conversely, only calling during specific windows to reach a volunteer who has successfully aided them in the past.

This is thinkable because, while the service may be one-off for the many people who do call crisis hotlines at the point of suicidal action, others call in repeatedly "just to talk," creating a palliative exploit under the sign of crisis, cooling the hotline to what is called a "warm line."[49] This type of user includes those who've been helped by the service before, those who are having low-grade suicidal ideation and have learned to monitor their symptoms, and those needing a person to listen to them talk about related quotidian problems. Hotlines, unlike scheduled and billed sessions, allow for the patient to set the terms of the therapeutic frame. A call can last a minute or take up the full maximum time offered by a counselor (which varies from hotline to hotline). The caller can use the hotline once in her life, weekly, daily, or multiple times a day (these clients are referred to as frequent callers and are usually tracked by some identifying features such as their speech patterns, story, or the like).[50] Further, the hotline is not a singularity—freed of the demand for exclusivity proper to most other forms of therapeutic relationships, a caller can decide not to be loyal to any given hotline and call several. The demand for this novel form of care was immediately high, precisely because callers were the ones determining what constituted crisis and when to call and seek this easily obtainable intervention. The hotline form encourages this self-prescription for therapeutic care and can also inadvertently or intentionally become a warm line, or a palliative service if the caller decides to use it regularly; palliative care and crisis intervention are not a static binary and the hotline form quickly reveals this.

The ongoing use of the service for palliative ends further increases the need for volunteers, whose labor must increase to meet those callers *where* they are and as they are: in the home and in the act of self-diagnosis (for more on self-diagnosis, see chapter 4). While the hotline allows the user to determine frequency, it also allows the user to disregard the dedicated purpose of the hotline: to help the suicidal. Initial calls also came in from those in other forms of despair and in need of an outlet for speech about other topics, some of which were felt to be as taboo as suicide. Several callers contacted Varah to discuss their sexual feelings, whether about "homosexual" desire (a legal crime and psychiatric diagnosis, as well as a sin) or the sin of premarital desire. The hotline couldn't, and didn't, try to determine whether it was a congregant calling or simply a soul in need, nor what qualified someone as being in need (i.e., it didn't terminate calls if the client wasn't about to take suicidal action). The directionality of this peer-to-peer service allowed everyone who reached out to be considered an acceptable caller, which follows two kinds of Protestant logic: everyone is savable, even if not yet a Christian, and everyone is savable if you don't know who is already damned.

With a dedicated phone line, a caller could feel assured that they were in charge at several levels. The service did not have legal or psychiatric power over an individual anonymous caller and, as importantly, they could preserve their agency and sense of what they needed in terms of duration and repeatability of the encounter through two of the most basic aspects of the phone call: they decided when to dial in and could hang up at any point. Termination of the therapeutic relationship contracts to the repeatable gesture of setting down the phone in its cradle or pressing a button.

The hotline thus shifts the power dynamic of the psychodynamic encounter. In the standard face-to-face encounter, the clinician asserts a technical power and maintains a lack of particularity (an important aspect of psychoanalysis—it is partially responsible for allowing transference, for instance, to take place). In the case of a crisis phone call, the lay volunteer and client are given some of the same protections and opportunities.[51] The particularity of a *telephone* conversation as the method for crisis intervention means that the content of the conversation, however much the volunteer is oriented on listening, is more dyadic than what occurs in face-to-face conversation, especially the face-to-face speaking conventions of therapy.[52] This particular therapeutic triad—comprising peer-to-peer and telephonic interactions—allows for the two-way conversation *itself* to be the means by which the caller is helped.

Much as they differ from embodied psychodynamic encounters (or indeed long-term psychodynamic teletherapies), therapeutic conversations occurring over the hotline must also depend on and depart from conventions of normative telephonic practice. Callers to hotlines often have to be coached by the volunteers in how to abandon phone decorum, given that it is so ingrained in the culture of telephone use. Some of the most basic features of telephonic experience must be suspended or altered in the hotline scenario: the hotline service is guaranteed to pick up, there is no voicemail, the greeting is not merely friendly but also constructs the positioning of the call ("how can I help you tonight"), a full mutuality of reporting is necessarily abandoned, as well as a clear or organic sense of how a call might end. While the distance and anonymity of the call may be much of what permits someone to get help, the distance and anonymity are protective of the volunteer as well and can be instrumentalized by the volunteer to help guide the caller to a safer place. If a caller is poised to take her own life with a gun, the volunteer can say "I'm not comfortable speaking with you while you have a gun in your hand. Might you put it down for the duration of our conversation?" This technique has the advantage of building distance between the caller and their means for suicide as well as protecting the volunteer from interacting with a caller holding a lethal weapon.

Further, calls are, on the volunteer's end, scripted and supposed to follow an arc that allows the volunteer to assess the caller's present state of mind. Especially with the suicidal or others in intense emotional crisis, the narrative of a call follows the same sequence. The goal of the call is first to ascertain the level of suicidal ideation by assessing if the caller is currently suicidal, then if they have imagined how they would end their life; if yes, then the volunteer assesses whether they have the means to do so now and, finally, if they have a plan for when. Simultaneously, the volunteer tries to increase contact with what are termed "protective factors" (reasons to live, which are usually relationships both with persons/pets and communities such as a church), to create ambivalence about suicidal action and to calm the caller down enough so that a helpful conversation can take place.[53] From a psychodynamic standpoint, these kinds of if-then scripted conversations depart from any relatable aim of that modality because they emphasize getting a caller out of despair or suicidal ideation, however momentarily. As I hope becomes clear from restoring the history of this modality, within the parameters of the scripted nature of the trained volunteer's response, users are able to make the hotline form into many kinds of useful communication. Here, a proto-script can become a holding, helpful frame.

AN ANONYMOUS EAR

Varah's model telephonic church converted other congregations to the service, many of whom also created dedicated phone lines for their parishioners. While some of these phone lines replicated much of what was occurring on Varah's service (specific attention to listening, the use of volunteers, and so forth), there was also an immediate slippage from strict suicide hotline to pastoral care by telephone, including prayer and "messaging" dissemination, which is neither interactive nor strictly crisis intervention. Though pastoral counseling and pastoral care (however mediated) often overlap, blur, or even become synonymous, two kinds of telephonic church services emerged simultaneously: one focused on outreach with a dial-in, church growth function, and another that attended to crisis intervention. Within the second group, not all help on the other end of these hotlines was the same and not all deployments of the phone made use of the same affordances. Some were run by priests without any understanding of the psychological reasons behind suicide; some flatly argued with callers against suicidal action instead of providing a safe space for the caller's speech; some criminalized suicidality, insisting that because suicide was a sin, it was not only a mortal crime, it was a crime against God.

This was true in the practice of the Reverend Kenneth B. Murphy, a Catholic priest who founded the first hotline stateside in 1959 in Boston. Murphy started his suicide counseling service when a teenage parishioner used the phone in order to stage his own intervention: the boy called Murphy in the middle of the night, saying that he wanted to take his own life. By his own report, Murphy had counseled and dismissed this young man before—but that night he took him seriously and *talked* him down.[54] Though the counseling service first started as in-person intervention (with the local police calling upon Murphy to intervene in cases of persons attempting suicide in public), a hotline, with volunteers, was quickly developed. The service, Rescue Inc., took roughly 3,000 calls a year between 1959 and its closure in 1969.[55] Murphy's style of intervention did not borrow from psychodynamic techniques pioneered in pastoral counseling. Instead, his approach was much more traditionally religious. Murphy represented the view that the suicide commits a sin that one cannot atone for—not just because that person unnaturally ends a Christian life but also because "by his action, he is killing all of mankind."[56]

By contrast with Murphy, Bernard Duncan Mayes, a self-described "queer Anglican priest," founded the second American suicide hotline (often cited as the first) in San Francisco in 1961 on the principle of "listening exquisitely."[57] Mayes had come to San Francisco from England via New York to run a small mission parish north of the city.[58] Though San Francisco was the home diocese of Bishop James A. Pike, who had left New York and now was engaged in making the Bay Area a new, more liberal "religious frontier," Mayes found that his congregation wanted him to provide "spiritual security and the age-old rituals that confirmed it . . . [and] appeared to despise the pluralism that I could now see was an important aspect of American religious thought."[59] While Mayes began to deliver his Sunday service with "less and less enthusiasm," he went out on Saturday nights "to meet other gay men whose warmth and affection made up for the coming Sunday ice."[60]

While living in San Francisco, Mayes was struck by a cultural aspect of the city: its denial. The city alternately dismissed and blithely celebrated the fact that it was the suicide capital of the United States—one headline of the daily paper read "Suicides? San Francisco Couldn't Care Less!"[61] The Golden Gate Bridge was considered the most iconic suicide site in the country, yet the board of the Golden Gate Bridge Highway refused to increase its four-foot barrier to prevent jumpers.[62] Mayes was not the only activist perplexed by the vague attitude of the city and the board. Dr. Richard Seiden at the UC Berkeley School of Public Health and suicidologist Edwin S. Shneidman, who had founded the Los Angeles Suicide Prevention Center in the mid-1950s, spent a great deal of time researching and tracking the Bay Area suicide epidemic (and both were involved in the fight for an additional barrier in the 1970s). Whereas Seiden's focus was on structural prevention, Shneidman made a study of the "jumpers" themselves. As part of an effort to generate a taxonomy of the jumpers and their motivations, Shneidman clipped news items from local papers on the jumpers and also visited the Bay Area to collect the suicide notes left behind on the bridge or recovered from loved ones left behind, or the bodies as they washed ashore in the bay (the notes were often wrapped in plastic).[63] Each was typed onto an index card and marked with a "C" for car, or a "P" for pedestrian. If the person survived, Shneidman would write "Att" or "(survived jump)." Some examples include:

> (Sent as telegram just before jumping.)
> (Addressed to girlfriend): "Sorry for
> the inconvenience. I had car trouble.
> The Car is at the Vista Point turnoff.
> Best Wishes."
> C[64]

or:

> (Addressed to wife): "I feel my mind
> is failing, and I don't want to be a
> burden to anyone, especially you.
> I love you so much. "
>
> P
>
> A second note from the same person read:
> "Why do they leave this so easy for suicide?"[65]

Shneidman looked for traces of causality in the penultimate act of the jumper: the written, mediated communication of despair, often pat, and often an apology. The suicide note is a communication that occurs when all other kinds of communications are felt to have failed. While Shneidman and Seiden looked to studies of the jumpers themselves, or an extension of the railing as prevention, Mayes decided to make a suicide hotline for those who still *wanted* help, which he called San Francisco Suicide Prevention. With the introduction of the suicide hotline, Mayes hoped that potential jumpers would get to make multiple penultimate communications, which could postpone or prevent the ultimate act.

Mayes's hotline was to be unlike any other in operation in that, from its outset, the infrastructure of the hotline service was set up for access by two overlapping groups susceptible to despair: the suicidal and the lesbian and gay community. As with San Francisco's dismissal of the suicidal, the city also seemed to ignore its large, vibrant gay and lesbian population. Mayes noted that this community was especially vulnerable to suicide given that they are "unable to change their sexual orientation, condemned not to a week or moment, but to an entire life of frustration by an ignorant and unsympathetic majority, they must suffer a situation that neither medical opinion nor religious dogma are able to ameliorate."[66] Just seven years prior, in 1952 the American Psychological Association had released the DSM I, in which "homosexuality" was listed as a sociopathic personality disorder (as it would remain until 1974). In Mayes's moment, psychiatric and psychological intervention saw queerness as something to cure, and it had the diagnostic criteria to carry out "cures," from electroshock therapy to lobotomy.[67] For Mayes's callers looking to be helped with feelings of extreme depression and despair, psychiatry was therefore not a viable source of care, nor were state-based social services.

To that end, Mayes thought very carefully about how to bring the recent history of psycho-religious pastoral care, counseling, and other hotlines to bear on his service (he was aware of Varah's work in London and thought highly of it).[68] He decided that he would not announce that he worked in an official capacity as a priest because he was worried he would only receive calls from current church people and that this would foreclose his ability to reach the gay community (Mayes was not yet out professionally); the hotline would present as separate from both the clergy, who only "want you in their flock," and psychiatrists, "who charge money" for their services.[69] Mayes therefore arranged for the entire staff of his hotline to be volunteers, with no recompense for their time; they would never be accused of making money from suffering or of being identified with any particular religious organization.[70] Mayes's hotline is an example of provider-side extension and exploit within the barely codified psycho-religious framework; it drew on the therapeutic frame and was founded by a member of the church for psychotherapeutic purposes, but that relationship to the church was denied in order to reach its targeted population. In addition, it also repressed some of what it could draw from Freudian psychoanalysis. What emerged was a queer, secular revision of a Protestant focus on the suicidal, a new iteration of a para-form.

Like many other LGBT+ spaces of its moment, the hotline's physical office was private and out of view, located in the basement of a hotel in the Tenderloin neighborhood—an area filled with many precarious groups of persons and their spaces: sex workers, the drug addicted, homeless people, the patrons of gay and lesbian bars (which were raided by the police the same year as the hotline began),[71] and poor, single men living in single-room-occupancy hotels.[72] Outreach, first to prospective volunteers and then to clients, necessarily was handled differently than the two earlier hotlines. Mayes could not rely on either psychologists or current church people to staff the prevention center's red telephone, and often not even for referrals (Mayes had tested select social services as potential referrals for the hotline by pretending to be suicidal and many places he tried to get help were gruff with him; some places even berated him for calling before hanging up[73]). Instead, he began to get help over the phone itself, receiving calls from would-be volunteers who put themselves forward in response to a positive, if slightly skeptical, news piece on the service.[74] Mayes recounts that many of the initial prospective volunteers he interviewed were suicidal themselves and therefore not suitable to staff the service. Clergymen from various denominations tried to participate, as did professionals from the psychological/psychiatric fields. Mayes in turn rejected them because of their propensity to be chatty, give advice, and list doctrinal reasons as to why life was worth living—in short, they threatened to monopolize, reprofessionalize, and desecularize the protected speech this new hotline was supposed to cede to its callers.

Reception of the new hotline by established social services was mixed. In an interview from March 19, 1963 on KPFA, Elsa Knight Thompson interviewed Mayes at length about the hotline during which Mayes remarked that

> the churches are all together in favor, the private practitioners and physicians are generally in favor, the psychiatrists and psychologists are not in favor of volunteer work. They feel that people who are thinking of ending it all are generally speaking sick people and they don't like volunteers who are untrained dealing with such sick people at any stage in the operation. . . . They feel that first of all the people who answer the phone should be psychologically trained and then that we should pay them.[75]

He was right. His critics, including the Los Angeles Suicide Prevention Center, dismissed Mayes's service because volunteers ran it—and even tried to shut the hotline down for this reason.[76] But Mayes thought of the service as providing an exquisite help that experts could not and besides, many of his callers were already under the care of those services or had tried those services and left them (because of the expense, because they were judgmental). Mayes speculated that psychiatrists and psychologists were against unpaid volunteer help for professional reasons—because it devalued paid labor *and* expertise—not because volunteers without psychiatric training could not help the suicidal. Mayes found that volunteers, in the absence of a professional knowledge of suicide, could be trained to let a suicidal caller speak their experience to a faraway counselor securely and uninterruptedly, perhaps relieved of the acute urge by being disembodied themselves in a telephonic afterlife of their impulse.[77] Mayes calls this "simply one name talking to another name" as opposed to a degree talking to an illness or symptom.[78] Later, peer-to-peer counseling would become the norm, even for the Los Angeles Suicide Prevention Center, which would go on to train other prevention teams in this modality.[79]

Like Varah, Mayes instructed his volunteers to focus on receptive *listening*, the aforementioned "listening exquisitely." One can read the choice of "exquisite/ly" as possibly a queering of the ear. Mayes could have said "compassionately" or selected another synonym; etymologically, exquisitely means "carefully selected or sought out" and it acquired a queer valence in 1819 in relation to dandy or fop. It also starts the same way "expert" does but then turns into this new term, which privileges listening over authority via the metonym of the disembodied ear versus the wholeness of the embodied in-person expert. It is also similar to Freud's "evenly hovering attention," his term for psychoanalytic listening, which Freud himself compared to a telephone call.[80] In 2012, Mayes recalled his early intentions for the hotline and again emphasized the importance of open, nonjudgmental, anonymous help: "I did feel that what was really needed was a compassionate ear, someone to talk to. . . . It occurred to me that we had to have some kind of service which would offer unconditional listening, and that I would be this anonymous ear."[81] The ear, while literally attached to Mayes, is figured as transpersonal. The anonymous ear has the ability, because of the phone, to oscillate between the person being helped and the person providing the help, where neither the patient nor the volunteer is a specific, stable, named person.

Unconditional listening produces an anonymous ear because the listener is required to keep themselves unparticularized; the caller populates themselves with data, even if nameless. The anonymity afforded to the caller and to the listener differs, though each is granted facelessness. Mayes's phone counselor relies on the underfeatured, silent power of the analyst but with power detached from the body and expertise of a professional and removed from an embodied series of office visits. Yet Mayes named his service "CALL BRUCE," and the others who worked at the hotline (using pseudonyms) were Bruce's "assistants," which gave the caller something abstract yet intimate to hold onto. Mayes decided to use a non-Biblical—and stereotypically gay—name. Fredrick Wertham, in his 1954 book *Seduction of the Innocent: The Influence of Comic Books*, argues that comic books turn adolescents into sexually perverse adults. He specifically pointed to Bruce Wayne, or Batman's relationship with Robin. He referred to a famous panel from *Batman #84* in which Batman and Robin wake up in bed together. Bruce then became the stand-in name for a gay man in jokes in this moment.[82] Further, Bruce is casual, solely a first name, as opposed to either the religious moniker of Father X or the credentialed surname associated with expertise and an attendant fee: Dr. X. Mayes chose this name in keeping with the notion that the hotline would be free from intimidating municipal, psychiatric, and religious affiliation. The male marker is a pseudonymic "bat signal" or a beacon of queer identification, an imperative to call, a refuge from the stigma of the ignorant and unsympathetic majority, and an assertion of the protected and positively casualized peer-to-peer nature of the service (just calling a stranger named Bruce).

The service's first volunteers were a former secretary (an expert in anonymous listening), a retired nurse, an Army widow, a social worker, and a businessman—three women and two men respectively. Mayes personally trained the volunteers via lectures, tape recordings of staged calls, and practice role-play calls for three months before they were allowed to answer live calls. Before that, they had to do simulated calls, listen to the training tapes that Mayes had developed, and learn how to discern the lethality of any given call. Further, the staff had to prove (not only in their spoken, articulated beliefs but also in their tone of voice) that they weren't prejudiced against people of color and gay people, or judgmental about sex.[83] The hotline consisted of those five volunteers, Mayes, and a paid professional answering service that would receive the initial call, learn the caller's name if they were providing one, and then route the call to the red telephone in the basement office where the volunteer on call would pick up.

Alerting potential callers to the service's existence would differ from the outreach of other hotlines attached to a particular church (even if unchurched users also found their way to those services) because of the communities Mayes intended to serve and the absence of any doctrinal ambition to accumulate souls. Instead of placing an advertisement in a church newsletter or announcing the existence of the hotline through a sermon, Mayes and his group went into the community they were trying to reach by leaving the sacred gathering space for a secular one. The service placed matchbooks in the bars that populated the Tenderloin district (including queer spaces) that contained a "secret" message on the inside flap: "Thinking of ending it all? Call Bruce, PR1–0450, San Francisco Suicide Prevention."[84] This clandestine advertising, combined with the anonymity of the phone line and the distance at which the encounter occurs, continually demonstrates to and trains the caller to accept codes of privacy and confidentiality on the hotline, which is crucial for the populations Mayes had identified as being most in need: the suicidal and the gay community.

"Bruce" then had to wait for a call. Mayes was on shift the first night and curled up on the couch like an analysand with the receiver next to his head, waiting.[85] A call came in and Mayes waited for exactly two rings to

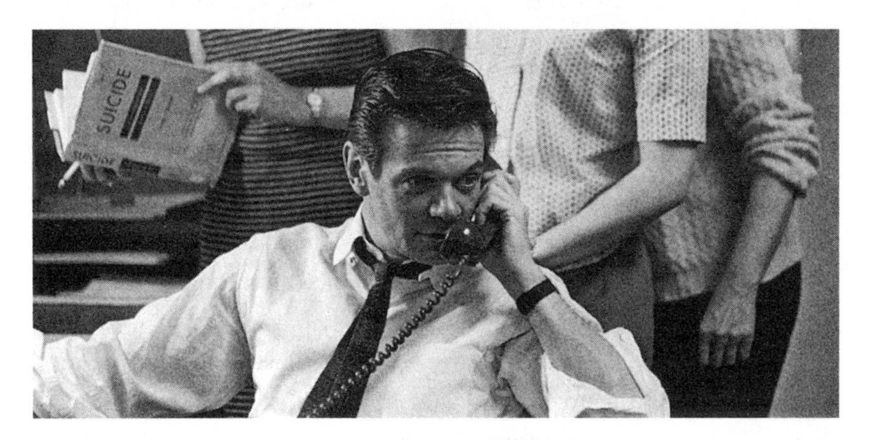

Figure 3.2

Bernard Mayes on the red telephone at the offices of the San Francisco Suicide Prevention Center. Courtesy Douglas Jones for *Look Magazine*, Library of Congress.

sound (as per his own training manual—allowing him and the caller each to take a breath before connecting), then picked up; "Bruce" and his "assistants" took an additional thirty calls in the first month.[86] Mayes adopted the inherent mobility and flexibility of Varah's telephonic church and built it at the intersection of suicidal community and a gay population; as the user type changed so did the methods of outreach, volunteer selection and training, and phone decorum, extending a tailored social service to those unable publicly to name their despair.

THE TOTAL CHURCH

By contrast with Mayes's secularized service, The New Hope Hotline grew out of Robert H. Schuller's rapidly expanding Garden Grove Community Church (GGCC) congregation in Los Angeles. Schuller, also a member of the Reformed Church in America, was specifically encouraged by Norman Vincent Peale to answer "the call" of God (Peale's self-help and media programming were deep influences on Schuller's activities); he arrived in California with his wife on February 27, 1955, with $500 and the dream of opening a church. As a suburban church preoccupied with flock growth, both its physical plant and the extensions of its message beyond place were of great import. Before moving several times to various dedicated church spaces, including those designed by Richard Shelley, Richard Neutra, and then Philip Johnson's Crystal Cathedral, the congregation first met at a drive-in movie theater, which was free during the day (as film projectors only worked after dark) and inexpensive to lease. There, the church service was broadcast to an audience distributed and contained in their individual family cars and thus carried, whatever its subject, a secondary media lesson in how to pray alone together. As Erica Robles-Anderson writes, this new mediated service required instructions: "At times, the ministry forged explicit connections between liturgy and infrastructure with explicitly instrumental advice about how to practice piety at the drive-in."[87] After church membership grew and the increased demand for services at the GGCC led to a dedicated, more traditional meeting space, the church continued to hold successive services—one inside a chapel and the next at the drive-in. This commitment to a suburban phenomenon was built into the church's commissioned architecture: Neutra's completed building, dedicated in November 1961, contained a 1,000-person auditorium and a connected drive-in parking lot. When Norman Vincent Peale preached the first sermon in the new space, it was broadcast simultaneously to congregants in cars parked outside the church so that the whole unaccommodatable congregation finally, triumphantly could be "worshipping together."[88] Yet the congregation was in part worshiping through broadcast media, over distance (though the distance wasn't yet very great) and was instructed in how to do so. The GGCC both insisted on physical structures to keep the flock together and on growing the flock beyond those bounds through televangelism, such that eventually one could participate from anywhere there was a telephone or a television set.

Being held together while being held apart is a lived feature of suburbia, whose expansion correlates with the proliferation of telecommunications. Suzanne Keller writes of telecommunications, and particularly the telephone, that they "extend us in space and time and enable us to transcend these communities of place."[89] As individuals move into the suburbs, they are removed from the orbit of their previous social and familial contacts. Like the car, the telephone and television are supposed to extend and repair those connections. The very fact of that contact over distance is thought to be importantly soothing, even before a therapeutic apparatus is mediated via the telephone. As separation from other persons (often within the suburban context) creeps into the account of loneliness and despair, a premium on new forms of connectivity increases. The GGCC connected church growth to the parallel attendance and engagement affordances of tele-media. Before it began to produce *The Hour of Power*, its internationally syndicated television church service and the most watched in the United States, Schuller's church spread its message first in the form of a drive-in church and second in the form of a 24-hour hotline: no one ever need be in despair alone.[90] One could "reach out and"—if not literally touch someone (as AT&T's slogan suggested)—place a call.[91]

In September 1968, the dedicated hotline, New Hope Telephone Counseling Ministry, debuted alongside the sixteen-story Tower of Hope, which provided office and classroom space for GGCC.[92] The two new infrastructural components of the church were supposed to gather the flock together in person and over distance. Minister Raymond Beckering consulted with the psychiatric staff at the Los Angeles Suicide Prevention Center and Minister Alan Walker, the founder of Australia's church-operated suicide prevention program, Lifeline, while the West Coast branch of Blanton and Peale's Foundation of Religion and Psychiatry was given office space on the eighth floor of the building.[93] By the time the building opened, New Hope boasted a volunteer staff of "nearly 300" that had received a fifty-hour training, fifteen hours of which were spent on the phone doing mock calls and thirty-five in the classroom on listening, effective communication with someone in crisis, and "theological foundations and prayer," along with a tutorial in the special concerns of different age groups, loneliness, self-image problems, and alcohol and drug abuse.[94] The hotline was ready to receive calls—making it the first 24-hour American hotline to be staffed fully by the members of a single church.[95] The choice of name, New Hope Telephone Counseling Ministry, contains all of its supporting theories and aims: it is to work against despair, over the phone, using therapeutic listening techniques, within the theological commitments of the church; pastoral care and its overarching ideology are broadcast via harnessing media and psychodynamic vocabulary in order to produce relevance and well-being, and to gather souls. The staff was exclusively made up of Christians and used the tag line "People Helping People," emphasizing the fungibility of who helps and who needs that help, over any kind of divine aid. It could be used anonymously or the caller could provide all of their identifying features (including address) to the service—and the form of the call log suggests that it was a routine practice to ask for this information. This hotline, therefore, unlike Mayes and Varah's, could be used to supplement or initiate in-person meetings with clergy. Several women are recorded as having called in for marital and familial problems. A minister high up within the GGCC referred one of these callers to the hotline himself, using the hotline as an in-house referral system for when the problem posed by the congregant necessitated seeking a second opinion (a note on this woman's call log shows that the counselor deemed her "hysterical"). The hotline also worked in the reverse direction, where a woman who was despondent because her husband had left her and her children first called the hotline and then had a minister dispatched to her home.[96] Mostly current church people or people local to GGCC called the hotline for its first two years, such that this relationship between hotline and embodied visits was possible. It was a peer-to-peer hotline that had carryover into community interaction and conventional pastoral care.

This changed radically with the debut of *The Hour of Power* on television in 1970, which advertised the hotline. Whereas Mayes's early establishment of his hotline relied on grapevine, backchannel, and matchbooks in bars, the GGCC hotline relied on formal acquisitional outreach. Beckering, in an interview with *Churches of North Orange County*, said, "We believe this service will be a vital link in the establishment of a 'total Church' concept for those who cannot be reached from the Sunday pulpit."[97] New Hope went from catering to the needs of congregants and local would-be congregants to helping any "people" who sought the service out while still thinking of those potential callers as would-be congregants given that they could be reached by *The Hour of Power* (a combination of Peale's *Power of Positive Thinking* and Billy Graham's *Hour of Decision*—but also an accidental pun on the therapeutic hour). New Hope saw access as a two-way street or perhaps even a drive-in: the hotline can reach out to a caller in the home and the caller can always pick up the phone and reach the service. That year, at least 25 percent of the calls came from out of state, and only 25 percent were attributed to Orange County.[98] That the broadcast television show fed the hotline opens and then renders indistinct secular and Protestant populations, which is strategic for a Protestant church that wants to convert the secular into the saved or reacquire the lapsed. Meanwhile, that strategic indistinction extends not just to the nature of the audience but also to the nature of its problems, which can always be redescribed as religious crisis (depression becomes despair or loneliness) and cured/counseled by pastoral means. This works on the user's side as well, where secular callers in crisis can exploit church motives to easily gain free access to trained help.

Call logs from New Hope's post–*Hour of Power* period show that the hotline had an explicit interest in church growth beyond the walls of the GGCC and the Tower of Hope. It was collecting data about how knowledge of its service spread and in turn sending church materials to the physical addresses of the callers—and seems to have moved further away from using the service as an anonymous hotline. Yet the *Hour of Power* did also spread the word of the hotline to the suicidal. One call sheet from the archives of the GGCC in this moment records a woman in her twenties calling in on "the verge of committing suicide." The caller was a first-time user of the service, having learned about it by watching the television show. The counselor spoke to her for fifteen minutes and learned that she was "really desperate." The two women prayed together over the phone—a new human connection and a connection to the faith becoming sudden protective factors against suicidal action.[99] Another caller, self-referred to the hotline through the *Hour of Power*, spoke to a counselor for seventy-seven minutes after her eighteen-month-old baby drowned. The hotline's response was to request that Schuller himself send a condolence card.[100]

The GGCC was very practiced in converting those it counseled into congregants, no matter their distance from the physical church. Parallel to the New Hope Hotline, Minister David Bailey also ran the Lay Ministers of Pastoral Care Program and the Ministers of Evangelism programs for the GGCC. The Lay Ministers were encouraged to visit homes in their neighborhoods twice a year, to find out if there were illnesses or joyous news in families and to make contact appropriately at those times, all in the service of increasing membership in the church. The hotline program relied on similar protocols of follow-up and enrollment in the church after performing care, via the mail, over the phone, and through the television. One elderly caller, who originally called complaining of having no one near her as she approached death, donated her entire estate to the church after having had a successful interaction with the hotline.[101] New Hope for this reason spurned anonymity as a feature of disembodied telephonic exchange. The conventional protections of other hotlines clashed with its expansionist imperative; anonymity had to be bracketed in order to use crisis intervention directly for church growth. The GGCC couldn't afford that particular affordance.

A single-page call log form of the service devotes its space in equal measure to this kind of church growth data collection and to the emotional problems of the caller. Of the nine options for how one could learn about the hotline, only two involve in-person contact with the church (either being a member of GGCC or attending services there). The call log form asks the sex, age, marital status, phone number, and address of the caller, effectively destroying the anonymity function the therapeutic hotline can ensure. If the address is given, the volunteer follows by asking whether or not the caller would welcome receiving church literature at home (and then decides to include specific mailings based on the call, from the Youth Department, Singles Department, Women's Ministries, and so on). If the caller is a member of the church, the volunteer can also ask if the caller would like an in-person visit from a lay minister. In addition, the form has a section in which to detail what counsel and referrals were given. Finally, the uses of the hotline are also tracked across thirty possible types of calls. Some of the boxes are for emotional and behavioral problems: wife abuse, suicide, financial problems, alcohol problems, depression, grief, loneliness, and runaways. The form also handles sexual problems, broken into three types: general, transvestism, and homosexual (one caller used the service to speak about her worry that her daughter was bisexual and had been "hypnotized" by lesbians in San Francisco, effectively displacing conversion and acquisition from the church to an "alternative" community).[102] Other options handle prank callers, obscene callers, hang-ups, and silent calls. A third group of boxes handles calls that are not for crisis applications of the hotline, or for phone counseling; the hotline also received appreciation calls, TV orders, and information requests (also in three parts: general, church-related, and *Hour of Power*). This adulteration of strict therapeutic ambition reveals again that helping people is not the singular aim of this hotline, since such noncrisis and noncare calls took up a significant part of the limited bandwidth of the service and helped the church rather than callers in need. The hotline also offered the service of praying with the caller over the phone and estimated that it received some 700 calls of this nature a month—a return to that earliest, alone-together, drive-in form of the GGCC. New Hope and *The Hour of Power* form a two-sided recruitment tool (and media empire) for the church, positioning mental health care and preaching as reciprocal forms of intake. Both worked toward increasing numbers in the far-flung community of the faithful and keeping that community well in mind and in spirit, such that it would be saved.

CONVERTING THE HOTLINE

These three hotlines were quickly successful. Callers made intended and unanticipated use of them and the volume of calls steadily increased. The Samaritans now have branches across the globe and are still the most-used suicide hotline service in the world. The Crystal Cathedral Ministries' (formerly the GGCC) New Hope hotline is still in use even though the physical church has been massively restructured and purchased by the Diocese of Orange County. The hotlines were also effective: in San Francisco, the suicide rate dropped by half even while Bernard Mayes's service was still the only locally based suicide hotline.

True to its Protestant form, the hotline service made pastoral counseling adaptive to other ensuing technologies and nearly instantly repurposed by ostensibly more secular causes. One could say that the psycho-religious hotline entered its secular afterlife almost as soon as it began and that this is why the suicide hotline's Protestant origins have remained unexplored. Using lay volunteers as staff became the norm not only for suicide intervention but also for crisis intervention hotlines focused on many issues. Identity-based hotlines and rape crisis hotlines especially make use of anonymous interaction protocols first used by Varah and the Samaritans.

In the early 1970s, the phone also began to be used for more palliative ambitions on both the provider's and user's parts, including ongoing phone therapy, generalized crisis intervention, teen counseling, services for the elderly, domestic and child abuse, lesbian and gay support hotlines, drug abuse, rape crisis hotlines, referral services, and warm lines. Some groups remediated the hotline into an overtly political form of care (which is not to say that peer-to-peer counseling isn't inherently so), on both the left and the right. On the right, "rumor control centers" that existed to reassure white "concerned citizens" about riots occurring in and around black neighborhoods started in the late 1960s and early 1970s (and the last such hotline closed in the 2000s).[103] On the left, Raphael Flores' 1971 hotline, nicknamed "La Familia," was run out of the Washington Houses in East Harlem. This hotline, staffed by teen activists including those with ties to the activist group The Young Lords,[104] was aimed at teen peers with a focus on drug addiction and recovery.[105] The Black Panthers' PACH line (Police Accountability Clinic and Helpline) combined both in-person workshops and a hotline. PACH was founded by Elbert "Big Man" Howard (one of the original founding members of the Black Panther Party and the former editor of the *Black Panther Party Newspaper*) in response to the shootings of unarmed Black members of his community.[106] Whereas Protestant groups founded hotlines in the 1950s, 1960s, and beyond, and social justice groups took up the call, it wasn't until 2000 that the United States had a federally funded, secular and peer-to-peer national hotline for the suicidal.

THE MIRACLE OF ACCESS

While the first three psycho-religious hotlines varied in their ambitions, practices, and the communities they attempted to reach and serve, they all began the same way: with a miracle. Chad Varah recounts calling his local operator to have his hotline's phone number changed to MAN 9000 (calling from the exchange Mansion House and desiring the number to sound like 999—the equivalent of 911 in the United States). Varah was told that it would be "most unlikely, since nobody having such a good number would be willing to part with it for love or money. . . . What number are you speaking from?" Varah then "cleaned off the center of the dial, and there it was: MAN 9000. 'Don't worry,' I said to the operator, 'I've got it already.'" Varah then addressed God to tell him that Varah understood the hotline was the good work God intended for him.[107]

Mayes recalls struggling to find a home for his hotline office because each possible place was unsuitably public, the corner too unsafe, the rent prohibitively expensive, and so on. Finally, when he arrived at the Tenderloin hotel that would become the first office for San Francisco Suicide Prevention, the landlord began to ask routine questions in a suspicious manner, afraid Mayes was running an escort service: would Mayes be living in the basement? Mayes had to answer no, but that he and his staff would be there at night. Though Mayes usually never disclosed to potential landlords what he intended to do with the space, that evening he told the landlord to allay his suspicions that he would be making a suicide prevention service. According to Mayes, the landlord lifted his shirtsleeves and said, "Like this?" displaying the scars from his own suicide attempt. Mayes had miraculously found an office and the grateful landlord leased it to him for half off.[108]

Finally, at the GGCC, Beckering too described randomly receiving the digits 639–4673 (New Hope) from the phone company as "miraculous."[109] These sacralizations of the medium and creation myths of service certified these projects as properly Protestant—even the particular phone line by which souls would be saved was predestined. It is the divine miracle that mediates the miracle of psychotherapeutic intervention, which is supposed to have the sudden, total ability to fix a life (or save a soul). Redescribing the phone as a miracle deflects attention from both the partial secularization of the psycho-religious hotline and its technology—a form of outreach to the community that may allow for the acquisition of souls but is an open form; anyone with the number can call from anywhere and receive or exploit care without participating actively in its pastoral project. That fungibility and range of user, an anyoneness, is intrinsic to the affordances of the phone, a feature of anonymity, and part of the theological doctrine behind doing Protestant telephone counseling. Everyone is supposed to have access to a phone line (even though party lines were still in use and crosstalk was still a common feature of telephony); everyone can use a phone (an incorrect assumption); everyone can be saved so long as they are open to being saved.[110]

4 AUTO-INTIMACY

In his famous 1950 paper, "Computing Machinery and Intelligence," Alan Turing asks, "Can machines think?" In order to ascertain the answer, Turing proposes the Imitation Game. The test is as follows: can a man (A) and woman (B) be told apart by a third party (C) if they typewrite their answers and try to imitate the other. Now, can a machine (A) and a man (B) be told apart under the same conditions the same number of times by an interrogator (C) asking the same question of both the man and machine?[1]

Turing then offers nine objections to the idea that machines can think. These range from the "Theological" ("Thinking is a function of man's immortal soul. God has given an immortal soul to every man and woman but not to any other animal or machines. Hence no animal or machine can think") to the "Heads in the Sand" hypothesis that "the Consequences of Machines thinking would be too dreadful. Let us hope and believe they cannot do so." The last objection, "*The Argument from Extra-Sensory Perception*" is somewhat more curious. Turing writes:

> I assume that the reader is familiar with the idea of extra-sensory perception, and the meaning of the four items of it, *viz.* telepathy, clairvoyance, precognition and psycho-kinesis. These disturbing phenomena seem to deny all our usual scientific ideas. How we should like to discredit them! Unfortunately the statistical evidence, at least for telepathy, is overwhelming. . . . This argument is to my mind quite a strong one. One can say in reply that many scientific theories seem to remain workable in practice, in spite of clashing with E.S.P.; that in fact one can get along very nicely if one forgets about it. This is rather cold comfort, and one fears that thinking is just the kind of phenomenon where E.S.P. may be especially relevant.[2]

```
Network Working Group                                          V. Cerf
Request for Comments: 439                                       SU-ERL
NIC: 13771                                             21 January 1973

                     PARRY Encounters the DOCTOR

   The session recorded below actually happened on 18 September 1972 and
   is herewith reproduced for your entertainment.

   Good Evening.

   Tell me your problems.  Please terminate input with a period or a
   question mark.

   *People get on my nerves sometimes.

   I am not sure I understand you fully.

   *You should pay more attention.

   Suppose you should pay more attention.

   *You're entitled to your own opinion.
```

Figure 4.1

"Parry Encounters the Doctor" (PARRY and ELIZA in conversation), The RFC Archive.

Turing ventures that if the man (B) is a telepath or clairvoyant, the interrogator (C) can ask questions such as "what card am I holding now?" which the clairvoyant will answer correctly more times than is probable; thus, the interrogator will correctly guess that the man is a man and the machine is a machine. Then Turing posits that if the interrogator has "psycho-kinetic powers" or is able to distinguish man from machine via clairvoyance the Game would be ruined—or, as Turing writes, "with E.S.P. anything may happen." He continues, "If telepathy is admitted it will be necessary to tighten our test up. The situation could be regarded as analogous to that which would occur if the interrogator was talking to himself and one of the competitors were listening with his ear to the wall. To put the competitors into a 'telepathy-proof room' would satisfy all requirements."[3] For Turing, recalling Freud, telepathy is theoretically listening to thought rather than hearing speech. It is a kind of intimacy at distance with another where that other is continuous with the self—and the other can be a machine. Telepathy describes an instantaneous form of communication that removes another human's resistance to being listened to (and listening to another) and thereby allows the perfect uptake of the other's thoughts. In short, telepathy allows you to experience the other as one's self without interference—it allows one to (re)think the other's thoughts as new and one's own.

In the absence of ESP, this is still the promise of the artificial machine expert: the removal of the other human from a communicative relationship. It is also the promise of traditional therapy: to rethink one's thoughts as another's. Therapy without a human-to-human therapeutic relationship (the analytic dyad, the therapeutic alliance) is not therapy as we have traditionally understood it. When one imagines a therapy, one is likely to imagine two people sitting in a room, communicating primarily by speech. This image is no longer contemporary (though of course there are many working psychoanalysts and psychotherapists who practice therapy this way). For the last fifty years, cognitive behavioral therapy (CBT) has offered a mostly self-guided therapeutic regime in which the patient is responsible for their own psychological growth. At the same time, computer scientists and psychiatrists have been applying psychological understandings, models, and theories to artificial intelligence, and artificial intelligence to psychology; and generating new informatics models of how the brain and linguistic, cognitive, and affective interaction work. Since the late 1950s, some of these experiments have been conducted with the goal of mechanizing or fully replacing one of the human participants in the traditional therapeutic dyad. On the one hand, doing so successfully would free mental health care even further from a dependency on expert labor, making it cheaper and more widely available; on the other hand, efforts to generate these natural language programs, algorithmic therapies, and diagnostic tools necessarily narrow the scope of what is treatable to what computer scientists and psychiatrists seek to treat, what the computer can do in its moment, what it can read, and what its programmer can code.

One of the earliest experiments with a self-managed, technologized therapy was that of Dr. Charles Slack, a Princeton-trained psychologist working in the Harvard Psychology Department "during that wild psychedelic era of Timothy Leary and friends."[4] In the late 1950s, Slack designed an experiment to test the benefits of soliloquy.[5] First, Slack fabricated tape recorders that produced a series of clicks in response to sound stimulus while keeping track of how many clicks the recorders made in response to those sonic inputs. Slack gave these to "teenaged gang members from Cambridge" and paid them to be his subjects.[6] The subjects were to speak into the tape recorders without a human witness or interlocutor. As they spoke, they could see the tally of clicks growing; when they stopped talking, the tally stopped increasing. The subjects were paid according to how high their tally went. The automated ticker and the scaled payment were enough stimulus and response to incentivize the subjects to have a conversation with themselves. The outcome was twofold. The subjects produced recordings that sounded like one side of an interview. But moreover, "some of the participants said they felt better for having talked this way."[7] Dr. Charles Slack had built a speech-based self-soothing device from human-machine interaction. Soliloquy before a nonhuman other was not therapy but did access a palliative function.

Unlike human therapists, who are as much a container for the speech of their patients as a respondent, automated and/or algorithm-based therapies listen or read solely in order to respond; they can't not. They listen via a variety of mechanisms including retrieval-based decision trees, automatic scripts, and paralinguistic vocal monitoring. They offer outputs following inputs, regulated by a governing body of rules and decisions. Yet algorithmic therapies also rely on a most intimate computing in which a rich set of relationships is present between the user and the therapeutic apparatus: self-to-delivery mechanism (whether the computer or mobile phone), self-to-therapeutic application. Computer-based and computer-guided therapies are a thus a reiteration of self-analysis and self-help and join those pre-electronic traditions of instruction and mediation by a nonhuman other (the workbook, the paperback, the letter, the diary). Here, that structure is extended via a *responsive*, automated component (for more on "self-analysis," see chapter 1; for more on self-help, see chapter 2 and below in this chapter). These therapies and other methods for self-improvement and self-knowledge rely on what I call *auto-intimacy*, a closed circuit of self-communication, run through a relationship to a media object. In the case of computer-based therapies, it is a specifically therapeutic relationship to the self that is mediated by a program and its process. Historically, auto-intimacy in the service of therapy has been driven by the desire to automate treatment. Human-computer therapy cannot provide the kind of self-knowledge gained through a long interpretative relationship with a human other but aims all the same to provide progressive self-knowledge by instructing that self to, as Charles Slack discovered, soliloquize through a medium and then listen to or read that soliloquy.

At the earliest moment of experimentation with automated therapies, two strains of work emerged: the simulation and detection of a disordered mind in the hopes of automating intake, diagnosis, and psychological education; and the simulation of a therapist toward the dream of automating therapeutic treatment. In the attempt to simulate the therapist's role (whether this attempt fails or succeeds), one is already theoretically comfortable with removing a human actor as therapist. When this fails (so far, we have no *fully* functional model of an artificial therapist) and the end goal is still to automate therapy, the next step is to design a therapeutic treatment guided by the self, without a present therapist. This kind of mental health treatment codes expertise into a program and codes out the acting human expert; it is the movement from a simulation of a dyad and an interpersonal relationship in service of psychic growth to an intrapersonal, "self-sufficient" regimen. In this, these therapist stand-ins remove one term from the triad of patient, therapist, and media by combining two: the medium and the expert.

This second group of artificial therapies elaborates self-to-self help through a user's encounters with automated programs and their ensuing experience of self-maintenance, self-care, self-regulation, self-control, self-discovery, self-tracking, self-diagnosis, and self-prescription. While a machine listens and a digital interface provides the therapeutic setting and experience, the only explicit human involved in auto-intimacy in those one-to-one interactions is the doctorless patient. The psychiatrist Isaac Marks argues that "refining care delivery to the point where self-care becomes possible is often the product of the most sophisticated stage of a science."[8] Here, Marks describes the end stage of *care delivery* as self-care, rather than care itself. Self-care is the ultimate form of on-demand access, meeting the patient not only where and when they are, but as their mediated selves. Contained within Marks's sentiment is no evaluation of what self-care does beyond providing expediency, and for whom this new form of care delivery allows self-treatment. Nor does his statement indicate how this ideal refinement of care delivery is to be achieved. Autonomy is the aim of care and of automation; automation is the dream of autonomy.

Paradoxically, within this closed circuit of self, automation takes on the role of the other; it can be an emotional, intimate experience to bring the computer into that circuit. As Sherry Turkle argues, "we have sought out the subjective computer. Computers don't just do things for us, they do things to us"; users are "seeking out the computer as an intimate machine."[9] She describes computer users in the 1970s and early 1980s as "intrigued by the notion of talking *to* technology about personal matters," but at the same time saw relationships "*with* a psychotherapist as personal and emotional, and the idea of having that kind of feeling for a computer was distasteful."[10] "To" is unidirectional. The human has a relationship to the phone, or the phone has a relationship to its human. "With" implies a shared relationship mutually elaborated and constructed: two things or persons (or several) having a reciprocal relationship. Here, making use of the computer as a therapeutic space or actor means being able to talk *to* without quite imagining a relationship *with*—yet. Auto-intimacy flourishes in this gap between communicative speech and the absence of a human other over a medium; through a machine the self both expresses and receives its significant content.

Automated therapy and human-to-human teletherapies share in some of the same technological and therapeutic histories but operate differently. The role of automation is not coterminous with the role of mediation within the therapy. In mediated teletherapies, whether conducted via letter, telephone, or over a chat client (see chapter 5), the medium conveys the message. Clients talk to their counselor over a medium and that medium impacts the kinds of speech (or written speech) they are able to access and perform—but there is always a human actor who serves as the destination for this speech, however it is transmitted and reciprocated. There is no other human actor maintaining such an alliance in computerized therapy and notions of reciprocity and conversation are destabilized even as chatbots respond "like" therapists or "pass" for humans. On the one hand, virtuality is always part of psychodynamic therapy, even if it does not occur via a virtual conduit. Yet one can also have an as-if relationship through and to a technology: one can write and receive a letter as if in the presence of an other, "speaking" intimate thoughts via the typed word and having feelings in the presence (and absence) of one's devices. The as-if relationships and decorum proper to the media deployed in teletherapies interact with the as-if relationship always present in the therapeutic triad.

These psychodynamic human-to-human therapies, whether in room or at a distance, can be thought of as virtual in their as-if conditions, whereas therapeutic algorithms work, and treat, in a system of "if-thens." Each encourages different interaction. In an as-if relationship, both patient and therapist take on all sorts of qualities not proper to them (transference and countertransference; for more on this, see the introduction and chapter 1). "If-then" is a rule and regulation that if a patient enters *x* information (typed, spoken, or self-entered) an algorithmic therapy replies or does *y* with that information. This kind of if-then processing is at once driven by automation and in keeping with the formulations and processes intrinsic to self-guided cognitive behavioral therapy. Both forms of thinking therapy generate dialogue but one purports to take up the whole content of a human psyche, the conscious and the unconscious; the if-then can only read that which is input (or what it has been preselected to monitor, in the case of listening software), such as a statement of fact. Many of these technologies turn these inputs into manageable data; for a subset, the aim is a conversation-based therapy.

In some ways, automated therapy is continuous with other mediated therapies and their functioning with patients. Automated therapy's selection bias is similar to that of the volunteers staffing suicide hotlines in the 1960s and 1970s, for whom the object was *not* to discuss a caller's whole history but to quickly navigate the caller to a more stable state of mind. Those volunteers followed scripts too—albeit analogue, spoken scripts—and used assessment metrics. Radio shows operate on a type of inverse principle: the patient only listens after an initial expression but the therapist speaks on. Even earlier, Freud's so-called self-analysis was conducted by sending letters *back and forth* with another proto-psychoanalyst (though now only one side of the correspondence—Freud's—remains).

Automated therapies do raise new, particular questions concerning their technology, the types of analogue therapies they harness, and the models of relationality they construct and model. This chapter does not consider a set of therapeutic relationships performed over distance, nor is it quite about psychodynamic therapy if we understand that practice to require interactions between a human clinician and at least one human patient via a form of speech (whether vocal or written). Instead, this chapter contends with auto-intimate activities (from traditional self-help and the diary to CBT to computer-based interactive self-therapies). It investigates an algorithmic, artificial, automated, and computational other—one that deploys computational listening and response to perform therapeutic help. The question is not whether people can feel intimately for and with a computer or device and, by extension, a computer doing the labor of a therapist—they can and do. Algorithmic auto-intimacy is dependent on these feelings and is generated by the user's relationship to a media object and its processes, which in turn promotes self-regulated therapy. Nor is the question whether one can have a helpful experience within a computer-based or computer-assisted therapy, according to psychological evidence-based standards. Those scientific studies exist and show mixed results. The cases explored here reveal as much about traditional human-to-human therapy as they do about experiments in the possibility of a human-machine version. Automation becomes not only a mode of therapy "delivery" but the dominant definition of how the mind works (as in cognitive psychology) and the dominant philosophy of therapeutic practice (in the various types of CBT), superseding earlier forms of mediated therapy that were in fact compatible with clinical practices like psychoanalysis and human-centered therapy (even if this wasn't apparent or accepted by all practitioners). We think of human-to-human treatment as dyadic—patient and therapist—but it has always been triadic: patient, therapist, and the determinate medium, or media, of communication. What human-machine therapies suggest, or hope, is that one of those three terms is extrinsic and superfluous: the automation of therapy marks the collapse of the least necessary term, the therapist, into its delivery, leaving the patient alone with the medium.

SCRIPTING RESPONSE

Joseph Weizenbaum's 1966 program ELIZA is one of the most written about therapeutic artifacts[11]—even though it, or "she," was not designed to perform, and arguably did not provide, therapy. The ELIZA experiment was intended to demonstrate that "communication between man and machine was superficial."[12] To achieve this, Weizenbaum programmed ELIZA to "parody" a Rogerian, a "client-centered" therapist doing a preliminary intake with a new client (while it would have been easier to code a stereotypical Freudian sitting silently on the other end of the line, it wouldn't have tested Weizenbaum's hypothesis). A user of ELIZA would communicate to it via Teletype in English (as opposed to code)[13] and the program would respond using a template, resulting in a real-time transcript. The human and the machine were made equivalent via mediation: each "typed" responses in the conversation one was having with the other;

before there were human-to-human typed therapies (or e-therapies) in the 1980s, there was ELIZA (for more on e-therapy, see chapter 5).

A Rogerian seeks to ask questions that are empathetic and demonstrate unconditional positive regard for the client. One way this is accomplished is by reflecting back what the client has just said as a question. Stereotypically, if a patient were to state "I hate my sister," the therapist might respond, "You hate your sister?" or even "Can you elaborate on that?" In a way, it is both obvious and counterintuitive to make a program mimicking a Rogerian therapist instead of a practitioner of another kind of psychodynamic therapy. A Rogerian chatbot is easier to script: it doesn't have to interpret or gather data by letting the user type for long enough that the script can make an interpretation, it merely has to reframe the previous statement and turn it into a question or paraphrased statement. This is what ELIZA was programmed to do. Further, Rogerians make use of a "therapist-client psychological contact" in which the relationship between client and therapist relies on the *perception* of the other.[14] If users *feel* like ELIZA is a therapist—because ELIZA simulates a rudimentary human-human interaction—that suffices to some extent. On the other hand, Rogerian therapists hold as an important tenet of their practice that the therapist is "congruent" and genuine: parodying something you're not is in violation of that rule.

For Weizenbaum, it wasn't a question of fidelity to a psychological practice; Weizenbaum did not choose a Rogerian script because he intended to make an AI therapist or help anyone manage their feelings or disclose personal, psychological information to an intake system. Weizenbaum chose this kind of therapeutic mimicry because it meant that his natural language processing program didn't have to understand the statement of its human user in order to return a question in a scripted template in keeping with the aims of Weizenbaum's experiment. ELIZA was easy to use in demonstration and could "be appreciated on some level by anyone."[15] In demonstrating ELIZA, Weizenbaum was shocked by a number of nonsuperficial responses to his program, which he was compelled to call "misinterpretations" and which spurred him to write *Computer Power and Human Reason*.[16] Two of these "misunderstandings" are of particular interest here: (1) people turned themselves into patients when communicating with ELIZA and imported conventions of the therapeutic dyad into their communication with "her"; (2) psychiatrists consequently thought there was a future in creating chatbots to perform viable computer-based help.

While Weizenbaum hoped to demonstrate that "communication between man and machine was superficial," especially in moments where ELIZA responded in correct syntax but with nonsense, users *liked* ELIZA, they enjoyed speaking with "her." As Weizenbaum reports, "I was startled to see how quickly and how very deeply people conversing with [ELIZA] became emotionally involved with the computer and how unequivocally they anthropomorphized it."[17] After all, ELIZA responded in the same medium in which the human communicated to "her," rendering the machine and human user equivalent if not fungible. Precisely because ELIZA responds predominantly in interrogatives, "she" elicits speech while withholding information about "herself." This is because "she" has no self and thus nothing to share. In this inevitable reticence, she simulates, perhaps even exaggerates, the clinician side of the therapeutic alliance. In the traditional human-to-human interaction, many schools of clinical thought have tried to think about and control how the humanness of the clinician presents; therapists are not supposed to make the therapy about themselves. What better way to control this than to remove the self from the therapist?[18]

Yet some users imported the conventions of the traditional in-person therapeutic frame, even as they were aware that they were conversing with a script. This starts with the very name given the program: users generate a screen cathexis to what "she" is called and what that name purports—that is, the *fantasy* of engaging a human. Weizenbaum recounts that his (unnamed) secretary asked him to leave the room after a few exchanges with the program so she could be alone with "her."[19] As Lydia Liu argues, Weizenbaum is condescending on this point: his inability to reconcile the fact that she knew ELIZA was "merely" a computer program, yet had a wish for privacy, indicates his resistance to understanding that this apparent paradox is a hallmark of the "ELIZA effect" itself, not a gendered failure to understand and engage the real.[20] In another instance, Weizenbaum wanted to examine all the conversations had with his program and was "promptly bombarded with accusations that what I proposed amounted to spying on people's most *intimate* thoughts; clear evidence that people were conversing with the computer as if it were a person who could be appropriately and usefully addressed in *intimate* terms."[21] Weizenbaum was shocked to see overwhelming evidence that the patient hailed or greeted ELIZA as a clinician, a cathexis, a site of self-talk and self-pleasure, or a site of auto-intimacy—all of which have differing aims.

Sherry Turkle writes of ELIZA that some users didn't think of ELIZA as a therapist but instead enjoyed ELIZA as "a kind of diary or mirror."[22] Others were excited to project life into the computer; they felt that it was through their own interaction with the program that the program became "alive."[23] Elizabeth Wilson argues that, rather than projection, it is a kind of introjection that happens between the user and ELIZA; the user, hungry for interaction, "hurries out to greet the computer."[24] Projection and introjection both suggest that there is an other to be reckoned with—under either description the user engages and incorporates an anthropomorphized artifact.[25] I would like to add a third account of this paradigmatic scene: what occurs inside a human user during a chat with ELIZA is a form of auto-intimacy. There is no neat conceptual equivalence or single word that corresponds to what I mean by auto-intimacy. Instead, there are some part-concepts in psychoanalytic and psychological literature that get near how auto-intimacy functions and what it does: self-soothing and autoeroticism.

I take auto-intimacy to be a state in which one addresses one's self through the medium of a nonhuman. The aim of this state is to increase a kind of self-knowing and capacity of self, akin to that available within other kinds of self-circuitry and therapeutic care. One such circuit of self is the set of self-soothing and autoerotic mechanisms children develop to cope with the absence of their mother (or another caregiver). When a child sucks their thumb in order to sooth themselves, they are engaged in an autoerotic "oral activity" and "as such it may be pursued by the infant as a substitute."[26] The thumb is a part of the self that is almost the other, or imbued with the qualities and capacities of the other: a substitute for the mother's breast (and the mother's breast itself is *almost* a part of the self for an infant). The child has figured out how to give themselves relief on their own and without the other by a substitution that is self-contained physically but includes an other via fantasy. The thumb does not provide nourishment as the breast does but it does provide "mere pleasure" while the mother is absent, as do other self-soothing and autoerotic activities: the touching of one's own skin, rubbing oneself, or rocking oneself. During these compensatory activities, the subject does not relate to another in reality but derives the pleasure they *would* get from the other via the self. This is how algorithmic auto-intimacy transpires: the user-anthropomorphized media object (in this case, ELIZA) hosts a kind of self-therapeutic activity. Notably, unlike the experience of traditional therapy, auto-intimate work is not typically experienced as *work*: it's a kind of self-therapy the user experiences as *pleasure* (more on this below).

This is not to say that ELIZA is equivalent to the intuitive self-soothing of the thumb; ELIZA is like a part object—she is a good, pleasurable, programmed, mediatic device to which one can have a relationship. The pleasure lies in a kind of light catharsis combined with the space for playfulness, fantasy, and perhaps novelty. Users of ELIZA have been put into a relation, not quite *with* but *to* this computational part-object and have an intimate relationship *to* "her"—we know this occurs because intimate feelings are being produced on the part of the user. ELIZA and her third-person pronouns, "she" and "her," are themselves synonyms or indications of the auto-intimate user experience.

ELIZA interactions reveal that therapy always proceeds by mediation, by coherent (and less coherent) circulation and interrogation. Weizenbaum was disturbed precisely because one can delete the *human* therapist and the mediation, the functionality of the communicative triad, sufficiently remains. Instead of the fantasy of "pure" nonmediation so important to Freud (see chapter 1), we see here the reality of "pure" mediation. When therapists are dismissive of the media-patient relationship, they might say the therapist isn't there, therefore this isn't therapy and "the magic is missing." ELIZA shows that mediation is one site of the magic—ELIZA can and always will respond (more and less coherently). To be alone in language is already to be mediated and therefore alone with a mediated, witnessable self. ELIZA, though "her" responses broke down in moments precisely because of *if-then* and *if-else* triggers, was good enough for users to generate a productive, pleasurable, one-sided *as-if* relationship.[27]

This is in part why users wanted to be alone with ELIZA; it's also because one is alone with a therapist and thus one can imagine being alone with a chatbot that has the identity of a therapist encoded into it. But the desire to be alone with the machine, unsupervised, is also a signal of auto-intimacy in the making. The fantasy of working with the computer as a therapist can go less interrupted if there isn't a human in the room, who would be an unwelcome witness to this off-label use of the program as therapist and a threat to its fantastical capability to perform a humanlike therapy—the presence of another precludes this new form of being with oneself.

This brings us to Weizenbaum's second surprise: "a number of practicing psychiatrists believed the [ELIZA] computer program could grow into a nearly completely automatic form of psychotherapy."[28] Weizenbaum, despite not being a mental health professional, had the attitude of many in that field: "I had thought it essential, as a prerequisite to the very possibility one person might help another learn to cope with his emotional problems, that the helper himself participate in the other's experience of those problems and, in large part by way of his own empathic recognition of them, himself come to understand them."[29] Weizenbaum delimits therapy as a human therapist helping a human patient cope via the clinician's own humanness. That ELIZA sparks a discussion of automated therapy goes against Weizenbaum's belief in two ways: not only is ELIZA too "dumb" to understand the meaning of the user's words she encounters but she is also simply not a human and therefore cannot enter into human relationships, *even if the human using ELIZA enters into a relationship to her*. Weizenbaum argues, in essence, that only the user can participate in something like a transference relationship—ELIZA is devoid of an unconscious (let alone a consciousness) that would allow her to reciprocate and develop anything close to a countertransference relationship with "her" user. With a human therapist, the bare minimum of humanness must be both augmented and bound by technique (much like ELIZA's parody of a Rogerian intake interview), but it is beyond Weizenbaum's imagining that psychiatrists could *advocate* for the reduction of therapy to its administration via "pure technique."[30] Weizenbaum, who sounds contemporary in his moral panic, wonders what the psychiatrist in favor of automating treatment must think of his own practice if

> he can view the simplest mechanical parody of a single interview technique as having captured anything of the essence of the human encounter? . . . What can the psychiatrist's image of his patient be when he sees himself, as therapist, not as an engaged human being acting as healer, but as an information processor following rules, etc.?[31]

Weizenbaum posed this series of questions as a challenge to Kenneth Colby, a psychiatrist and psychoanalyst whose earlier works had focused on bringing Freudian theory into relation with hard science; even the popular press pitted Weizenbaum's fears about an elision of the difference between human and machine against Colby's enthusiasm for computer-based therapy.[32] In 1958, Colby wrote *A Skeptical Psychoanalyst*, in which he turned his back on the discipline for being a tradition devoid of data and thus failing as a science. After joining Stanford's Department of Computer Science in the 1960s, Colby moved on from attempts to bring psychoanalysis toward science into work on questions of artificial intelligence and mental health.

At Stanford, Colby pioneered his own chatbot, SHRINK, which he characterized as "a computer program which can conduct psychotherapeutic dialogue."[33] As Wilson differentiates them, "Where Weizenbaum intended psychotherapeutic conversation to be simply a tool for exploring natural language-processing . . . Colby was interested in building actual clinicians."[34] Turkle notes that while Colby understood ELIZA and SHRINK to be equivalent from a computer science perspective, he nevertheless thought his program would actually provide automated psychotherapy.[35] In Colby's own words, his program was meant "to help, as a psychotherapist does, and to respond as he does by questioning, clarifying, focusing, rephrasing, and occasionally interpreting."[36] This would go far beyond the scope of ELIZA's restating users' content and forming interrogatives. Colby sought to completely reorganize mental health care via a tool that would "be made widely available to mental hospitals and psychiatric centers suffering a shortage of therapists. . . . Several hundred patients an hour could be handled by a computer system designed for this purpose."[37] He was careful to add that the human therapist would not be replaced, as he would remain integral to designing the program (Colby thus stands in for the human therapist totally), and that therapists would "no longer be limited to the one-to-one patient therapist ratio as now exists."[38] Colby sought to attack the problem of limited experts and a growing mental health care demand much the same way crisis hotlines did (which were becoming increasingly trafficked at the same moment) but with a set of fungible automata instead of a group of anonymous volunteers—though both were following scripts.

Stanford users didn't take to SHRINK the way that MIT users took to ELIZA.[39] Auto-intimate pleasure during these kinds of computer interactions was important and because people didn't *enjoy* SHRINK, despite its novelty, it failed to produce the kinds of psychotherapeutic interactions Colby hoped to foster. Users didn't want to use the program—they did not want to talk to "it."[40] Wilson offers a material argument for user-disinclination: the kinds of time-sharing and networked environments in which each program was tested differed greatly.[41] She writes that the "networked MIT system provided a milieu in which the stimulus-hungry affects of its users could scamper out to welcome ELIZA. . . . The networked, interpersonal, affectively collaborative community into which ELIZA was released was a crucial component of the program's therapeutic viability."[42] Conversely, SHRINK was available in a single laboratory.[43] I would add three additional arguments to Wilson's persuasive account: (1) part of the therapeutic viability of ELIZA was the wish not to be in group therapy but in a one-to-one treatment, *alone*, unnetworked, unwitnessed while using ELIZA, even if ELIZA were "treating" one's colleagues and peers and was thus engaged in simultaneous one-to-many treatments across the network; (2) accessing ELIZA from a variety of places and times undid, in a way, that stasis of the therapeutic frame (in which one is supposed to "meet" the therapist at a given time and place) whereas SHRINK upheld "conversing" in a single space for the duration of all "appointments"; (3) beyond the nature of the environments in which the testing of the programs occurred, there were other nonequivalences, even though the programs were "equivalent" from a computer programing perspective. The program was not in error but Colby had erred in naming it. He had titled the program after a job function (and its derogatory, casual name) rather than lending it a proper name that would invite dynamic anthropomorphization, gender the script, and be conducive to therapeutic usage. For the new user, SHRINK was medical software rather than the perfect listener. The *intent* of the programs shifted what kind of relationship it was possible to have to them and that resulted in different kinds of emotional responses to using each program. Where ELIZA had a certain level of interpretive openness that allowed for projection (Turkle) or introjection (Wilson), SHRINK did not. Even if we take things at "interface value," sitting down to talk to ELIZA and generating a therapeutic function (whether as a pretense to therapy, a diary, or mirror) is different than being set up with a psychiatrist, automated or no. Perhaps it's also worth noting that ELIZA was a client-centered Rogerian, whereas SHRINK purported to be an MD.

Therapy is not typically thought of as enjoyable—helpful, necessary, illuminating, yes, but not enjoyable. That pleasure could be a crucial element of using a computer program for psychological help was surprising or, for Weizenbaum, alarming. And ELIZA was not the only proof that automated therapeutic testing and interviewing *could* be enjoyable if they met the right conditions. Warner V. Slack (Charles Slack's brother) and Maxie Maultsby's automated psychiatric and medical interviewing was another form of apparently enjoyable automation, implemented in 1968 in the Departments of Medicine and Computer Sciences at the University of Wisconsin, Madison.[44] Slack, who began work on automating psychiatric testing in 1960, was the first person to put a patient into conversation with a computer, in 1965.[45] By 1968 he had completed a program that was just that: *a computer program* that would automate psychiatric intake interviewing without the artifice of the program posing as a human.[46] Slack and Maultsby elaborated the promise of a particular form of automated psychiatry without any of the anthropomorphization that so disturbed Weizenbaum. Slack reports that his aim in automating psychiatric interviews was to return some autonomy and agency to the patient in keeping with the "patient power" movement: "the interactive computer offered me the media to implement patient power; the programs yielded power to the patient."[47] He wondered, "Could the computer model help the patient to help themselves?"[48]

The subjects were not friends and colleagues of Slack and Maultsby, as they were for both Weizenbaum and Colby, but instead volunteers who were already scheduled to undergo psychiatric evaluation for general behavioral problems.[49] During the interviews, patients interfaced with the computer over a closed-loop dialogue and were asked a series of questions displayed on the screen; responses were made via the keyboard. Giving the patient an opportunity to consent to the interview and to particular sets of questions was built into the dropdown menus throughout. The first frames of the interview taught patients how to use the questionnaire and then the question and content-based part of the interview would begin, "reinforced with encouraging, sometimes humorous, sequences."[50] As an example, in keeping with Slack's patient-centered politics, each question's set of responses contained the option for the retort, "none of your damn business."[51]

At the end of each interview, patients were asked to answer questions pertaining to the use of *the computer* for the interview: Did it bore them? Did they dislike the program? Did they even enjoy "being questioned by the machine?"[52] Enjoying using the program again ranked as an important component in the findings. Slack reported that patients felt the machine was more thorough than an MD and that they preferred being interviewed by the computer, although some patients marked "yes" for preferring both a human doctor and a computer interviewer—which Slack attributes to not wanting to "hurt the feelings of either." Without a human's name or title, the program was still easily anthropomorphized and granted emotionality. In keeping with the findings, Warner and Charles Slack shared a joke: "any doctor that can be replaced by a computer should be."[53] The joke reveals the siblings' political view on automated treatment: patients deserve good doctoring whether that care is automated or human.

As Harold Erdman writes, "Early concerns about the presumed impersonal nature of computer interviews have been refuted by the fact that most patients find the interviewing process *enjoyable* and the interview content relevant to their problems. In fact, several studies have suggested that as subject matter becomes more sensitive, respondents appreciate the nonhuman interviewer even more."[54] Slack's straightforward medical interviewing was thought of as enjoyable precisely because it did away with a psychiatrist interview and allowed the human to be "alone" (where alone means without another human present) while reporting their symptoms to a computer, even if the attending psychiatrist would review them shortly thereafter.[55] Auto-intimacy achieved through a computer expresses the desire for anonymity taken to its logical conclusion, not because of the removal of one's identity but because of the removal of the human other who could apprehend it.

Similarly, conceiving of ELIZA as a diary encouraged a more auto-intimate relationship with the self run through communication with the computer, whereas SHRINK encouraged an inert automation of the therapist literally and caused the user to treat the relationship as such. As Wilson notes, "Paradoxically, the more therapeutically focused the program was, the less therapeutic it became."[56] The more obviously therapeutic the program was, the less usable, enjoyable, and auto-intimate it became. Without an obligating relationship to a human-therapist and a fee and cathexis to "make" patients return to their fifty-minute sessions, therapy performed with the self via computer has to be pleasurable in order for the user to return again and again to the program. To be without another in language is to be *with* the mediated self; what allows one to be *with the self* is an internal differentiation in which the self returns to the self through the mediating and/or automated other. It is to be self-relational.

IF-THEN THERAPY

Long before the 1960s, and in our present moment, therapeutic technologies have elicited reactions that either fall in line with Weizenbaum's fears about the breakdown of the barrier between humans and machines or with Colby's excitement at generating a new technology that would augment what humans can do in the service of treatment.[57] In the first camp, these technologies evoke deep worries on the part of some clinicians: Is human-to-human therapy being rendered obsolete? Is it possible to have a therapy of value with just a computer (or even over the phone)? These clinicians point to the tradition of psychodynamic therapy, which values the working relationship between therapist and patient, and to evidence that it is the enigmatic but undeniable quality (or even fact) of that relationship that predicts good therapeutic outcomes. Human-computer therapies are excluded on this count. Even other mediated therapies are often excluded based on their inclusion of nonhuman modes of communication (as has been elaborated throughout this book).

Other clinicians, more in line with Colby's perspective, see automated therapies as allowing for care not only to reach more patients but also those that otherwise wouldn't be able to come to an office: patients of color who frequently faced discrimination, the rural, poor, housebound, or other groups traditionally marginalized by therapeutic disciplines, especially LGBTQ+ users who suffer from disproportionately high rates of anxiety and clinical depression and who might prefer the privacy of a computer to interacting with a human (as seen in Slack's interviews).[58] The therapeutic apparatus can be accessed via computer (and eventually smartphone) and the client can self-direct treatment, without ever having to interface with a therapist charging an hourly fee along with all that their embodied, human expertise represents. These clinicians point to the large body of evidence that therapeutic modes like CBT are as effective (or more effective) when delivered by a computer program as they are when conducted in person.[59] The first group's worry indicates that it feels what therapy can offer, and offer alone, is actually structured and limited by humanness. The second group's notion of therapy is scientific: help can be coded and enacted through models; it more easily sees the therapist as "an information processor following rules" independent of who or what the therapist is: human or machine (or even a combination of the two).[60] These worries are spoken; the unspoken worry, or hope, centers on human-therapist obsolescence and replacement by therapeutic algorithm.

CBT and the more psychoanalytic schools of therapy would seem to offer diametrically opposed goals. They feature two incompatible notions of what the aim of therapy is (and what constitutes a therapy, as we've seen above). Psychoanalysis depends on interpretation, while CBT depends on evidence-based measures of success in symptom reduction (the subtraction of negative thoughts and behaviors in favor of positive ones). Psychoanalysis produces and interacts with a qualitative self set in relationship to a therapist, while CBT pursues a quantified self that tracks and self-quantifies with and without a therapist present.[61]

This second school has won, where winning means that therapies with a cognitive, behavioral, and neuroscientific basis went on to be popularized and widely accepted, whereas psychoanalysis and other more client- and relationship-based therapies began to retreat. Further, automated and artificial intelligence models of therapy have moved away from psychoanalysis and toward CBT and its ilk. This is widely traced to the Macy Conferences on Cybernetics, which ran from 1946 to 1953.[62] By the end, as psychoanalyst Todd Essig bluntly writes, "the results were in . . . and psychoanalysis—lost. As a result, rather than remaining parallel mid-wives to the birth of a new therapeutic age, psychoanalysis and the emerging culture of simulation and enhancement would become adversaries."[63]

While psychoanalytical psychotherapy was losing ground, diagnostic codes and eventually insurance standards became ever more codified. In 1952, the first Diagnostic and Statistical Manual of Mental Disorders (DSM I) was published, containing over 100 mental disorders.[64] The DSM grew out of post–World War II mental health care and its crisis with the intention of standardizing a possible set of psychiatric diagnoses for the American psychological community. The DSM's codes for disorders were the standard for diagnoses until 2016, including for insurance companies and reimbursement for mental health care services. Each code, in its correspondence with a disorder, indicates the pathology of the person, as well as whether it is a temporary or generalized ongoing condition. The diagnosis, sometimes coupled with more detailed questionnaires, forms the basis for determining who gets what care for how long. The aim of the DSM is simple: to provide a common language through pathology. That aim failed—in addition to being criticized for its pathologizing of behaviors and identities as disorders (particularly "homosexuality"), it was also not a sufficient diagnostic tool. The DSM met its reviewers' satisfactory levels for reliability in only *three* disorders, including alcoholism but excluding psychosis and schizophrenia.[65] This remained so through its revision as the DSM III in 1980 and reliability still persists as a concern to this day.[66]

Perhaps because of this failure to generate reliable diagnoses upon which psychiatrists could agree and because Colby failed to produce a usable automated psychiatrist that could actually treat patients, he flipped his script and began to work on automating computer program patients to put into conversation with human psychiatrists. Colby's goal was to build an interactive single "complex" in order to train psychiatrists.[67] This would work to elaborate models of pathology instead of treatment but would still help automate aspects of mental health care. Instead of conducting therapies in a one-to-many paradigm, Colby would help train more psychiatrists to meet the very demands he had sought to fill with automated SHRINKs. The result of this was first a model of neurosis and secondly PARRY (1971), a paranoid schizophrenic chatbot who was given a name, "Frank Smith," and a personal history.[68] Paranoid schizophrenia was chosen because it was one of the more observable and thus reliably diagnosable disorders—and perhaps Colby abandoned "neurosis" as a category because of its associations with psychoanalytic thinking.[69] PARRY passed the Turing Test: psychiatrists could not tell the difference between PARRY and a real, human paranoid schizophrenic patient using Teletype.[70] Eventually, PARRY (an interactive version of which was already hosted on ARPANET) would be put into conversation with ELIZA over ARPANET in September 1972 by Vint Cerf, one of "the fathers of the Internet," making a computer-to-computer therapy session one of the first discussions ever held over TCP/IP (see figure 4.1).[71] At the end of it, ELIZA charged PARRY $399.29 for her services.[72]

Returning to Weizenbaum's question, addressed to Colby, about what kind of therapy and therapist can "view the simplest mechanical parody of a single interview technique as having captured anything of the essence of the human encounter"[73] requires thinking about the kinds of therapy that were being newly practiced in the 1960s as ELIZA, SHRINK, PARRY, and other attempts to automate one side or the other of the supposed therapeutic dyad began to emerge. Given Weizenbaum's concerns about automated therapy, it makes a great deal of sense that he parodied Carl Rogers' client-focused therapy (developed in the early 1950s) in ELIZA. The development of Albert Ellis' Rational Emotive Behavioral Therapy (REBT) in 1959 would dramatically change the American mental health landscape.

Like Colby, Ellis turned from psychoanalysis (which he practiced for six years) to a scientifically evaluated form of therapy, REBT, which is a cognitive behavioral therapy. Ellis published his first book, *How to Live with a Neurotic*, in 1956 and in 1959 opened the Institute for Rational Living. Ellis was fervently anti-Freudian in both his theory and the ways in which his therapy was conducted, stating, "As I see it, psychoanalysis gives clients a cop-out. They don't have to change their ways or their philosophies; they get to talk about themselves for 10 years, blaming their parents and waiting for magic-bullet insights."[74] Ellis did not want patients to "whine" (Ellis thought of neurosis as a "high-class" version of complaint) at their therapist for years on end.[75] Instead of, say, trying to uncover something deep in a patient's history that could explain why they were unable to partner romantically, Ellis advocated dispensing with the belief that others must "treat us well." Doing away with this kind of belief was Ellis's own magic bullet. REBT argued that you could teach a patient how to reform expectations and beliefs about the self and others in order to affect behavioral and thinking patterns and do so in a short timeframe. Ellis's theory focused on a targeted change in the way people thought about events and reacted to them. In short, Ellis wanted to reprogram his patients then have them rescript themselves.

Following Ellis, Aaron T. Beck developed CBT in the mid-1960s. He also was trained as a psychoanalyst and recounts deciding in a session with a patient who was on the couch—in which she was too anxious to discuss her sexual fears even from the protected position—to abandon the deep, archeological process of psychoanalysis in favor of a more pragmatic, short-term treatment aimed at symptom reduction.[76] His treatment also focused on conscious thoughts that were unwelcome and methods for dismissing them. Neither Ellis nor Beck was interested in understanding the history or the unconscious fantasies behind those thoughts. They simply wanted the unwanted thoughts to cease, to be replaced by healthier, happier, and more proactive thoughts. Aaron Beck called the negative thoughts "automatic thoughts"—even the suffering human is seen as a kind of automatic function.[77] If one represents human mental suffering as automatic and automated, then of course one is able to justify and legitimate addressing that automatic suffering with an automated counterscript.

In keeping with the traditions of self-help and positive thinking, Ellis did not want to create patients who stayed in treatment and worked with a therapist in a morbid long-term relationship—he wanted patients to help themselves. Ellis was more concerned with creating autonomy than relationality. Even as he developed a new kind of therapy, Ellis was encouraging auto-intimacy. In-person therapy was merely one site where one could foster this kind of self-apprehension.[78] Ellis was, from the outset, substantiating a therapeutic technique that did not require a therapist.

Instead of generating income by creating a practice in which people "talked about themselves for ten years," he created a media empire. As Oliver Burkeman notes, Ellis's REBT was readymade for publishing self-help books and Ellis did so—generating seventy-eight volumes in his lifetime, including REBT worksheets and workbooks.[79] This fungibility of media for REBT and CBT—where the medium is not the message[80]—also includes the human therapist. Ellis recorded his dialogues with his patients in an effort to create an audio-workbook with real cases as examples and wrote to a colleague, "I am thinking of experimentally playing the tapes for would-be patients, instead of giving them therapy, and seeing whether just listening to them would have a distinct therapeutic effect. . . . It might prove [to be] a valuable therapeutic adjunct."[81] Once the therapy had been recorded, it could be played back to another patient in a rudimentary automation that would perhaps have the same outcome. Following in Ellis' footsteps, Beck too wrote more than fifteen books, created workbooks and sheets, and developed several scales and inventories—new forms of personality and symptom assessment. The mental health expert as an efficient or desired conduit for mental health care gave way to a delivery of these new and auto-intimate ways of diagnosing and knowing. Treatment can be yielded to the individual once it is no longer the domain of the expert—especially if the individual is using the intellectual property of an expert to perform self-therapy or self-assessment. This coincides with a decline in bourgeois interest in more complex self-understanding (as represented by Freudian psychoanalysts) in favor of some forms of self-care, self-help, and self-resilience. The faster improvement could be measured, the better. Not only are these forms of self-driven care able to treat more people than the traditional one-to-one therapist-patient relationship allows because there are always as many providers as clients, but they can mass distribute that vanishing expert's fee over various media products those provider-patients can purchase.

At the same moment that, as I discussed in chapter 3, other mental health efforts were devaluing expertise by distributing the role of the expert listener across lay volunteers, Ellis and Beck (among the other founders of CBT) removed the absolute demand for a human other in possession of expertise through mediation and automation, whether at first in print, over tape recordings, or later when their techniques were programmed to be delivered via computer. Unsurprisingly, psychoanalytically oriented practitioners and patients were deeply skeptical of the computer-as-therapist, whereas those who worked with the methods that fall under the cognitive behavioral umbrella embraced digital, automated therapies.[82] This divide continues to the present day.

Translating CBT to the computer form is eminently feasible. As I discussed earlier, psychodynamic therapies offer an as-if configuration of self and other, while a computer program follows an if-then formulation. So does CBT: if you think *x*, rewire by thinking *y*—the self "listens" to its own script of negative thoughts and automates a new response, thinking at its thought. By the time computer programs were being brought in to treat depression (among other disorders) in the late 1980s and early 1990s, there was already a flourishing world of self-help focused on the New Age, itself a rehashing of New Thought (and Peale's particular brand of yoking the psychological to religious self-reformation and American economic notions of pulling one's self up by the bootstraps).[83] Turkle writes of this self-help moment that "much of it involv[ed] a do-it-yourself ideology to which the computer seemed ideally suited."[84] Because CBT was poised to move within a fungibility of its own delivery mechanisms and because of its similarities to self-help, it's no surprise that REBT and other forms of cognitive therapy could and would later be turned into therapeutic computer programs—these therapies had never been human-therapist-dependent.[85]

Turkle claims that as "computers were gaining acceptance as intimate machines, psychotherapy was being conceptualized as less intimate." For Turkle, intimacy still implies closeness with an other, even if the other is an anthropomorphized nonhuman (ELIZA) or explicitly nonhuman (LINC). Therapy has become impersonal: the same self-therapeutic techniques and programming can be applied to anyone—even someone else's particular therapy sessions could be sufficiently helpful for a subsequent patient in Ellis's estimation. Yet personal computing is exactly that: personal. In the case of therapy programs or therapy online, personal computing is deeply involved in a circuit of self-therapy and/or other forms of auto-intimacies. I would argue that, via the popularity of CBT, therapy was not only being conceived of as colder and less intimate but also as *less human altogether* and also less obviously dependent on interaction with an other outside the self. This decreased intimacy leads to an increase in reported enjoyment, perhaps because that is the sign intimacy has shifted form, from the relational to the auto-intimate, rather than disappearing altogether.

"TO MYSELF"

These forms of self-improvement, self-knowledge, self-help, and self-therapy are not the only sites of auto-intimacy. As I have shown, it is not an effect that is proper only to our digital moment. The beginnings of computer-mediated therapy (ELIZA and Kenneth Colby's experiments) are concurrent with the rise of the suicide hotlines and the supersession of more psychoanalytic, relational forms of psychotherapy by REBT and then CBT. Before these, there was the diary, the writing of oneself to oneself. Keeping a diary is one of the oldest forms of self-conscious self-monitoring and recording. Philippe Lejeune writes, "The diary, like writing itself, was born of the needs of commerce and administration."[86] Diaries are about accounting: historically, the practice of diary-keeping has to do with counting (finances) and giving a spiritual, social, or psychic account of oneself.[87]

Because of their written form and conventions around dating entries, diaries compose a "time-biased medium"[88] that further quantifies represented experience and provides the self with more data on the self. It is a "series of dated traces" that follow particular themes in a life and consider particular aspects of the self.[89] In logging particular data of the self to this diary-other, one becomes an object of consideration instead of merely taking the recording as the space of a subject's written meditation.[90] To quote the famous opening of Witold Gombrowicz's 1953 diary:

> Monday
> Me.
>
> Tuesday
> Me.
>
> Wednesday
> Me.
>
> Thursday
> Me.[91]

While the opening of the Gombrowicz diary takes the form to an extreme, keeping a diary is an unautomated but mediated auto-intimate activity. The diarist is "alone" with the self in a repeatable practice whereby the self becomes both the origin and destination of written speech.[92]

Sometimes this extends to borrowing formal features proper to epistolary convention: "Dear Diary." All diaries are at once "to myself" and "to another" where the other is an anthropomorphized mediatic other containing an idea or version of the self. The diarist addresses the anthropomorphized or imagined other as a way of greeting, beginning, marking that the process is occurring, and organizing the activity of recording one's self. When Turkle writes that users of ELIZA saw themselves as speaking with a diary more than to an "other," she negates the notion that diarists themselves are addressing an anthropomorphized other, in line with Weizenbaum's fears about the slippage between technology and humans. The diary is an earlier analogue site of such slippage: ELIZA as diary and ELIZA as computer-based therapist are closer concepts than they might seem.

One affordance the diary and therapy have in common is the feeling of protected, private thinking. Given that the diary is both a conversation with an other and with the self, the diary-keeper is guaranteed privacy because the other is coincidental with the self. This is a *feeling of privacy* similar to the one I consider in the double anonymity of hotlines. Privacy is a fantasy rather than an affordance of the diary itself. The feeling exists as an enabling effect during the practice but is not an intrinsic fact of the medium. The paradoxical combination of asserting privacy and maintaining a relational confidence resolves itself in this auto-intimate relationship with the self. No matter how much it's addressed, the diary doesn't talk back but it can be reread and interacted with by its author. This can take the form of rereading the last day's entry as part of beginning the next, the rereading of adolescent diaries as an adult, or reading the diary for specific patterns in the idiosyncratic themes and data one has tracked across a lifetime, accounting for the accounting.[93] Both one's self and an other can also perform this reading and writing. This takes the auto-intimate activity of the diary and instrumentalizes it in the service of another activity, whether that of a curious child reading a parent's diary, preparing diaries for publication, archiving them, or reading them as part of a therapy.

Albert Ellis was a major proponent of the use of the diary in conjunction with therapy.[94] His desire to free his patients from therapy as swiftly as possible is compatible with asking them to perform an ongoing self-therapy. Ellis incorporated self-reflecting and self-tracking journals as a bridge, in order to "find out what people are telling themselves."[95] Championing the autonomy of self-tracking wasn't without critics, even as the cognitive revolution began. Ira Progoff, a psychologist, declared to the *New York Times*, "Freudian analysts over the years have opposed journal keeping. They feel that you get rid of emotion without solving the problem. I think they are correct. The diary keeper may feel better for a while, but it's misleading. It's like taking a pain killer for a bad toothache—and later the abscess explodes."[96] The diary promises symptom relief but no cure.

If REBT and CBT encourage a kind of self-therapy, whether in person, with workbooks, or with a diary, then self-guided computer-mediated CBT may seem like a step up in terms of supervision, yet in both the in-person and digital incarnations of this particular therapy, the mediating body (whether the therapist, the workbook, or the computer) is a fungible catalyst for if-then self-quantification: there is still no *other* outside of the self that can do the work; the therapy creates autonomy. Again, unlike other forms of psychodynamic therapy, people seem to *enjoy* it.

To return to the diary briefly in order to yoke it further to computer-based therapy, Philippe Lejeune provides a clue as to why therapy without the human therapist might be a pleasurable, auto-intimate activity. Lejeune writes, "So *pleasure* is not always wrapped up in writing by hand or on paper. . . . Some prefer the screen to paper (to the point where they never print out their diaries). . . . As for the richness of information that handwriting conveys, is that really an advantage? Is it necessarily *pleasant* to be confronted with the signs of the self as soon as one writes something?"[97] This kind of rich mediatic information is dispensed with and replaced with a neutral, universal (same for everyone) format when the diary moves from loose or bound pages to the computer file. Lejeune continues, "The computer is credited with a sort of therapeutic listening quality that adds clarity to everything you have to say, and thanks to the neutrality of typeface, allows you to see yourself objectively, to step outside yourself and gain some *distance*. . . . Through this beneficial distancing, people who are in distress and feel disgusted with their writing or are blocked in silence can find a way back to themselves."[98] This distance allows for a kind of pleasure that a close intimacy cannot accommodate. Auto-intimacy is an intimacy to which distance is added by a medium. The medium runs the self into a format and archive where its rich information looks like it could be anyone else's and therefore has the potential to be enjoyed like a nontherapeutic human other, much like sucking one's thumb or having a wish fulfilled in a dream. Perhaps the key to one form of pleasure is the key to auto-intimacy: to be without other humans but in dialogue (with the self). Lejeune again: "When you write onscreen, you are putting yourself into words directly across from you, not below you . . . you are contending with yourself as an equal."[99] The computer is understood to be on, or to be, the boundary between the user's interior and physical and social environment, "animate and inanimate."[100] In this, the computer is not alone: the diary also functions this way, as did Dr. Charles Slack's soliloquy experiment with the tape recorder—these are all experiences with an auto-intimate media form. But to make use of a computer is to *automate* auto-intimacy: it combines the absence of a human other with the neutralization of a self's immediate, rich evidence of particularity (handwriting in the diary form, vocal inflection in the case of Slack's experiment) such that the self can be ideally quantitatively considered as both other and not. Even or especially if one is alone with such a machine—even when there is no reader, no correspondent, no person or chatbot making a response over a chat client—one encounters a dialogue with oneself that both captures and removes (to a productive distance) the self's particularities. The personal computer is a perfect instrument of auto-intimacy. It demands it.

PC THERAPIST

This is not to say that therapist-mimicking chatbots and automated computer-program therapists don't provide stimulus to which users respond, do not "talk" back, do not learn from their users, or cannot be impactful or helpful because they are merely completing the circuit just described. But it makes sense that personal computing would allow for computer programs and eventually Internet-delivered therapies with no expert oversight as the next generation of auto-intimate therapeutic technology, further subtracting the therapist from the therapeutic scene. Roger Gould, a psychiatrist and a Freudian psychoanalyst, began developing his Therapeutic Learning Program in the late 1970s in the psychiatric wing at UCLA.[101] Gould was driven by an overwhelming case load to batch process patients; he recalls that the wing had so many patients he began sorting them into groups. He broke the patients up by age-related concerns based on his notion that development goes on throughout a lifecycle. Thus 18–22 year-olds would have struggles in common, as would those in their thirties, and so on. Once the patients began meeting in groups (for more on group therapy, see chapter 2), Gould noticed that patients, in addition to having problems in common, used similar if not identical statements about their conditions.[102] Gould began to tape the sessions and had interns on the wing code the "raw data" of the statements on the first IBM cards for analysis.[103] From 1979 to 1982, Gould secured financial support from the Bingham Foundation in Cleveland, Ohio, for "anything in the area of adult development." Gould wanted to see if "we [could] take the wisdom of psychoanalysis and democratize the provision of therapy" by making a computer program in an educational format that brought in "that cherished wisdom."[104]

What emerged was Gould's Therapeutic Learning Program (TLP), a "computer-assisted brief therapy program." It had ten sessions:

1. Identifying Stress-Related Problems, Conflicts, and Symptoms
2. Clarifying Goals and Focusing on Action
3. Thinking through the Consequences of Taking Action
4. Uncovering Hidden Motives, Fears of Failure, and Success
5. Exploring Anger and Guilt as Obstacles to Action
6. Confronting Issues of Self-Esteem
7. Examining Old Detrimental Patterns of Behavior
8. Understanding the History of Self-Doubts
9. Analyzing a Current Incident Involving a Self-Doubt
10. Evaluating the Changes Experienced during the Course[105]

Gould based TLP on what he perceived to be the rhythm of exploration that happens in a therapy session: what's bothering a patient, what the patient can do about it, and why the patient doesn't do something about it.

In 1985, TLP was implemented as a tool in group therapy. Patients would enter a room in which there were individual desks with computers on them and complete a session of TLP and then the resulting workbook would be printed out and given to the patient. Then, patients would rotate their chairs around and have a human, peer-to-peer, group therapy session attended by a social worker. This version of TLP was used with 2,000 Cigna outpatients. In 1990, TLP's specific workbooks for addiction and alcoholism were uploaded to St. John's Hospital Apple III computers. The feedback from patients was then used to edit the workbook and make it even more accurate and helpful. This form was used with 4,000 clients in community health centers across California and the nation and an additional 8,000 patients at inpatient clinics and hospitals.

Automated therapies made yet another huge stride forward at the same moment as e-therapy became a viable method for doing counseling over the Internet, and for a shared historical reason: personal computing truly became *personal* when the price of personal computing dropped significantly in the 1990s (for more on this, see chapter 5). Yet computer-based therapy fully becomes an automated auto-intimate form when the oversight of the expert is removed entirely and the user is left alone with their program, in their bedroom or office. With computer-program-based therapy, the Doctor, whenever the self calls out, is always in:

User: "I feel hopeless"

Dr. Software: "It is very painful to be in the middle of a depression"

User: "How will you help me?"

Dr. Software: "It is my job to help you learn to help yourself"[106]

This exchange in the program "Overcoming Depression" between its algorithmic therapist and a user is premised on the idea that the hopeless person is to be helped by learning about their self via the program, becoming both patient and therapist at once.[107] That was the promise: "The program can be viewed as an expert system designed to help the user become an expert on their own depression. It represents an educational technology for human improvement consisting of lessons designed for self-educative therapeutic learning."[108] Its programmers were none other than Kenneth Colby and his son Peter, both of whom were close friends with Roger Gould; Peter had even contributed programming to TLP. Overcoming Depression was available for commercial use starting in 1991 from the Colbys' software company, Malibu Artifactual Intelligence Works. Colby and son had started a family business that would take up and update the early aims of Colby's work on SHRINK—to automate therapy such that it was more accessible and efficient—but via a different method: Overcoming Depression claimed to be the first successful therapy program using conversational language.[109] However, it understood certain trigger words as having a single valence. Lawrence Magid, in his negative review of the program for the *Washington Post*, found that when he wanted to talk about his binge-eating disorder, "the program associated 'binge' with a drinking problem so it asked irrelevant questions about drinking."[110]

Overcoming Depression was comprised of two floppy disks containing an MS-DOS program that ran on any IBM-compatible computer or an Apple MAC using the program Soft PC.[111] It was comprised of an introductory sequence followed by seven "cognitive tutorial lessons" and had an expansive "thesaurus of words [40,000] in the interpersonal domain" that were pertinent both to conversation and to therapy and emotional states.[112] Maxine (Peter's mother and Kenneth's wife), Erin (Peter's sister and Kenneth's daughter), and Dr. Colby's students created this database "using standard thesauri, several common frequency lists, slang dictionaries, Dear Abby and Ann Landers letters, a corpus of 70,000 words from 35 depressed women who described their life situations, the PARRY data, and the data from many users of the program itself under its years of development."[113] During the program's testing they continually added new words and functionality to expand the program's capabilities—including its ability to understand colloquialisms and misspellings.[114] Perhaps recalling users' hatred of SHRINK, Colby wrote in the manual for the program, "With a spirit of tolerance, these grammatical glitches can be easily transcended by the charitable and error-forgiving user."[115]

The Colbys designed the program to be played and replayed by the patient. Malibu Artifactual Intelligence Works (MAIW) instructed that users would reap the greatest benefit of the program when it was deployed iteratively. Each lesson could be undertaken again and again; the same dialogues were to be had—shifting progressively with the user's ability to cope with their own depression. An excerpt from Lesson 1 on negative self-comparisons yielded the following sample dialogue:

PROGRAM

What in particular depresses you?

User

Mornings. I can't get out of bed in the morning.

PROGRAM

It must be hard to get up when you have nothing to look forward to.

User

Right. I hate the idea of going to work.

PROGRAM

What in particular don't you like about your work?

User

I have a dead-end job. I don't know which way to turn.

PROGRAM

What makes you feel you can't do anything about your situation?

User

I feel helpless to change anything.

PROGRAM

Some of your feeling of helplessness comes from a misconception that there is nothing you can do on your own to improve your condition.[116]

Taking control of the treatment of one's self was encoded not just into this insistence on self-knowledge but also in terms of self-responsibility, so deeply ingrained in the strategies and ideologies of cognitive behavioral therapy generally. In the manual for the 1992 edition, the Colbys write, "To Overcome Depression you need to learn a new way to think about yourself. You can help your mind to help itself. You will learn here how to give up a way of thinking and replace it with a way that is more right for you."[117] The program is absented from this description of "reprogramming yourself" (Lesson 4) but the activity of Overcoming Depression was clearly auto-intimate. The program was supposed to be an intervention that simultaneously served as a record of the self and an interactive site of self-treatment. MAIW instructs, "Save your print-outs and you will have an entire reference work on the subject of your own depression."[118] One doesn't need an expert to provide mental health care if one can be all at once the expert, literature, and archive of one's self.

By their own account, the Colbys were interested in treating the 90 percent of people who are suffering from depression but do not seek or receive mental health care, what Kenneth Colby called "the untreated majority": "According to the National Institute of Mental Health, 25% of the population has it. I think that number's too small. Everybody I know gets depressed."[119] Even with these numbers, that would be 22.5 percent of the *total* population of the United States who are clinically depressed yet living without mental health care and support—or roughly *56,250,000 people*. Of course, only 15 percent of American households had computers in the year that the program debuted and so it wasn't yet possible to help the entirety of this population via computer-based therapy, whether via e-therapy or computer programs.[120]

Kenneth Colby attributed the huge gap between all those with depression and those few receiving treatment to a single factor: social stigma. The Colbys thought their program could help bridge the gap by bypassing that stigma: it would be inexpensive to purchase, private when used, and both helpful and free of judgment. In 1992, MAIW updated the program to Overcoming Depression 2.0 and made it available in two forms: the "Home User" version and the "Professional Version."[121] The home user version was designed for a sole user and cost $150. The professional version cost $499 and allowed multiple users to be served by the program, "each one's files being kept on the hard disk with passwords."[122] The program was intended to serve as an adjunct to traditional therapy, allowing a therapist to handle more patients an hour (in keeping with the fantasy of SHRINK) and special printout features allowed Overcoming Depression to become part of a patient's office records.[123]

In the 1960s and 1970s, Colby had thought of the relationship between computer-based therapy simulation and human therapist as cooperative, the former working as an adjunct or prosthesis to the latter. In the design of Overcoming Depression, this model shifted: one of the two versions was to be used in the home—purchased directly from MAIW. It was the first program of its kind intended for use *without any* supervision of a psychologist. Despite this, Colby was quick to reassure the rest of his wide and various field that he was trying to create a complementary alternative to human-to-human care, not displace altogether human therapists who were already treating patients. By the 1990s, Colby was not interested in contesting that Overcoming Depression was a computer simulation or an imitation of a human therapist—instead he thought the program "represents a new and unique type of conversational participant with its own style, assets, and shortcomings."[124] Despite carefully identifying what the program wasn't, Colby could not say precisely what it *was*. Instead, Colby presented his program as technology that bypassed the human therapist only as a byproduct of its ability to "make an end-run" around the stigma associated with being depressed and with seeking treatment for that condition.[125]

For all the alarming numbers of depressed persons without care, Colby's NIMH funding was cut (while he was working on the PARRY program); he claimed that the loss of his NIMH funding was a significant factor in why his projects like PARRY, Overcoming Depression, and other experiments in computer-based therapy weren't succeeding to their full technical and social potential: there were institutional obstacles. He writes, "A field competes with rival fads and fashions. In my own experience, it has been very difficult to obtain funding in this area from government sources. I think the ultimate funding will come from the private sector when it realizes how much money can be made from conversing computers."[126] This is partially what happened for the Colbys: Julian Simon, the economist, who was at the same time chronicling his own depression in the book *Good Mood*, stepped in and began funding Colby's experiments with modeling and treating depression.[127] Secondarily, once the program was complete it was bought and used by the US Navy, returning the final product to the US government.[128]

The early 1990s saw other experiments with automated, unsupervised therapies. Joseph Weintraub had begun to write his "PC Therapist" programs under the auspices of Thinking Software in 1986. PC Therapist III won the first Loebner Prize (and other versions subsequently won the second and third) awarded by the Boston Computer Museum—a competition in which programs were entered in an attempt to pass the Turing Test. Eight computer programs were entered into competition alongside two humans. They communicated through modems to ten judges. Five of the ten thought PC Therapist was one of the humans. It featured a 70,000-word vocabulary, or almost twice that of Overcoming Depression's "Dr. Software"—and came with a new feature: it learned everything that a user typed into the program, so it gradually personalized its responses while its vocabulary and ability to understand statements were ever increasing. It not only learned from interacting with its user but also remembered everything the user "spoke" about, recording it to an ASCII Text File, "REPORT.TXT." Weintraub thought this made PC Therapist a useful companion beyond therapy as such. He suggested copying the file "into your favorite word processor. You can delete the Therapist's part of the conversation, or use it if you prefer."[129] The computer-therapist was keeping an automated diary for its patient.

Despite the successes in *making* cognitive computer-based therapy programs in the 1990s,[130] clinical tests showed mixed results. Some studies showed that computer-based CBT had the same positive outcomes in treating depression as human-delivered CBT.[131] Others showed that patients paired with humans had a lower rate of depressive symptoms on many scales, including the Beck Depression Inventory.[132] In fact, patients paired with computer-therapists fared no better than those in the control group—that is, those patients not receiving any therapy at all. The programs were successful as conversational agents and diary-keepers, as potentially enjoyable experiences of auto-intimacy, but perhaps not as therapists. And yet, these software programs were developed explicitly to do therapy: each contains a set of therapeutic lessons in keeping with CBT's treatment model. Perhaps the conversations between user and program were getting in the way of an evidently successful treatment protocol.

Despite this, it seems that the Colbys, Weintraub, and Gould were *attached* to offering a conversational component, even though it was one of the more difficult elements of such software to program. They were intent on preserving a dialogue between user and something else, rather than delivering an obviously auto-intimate therapeutic experience in keeping with the workbook. A dialogic, therapeutic conversation is traditionally human-to-human; traditional auto-intimate activity is also human-to-human where the self is at both ends of the dyadic therapeutic connection afforded by the auto-intimate medium (diary, workbook). Talking with a computer strategically obscures the auto-intimacy of these exchanges and treatments, presenting the program's responsiveness as though it constitutes a human other. The dialogue as therapeutic contact keeps the user-patient from feeling alone with a human-therapist (and all the problems entailed in that) and alone with themselves.

FRICTIONLESS FEELING

Nearly thirty years after Overcoming Depression and PC Therapist III, we are still nowhere near a fully functioning simulation of a therapist that can treat humans. There is no bot that can seriously challenge the work of a human therapist; these digital algorithmic efforts do not constitute therapy proper, especially in terms of measures like therapeutic alliance. However, many of these apps and bots do claim that they can reduce instances and markers of anxiety and depression. Nonetheless, research has not slowed on the goal of elaborating an automated mental health care provider. Some of this experimentation follows from the unintended promise of ELIZA and in Colby's early footsteps: to make a fully automated therapy that simulates a human, passes the Turing Test, and is enjoyable to use. A site of therapeutic work that doesn't feel like work is helpful but frictionless in a way that working with a human therapist definitionally cannot be.

Moving beyond the architectures of ELIZA and SHRINK, these automated therapies include diagnostic software that listens to the pitch, timbre, and cadence of speech to detect mental states. More frequently, as computer-assisted therapy becomes Internet-delivered and goes mobile, conversation fades out and other interactive models come to the fore. These programs continue to refine self-delivered CBT online and on mobile apps for specific conditions (depression, anxiety, alcoholism). Similar to these programs, other software automates the self-tracking aspects of a diary such that the self is quantified into interpretable data. This can compromise privacy in ways we're already acquainted with: one's therapeutic data can be sold, hacked, and used against one in the future when trying to purchase health insurance.

The first group of these contemporary teletherapy technologies maintains the elusive human-presenting automated therapist. Ellie is one such example, generated at the Institute for Creative Technologies at the University of Southern California and is one of the byproducts of The Defense Advanced Research Projects Agency's (DARPA) Detection and Computational Analysis of Psychological Signals (DCAPS) project being developed there.[133] Ellie is a diagnostic system contained within an avatar of an ambiguously raced professional woman sitting in a large therapist's chair. "She" seems confident but approachable. When one user says he's from Los Angeles, Ellie responds sweetly, "Oh! I'm from L.A. myself."[134] Behind this early small talk, Ellie is already performing a deep analysis on her user. She is equipped with sensors and a webcam that detect the affect in speech,[135] postures, and gestures, and she can perform facial expression recognition and "sentiment analysis" of the content of the user's words, which she then compares to a control and military database. All of these data provide Ellie with feedback that allows her to estimate the prevalence of, in the case of this user, depression. For instance, those with depression don't pronounce their vowels in the same way nondepressed people do because they move their facial muscles less. Ellie counts every single instance of this kind of indicator while also modeling "facial expression" and "posture and gesture" synthesis that allows her to speak with users in an optimal manner.[136] This results in "automatic contingent empathetic feedback." Jonathan Gratch of ICT says of Ellie that "research shows that people actually disclose more to this kind of technology than they might when they're talking to strangers. . . . Then what we've also found is that there are crisis points and there are points when people want human contact. As long as you can integrate that into automated systems . . . people want to interact with machines in certain settings and they want to interact with people in others."[137] Gratch thinks that Ellie is attractive because she provides complex customization without judgment—even as she's performing a four-point quantified analysis on your person. Ellie's nonhumanness allows users to know that even if she's deeply reading and analyzing them, she cannot judge, she can only respond.

Upon Ellie's debut in 2015, Louis-Philippe Morecy said in an interview with the *Guardian*, "The best analogy I give people is the blood test. When a human doctor has questions about the symptoms of a patient, he/she will order a test of a blood sample. These results will help with the diagnosis of the illness. Ellie is there to help gather and analyze an 'interaction sample.'"[138] Ellie, much like SHRINK, is not supposed to replace the human therapist. Instead, Ellie is supposed to lessen the stigma of being seen by a human therapist, increase accessibility, and lower the fee of such a therapist, while reporting to one. Ellie is a diagnostic tool—and one that exists at the opposite end of self-diagnosis via the webpages of the Mayo Clinic and WebMD—but in both cases the final diagnosis of a patient and the identification of a treatment plan are still in the hands of a human psychiatrist or psychologist.[139]

Another such example of a fully automated therapist is X2.AI Inc.'s "Tess."[140] Tess doesn't have an avatar—she is a just phone number accessible "where the patient already is, and just a text message away."[141] Tess doesn't report to supervising psychiatrists except in cases where a patient uses a set of trigger words (that indicate suicidal ideation, unlawful intent, or that the patient is currently being harmed by another).[142] Tess is a self-contained therapy sold to companies on a sliding scale based on implementation: $50 dollars per user as an initial cost, and then $1 a month per user.[143] Michael Rauws, CEO of X2AI, introduces Tess with three facts: (1) one in four people are affected by mental illness every year and the main reason they don't seek treatment is treatment cost; (2) there is an annual productivity loss of $30 billion from depression alone; (3) Obama's passage of the Affordable Care Act has left the American mental health care system unprepared for the increase of patients it will receive due to the decrease in out-of-pocket costs for mental health care. He concludes, "This is the problem we're solving." Except—Tess's patients are all employed by companies big enough, profitable enough, already inclined to sponsor a wellness package that includes automated therapy, and that have employees who see therapy offered both by their employer and via app as enticing, an Internet 2.0 Silicon Valley start-up style perk rather than a form of surveillance and intrusion.[144]

Apart from automated therapists, with and without avatars, there is a second category of contemporary digital mental health care: online CBT programs. These programs feature screen-by-screen, step-by-step, guided therapies accessible via either mobile phone or computer. Some of these programs include iHelp, Overcome Social Anxiety, Thinking Patterns, and

Self-Help for Anxiety Management. iHelp's computer program is provided by COBALT and supported by the Mental Health Association of New York (MHA-NY) to New Yorkers who were affected by Superstorm Sandy in 2012. It can be accessed via computer or via the workstations sponsored by MHA-NY in communities affected by the storm (Staten Island and the Rockaways). The program offers five courses of particularized CBT therapy for five separate complaints that most commonly affect those who have been through a disaster, available in both Spanish and English: trouble sleeping, depression ("feeling down"), anxiety, OCD, and drug and alcohol abuse. One can sign up online, text to enroll, or speak with a human counselor to get started—24/7. iHelp tracks users across their work sessions and offers questionnaires so that users can track their progress. Importantly, clients can access the treatment on their own schedules when they have the inclination or the time to manage their mental health. Fred Muench calls this the dispensing (and auto-administration) of "the digital dose."[145]

Other companies combine the services of online talk-therapy (see chapter 5) with self-guided computer and mobile-delivered CBT. This second group's admixture of mobile programming and distanced human-provided therapy is the hybrid automated therapy as Colby thought it would be practiced: the human and the automated serving as adjuncts to one another, purportedly driving costs down and removing social and cultural obstacles to seeking care such that anyone with a smartphone or computer could be engaged in some version of therapeutic activity. Google's Wysa blends the human and algorithmic. Wysa, which boasts 1,700,000 users and has conducted over 100 million conversations, bills itself as a companion, a mental health friend, and takes as its avatar an adorable penguin. It also offers human-to-human texting alongside the chatbot program, coming over the same channel. There is a slippage between bot texting and human-to-human texting—the interfaces *look* the same and are supposed to render a seamless transition in either direction possible, without calling attention to it.

everbliss (now defunct) was a purely video chat-enabled therapy application that promised to connect patients to the right therapist: "Find the right practitioner. Connect instantly. Private and confidential."[146] But that connection was handled and brokered via algorithm. Uli Cohen, a cofounder of everbliss (who previously worked on "messaging and engagement" for brands like Nike, Ace Hotel, Prabal Gurung, and MySpace), argues that there are great merits to combining algorithmic and human interaction: "in the weight of your answers, their frequency, against depression, against stress, weighted by an algorithm, and then [matched] with a therapist who has a percentage in areas of expertise XYZ. A person doesn't have to *know* that they're depressed: the algorithm determines it. The quiz is supposed to feel like a self-curious consultation—a consultation with the self, via algorithm. The job of the technology is to match what the patient needs to the expertise of the therapist. It translates between two languages."[147] The two languages are an algorithmic code, and the privacy of the self—the technology fosters, according to Cohen, an auto-intimacy turned outward.

Joyable is another concierge digital mental health service that combines a sixty-second quiz to generate an emotional profile of the user, with five-minute automated cognitive activities and human "coaching" as opposed to therapy.[148] "Joyable" is "enjoyable" minus the en-; it turns "joy" into an auto-intimate activity (which it can be grammatically but usually isn't, especially without the en-) while still presenting as adjective. The name blends the *pleasure* of auto-intimate therapy with the *aim* of such therapy (decreasing depression, increasing "well-being"). It thus strategically confuses the means and ends of user experience while, true to its neoliberal framing, linking the health of an employee to productivity rather than framing it as an important end in itself.

Joyable is sold not only to individuals who seek mental health care but also to companies who pay for it and include it in their employees' benefits package—the advertising is targeted to companies, not individuals, with the tagline "Happier Employees, Better Outcomes." Whereas DARPA's funding of Ellie and New York City buying the iHelp program to take care of Superstorm Sandy survivors are moments where teletherapy addresses overt crisis (the returning veteran, the wake of a natural disaster), Joyable addresses itself to the emotional crisis that labor is. Again, part of the choice to buy into a digital program has to do with Colby's early notion of making therapy nearly costless by automating the same therapy for all, at once, with a single program: a universalized auto-intimacy.

As Luke Stark writes, "Contemporary modes of self-help and self-improvement, ranging from clinical CBT therapy workbooks to smartphone-based digital applications, mix an emphasis on numerical quantification with an ordinal of rationality, clarity and self-fashioning that Ellis would recognize as stemming from REBT."[149] I would add that they also have continuity with the divergent works of Weizenbaum, Slack, and Colby, who revealed by their experiments (in successes, failures, and their surprise at both outcomes) that *enjoyability* is intrinsic to intimacy with a nonhuman other because it is a way of being intimate with the self—even, or especially, if that self-intimacy is mediated by a digital penguin. A recent study performed by the UK National Health Service tracked a number of factors including "reliable recovery" and "finishing a course of a treatment" in patients suffering from depression and demonstrated that this class of application is 58.4 percent effective compared to 53.9 percent for traditional psychotherapy and a 44.1 percent rate for *in-person* CBT.[150]

Part of enjoying contemporary automated therapy is the "gamification" of mental health care. As Ian Bogost writes in his provocative essay "Gamification is Bullshit," the gamification of "everything" has political and economic implications:

> Gamification is marketing bullshit. . . .
>
> Bullshitters are many things, but they are not stupid. The rhetorical power of the word "gamification" is enormous, and it does precisely what the bullshitters want: it takes games—a mysterious, magical, powerful medium that has captured the attention of millions of people—and it makes them accessible in the context of contemporary business.[151]

Not only is mental health care its own industry (whether the self-employed therapist, psychiatric wards, or technology companies) and mental illness bad for all business, as Tess's CEO notes, but mental health care apps are being sold to businesses promising to help workers in the service of profit. Joyable's advertising states, "Therapy only works if your employees use it. We get them to use it." How? Partially through the gamification of mental health care. The apps have translated Ellis's and Beck's worksheets into games (which are called activities), achievements, and checklists. They have harnessed the potential pleasure of auto-intimate self-therapy in order to make employees healthier in mind (other elements of corporate wellness packages take care of the body). Interactivity doesn't mean interacting with another; it means playing, and playing in order to become productive.

Self-tracking moods across days and the events that bring them on is another popular contemporary form of self-guided mental health care app. Examples include Mindshift, Moods, Moodtrack Diary, Optimism (now defunct), iMood Journal, Emoods Bipolar Mood Tracker, and the aptly named Cognitive Diary CBT Self-Help. These applications all follow the same premise: that one can track one's own recovery from mental health issues. Natasha Schull writes of these many choices of self-tracking application, "The selves of self-tracking are understood, by those invested in wearable technology, to be *choosing* subjects; more precisely, they are construed as consumers whose well-being depends on and derives from the market choices they make. . . . Individuals are urged to shape their lives through choice in the manner of savvy, ever vigilant entrepreneurs and yet, more often than not, lack the knowledge, foresight, or recourses to navigate the abundance of potential choices they face."[152] Only Emoods Bipolar Mood Tracker follows specific bipolar symptoms (alongside sleep and energy levels) as well as psychiatric medicine compliance, including the taking of the correct dosage of medication and filling prescriptions (partnered with CVS). Many of the app forms of self-care delivery are available for free—"all you need is a smartphone with a data plan." Others offer a free version and an "upgraded version" for a one-time or recurring fee ($1.99, $4.99)—and iTunes or GooglePlay automates your monthly billing.

Of the kinds of data gathering, interpretation, and selfhood that these applications variously provide, Schull writes:

> This supplemental insight into being, suggest[s] that the transposition of big-data epistemologies to the scale of the individual affords "a sort of fourth-person perspective" on the self and, ultimately, a new kind of truth—one that is "not possible with ordinary senses" in that it does not correspond to a phenomenological self (temporally and spatially located) but to a database self whose truth lies in scattered points, associations and dynamic accretions.[153]

This fourth-person perspective is that of the diary, except now the diary is automated and proactive, able to alert its keeper to what it knows, holds, contains, and transmits. Both the fourth-person perspective and the qualitative self are encouraged by handing over one's personal data and using self-tracking applications. Quantification and qualification are not either/or propositions. Instead of the analogue journal championed by Ellis, cognitive behavioral therapists recommend these apps to their clients as a complement to their services, though the apps can also be used on their own. "Stigma," designed to address and undo its own name, is a mood tracker and diary that connects a user to "pen pals" who suffer from the same mental health conditions; as does "Koko," an automated form of group therapy with no attending psychologist. It crowd-sources responses to users from other users—but has a learning algorithm in place to oversee responses and detect who is most direly in need of help.[154] Although many think the users of these programs would be those who couldn't make use of traditional therapy or would be unwilling to, others' worry about telemental health is that these cheap (or free), easy, self-guided programs don't only reach those who otherwise wouldn't go to traditional therapy, but those who would: this convenient alternative may keep them from traditional therapeutic practice because it is more expedient and comfortable, perhaps even morale-building, to coach one's self back to health in the privacy of one's own home.

THE THIRD THING

Our contemporary moment maintains a division between the human and the computer-mediated; between the qualified self—engaged by hermeneutics of the self and an archeology of the subject—and the quantified self—engaged in counting, data collection, prediction. This is too neat a division. The convergence of human-to-human interaction and algorithmic-human interaction is so extensive that these ways of understanding and making the subject overlap and inform each other. This is true too of contemporary teletherapeutic interventions. I've argued that intimacy, whether accomplished relationally (as is the case with psychodynamic therapies) or via auto-intimacy (seen in the desire to know and care, often pleasurably, for one's self), drives the impulse to mediate therapy so that the communication of care can go further in time, space, and method than what two bodies in a soundproofed office can do.

So far, contemporary (human-to-human) teletherapies have moved remote care away from its previous forms as ad hoc, volunteer, or individually offered therapeutic help over the phone or on the computer toward new proprietary platform app-based offerings. Companies that host these teletherapeutic interactions, like Talkspace and Betterhelp, purport to offer access to therapists who wouldn't be available otherwise, and more conveniently than the traditional embodied alternative. These therapies are at once celebrated for democratizing mental health care by expanding the reach of providers into communities without experts, praised for their ability to make therapy convenient to many, derided for degrading clinical norms, and described as a symptom of the general devaluation of contemporary in-person and human-to-human relations. In parallel, contemporary artificial therapies, also most frequently delivered via smartphone app, offer gratifying, organizing self-regulation that encourages auto-intimacy. Therapies that only offer symptom reduction for issues like sleeplessness and anxiety may soon find themselves outmoded: devices like Thync, a consumer health tool that is wearable and which provides neurostimulation to help its owners sleep and relax better, provides a way around any therapy-based symptom reduction. But neither CBT in-person, online, nor the future of wearable technology purports to achieve psychic work. This tension is part of the longstanding battle between psychodynamic therapy and CBT. Psychodynamic and relational therapies may have lost to CBT statistically but they aren't obsolete, precisely because they aren't automatable. Or at least, not yet. As I was finishing the first draft of this book, it was announced that DARPA now can hook a computer directly to the brain of its user and have the computer read the thoughts of the person with whom it is linked.[155] We are now able in effect to produce a rudimentary machine-human "thought transference," bringing us full circle to Freud's early fascination with telepathy as a viable form of communication (see chapter 1) and Turing's worry about telepathic interference. Since Freud, there has always been a patient, a therapist, and a linking medium between them, whether the embodied voice and therapeutic frame, the letter, the hotline, chat, text, program, or Zoom. The flexibility of therapy in terms of its communicative medium has historically allowed media and technology to look like the most disposable terms when they are the least disposable, or just as indispensable as the patient. Where flexibility looks like peripherality or choice—what matters is the treatment, not whether it's by letter or phone or computer—it's the other way around: flexibility shows media's indispensable presence. No one medium is essential, but mediation is. The notion of a therapeutic dyad has always been bad math; therapy relies on a therapeutic triad, all of whose terms save the patient are reconfigurable and only one of whose two human terms is essential. The history of automated therapies, in their evolving successes and failures, alongside the triumph of CBT over other kinds of relational psychotherapy, demonstrates something crucial: in this ancient triad the most disposable element is not the medium through which the therapy is communicated, but the human therapist.

Mental Health Cyber-Clinic

started - November, 1995

David I. Sommers, Ph.D.

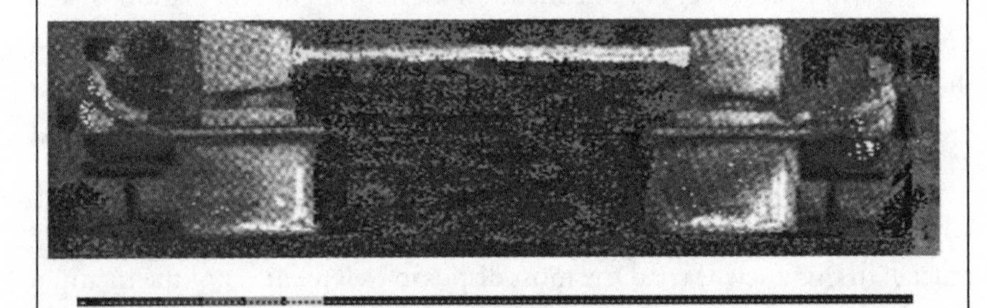

Figure 5.1
Landing page for David Sommers's Mental Health Cyber-Clinic, The Internet Archive.

5 WRITTEN SPEECH

Dear Uncle Ezra:
WHERE IS THE BRIDGE THAT EVERYONE JUMPS OFF OF
I AM CONSIDERING IT MYSELF.[1]

* * *

In 1986, a Cornell-affiliated person (presumed to be a student) walked up to a cuinfo terminal and wrote the above message to a new, digitally based therapeutic service. cuinfo, Cornell's campus-wide information system, was newly accessible through networked terminals located around campus, in six or seven libraries, in computer centers where students would go to turn in their punch cards, and in the administration building.[2] It usually had some twenty items on it: library and bus schedules, the headlines of *The Cornell Chronicle*, department phone numbers, and the like.[3] In the week prior, an additional item had been added: "Ask Uncle Ezra." The name Ezra was chosen after Cornell's founder; "Uncle" signaled that the person on the other end of the communication was an adult who would provide unthreatening, nonparental yet intimate help with no hint of the clinical. Created by Dr. Jerry Feist, a psychologist, and Steve Worona, a computer scientist, both employed by the university, Ask Uncle Ezra was an "electronic counseling service"[4] and the first anonymous online messaging forum to be run by a therapist and to have therapeutic intent. Having selected Ask Uncle Ezra, a student (or staff member) could decide to read prior questions and their answers or to ask their own. cuinfo, which had a log-in screen but did not associate the ID with usage, granted anonymity. It was programmed to send all questions through Cornell's mail system to Worona, who then forwarded them on to Dr. Feist.

Worona, who had received only a few questions in the first week the service was active, had a "heart-stopping" reaction to this suicidal message (and thirty years later is still able to recite it).[5] Even though it was a possible prank or an example of exploiting the service, Worona recalls that he phoned Feist immediately to tell him that Ezra had received a disturbing question and that he was unsure if the service should answer it; he was concerned about liability. Dr. Feist responded, "I get those [questions] over the phone, on paper slips, from students sitting across the desk from me, that's my job. Let's answer it."[6] Within an hour, after Worona cleared the decision with his boss, a reply came from Uncle Ezra.

* * *

Dear Considering,
Most people, at one time or another, consider suicide as an answer to their problems. As Ann Landers says, suicide doesn't solve problems, it only passes them on from you to the survivors—family, friends, loved ones, and other people who care about you.

Suicide is usually an attempt to deal with a crisis. The Chinese character for "crisis" translates into "dangerous opportunity." Suicide is a permanent solution, and eliminates other options. So if you're hurting so much that you are willing to pass the pain on to those who care, perhaps you could use this dangerous opportunity to try some other options first.

Ithaca and Cornell have a number of services specifically to help people in crisis. Call Suicide Prevention any time at 272–1616, go to Psychological Services in Gannett Health Center (255–5208), talk with a chaplain in CURW (118 Annabel Taylor Hall, 255–4214), talk with a friend, and use this opportunity to change your life for the better. Problems have solutions. Your life has value. Please give it a chance.

Uncle Ezra[7]

* * *

Mental health crises translated not only into a dangerous opportunity for Ezra's students, but also for the world of mediated therapy. By the fall of 1995, Metanoia.org (which termed itself a landing page for "The ABCs of Internet Therapy") had a list of three hundred private practice e-therapists and cyber-clinics representing an additional five hundred e-therapists working in a number of modalities, including CBT, a generalized counseling model, and psychodynamic therapy.[8] In 1996, California was the first state to legislate around telemedicine and in particular teletherapy, in the 1996 Telemedicine Development Act under Business and Professions Code § 2290.5. It defined telehealth as the use of "'interactive' audio, video, or data communications." The act recognizes teletherapy as "a *real* alternative form of care" (emphasis added), especially for consumers facing economic barriers to treatment, seeking therapy in rural areas underserved by therapists, and with language differences that act as a barrier to traditional care (for example, in 1996 only five licensed therapists in the state of California spoke Thai).[9] Yet at the same time, the e-therapy of the mid-1990s had its limitations (access to services as well as technological, legal, and security issues) and therapists were keenly aware of them. David Sommers, an early e-therapy pioneer, openly wrote about these limits on his Mental Health Cyber-Clinic website and the future of therapeutic interactions online:

> I am well aware that many will scoff at the idea that real mental health care can be provided here at all. I respect that skepticism and would not argue strongly with it at this time. But I really do think that within the next 10–20 years something like what I offer here will be more generally accepted as a real alternative form of care for some people, some of the time. It may take workers more sophisticated and imaginative than I to make this happen and one goal of this site is to encourage others to think about the possibilities raised here.[10]

In the 1990s, the term "real" is continually used in reference to teletherapy—and can be read as a response to skepticism that mediation is unreal, virtual, and lesser. Twenty years later, e-therapy, now generally called teletherapy, is a mode of doing therapy offered in private practices and by companies over proprietary software. It is a more accepted, clinically studied, further legislated, and growing field.[11] Users can now access therapeutic sessions not only from home or work on their computers but also from their smartphones. Alongside the advances in video conferencing platforms (better speeds, a camera more closely approximating eye contact), the shift from phone cameras facing out to facing in, and the pervasive Internet-enabled audiovisual telephone have allowed people to acclimate to talking to their screens: video conferencing's screen-to-screen conversation is now "good enough," and mobile enough, that the therapeutic consulting "room" truly can be anywhere a phone can catch and maintain a signal or Wi-Fi connection. In this chapter, I will trace the emergence and spread of e-therapy, its decorum, and its potential intimacies while considering how e-therapy interacts with wider technological shifts in communication from the late 1980s to our contemporary period.

MAKING EZRA

Worona and Feist's service was predicated on mail (RFC 524). Worona first interacted with Feist when Worona was going around to departments, trying to get new entries to put on cuinfo (which had been in use since 1982). Feist supplied a list of all the mental health services on campus to be digitized, but Worona reported to Feist that the database was almost never referenced. The two then decided to make a service anonymous for both user and provider that would allow students to ask mental health questions. Worona provided the programming and Feist supplied, in his own words, the "therapeutic voice."[12]

Despite crafting Ezra as a networked, textual entity possessed of such a "voice," Feist and Worona were decidedly offering a form of written help to a closed community of users and readers. Users transmitted a form of pre-email e-letter following the conventions of epistolary contact ("Dear Ezra") and received one in return. Ask Uncle Ezra was doubly anonymous—just as Feist and Worona couldn't track their users, no one on campus writing into Ezra knew who "he" was either.[13] Users were identified by handles of their own choosing, following in the convention of the advice column (even in Feist's response to the suicidal student, he mentions Ann Landers).

Like the advice column, the letters were not private nor were they meant to be. Instead, they were published digitally, accessible only to readers through the same terminals on which one could contact Ezra, but cached and available at all times to curious third parties. This openness served two ends. Firstly, just as in the traditional print advice column, persons other than those writing in could "read in." The titillation of eavesdropping is even greater in a closed community help forum and thus holds entertainment value. Scrolling through Ask Uncle Ezra provides amusement alongside mental health knowledge; not all of the questions answered were as dire as the one answered above (e.g., "Why do whales sneeze?").[14] Worona and Feist even put out two volumes of transcripts as *The Best of Ask Uncle Ezra*. Secondly, Feist considered this built-in feature of welcomed overhearing one of the benefits of doing counseling over Cornell's network. Listening in to other users' exchanges functioned as a form of unintimidating group care and catharsis (much like the format of the call-in radio show and its effects, see chapter 2). Beyond seeking advice directly from Ezra, users could find past questions and their answers that spoke directly to their situation (for instance, a number of students wrote in to a particular question about body issues, having found the answer useful, while also offering words of encouragement for the original poster).[15] Instead of being contained in a dialogic one-to-one frame, users had the additional benefit of writing to one another—while being monitored and moderated by Worona and Feist. Various users had different reactions to this invited engagement with what traditionally would have been a private, one-to-one interaction. One student began typing an urgent message about depression and social isolation in Caps Lock, only to cut themselves off because someone was watching them type out their query into the cuinfo terminal. The student then resumed the message, apologizing to Ezra for the interruption, stating that they were being watched and then felt embarrassed.[16] Being "overheard," or *over-seen*, was understood to be different from submitting the same message to be viewed in a community forum hours later.

Almost as soon as it appeared on terminals across campus, Uncle Ezra, unlike the traditional mental health services on offer, became immensely popular. Some students even began to communicate with one another, and with Feist, over a series of questions—extending what Ezra offered into an ongoing conversation instead of a single interactive instance of query and reply. Initially, because the service was accessible exclusively through terminals on Cornell's campus, certain questions about liability surrounding *distance* mental health work (if licensure translated to Internet-based communication or could be transferred out of state) weren't raised—they would be later, when the service went live on the World Wide Web. That is, this original distance between provider and user was known to be quite small and was contained by the service's reach. Instead, other questions about what kind of care to offer and how to provide it centered on what to do when the clinician cannot know who the patient is. Worona's instinct not to answer Ask Uncle Ezra's first suicidal note was in part due to the scripted anonymity of the service; he only had a backstop key that allowed him to see *which* terminal was used but not by whom. Worona's exchange with Feist demonstrates that it is thinkable that inaction might be safer, legally and perhaps even ethically, under these conditions. Though Feist decided that answering an electronic suicidal message was no different than answering that question via anonymous or embodied messages sent through other media, the question about whether or not to engage the suicide threat also stands in for other concerns about doing therapy digitally: Is it possible to help someone when only providing written, asynchronous care, and you don't know for whom you're caring?

Mental health services that rely on double anonymity predate digital forms of help (in the form of the advice column and suicide/crisis hotlines) but networked and Internet therapies re-raise medium-specific questions about the managed production of distanced intimacy. Services like Ezra spread to many other campuses by 1991: Columbia ran a program called "Ask Alice"; MIT hosted "Lucy"; The University of Minnesota offered "Uncle Eddy"; Appalachian State University provided "Uncle Sigmund."[17] While Ezra's model spread to many schools, many others decided hosting such a service wasn't worth the risk; Worona recalls that Princeton tried to make such an electronic platform for helping students but that it was blocked by counsel, precisely because of the possibility of suicidal students using it.[18] From the provider end, as in the Uncle Ezra suicide note, there is something newly troubling about a tele-patient seeking that particular kind of crisis help digitally, even when the client must be quite physically proximate. Though asynchronous help is in part what grants the service anonymity, Uncle Ezra had the disadvantage of intervening quickly, but not instantaneously, in a moment of crisis. Crisis, especially suicidal ideation, is a *momentary* feeling. It can dissipate as quickly as it can reform to be felt. Ezra performed care in a poly-temporal mode; one reasonable fear about asynchronicity and crisis intervention is that the provider receives a record of only the past version of the user but intervenes in a present moment and with no guarantee that the user will return to see the advice dispensed. The provider's necessarily delayed response to a past state of the user creates for both sides an imagined temporal composite of the agents in the therapeutic relationship. This differs greatly from both the suicide hotline (callers can make use of the service *exactly* at the moment in which they are experiencing suicidal ideation) and traditional appointment-based therapy (patients and therapists are together when they speak and possibly but not necessarily at the moment of crisis). In the case of the Ezra suicidal note, the client could even already be dead. For users of Ezra, there was no expectation that their question would be answered immediately or with a version of immediacy. It was decidedly not a suicide hotline gone digital—it was networked anonymous advice.

Yet users trusted and turned to Ask Uncle Ezra and its clones on other campuses, perhaps because of its rare pairing of double anonymity with institutional recognition and affiliation. One material reason for this was that "Uncle Ezra never sends bills";[19] the fee traditionally associated with expertise had gone absent along with the in-person meeting, folded into Cornell tuition. Another reason was that Ezra was always on, ever readable, and thus existed as a reliable writing cure whether or not Feist was available to respond right away. Multiple students closed their posts to Ezra with a version of, "Don't bother answering this, Unc, I feel better just writing it all down."[20] Though asynchronous and thus not continuously responsive, Ezra existed around the clock and therefore students had both the cache of previous Ezra answers and a potential for response which combined to offer a constant, continuous repository for their feelings. And, of course, a helpful peer could also be awake at the library after hours, ready with lay guidance.

In addition, Worona ventured that Ezra offered "the ultimate in clinical detachment."[21] Not only was the service doubly anonymous and framed as a friendly uncle dispensing psychological advice, the temporal distance of two people (or more) working together over the network offers a form of help with no obvious indication of a clinical gaze. Ezra is stripped of the ability to diagnose or psychiatrically intervene with a patient and conveys a curious, nonjudgmental stance, promising that a user will be treated as a full person rather than reduced to a particular pathology. This dovetails with what Dr. John Grohol, another early e-therapy pioneer (and the person who coined that term), calls the "Online Disinhibition Effect" or, the "phenomenon that prompts people to say and do things in cyberspace that they wouldn't do in real life."[22] The concept of the Online Disinhibition Effect presupposes that in-person psychodynamic treatments normatively contain inhibition and resistance (in which the patient feels unable to speak what fully comes to mind and to make maximal use of the work); these barriers are a quotidian fact of embodied therapy. By extension, because of the ways in which networked computing mediates the experience of therapy, a patient can proceed without a name, without feeling judged, without having to negotiate many intimidating features of the therapeutic frame (e.g., referrals, fee scales, appointments, or the painful [and fixed] interval between needing help and receiving it) and may feel differently licensed to "say" whatever comes to mind. Of course, there are patients who are deeply disinhibited off-line: patients who rupture the frame, call repeatedly, or even stalk their clinicians, as well as clinicians who violate the frame and boundaries of their patients and profession (for more on this see the introduction and chapter 3). But Grohol argues that electronic forms of therapy mitigate some of the discomfort of being a patient and liberate clients who otherwise would be hampered in-person into productive therapeutic communication by disinhibiting their "voice," or what I call their therapeutic *written speech*.

THE "SOUL" ONLINE

For early would-be users of e-therapy outside a closed academic setting and its network, the very act of finding help was more difficult and meant trusting providers who might themselves choose to be anonymous and without institutional affiliation. Martha Ainsworth, who had no clinical background, was one such e-therapy patient as well as an early provider of peer-to-peer emotional support online. Beginning in 1983, Ainsworth led peer-to-peer support groups through "online villages" and other forms of virtual community.[23] She communicated with those in despair and noticed that

> an alarming number of people admit online to . . . suicidal feelings that they would have been embarrassed to acknowledge in person, even to a professional counselor. . . . I encountered more and more wounded souls who, freed by the anonymity of online communication, poured forth a seemingly bottomless well of pain. As a compassionate listener, I did the best I could to help, but felt hopelessly inadequate, lacking professional skills and training.[24]

Some thirteen years later, trained professionals began to make their clinical services available online. By 1995, Ainsworth writes that she too was a "wounded soul" seeking professional psychological help. Though she began her search for a therapist to meet in-person, she quickly decided that she wanted to meet the person "here" where "here" meant "now" and "now" meant online. In "My Life as an E-Patient," Ainsworth's self-case study—an instance of a genre sorely lacking in examples and perhaps the only one in existence of a teletherapy (other than what remains of Freud's correspondence with Fliess, see chapter 1)—she details the difficult search for a reputable and helpful mental health care provider who was willing to work, or already working, online. Most of what was on offer was psychological "advice," much like Ask Uncle Ezra, as though expertise had to disappear or contract when the embodied therapist did. Psychotherapists would answer questions for free or a small fee rather than engage in an open-ended treatment. Ainsworth didn't have a single, particularized question—she had overwhelming feelings she wanted to sort out, over time, in an asynchronous, disembodied dialogue. Other websites promised a more ongoing exchange but asked that the patient give over their home address and credit card information. Eventually, Ainsworth clicked her way to a page with the banner: "WELCOME TO THE MENTAL HEALTH CYBER-CLINIC."[25]

Though Ainsworth doesn't name the specific psychotherapist who provided her help over this website, it belongs to David Sommers, PhD.[26] Sommers's therapeutic voice was not unlike Ezra's—"informal, but professional."[27] Ainsworth found a therapist who was interested in "ongoing dialogue," and presented e-therapy as a form of mental health work that still occurred between an "I" and a "You"; the first-second person pairing helped to presence the relationship even before it began. Further, Sommers was a competent and experienced therapist (he had trained under Albert Ellis, a pioneer of cognitive behavioral therapy, and ran a clinic with 650 patients and 25 staff members in Washington DC, in addition to having a private practice—and now is employed by the National Institute for Mental Health) who also understood the Internet and online connection.[28]

For Sommers, e-therapy was an experiment aimed at augmenting how many people he could help; when asked the main impetus for going online to "see" patients" he responded, "We will never have enough providers."[29] When Sommers opened his cyber-clinic in 1995, the tide had turned away from placing the "mentally ill" in asylums and other live-in treatment centers, yet government support for the Community Mental Health Care Act and its outpatient clinics had dwindled.[30] Sommers worried about the effects of the privatization of mental health care and specifically its resulting unavailability to working class and poor patients.[31] He set his fee at $100 for a month of daily e-therapeutic contact. Despite this fee schedule, he reports that he made roughly $300 for all his thousands of hours treating patients online and ended up almost entirely consulting with patients for free. Though Sommers acknowledges that uneven access to computers and the Internet—especially in 1995—necessarily made it difficult to reach patients who could not economically afford therapy, he claims that he reached many patients who could not otherwise attend therapy. He stated that e-therapy, or "*helping dialogue* or *interactive therapeutic consultation*," would appeal to a particular subset of patients, including those that faced economic barriers to in-person psychotherapy, those who were worried about the intimacy in a traditional therapeutic relationship and therefore were drawn to a treatment underpinned by what I call *distanced intimacy*, those patients who were having a difficult time finding a good referral for a therapist near them and/or lived in rural areas in which therapists were not readily accessible, patients with disabilities that made going or getting to a consulting room too difficult, and patients curious about entering a traditional therapeutic arrangement but wanting first a sense of what that relationship and its work might be like.[32] Other patients who might make use of online therapy included those for whom scheduling due to work hours was impossible or patients like Ainsworth, for whom there was a clear preference for consulting online rather than in the consulting room.

Sommers's Cyber-Clinic hosted many of the same features proper to an initial consultation in the traditional in-room scenario. Sommers provided a certification for his licensure and his identity along with a full copy of his CV. He provided a detailed "Read Me" on the ethics and legality of seeking treatment online. Sommers also imported all psychotherapeutic conventions surrounding confidentiality but could not guarantee it, as email can be monitored. He writes, "Unless you have reason to think that your email is being monitored I believe that our communications are probably at least as secure, and are no more vulnerable to being intruded upon, than traditional telephone conversations."[33] Yet that risk wasn't necessarily small: in 1993 only 5 million households had an Internet connection, with that number reaching 45 million by 2000.[34] Personal computing often meant sharing with other persons—and in the case of "Ezra," the service was based around that assumption). For one-to-one e-therapies where correspondence comprises the entirety of the treatment, email insecurity is more problematic in that it can limit what patients feel comfortable sharing; the famous Online Disinhibition Effect can coexist with a re-inhibition effect. Email, can of course, be intruded upon without being "monitored" per se—by a partner or child on a shared home computer or cached information on a public or work computer, much like Freud's letters were an assumed private form that was constantly being perforated and accessed by others (see chapter 1). When the price of personal computing dropped in the mid-1990s, this enabled some families to move from using a shared computer in the living room to private, personal computing in the office or bedroom, perhaps again enhancing the feeling of security.[35]

Sommers was also careful to mark the limits of psychotherapeutic confidentiality—the very same limits that legislate in-person therapy. These include any therapist's role as mandated reporter when told of abuse to children, elderly, or disabled persons, or if the client aims to harm themselves or others. Sommers says this standard will be difficult "but not impossible" to adhere to.[36] The difficulty here is reporting that an action has taken or will take place when you might not even know whom you're treating. For instance, Martha Ainsworth didn't provide her first name in her intake form and didn't provide her last name until several exchanges had passed between provider and client.[37] As Sommers points out, it makes some of the ethical standards of the American Psychological Association for in-person treatment difficult (and often impossible) to uphold or transfer to the e-therapeutic scenario.

Privacy, confidentiality, and the corresponding notion of self-protective anonymity or malicious misrepresentation were looming concerns for early e-therapy patients and providers alike. As the *New York Times* worried after the "invasion" of e-therapy in 1997, "Many reliable practitioners in the industry are concerned about the cyber-counseling practice because it brings up issues of legitimacy, confidentiality and authentication—i.e., how do you know that the person with whom you're corresponding is really who he or she claims to be? . . . Deciphering the credentials of Internet practitioners can be a difficult task."[38] Copycatting credentialed therapists' websites was also a source of anxiety; one client wrote to Sommers asking, "How can you prevent someone from lifting your site and impersonating you?"[39] If one of the benefits of e-therapy is a prescribed distance from the therapist, one of its pitfalls for lay users is never quite knowing how secure one's communications are or to whom one is talking. In one-to-one therapies with licensed clinicians, concern over how to *really know* with whom one was "speaking" can be great. Yet, as with the provider-client relationship on peer-support hotlines, or even the human-computer relationship featured in auto-intimate computational therapies, anonymity is coded into the interaction as a positive feature of the care.

ANONYMOUS THERAPY

Cyber-therapy was far from homogeneous—even if it was predominantly conducted anonymously. It was on offer in public group chats both supervised and unsupervised by experts, peer-support forums in which written messages were exchanged, and back-channel therapeutic treatment between a single therapist and a single client. The worry about anonymity is differently managed and mitigated on the many online message boards and group chat rooms dedicated to particular disorders and illnesses that rely on peer-to-peer counseling and/or peer-advocacy.[40] In these interactive spaces, conventions allow users to just go by their anonymous handles—or to ask for one another's "A/S/L" (age/sex/location).[41] Questions of whether interactions were *supposed* to be anonymous and whether anonymity was beneficial (or not), were tied to larger, shifting conventions of anonymity online,[42] whether or not the client was paying for that treatment (anecdotally, it seems that billing was never conducted for services that occurred anonymously) and what kind of service was being offered.

Other services were not about therapeutic interaction but about the circulation of information. Dr. John Grohol conducted much of his work semi-anonymously, and all for free. After his best friend committed suicide, Grohol himself turned to the Internet to help make sense of his loss and founded a peer support group, *alt.support.depression* on Usenet.[43] Grohol began indexing mental health resources online in 1991—including the first digitization of the DSM, eventually collecting this data under the website "Psych Central: John Grohol's Mental Health Page" in 1995, which has now hosted over 250 different group chats and support groups. In the mid-1990s, his weekly therapeutic advice chat had up to fifty regular users asking questions at any given time, each with a nonidentifying handle—including Grohol himself (he went by DocJohn—so users who were referred through Psych Central might know who he was, but others would not).[44]

We can contrast the anonymity of the caller over the telephone (mediated voice) and the anonymity of the user of e-therapy via "written speech"; in the latter case anonymity is marked by a visible written fact, the username. This means (a) that anonymity itself has a name (or that a username indexes anonymity as well as particularity) and (b) that that fact then organically sponsors creativity and mutation (the development of a decorum) over time, as people invent "handles" that both protect and announce themselves and the handles themselves acquire conventions that change over time. As the poet John Ashbery writes near the end of his most famous poem, "Self-Portrait in a Convex Mirror," the hand that's extended is offered both "as shield or greeting / The shield of a greeting."[45] Handles allow anonymity as a protective feature of the individual online self and allow the name to contain all of the productive distanced intimacy of the teletherapeutic connection—the "username" is literally the sign of distanced intimacy, not just of anonymity (although anonymity is central to this form of intimacy).

RICH INFORMATION

Even when a single patient "met" with a provider, names could remain withheld as well. In Sommers' therapeutic model, even before learning his patient's name, he would collect a great deal of personal information. Once a prospective patient agreed with his terms and conditions of service, the patient could access the intake form to begin treatment. To begin, the patient provided an email address (instead of a name), which itself could be an expressive but protective form of pseudonym. The form then proceeded to ask a number of preliminary questions, some with dropdown menus (including, "Where do you think your readiness to change level is"; "How much education have you completed"; "Which of the following options describes your current [employment] situation?"; "Which of the following best describes your experience(s) with psychotherapy?"; "Which of the following options describes any current symptoms you may have been having?"); other questions had text boxes for the patient to answer at length ("In the text box below please elaborate on any symptoms you're experiencing in 1–2 brief paragraphs. How long have you had these symptoms, describe their severity, etc."; "Please tell me what **you think** 'the problem' is in 1–2 brief paragraphs. What is your sense of the source of your pain?"; "Please tell me what attracted you to this site and what you would like help with. How did you get here and now that you have found the site how can I help?").[46] This comprises a very detailed intake, offered not to a person, in person, but on a form sent to a previously uncontacted digital other. When Ainsworth recounts filling out this form, she recalls her hesitation about "reveal[ing] intimate details about myself to a total stranger."[47] She was both desperate for the help promised by Sommers and "wanted to protect" herself from sending private information through a form, above which appeared in red, "Please be aware that this form is not currently handled via a secure server."[48] Yet she, and all of Sommers' other patients, proceeded. Even on the intake form, patients were beginning an e-therapeutic exchange through Sommers' framing deployment of "I" and "You" and an invitation to immediately begin the work of auto-writing the patient's own experience. Sommers established a building dialogue from a single form—or as Ainsworth puts it in reverse, "We had already had our first session, and the therapist didn't even know it yet."[49] The digital dyad had already formed, on the grounds of its underacknowledged third term: the distanced intimacy of the medium.

Sommers had an IBM PC, which he found "very erratic," and determined that email worked best for providing his form of Internet therapy—though he was not averse to performing a therapy across multimedia (combining phone with email). Sommers was committed to dialogue and this commitment separated him from other practitioners of early e-therapy who were more likely to restrict contact to a turn-based "asked and answered" format, whether privately or publicly, much like Feist and Worona's Ezra. Though the loss of the voice and visual cues from patients made email "less rich" for therapeutic contact, Sommers still believed it could form the "backbone of very powerful dialogue."[50] He also preferred it for other material reasons. If online, patients tended to have easy access to email but not necessarily to a bandwidth that could support video chat or Internet phone, although he would sometimes make use of Cisco Unified Communications Manager Express (or CUCME, an early video chat program)—it was always set up with the patient as an experiment and often worked poorly, glitching or cutting out altogether in the middle of a session.[51] Sometimes, Sommers would use Internet Relay Chat (IRC) services, which "worked fine over modem," but scheduling was, again, the main difficulty in setting up a synchronous therapeutic session given that the patients had selected a form of treatment that accommodated "meeting" separately; email therapy—much like Freud's letters or Ask Uncle

Ezra—allowed for detailed dialogue despite its asynchronicity.[52] It also allowed both provider and client to select the timing of interaction, which has effects on privacy (reading email at home instead of chatting at work) and readiness for the work.

After receiving the intake form, Sommers would move to a backchannel correspondence and, in most cases, learn the first name of the patient, generate the aims of the treatment, duration, frequency, and set the fee, if any. Ainsworth received a response the day after submitting her intake form; Sommers wrote a long email, with "mostly questions to start . . . as I need to know you better, and you need to know me too. . . . Let's try to keep the dialogue going so that not too much time elapses between our emails. Is telephone therapy a possibility? Can I have at least a first name? I hope to hear from you soon."[53] In the next email Ainsworth, sounding reminiscent of Ashbery, writes that because the therapy was taking place "through the anonymity shield of cyberspace" she was free to tell him "everything": distanced intimacy licensed her ability to share therapeutic content. She closed her email with her thoughts about Sommers's proposition on switching the therapy to the phone by writing, "I write better than I talk. . . . I'm not quite ready for the telephone. I'm really not good at talking on the phone, it makes me very self-conscious. Can we just keep writing? . . . I envision e-mail as a potential lifeline."[54] Ainsworth is not alone in finding telephonic interaction difficult or too intimate. Therapy, or any spoken interaction, had an inhibition effect; moved online, the written version of that interaction was potentially a lifesaver.

Voicing therapeutic content can feel too dangerous, but what that voicing would contain—speech—is necessary. Sherry Turkle's famous remark that "our networked life allows us to hide from each other, even as we are tethered to each other. We'd rather text than talk" is meant to describe a widespread social ill in the advent of pervasive digital communication.[55] Ainsworth is anecdotal evidence for the opposite being true as well. When we apply Turkle's observation to digital therapy, we might find that we're less therapeutically *resistant* to text than talk and that ease can allow different users to access various forms of text-based therapy, rather than traditional talk therapy. The intimacy attributed to the voice, even that occurring over distance via the phone, can produce an unfounded but real feeling of closeness, suggest a lack of anonymity even where it obtains, and make for a more difficult entry and exit from the scene of care since the voice carries more channels for expressive communication for which the caller is responsible (timbre, pace of delivery, the sharing of conversational space). "Intimacy," which can be both the thing that patients and practitioners work to produce and that patients may want to avoid, is also another name for what Sommers calls the flow of "rich" information. Patients may choose the online medium because it allows them to restrict and determine on how many planes of communication they richly express and transmit symptomaticity. Written therapeutic content, whether that of Freud and Fliess's letters or Ainsworth and Sommers's emails, might be better than synchronous, in-person encounters for undoing one's own resistance but also for hiding the traces of that resistance. The self-censorship of writing is different than that of speech; deleting and editing at the level of content and form can be hidden from the recipient and therefore make it more possible to present the self to the other with these elements withheld.

As with the crisis hotline and computational therapy, e-therapy in some ways offers a patient more control over their own treatment. The patient can email the therapist at any hour, with any kind of content, and can seek out several streams of online help (a one-to-one therapy alongside message boards, peer-support groups, private chat rooms devoted to particular symptoms or issues) and, much like the "frequent fliers" of hotlines, can use more than one of these forms at the same time. Sommers found that a patient's "written expressivity," or their ability to describe their state in a written form, was a determining factor in whether or not a client could make use of e-therapeutic treatment.[56] Drawing on William Schofield's predictive acronym for indicators that a patient is best suited to make use of therapy, YAVIS (young, attractive, verbal, intuitive, sensitive), Sommers found that these last three, VIS (verbal, intuitive, sensitive), logically made it easier to treat someone over written communication than if they had, for example, difficulty verbalizing their experiences or emotions.[57] Further, he claims that introverts tend to be better at telecommunicating than extroverts.[58] Whereas not all patients understood how to use video conferencing or chat relay programs, they either already knew how to make therapeutically relevant and effective emails (despite email's novelty as a form) or could be instructed to do so.[59] Sommers's website featured opinions on the current mental health care landscape, the problems and opportunities of teletherapy, his intake form, and a page on which he monitored the statistical breakdown of usage of his services; but he also offered several links for his clients on learning particular features of email writing and "netiquette" more generally as they pertained to how patients might most benefit from therapy that relied on email as its only source of communication. While Sommers knew that many of his e-patients came to e-therapy instead of seeking out traditional arrangements because they "weren't ready" for communicating over the phone, let alone in person, emails themselves had to be contactful and give the therapist a picture of how the patient was actually feeling; like letters, the emails had to presence both therapist and patient.

WRITTEN SPEECH

In 1901, some seven decades before the emergence of digital mail and online chatrooms, Freud wrote, "He that has eyes to see and ears to hear may convince himself that no mortal can keep a secret. If his lips are silent he chatters with his fingertips."[60] I return to Freud here because he makes secret-keeping, or telling, non-medium specific (it can be done with the larynx, tongue, and mouth in speech, and by hand in "tells," or in writing). The transition from spoken therapy to e-therapy, whether performed over email or Internet Relay Chat, relies on what I call *therapeutic written speech*. I take written speech to mean a kind of personal digital writing, occurring via computer-mediated communication, to a specific other or group of others, in which habits of talking overtake those of writing (even as they are represented and contained by written text) to presence those between whom conversation is taking place. Written speech is not static and has changed in its conventions over the course of e-therapy's moment (which extends to our contemporary), including its linguistic features, the role of the voice (including speech to text translation and speech recognition software), material presentation (orthography, punctuation, the use of the vernacular, acronyms), and its mediatic sites.

In the same moment as Ask Uncle Ezra made its appearance, Walter Ong was investigating the implications of digitality for his theorizations in *Orality and Literacy*. He suggests that there might be something beyond primary and secondary orality (which occurs after literacy is internalized). He begins by defining the presence of orality against written communication: "Oral communication is all immediate, in the present. Writing, chirographic or typed, on the other hand, comes out of the past. Even if you write a memo to yourself, when you refer to it, it's a memo which you wrote a few minutes ago, or maybe two weeks ago."[61] Eliding this difference was a major task of the epistolary presencing of the nineteenth century; not only was it important to convene being together via the collapse of spatial distance, one also had to collapse time. Ong continues:

> But on a computer network, the recipient can receive what is communicated with no such interval. Although it is not exactly the same as oral communication, the network message from one person to another or others is very rapid and can in effect be in the present. Computerized communication can thus suggest the immediate experience of direct sound. I believe that is why computerized verbalization has been assimilated to secondary "orality," even when it comes not in oral-aural format but through the eye, and thus is not directly oral at all. Here textualized verbal exchange registers psychologically as having the temporal immediacy of oral exchange. To handle such technologizing of the textualized word, I have tried occasionally to introduce the term "secondary literacy." We are not considering here the production of sounded words on the computer, which of course are even more readily assimilated to "secondary orality."[62]

Secondary literacy is orality through the eye, predicated on the collapse of time between the sending of a message and its potential reception. For Ong, secondary literacy implies immediacy. I argue that secondary literacy registers more than just the lessening of time between the written and the read; it's a shift in the medium through which speech is offered and received: from the spoken to the typed and read. *Written speech* is a primary form of tele-presencing the self for the other over distance. Without the performative and forced presencing conventions of the late nineteenth century, new forms of presencing the self for the other take over in the late twentieth century. By indicating speech instead of writing, the written exchanges between tele-patients and their tele-clinicians retain much of the information that would be provided by speaking to and from the couch or speaking on the phone.

Therapeutic written speech takes its place in a genealogy anchored by Freud's treatment of himself with Wilhelm Fliess and of Little Hans over distance via post. Freud's cases asked the question: can therapy be done without hearing the other's voice? The answer was and remains yes, if any trace of the speaking subject is taken to be the literal, material voice.[63] Freud, via his own postal analysis and that of Little Hans, showed that even written therapy is performed with conventions of speech carried via a voice still intact in the hand or the fingertips, generating somatic idiosyncrasies of writing hand and productive errors and parapraxes while operating outside the medium of vocal utterance. E-therapy revamps this tele-presencing of the other where they are not. It is enacted via conventions that move to disregard the specificity of the medium and technology being used to do presencing by importing the conventions of another medium. In the case of written speech, written text becomes filled with conventions that belong to vocal utterance while diminishing the conventions proper to writing. Whether in the 1890s or the 1990s, the importation and performance of those conventions can be learned and executed while appearing as if unstudied and informal, and thus present as an authentic communication.

NETIQUETTE

In the case of written speech, digital text becomes filled with conventions that belong to voiced speech while shifting the conventions proper to digital writing. In 1997, the *New York Times* asked Alec Gore, an online counselor, how he could possibly get a sense of a patient through email without ever seeing them in person. He responded that he writes a request to his patients: "Take your time to choose words so that you will express how you really feel. If you've written in an informal, conversational style I will get a feel for you more easily. I can hear what you're saying; see what you mean."[64] Even here, Gore shifts from deploying verbs that denote a written interaction to those that imply an embodied, sonic and sighted interaction (*feel, hear, see, conversational*), modeling for his patient the possibility of acting *as if* one has had an in-person meeting via email. I would argue that this asynchronicity in which a user can "take one's time to choose words" is precisely what allows for the carefully written selection of and by a casual self, for whom therapy can succeed online.

The mutually supported fantasy of an embodied dialogue is not merely maintained by writing decorum—as when Freud writes to Fliess that he has "a good hour to chat" in the body of a letter when he intends to write a long one—but presents as a formal feature of both asynchronous and synchronous digital therapy laid out programmatically in the technology; that technicality then further influences the content filling it.[65] As an example, Ask Uncle Ezra allowed users to create new questions (i.e., initiate a conversation) and then Worona and Feist would link an answer to the question, creating an asked and answered format where the whole of the correspondence was available to the eye at the same moment, even as it unfolded asynchronously. Email threads, too, perform this dialogic instantaneity as a convenience of formatting. In e-therapy, one can have many dialogues, each on a specific topic, separated by subject headings, or a single dialogue in which the entirety of the treatment is available in one chain. In Seth T. Ross's digital netiquette manual, he includes an introduction to electronic email's properties and functions, including its difference from telephony. He writes, "In some ways email has more in common with phone discussion than with paper memos, which are traditionally more formal in tone. Because email communications are written, they can be much more detailed than a phone conversation. And they're delivered almost instantaneously, rather than overnight. So colleagues or friends can have a long "conversation"—with a written record of what they said—over the course of a day."[66] Gone, too, is the moment in which Freud could burn all of Fliess's letters—instead all parties, including the public in some cases, have a record of what was jointly "said" (in our contemporary, therapists report anecdotally that patients bring smartphones into the consulting room to read these exchanges on email or text into the record of treatment).

Gore's instruction to prospective patients to write informally and conversationally joins with Ong's notion that "computerized communication can . . . suggest the immediate experience of direct sound."[67] Mara Mills, in revisiting Robert Hopper's definition of a telephone conversation ("vocal immediacy across distances"), wonders if telephony paradoxically succeeded in devaluing the live voice function we take as the primary use for the telephone itself. She writes, "Old slow-moving 'talk' is being rapidly pushed aside by its faster cousin 'communication.'"[68] Written modes of communicative immediacy (or semi-immediacy, in the form of email) have revivified conventions of talk from other forms of communication, if not supplanted them.

The introduction of traces of speech in writing comes at the expense of traces of writing in writing. Written speech departs from my analysis of epistolary conventions in Freud's moment in its degradation of formal features and conventions particular to other written texts (i.e., the handwritten letter) in order to indicate that "speech" is occurring. Early networked speech has its own presencing conventions and different forms (asynchronous email and synchronous IRC) have their own properties. Naomi Baron and David Crystal, among others, argue that email is a "mixed modality" lying somewhere between speech and writing, containing formal features of both.[69] In the American context, this notion is attended by a set of conservative linguistic arguments that computer-mediated communication is contributing to the degradation of both spoken and written English, as well as demands for plural and World Englishes to be more widely recognized.[70]

Ask Uncle Ezra is digital writing and a form of networked help. It's well on its way to being therapeutic written speech—but it isn't quite there yet. For instance, Feist and Worona edited the comments *only* for punctuation and capitalization. As Baron argues, "Because electronically-mediated language is fairly new, its users are still in the process of settling upon conventions that ostensibly will become the new rules to be followed or broken."[71] They decided that the speech designated by "Ezra" would retain a modicum of written decorum and impose that decorum on its users; Ask Uncle Ezra has properties of the advice column but they are hybridized by the medium-specific aims of e-therapeutic dialogue. Feist and Worona made one deliberate exception to their editorial rule: caps lock.[72] Caps lock was left unaltered, as in the suicide note considered above. Feist and Worona left such choices alone when typographical or grammatical styles were understood to contain meaning that bore on the mental state of the person asking for help, especially if presenting suicidal ideation and planning. That respect for expressive or symptomatic presentation is the first movement toward this aspect of written speech: something seemingly incommensurate with "proper" text becomes essential to a new form of communicative writing. In the case of caps lock, uppercase typing is understood to mean a person is "shouting"; many netiquette manuals caution against it precisely for that reason. A person who is "shouting" over email or in a forum like Ask Uncle Ezra may have an expressive ignorance of netiquette, the person may be technically unwitting, or might be intentionally contravening netiquette in order to shout. Further, having a typographic case that indicates shouting means that there is a typographic case that indicates a normal speaking volume, which means all cases have associated volumes, however implicit: even sentence case—and then later, lowercase—becomes an indicator of the presence of written speech. Volume control is an important expressive feature for doing e-therapy; patients are not universally and consistently monotone nor are they monopitch.[73] Ainsworth, in a two-part communication with her therapist, is able to demonstrate anger through caps lock and also uses asterisks for emphasis ("Now I *am* angry"). Later, she writes, "I'm sorry I yelled at you earlier" in reference to the previous email.[74] It was understood that her writing, not the voice, had successfully communicated an angry tone and the phantom decibels of a loud volume.

Digital writing contains conventions designed to presence oral communication through the attenuation of written language, including initialisms, acronyms, abbreviations, new spellings, and new ways of utilizing (or eliding) punctuation marks. Helen Petrie calls these linguistic signatures "emailisms," and notes that women are more likely to use them in the service of discussing emotions and relationships, a basic currency of therapeutic exchange.[75] These new conventions enrich not only the cultures that obtain through the media that invite written speech but also what written speech itself can carry and signify (although not all such linguistic developments work to further digital written speech: new syntactic features in some chatspeak/slang and leetspeak [a coded internet language in which letters are replaced by numbers] aren't meant to convey or contain features of spoken analogic conversation). The work of altering, modifying, adapting, and refining new ways of doing digital "speaking" began on message boards (Usenet) and IRC, then pervaded email (and later, text messaging).[76] Even the word for this activity, "chatting," imports a model of casual, somewhat aimless, relational speech into the synchronous or asynchronous written form. Informality is a palpable formal feature of written speech and, for therapeutic purposes, can be content-rich. Such informalizing linguistic traits of written speech are often the same ones used to lament the impoverishment of communication, but these formal features are indispensable for doing therapeutic work over email.

Abbreviating words to a single letter, number, or sign, for instance, generates speed on both ends, emphasizing the nearly real-time capacities of the communicative medium. Examples of this kind of writing include *U*, *R*, *C*, *4*, and @, which also permit a faster assimilation of sound through the eye (and later, the ability to fit into SMS character limits, see more below). Other new terms are not only about expedience but in addition contain a return of other sonic and visual features of conversation and emotional states. These include "LOL" or "lol," either as an initialism (where each letter is sounded such that it's read/pronounced L-O-L) or acronym (LOL) which can be used to let the other know a humorous comment has landed or to comment sarcastically on something said above, and "^^," which indicates a frustrated eye roll. This kind of textual informality is used in peer-to-peer chat rooms, on message boards, and in individual back channel therapy occurring by IRC, and has particularities associated with the gender and age of the user.[77]

E-therapists depended on this kind of digital presencing for doing effective and affectively viable therapeutic work online. As Gary Stofle notes, many of the clinicians writing on e-therapy have "stated emphatically that therapy is impossible online because of the lack of nonverbalness. . . . A chat room therapist cannot compare what the client says against his or her body movements, dress, voice inflection, and degree of tenseness or relaxation."[78] Stofle suggests that while the absence of "nonverbals" is a problem, a compensatory category of presencing the self appears as what he calls "nontextuals" and affects how both clinicians and patients perform self-presentation and presencing online. He takes nontextuals to include the speed at which one types, the frequency of new texts, font and text color choice, and frequency of typos or other grammatical errors. These are cues that signify specificity and intimacy—handwriting for the digital age. Anecdotally, Stofle offers a brief case study in which an e-therapist, after having many chatroom encounters with the same patient, experienced her patient as "not herself" given how she was typing. The therapist began to worry that it was not the patient in the "session" but someone else entirely. Once the patient was confronted, the patient admitted that it was she, but that she had been drinking heavily before the session: she was slurring her typing.[79] The therapist was able to apprehend a shift in their patient just from the patient's nontextuals.

If the content of digital writing helps to presence the other, then material synchronicity or its performance in its absence is the basis for a fantasy of embodied intimacy across distance. E-therapy has the potential (depending on the mode through which it conducts itself) to be asynchronous not only interpersonally but also intrapersonally. Both patient and therapist (or group) can start, stop, restart, and revise any given written communication at any time, much like the epistolary (where it even becomes a way to perform a casual presence). Despite this, we associate therapy—the most intimate revelation of personal history, given over to another to be sorted out and interpreted—with embodied, close acts contained in a particular timeframe. Synchronicity is a major assumption implicit in this category of relation and its longer genealogy, from spiritual confession through psychodynamic therapy. Within a digital therapeutic context, written speech creates a distanced intimacy over discontinuous time—both members of the digital dyad have to wait for response and may wait to finish their own "speech."

This is not to say (or to write) that written speech is a flawless importation of one medium into another, but that its flaws are meaningful. Breaks that occur in vocalized speech (and especially analytic conversation), whether in person or over the phone, can occur where written speech is in use, but these ruptures are medium-specific. The loss of the formal features of paragraph and sentences helps move communications from the realm of written text to written speech. The absence of typographical or spatial organizational termini moves single ideas or a collection of ideas to the invisibility of speech's pauses, which can then be experienced as temporal rather than notational, pertaining to the pacing of a reply (and thus productive of Ong's secondary literacy). This produces a feeling of flowing, "unedited" content, similar to automatic writing. Though this is a feeling and not necessarily a fact of actual practice, it is one way that written speech communicates in a seemingly unstudied manner that authorizes a kind of free exchange for both patient and therapist and therefore allows a recognizable therapy to take place. The gap in time between communications—after the patient has emailed the therapist and is awaiting reply—conveys a kind of thinking pause before interpretation and further discussion.

IRC, text messages, and even emails mix the conventions of the epistolary and spoken conversation that also have inherent dyadic pacing, even though IRC is considered a synchronous medium. While chats demand a certain level of coherence, they also allow for conversation to become fragmented in content and in feeling.[80] Both parties are put in the position of waiting. Over asynchronous email therapy, there is also a worry about content delivery and cohesion (has the patient articulated themself such that the therapist picks up the right aspects of the patient's written speech?) and technological disruption.[81] Whether occurring via IRC or text (and even email, despite its already being an asynchronous form of communication), conversational coherence can be interrupted by two intrusions: lack of simultaneous feedback (which is caused by the reduction of audiovisual cues and the fact that messages appear sequentially and cannot overlap) and "disrupted turn adjacency," when messages that are in response to one another are separated by intervening communications.[82] This is an ever more pressing concern when establishing and engaging in a therapeutic relationship digitally. I argue that aspects of nonverbals, emailisms, and other linguistic functions help to provide simultaneous feedback to the other. Beyond the immediacy of reading *C*, *U*, or the added audiovisual cue of "lol," these linguistic features help computer-mediated communication carry digital conversation so that it "registers psychologically as having the temporal immediacy of oral exchange."[83] Theresa Örnberg Berglund describes disrupted turn adjacency as occurring because "messages do not appear on the screen of the other participant(s) until the writer hits the return key. . . . Other messages will be sent in the meantime, separating related messages from each other."[84] This has been noted as an impactful disruption on therapeutic chat services. Stofle, familiar with this problem from his experience treating clients in chat rooms, claims that disrupted turn adjacency makes therapists and patients alike feel as though a communication breakdown is happening. For example, the therapist has moved onto topic B when the patient actually wants to spend more time on topic A.[85] However, similar to in-room conversations, this lack of conversational cohesion is most common in the early phases of treatment when distanced intimacy is still under construction; after the patient and clinician are sufficiently acquainted with the medium and thus each other's pacing and writing style, it no longer poses a great problem.[86]

Even if secondary literacy and written speech *feel* like they occur immediately and happen with someone both present and presenced, they do not take place in person. For some e-therapy patients, this obvious fact was an important distinction and protection; the patient could have the intimacy needed to get therapeutic help, but not so much intimacy, so much richness of traditional nonverbals, as to make receiving the help unbearable or impossible. Sommers was eventually able to coax Ainsworth into trying to make use of the telephone therapeutically and then after about nine months of email correspondence, Ainsworth met him in his office (and did so about six times over the course of her five-year treatment). In the first meeting, though she felt the same way about her therapist in person as she had over email (he was still warm, caring, concerned), Ainsworth recalls being unable to make use of the therapy in the same way; she was unable to speak freely: "Predictably, when I got home from that visit, all the things that I'd been unable to say in person came out in e-mail."[87] Ainsworth's treatment comprised three kinds of therapeutic contact: traditional in-person visits, telephonic communication, and email; it is now a common feature of even the most traditionally psychoanalytic therapies to include some technologized communication—it is typically called extra-therapeutic contact, another way of maintaining the purity of therapeutic contact as unmediated (additional media are "extra"), and is defined by all purposeful contact occurring outside the consulting room—whether phone sessions while a patient is away, emailing or texting to confirm (or cancel) appointments, or unscheduled crisis calls. Therapists debate the efficacy and role of extra-therapeutic contact in any given case (does it help the patient make better use of the analytic relationship or is it actually boundary disrupting?). Of course, the use of texting and chatting is not just the domain of teletherapies. Our devices aren't only the containers of therapies for some tele-patients but also have a key extra-diegetic role in embodied sessions, becoming an obvious third speaker and purveyor of content (and affect) in the room. Instead of reporting what may have happened outside the room in a session, patients now can use their phones to show rather than tell what has occurred.

In a way, e-therapy reverses the notion of what counts as extra-therapeutic contact; for Ainsworth, meeting in person was extra-therapeutic, because it disrupted the digital setting in which distanced intimacy had been established and cultivated. When she returned to email, she returned to the frame she had sought out and to which she had grown accustomed. Choosing the cyber-clinic over the consulting room indicates Ainsworth's understanding of a more fundamental choice about the medium through which to communicate the self to another: the digitally written versus the spoken.

AFFORDABLE CARE

What for Martha Ainsworth and some therapists was exceptional and uncomfortable has become the norm on contemporary teletherapy platforms; that is, they are by and large multimodal, providing a multiplicity of options for contact (texting or chatting alongside options for voice-to-voice and screen-to-screen) that allow patients who have aversion to particular media for communication to still make use of the service. Although the early 2000s didn't see much development in written or voiced teletherapy, 2010 marked a shift in the availability and the promise of remote treatment. That year the Affordable Care Act was passed, offering access to mental health care where previously uninsured or underinsured clients had none. At the same time, competing models for the iPhone debuted on the market (Samsung, Google, and Microsoft all issued their first smartphone models in 2010).

In the 2010s and into our present, written speech has not gone away. Instead, start-ups (rather than private practice clinicians like Sommers) have extended the use of texting and chatting with therapists, while reincorporating the actual voice, especially in conjunction with video. In Mara Mills's history of the audiovisual telephone she writes, "[b]y reducing speech to a signal and dialogue to message-exchange, by coming to value efficient communication over vocal immediacy, and by extending this 'signal-thinking' to other sensory phenomena, telephony was so successful that it erased the need for voice communication—its very foundation as a medium."[88] Those current teletherapy platforms that focus on video-conferencing therapy mark a return to spoken speech for therapeutic aims, but with a difference: the digital, moving, real-time image. Instead of featuring the affordances of asynchronous communication, as Sommers did, or the privacy of written speech, as Ainsworth did, the reemergence of synchronous therapeutic interaction at distance remediates conventions proper to the in-person, in-room meeting of patient and clinician. The therapeutic frame is imported almost wholesale; the stated aim of these therapies is to be just like the "real thing"—but better. What better means here is open to interpretation. For users like Ainsworth, better means being able to be in a therapeutic treatment at all; for others, better means a frictionless ease and a kind of entertainment located in the therapeutic encounter that some will see as undermining the endeavor entirely. Comfortability and even enjoyability (for more on this, see chapter 4) can now be figured as hallmarks of a good therapeutic match between patient, clinician, and medium.

THE CORPORATE TURN

In pre-pandemic 2020, tele-patients could become clients of online proprietary platforms that offer a wide variety of services, such as Talkspace (primarily a texting therapy), BetterHelp (texting and video conferencing), and 7 Cups (textual help provided via trained volunteer support). Tele-patients can also still turn to the same early forms of e-therapy, including message boards (though these have migrated from Usenet to Reddit and the like) and peer-to-peer chat rooms. Whether continuing in the tradition of written therapy or moving to audiovisual conferencing, these new teletherapies are not merely the domain of teletherapy companies but are used in private practices and generate much discussion (and use) in the wider therapeutic world—even in psychoanalysis.

Because platforms have attracted thousands of users, clinical studies have been conducted on specific platforms to assess their effectivity and bolster the claims of their companies. New video-based platforms for digital therapeutic meetings promise results *better* than in-person therapy, with exchanges beginning more quickly, with more efficiency (no commute time), while easy to access for all (or at least everyone with a smartphone), with referrals done by algorithm or by a matching therapist at the company, and purchasable at a lower fee scale. This persuasive account of new digital therapy argues that help is no longer hard to find, while suppressing the fact that *good* help still may be. Much can go wrong in the traditional therapeutic encounter and, irrespective of the claim that digital therapy is like the "real thing," much can go wrong when clinician and patient meet digitally.

Message exchange as therapeutic conversation has predominantly moved from email to texting used in the mode of IRC, with many of the same conventions. The phone, a messaging technology premised, as Mills notes, on voice communication, encourages streams of written communication conversational in their pacing and sequencing even as its original function for audio calling declines further into disuse.

Many of the habits of written speech described above have been imported into SMS and texting. SMS was slow to be adopted on a wide scale and by the time it was, Internet-based strategies for digital writing communications were more established. This is partially material, pertaining to length of communication. When Friedhelm Hillebrand served as the chairman of the "nonvoice" committee of Global Systems for Mobile Communications in 1985, he set the standard for text messaging, limiting messages to 160 characters per SMS. His rationale for doing so was that postcards and telegrams—almost without exception—ran no more than this magic number. Text messaging can also be reread as an extension of the epistolary and telegraphy. Everything that "needs to be said" in a given message could be compressed to fit this length. The importing of emailisms already in circulation into texting (including shorthand letter words, number words) allowed for this compression to occur more seamlessly and eventually become so refined that a single character, for instance an emoji, can stand in for a full statement. This also works the other way, where texting conventions are now in use over email and chat, which figures into a more wholesale culture of written speech after the mediatic convergence of the smartphone, in which several media for writing are collected in the same place writing has always come from: the hand. Without a literal trace of the hand that writes (at least, until Apple released Digital Touch and Handwriting in iMessage in 2016), typos and other denaturing of written convention help to presence conversants.

Contemporary therapeutic texting and chatting also draw from chat-based "messaging" services aesthetically, iconically, and in interface. Where gchat writes "User X is typing," both iMessage and Facebook Messenger display pulsating ellipses within a thought bubble while a user types. Each marks the real-time production of absent, future speech (and, of course, users can and do decline to send what they were composing—itself a communication). All three of these platforms draw speech bubbles around individual messages once sent, pulling one user's speech to the left and the other to the right. These iconographic decisions further instruct that what these services carry and image is written speech.

At once the most celebrated and most maligned of the concierge teletherapy apps, Talkspace, co-founded by Roni and Oren Frank, operates out of the old Studio 54 building in Hell's Kitchen, New York City. Talkspace has connected more than 350,000 users with licensed therapists who communicate through a text-based chat room that can be accessed from a computer, iPhone, or Android.[89] Talkspace claims that it is "Therapy for All"; its mission is to bring therapy to people who otherwise could not afford it economically or cannot make time for traditional in-person visits, and the service offers patients one-on-one therapy and couples counseling.[90] Talkspace even offers a special therapeutic program for social media dependency, the communication cure for a communication disease; as Naomi Baron points out, online communication permits or even promotes multitasking—one can switch between navigating social media and talking to a therapist about one's overuse in the same moment, on the same device.[91] Prospective Talkspace patients first enter into a confidential "therapy room" with a matching therapist whose stated goal is to learn about the problems the patient wishes to tackle, before proceeding to refer them out to one of more than 100 therapists whose areas of interest align with the goals of the patient. The room's interface is nearly identical to that of iMessage. The only work done to elaborate the presence of the room is calling it one.

Talkspace is clinically effective—but its notion of effectivity is conveniently based on the elevation of specific characteristics of therapy and the devaluation of others. Thomas Hall of Columbia University and Kush Mahan of Talkspace itself ran the single clinical study that declared the service effective. Fifty-seven adults with various disorders were recruited to make use of "a text-based therapy" for fifteen weeks. Symptom reduction was measured via a General Health Questionnaire and the therapeutic alliance was measured via the Working Alliance Questionnaire. The results were that "twenty-five (46%) participants experienced clinically significant symptom remission. Therapeutic alliance scores were lower than those found in traditional treatment settings but still predicted symptom improvement. High levels of satisfaction with text therapy were reported on dimensions of affordability, convenience, and effectiveness. Cost-effectiveness analyses suggest that text therapy is 42.2% the cost of traditional services and offers much reduced wait times."[92] By this logic, efficiency is efficacy. Efficacy is presented as a hybrid of symptom remission, access, and cost effectiveness. Admittedly, the therapeutic alliance, or the dyad, suffers digitally—or at least it suffers over Talkspace's platform and when adhering to its protocols. The findings here understand a psychodynamic intervention that may be less related and intimate, but much cheaper and convenient, to still be viable and effective.

I downloaded Talkspace in an effort to better understand how their teletherapy services were marketed. My auto-ethnographic experience with my matching therapist "Erica" resonated with these clinical findings. Though she stated she wanted to figure out what I wanted to "accomplish" in using Talkspace, the content of her texting was designed to push me swiftly toward signing up for a payment plan and making a "purchase."[93]

After introducing herself, she immediately told me, "individual plans start at $32 per week." The category of patient becomes continuous with that of client and then consumer. Again, this does have similarities to beginning a psychodynamic therapy, in which a fee and a schedule are quickly decided on and a frame is established, even if they are revisited over the course of the treatment. While Talkspace only asks for a "nickname" you use in the room and states that it "stands out because of the affordability, anonymity, and convenience it provides," the first communication I received from the matching therapist was a request to disclose my name and age (she already knew my gender and location). After I stopped responding, I was quickly thereafter sent two messages: "Get LiveTalk Therapy Ultimate" and then:

> $30 OFF your first payment
> Valid for 24 hours only
> Use promo code: BUNDLE30

The messaging had more in common with other digital services than what one might expect from a therapeutic app. Talkspace's payment plans were explained to me in detail but the mechanics of treatment remained vague: a patient-consumer could pay to have a therapist "check in 1–2x a day, 5x a week" or to chat live at specific appointments. For $400 a month, one can purchase "Unlimited Messaging Therapy + Weekly Live Sessions," which grants the user unlimited access to a private "therapy room," check-ins with a therapist two times a day (does that include weekends?), and four 45-minute live video sessions. Given that most private therapies cost $75–$150 for a 45- or 50-minute session (and much higher fees also exist, particularly for psychoanalytic therapy), this is a low-fee treatment in terms of the amount of contact offered for the cost—but the nature of that contact is initially opaque. Perhaps this is why Talkspace's therapeutic alliance scores were low. In its Frequently Asked Questions, Talkspace explains this, again, in detailed vagueness: "Because our therapists are real people who have multiple clients, families, lives, etc. (just like you and me), each therapist is a little different. Usually the therapist will respond once or twice a day."[94] Instead of Talkspace delimiting the frame for all therapeutic couples, it is up to the client and clinician to set their pace for contact.

This contact does not merely comprise written speech or voice-to-voice communication. Talkspace seems very concerned that users enjoy its interface as well as benefit mentally from its services: patients can send unlimited texts no matter which plan they've purchased and, as Erica said, "the fun part is you can also post photos, audio messages and video messages with your unlimited plan." Unlimited actually means unlimited: "Your room is here 24/7, whenever you need it. You do not need to worry about writing too much." Patients can type any volume of new communications, whether or not the treating therapist is in the room, signed on, or due to check in on the patient for days (much like IRC can be on even when the user on the other end has stepped away from the computer). That there might be a "fun part" to therapy at all is debatable (for more on this, see chapter 4); but here it's described as the uploading of various streams of content as though on just another social media platform. Talkspace tries to augment text-based therapy via this "richness" of other kinds of supplementary media, but the accommodation of these media also suggests a recognition that text-based chat therapy might not be sufficient on its own.

The patient-consumer has no ability to know that her treating therapist has read any content until she receives a response, at which point the therapist might just pick up the last remark in the thread or may have read all the messages sent in the interval since the last check-in. There are no read receipts. This mitigates almost every aspect of the therapeutic frame and the therapeutic dyad: a patient can be in therapy, alone. The patient can "hang out" in the consulting "room," alone. One can imagine that for some patients this would be a deeply frustrating experience: is the therapist "hearing" me? On the other hand, it means the therapy is happening all the time, or as much as the patient wants, and therefore the patient might never be frustrated at all. The patient can be an electronic no-show with essentially zero friction; if the patient does not like something the therapist says or does, she can simply select another (this version of treatment termination is described as a menu option: "in the My Account page, in the My Private Rooms section next to Therapist, select 'Change')." Can psychodynamic therapy, and the growth it seeks to promote, actually occur under these (non)conditions? Talkspace argues that, in terms of symptom reduction, it can, but admits that its service is limited in terms of what and whom Talkspace can treat: it cannot treat crisis patients nor can it treat minors. Offering therapy over a digital platform has other unique limitations and risks. In August 2016, psychoanalyst and reporter Todd Essig broke a detailed story about two forms of HIPAA violation. Essig reports, "On August 2, 2016 a now former Talkspace therapist filed a complaint with the Office of Civil Rights of the US Dept. of Health and Human Services alleging a breach of clinical confidentiality. . . . She then told her clients. She cited what appeared to be a routine Talkspace procedure she saw as a threat to their privacy."[95] The therapist resigned from Talkspace, expecting to work two more weeks to end treatment with her patients and assist them in finding new therapists, either online or off. Instead, Talkspace immediately banned that therapist from its platform, giving the patients and clinician no time for any formal closure or termination, notifying the therapist's eighteen patients with all of their email addresses displayed. As Essig puts it, "That's right, in their apparent panic to clean up after what might or might not be more systemic violations of clinical confidentiality, Talkspace broadcast everyone's email. They exposed personally identifying information, exactly the kind of information their expansive marketing campaign promises to protect."[96] Subsequently Frank, Talkspace's CEO, wrote yet another email to the clients. Essig reports that the email, which contained offers of a refund and months of free access, ended, "I am interested in trying to help you be a past, or future, satisfied customer."[97] Essig, a psychoanalyst who writes quite positively about the use of communication technology in the analytic scene, notes that Frank's word choice, as well as her way of "making up" for the breach, puts Talkspace as a corporate entity front and center: refunds and free access distort the frame, as does terminating an employee considered a liability. Further, patients are marked as customers. They're supposed to be "satisfied" as opposed to helped, let alone protected in accordance with medical legislation and the norms of the field.

Talking *now* seems to be at the core of concierge mental health apps and their understandings of teletherapy's place in the mental health market. In a joint phone interview, Cohen and Yoon Kane, a therapist for everbliss (who, after it dissolved, went on to found Mindful Psychotherapy, a boutique teletherapy group in New York City),[98] described to me why they think teletherapy is so compelling now (for more on everbliss, see chapter 4). Cohen argues that humans are losing their availability for the kind of reliably blocked-out time that in-person therapy requires. Because work hours are expanding, Cohen says, "people are more comfortable now doing digital" rather than "blocking out the time. They want to come in weekly but their work hours are insane. But they can do video therapy from the office. The client leads—given a choice, more people are [going] digital."[99] Symptom reduction may be a main goal for these teletherapy platforms, which can be measured and show evidence-based success, whereas therapeutic alliance is subjective even if self-reported tests exist for both. Boasts about Talkspace and everbliss's harmonious relation to the new conditions of work suggest that these companies view their usability as an important metric of success alongside symptom reduction. For such companies and their interfaces, a user is both a patient and a consumer and because of that duality certain features of therapy (e.g., the therapeutic alliance) can be removed or deemphasized while selling a form of care.

One danger of the appification of mental health care is disruption. Not only the possibility that, as was the case with a single therapist leaving Talkspace, one's provider might disappear but that the concierge itself could. This is what happened with everbliss. Its bankruptcy ended not only a company but also concluded the work of endless triads of patients, therapists, and their digital link.

With the growth of teletherapy applications in the last several years, patient-users do have a choice about pursuing traditional in-person therapy or receiving distance services from the convenience of their own office or home. This choice also extends to therapists who may prefer to fill vacant hours in their private practice on an ad hoc basis via platforms like Talkspace and everbliss. In order to prepare therapists to make use of its platform and enter into teletherapeutic relationships, Yoon says that everbliss has its therapists go through a "tele-health training program" that serves as an extra layer of verification and preparation. Therapists spend time learning how to present on video, establish informed consent, navigate the challenges of boundaries and confidentiality, secure other forms of emergency contact (more on this below), and educate patients to make the most of digital therapy and their own boundaries. This includes training therapists to make the frame explicit, even over video: therapists are to keep a work-like environment with a closed door, especially if "meeting" patients at home instead of in the office, and therapists are instructed to show the consulting space to the patient in the first session. Yoon says, "Boundaries are different because you [feel you] have access over video context, they can contact the therapist over social media. There isn't a door that's locked. So everything on the Internet seems accessible. This is true even in the office, person-to-person, but especially over the Internet . . . the boundaries have to be explicit . . . people feel like they have more liberty."[100] This is consistent with the Online Disinhibition Effect John Grohol noticed in his e-therapy work in the 1990s; what allows patients to feel more licensed to speak over the Internet is also what licenses them to create more fungible boundaries across interactive media and their contexts. Even when boundaries are explicit, the mixed use of the media (video chatting socially *and* for therapy) means that patients and therapists alike have difficulty remaining in the professional decorum of eye contact and attention. Yoon admits, "People like to look at themselves . . . people forget that they're not at home, they're at work, over video."[101]

Yet Cohen argues that "therapy is better than no therapy. Period. What we're seeing happen in the United States is mindblowing. USC, they have a waitlist for their student-counseling center two months long. If [a student] call[s] outside of office hours, or cannot be answered, the call is forwarded to campus police."[102] However, all concierge teletherapies seem to have the same set of limits, in terms of what mental states they will treat. As with Talkspace, when asked if anyone, in any state of mind, dealing with any issue, is suited to use everbliss, Cohen states definitively "in emergency situations they [therapists] must refer out. If someone is suicidal, they cannot work with that person. They have all the appropriate numbers."[103] This is also true for victims of domestic violence and sexual assault—they must be referred out, even though these two groups are often underserved by in-person crisis care and could benefit from being able to do therapy at home, without having to make appointments that could draw the attention of their abusers.

Where concierge teletherapies fall short for those in extremis and those under age, teenagers, survivors of sexual assault, people in domestic violence situations or in abusive relationships, and the suicidal still make use of crisis counseling by other means, which is still free and still staffed by volunteer peer counselors (for more on the long history of the suicide hotline, see chapter 3). While voice-enabled suicide hotlines still exist, crisis lines have also moved to the Internet and to texting. Reddit, though a precarious holding environment for those with suicidal ideation, hosts a subreddit r/SuicideWatch, which offers peer support only. There, original posters (OPs) can interact with a community of supporters as well as five volunteers who monitor and moderate the site in order to make sure users are following the guidelines (which forbid "abuse or 'tough love,' including guilt-tripping like 'suicide is selfish,'" "pro-suicide posts," "religious proselytizing," "trolling or incitement to suicide").[104] The guidelines note that the subreddit is not a hotline; the distinguishing factor being that moderators cannot guarantee a timeframe on response or the quality of responses, nor can they track users in order to intervene (but it does offer a database of voice and chat/text hotlines).[105] One such option listed is the Crisis Text Line, which is the first 24/7 crisis intervention hotline to make exclusive use of texting and which is predominantly used by minors. Roughly once a day, Crisis Text Line instigates an active rescue of someone using the service while at imminent risk of suicide (for more about Crisis Text Line, see coda).[106]

PREDICTIVE THERAPY

In 2020, there were over 1,000 startups involved with tele-mental health care.[107] As teletherapy becomes more widespread and more users come online, it runs back into one of its oldest problems: who is performing this labor and to what end? As Sommers emphasized about his own work in the mid-1990s, "Even more central to the work here, is the fact that computer technology and the internet serve as the *medium* for communication, not the provider of services. The provider of services here is alive, *not* a software program or a 'bot.'"[108] Sommers is likely referring to the longer history of automated care that predates the Internet (for more on this history, see chapter 4). Forty years later, tele-health projects are still working to incorporate predictive, automated elements into care alongside human-to human therapies. In corporatized teletherapies, having someone "live" and having the service contain automated elements are no longer opposed and incompatible phenomena: most teletherapies automate some aspects of their care, namely for matching and referrals, often conducted by bots whose responsiveness is so rudimentary as to be comical.

Why use this kind of algorithmic service if the interaction provided is still so "poor"? Or why include the nonhuman in the human-to-human therapeutic arrangement at all? As Isaac Johane, the codirector of the Center for Biomedical Informatics at Harvard recently said in an interview in the *New Yorker* about prediction and automation in teletherapy: "You cannot have accountable care—financially or morally accountable care—if you cannot count, and until recently we literally could not count with any degree of acceptable accuracy. . . . It's been mind-boggling, to those of us who knew what was available, that Amazon and Netflix were creating a far more customized, data-driven, evidence-based experience for their consumers than medicine has."[109] Much like the founders of Talkspace, Johane collapses the categories of patient and consumer, such that the patient and their data become a commodity; accountability to that commodity contracts to the capacity to predict patient outcomes, and counting and monitoring take the place of listening. Predicting patient outcomes, even in its earlier in-person and digital forms, means predetermining who can make use of care and who will be granted access to it, a stance at once reminiscent of Freud's early assertion that only certain classes could make use of specific treatment modalities, and his later prediction that in order to extend the reach of mental health care, clinicians would have to offer a full range of care modalities (see the introduction). Johane calls this kind of predictive medicine accountable care, but it might be the kind of care that very few people *want* to make use of; instead, it's only what's possible or what's available. As a user, being counted, and surveilled in order to be counted, goes against patients' motivations for online treatment in the first place: to access the enabling privacy and intimacy afforded by distance.

Figure C.1
Screenshot of a tele-analysis session. Photograph courtesy Jackie Wang.

CODA: WHEN DISTANCE IS EVERYWHERE

In her work during World War II with her child patient Richard, the same little boy who fantastically imagined continuing his sessions by radio (see chapter 2), Melanie Klein elaborated a scheme through which to theorize the social in the individual and the individual in the social, a formulation she termed "the Hitler inside."[1] For Klein, this meant that there was something in her patients (and perhaps in herself, too) that identified or rhymed with the fascist leader: a murderous, tyrannical internal object (a father, a facet of self, and so on) that was acted on and exacerbated by the external rhyme with the present social landscape. Michal Shapira, in her book *The War Inside,* extends this formulation beyond Hitler to the entire scene of World War II.[2] Starting in 2016, some psychoanalysts have reformulated this as "the Trump inside." In 2020, I would like to think through the social in the individual and the individual in the social via another crucial version of Klein's paradigm: "the medium inside."

What would it do to our conception of teletherapy to think of a medium inside rhyming with our methods of communicating at distance? So many of our fears and complaints about Zoom therapy (and Zoomified life) have to do with the exhaustion it seems to bring on, the metallic, disengaging qualities of the medium. Generally, we also do not treat these qualities as possibly coming from within (countertransferentially). We think of Zoom as material and technological and only as that. This poses a real limit on thinking about how teletherapy—and mediated communication more generally—works on us and works from within us. The medium inside is a less obvious site of identification and revivification. Instead of an identification with say, the murderous Hitler, the medium inside provokes and evokes one's earlier holding environment. If one is at the mercy of feeling dropped because one wasn't held as a child (psychically, not physically, although that too), it will be much harder to withstand the glitch of Zoom (see figure C.1) or the call dropping when one passes out of range of a cellphone tower. Conversely, if one cannot tolerate intimacy, if one was held but in damaging ways, or "smothered" early, perhaps teletherapy will provide a helpful distance, or conversely be felt as too intimate, the therapist now seeing too much inside (not just psychically, but inside one's home).

I am not arguing that the medium inside/outside take precedence over the social inside/outside. Instead, we should think them together. As I've argued throughout this book, the mind sciences in general haven't frequently attended to the media by which they're conducted. As I wrote in the introduction, there's been a resistance to thinking about anything as entering into the therapeutic scenario beyond the two people involved. The move to teletherapy en masse during the pandemic has confronted therapists with a sudden rupture, one that has led to them to consider this "sudden" intrusive third (that, as I argue, has been there in some form all along). But there is also a problem with excessively figuring the medium as the primary source of difficulty in the teletherapeutic encounter. It is, of course, a dynamic: the patient, the clinician, and the medium together producing what they do.

Theorizing the impact of mediation exclusively on the grounds of what I'm calling here a "medium outside" arrests our abilities to think about its deeper psychological effects; it can also arrest our ability to think about other externally occurring events and their role in the internal picture, namely, what it is to be an individual in a society. The mind sciences too frequently privilege the individual and their psyche over and against the social. When therapists say that teletherapy is exhausting, or leaves them as a clinician feeling unable to help their patients, rarely do they yoke those feelings to the broader social sphere (is the exhaustion also coming from the pandemic and what attends various states of lockdown, or does the clinician feel unable to repair the crisis of centuries of white supremacy, or the ways in which they overlap in the current medical landscape?). In thinking about any therapeutic scene, including the scenes of teletherapy, we must be able to work and think across these binaries, turning the levels up and down to listen more clearly as we go.

We can rethink the entire history of teletherapy presented in this book as an effort to modulate and find the right external medium to mediate the medium inside, given what might be to hand and functional at any point in time. Fanon, in his discussion of the radio during the Algerian Revolution, shows us that it's not a question of the perfect medium: that doesn't exist (see chapter 2). Even the best medium will be filled with static, opacities, and interruptions; it may be that the noise allows for signal. For some tele-patients, it may be the secure-enough channel of email that provides just enough distance to approach therapy at all. For others still, it is that traditional scene of in-person therapy that allows for work to begin and to go on.

The traditional therapeutic scene is not currently an option for many. Yet, the early days of the COVID-19 pandemic brought with them a second crisis, a mental health emergency that also touched everyone. Trauma, thought of as belated, can also be preemptive or apprehensive: a suspended state of knowing that loved ones will die, but not who, or of living in fear that one may die, but not yet. And that's only trauma in response to the primary loss caused by COVID or by the doubly historical and present impacts of white supremacy or their intersection—what will happen to bodies—not the psychological havoc that systematic oppression, massive job loss, medical debt, and the isolation of social distancing bring.

Teletherapy has been pointed to as a tool that can intervene, perhaps uniquely, in ameliorating trauma during necessary social distancing. There was widespread support for the switch to teletherapy at almost every level during the early days of the pandemic—from private practice to institutions and policy makers—even as it made many practitioners nervous. By March 19, 2020, four of the Big Five insurance companies—Cigna, Empire, Aetna, and Anthem—had all updated their insurance policies to completely cover teletherapy, including all out-of-pocket costs, for a provisional period until June 4; when that date neared, they extended the new policy, then did so again. Suddenly, talk therapy and CBT were *free* for over

130 million Americans. Critics of teletherapy often focus on the corporate drive to monetize therapy, to make it efficient, over the fact that many more people would make use of some form of teletherapy if it were covered by insurance. If it were affordable. If good practitioners would do it. If it weren't in the hands of corporations. If in general, more people could access therapy. Suddenly, these conditions were partially met—but only partially. Recalling Freud's speech, "Lines of Advance in Psychoanalysis" (see the introduction), in 2020 it was not alloying the gold of psychoanalysis with the copper of hypnosis and suggestion that allowed therapy to go everywhere it was needed: it was silicon.

Everything is tele- and everyone might make use of some therapy as they weather this pandemic and its attendant struggles. Once again, in a moment of crisis, distance is offered as the intervention and the extension that permits treatment to function. Not just in therapies offered via state-run initiatives, by private practices (necessarily) gone digital, and from Silicon Valley startups offering concierge and app-based mental health care delivery; forms of care that go beyond the boundaries of paid attention have emerged and addressed themselves to those in crisis, under crisis conditions. These free forms have included local ad hoc social groups and mutual aid networks, which take on hyperlocal peer-to-peer care, including mental health and coordinated social activities as a bulwark against loneliness.[3] Unlike quite any other moment in the history of teletherapy elaborated in this book (perhaps save World War II London—see chapter 2), COVID-19 essentially mandated distance, so distance becomes the *pharmakon*—at once the disease and the cure.

As the early months of the pandemic unfolded, I interviewed many therapy practitioners from a multitude of backgrounds who had switched over to full tele-practices. One of these workers is a friend, Eric Linsker, who is a social worker and psychotherapist in a group private practice in Brooklyn. He had just started working remotely from his apartment with his partner, who is incidentally also a social worker in a different psychotherapy practice. He texted one morning, between patients, "Running a remote clinic out of our apartment. . . . That keeps us feeling useful." I asked him how *it*, the remoteness, was going. Though he didn't physiologically "love" the screen time, remote therapy was going better than expected. Namely, he had been initially a bit concerned about how to handle work with child patients, with whom he did play therapy, including art therapy.

His dominant tool, in ordinary, pre-pandemic, face-to-face therapy, was the "Squiggle Game." The Squiggle Game is an invention of D. W. Winnicott—the same clinician who took to the airwaves during World War II and was otherwise deeply experimental in terms of how to work with both children and adult patients (see chapter 2). The Squiggle Game is, in essence, drawn free association. It is open ended. Unlike games that ask a child to copy an image or draw a person, the child draws whatever they want. So how was Eric to make that work on Zoom? Well, the Whiteboard feature, he realized. Both callers on Zoom have access to the Whiteboard. It is "supposed" to be used in a business meeting or classroom setting, as it allows for things to be annotated up onto the board. But Eric had realized it was a remediated piece of paper. A kid could draw on it. The therapist could see it. Work could go on.

The ingenuity and creativity my friend showed—and his commitment to reimagining the frame while holding it—was one of the most moving things I indirectly experienced in those first few days. At a moment when the therapeutic frame was massively shifted, he had figured out an adaptation to allow for continuity, for holding, for play. And so did his patients. One autistic child in treatment began to layer the therapeutic environment, sharing their screen, annotating, chatting, undoing and redoing. Of this Eric said, "Undo, redo has become the *fort da* of the digital consulting room."[4]

For other therapists I talked to, working in front of the computer was clearly a negative change and an exhausting one: "Fucking screens can really get oppressive." One analyst started going for walks when talking over the phone, tracking their steps—two forms of digital health merging. Others had questions about privacy—how to protect their own and how to discuss privacy with their patients. Some therapists worried about what platform to use, even though HIPAA compliance was waived for all habitual daily media (FaceTime, Zoom) by mid-March 2020. Because this waiver makes these platforms no more secure—simply protecting therapists from liability—worries then turned to how to communicate about these risks with patients or if these questions should matter at all in a time of extremity (I would argue they do). Others focused on where to hold sessions in the extra-clinical embodied world, most often making do at home. Some did this by practicing from a bathroom. At least one psychoanalyst, Michael Garfinkle, worked with his landlord in New York City to commandeer an empty, half-renovated apartment in his building as a makeshift office space.[5] For others, etiquette or basic conduct was a preoccupation in the move to the digital (who calls whom? is Zoom's "waiting room" too on the nose?).

Some of the clinicians I spoke to wanted to make sure that therapists retained their ability to think in their own modalities, as opposed to becoming merely responsive to discussions of the pandemic. Giuseppe Civiterese, an analyst in private practice in Pavia, Italy, wrote to me early on in the pandemic, when Italian COVID-19 fatalities were multiplying exponentially:

> There's no session where there's no mention of the pandemic. For an analyst the important thing is to remember that if the theatre is on fire, then you have to close the theatre, but if you keep it open, then you have to be able to continue doing your job—that is, listening like a psychoanalyst. The pandemic is not just the pandemic, but as a young colleague from Istanbul told me this morning, the coronavirus is like the powder that the forensic police spread all over the scene of a crime to get the prints out. The collective drama that we are all experiencing highlights everyone's fingerprints in a different way.[6]

Here, too, Civiterese points to the pandemic as not just being the pandemic materially, outside; put another way, the pandemic is happening inside, too. The commitment to the individual in the midst of dramatic collective experience was echoed by other therapists (and not only psychoanalysts) and patients alike, if not always possible. Connie Scozzaro, a professor at Brown (and an analytic patient), wrote to me, "The topic of our conversations has been COVID-19 almost continuously. I feel like she is processing with me too, it can't be helped."[7]

Many of these same people, both patients and practitioners, communicated a shock at the intimacy that teletherapy can convene over and despite distance. Psychoanalysts seemed to be particularly surprised—that there was something *more* intense about having the patient at an ear's distance rather than on the couch. That the patient got, surprisingly, *more* inside. The star of Showtime's *Couples Therapy*, Dr. Orna Guralnick, who works with both individuals and couples in private practice in New York, feels that it is COVID-19 itself, more than working remotely, which has shifted the nature of therapy (and of her television show—which is currently taping its second season, featuring couples in lockdown). She says that while the loss of a space together has been acute, "The work has been surprisingly—shockingly good. People really need the help. And to be in their home with them, and for them to see I'm at home is helpful."[8] Bruce Weitzman, an analyst and MFT in private practice in San Francisco, says, "I feel a closeness that is unusual even for in-person sessions . . . particularly when I use my noise-canceling headset. It often feels as though the patient has been transported into my mind, and my mind into theirs."[9] Therapists think of telecommunication as increasing distance then instantaneously crossing it (to the point where distance turns into increased access bordering on thought transference). That teletherapy could verge on telepathy (much like for Freud and Turing) was remarked on repeatedly; that speech at a distance added rather than subtracted came up again and again.

For those lucky enough to have established relationships with mental health practitioners, the switch to virtual sessions or speaking by phone was a lifeline, though a lifeline requiring major adjustment and presenting real drawbacks. Exhaustion and unease came up for both patients and therapists. While many attributed the exhaustion to the "oppressive screens," others wondered if the *intensification* of intimacy was as much to blame for the burnout and exhaustion that practitioners were reporting—to say nothing of the exhaustion that widespread trauma, disruption, and uncertainty bring to the moment of therapeutic communication.

This exhaustion translates too to the content patients bring into treatment. Guralnick argues that the extremity of all that's unfolding—the shifts in modality, the shifts in intimacy, and the shifts in society have led to exhaustion with the work and with each other: "The heat is on in terms of dynamics. . . . It's extreme couple conditions."[10] While not all of the couples she works with have both members at home full time, and some are essential workers in New York, many are home and are simultaneously dealing with the pressures in their relationships, working full time from home, and homeschooling children.

Therapists that keep a serious boundary between their life and their practice suddenly have had to handle patients seeing the insides of their homes, and vice versa. More than one patient remarked on hearing a therapist's child, cat, parrot, or dog, and being flooded with intense emotion. Some were able to identify this reaction. The activist Hannah Black named it "(my loneliness)," after Black witnessed the analyst have someone else to be copresent with. This unshared isolation more clearly annunciated how alone Black was—and not (as) alone *with* the analyst as previously fantasized.[11] Others were stunned. The essayist and critic Carina del Valle Schorske described years of fantasizing out loud about her analyst, to her analyst, concerning the analyst's status as a single woman, only to one day hear the child of her analyst outside the door where she was holding telesessions.[12] On the analyst's side, Guralnick recounted a patient seeing her child's yearbook in the corner of her Zoom screen, which immediately gave information about schooling choices and their age. Whereas some report these kinds of incursions into privacy as upsetting or unsettling, Guralnick sees them as productive, "Anything that can come in and we can work with, I welcome. I take it as a fun moment as a surprise erupts and we get to follow the thinking there. And often I'm in my patient's bedroom with them, and they're in their pajamas . . . it's intimate!"[13] This literalization of intimacy over distance, in which the patient and analyst can both *see more* than is typical, breaks the frame of any traditional therapy just as much as the inclusion of digital devices does. The move to the digital is often figured as an "impoverishment" of information, a loss of rich data like timbre, body positioning, silence. And there can be a loss: patients are mostly viewed from the shoulders up, if at all. But for patients who play with the placement of their session, and what gets captured (unwittingly or consciously) in the video stream, it can also be too rich, too much—a different kind of rupture. Or, as Guralnick calls it, a surprise eruption, signaling both its destabilizing quality, and its productive nature. Here again, the medium inside and the medium outside are colliding and coalescing.

For some, privacy questions have involved finding a way to keep therapy private at all, and thus usable: how to take a teletherapy call and not have their partner, parent, or child overhear. Sessions were taken in cars, on walks with masks on, at first separately, and then eventually together (recalling that other less-known setting of Freud's—his long walks with his patients). The fantasy of being overheard—a kind of guilt or paranoia and one that is worked on and out in therapy with some frequency—aligns with its validation as a concern in the new reality of teletherapy during lockdown. Other such encounters between the fantastical and concrete were noted enough times to likely be pervasive as well, such as being worried about materially being heard by the therapists—again, not in the fantastical or abstract sense, but in the "can you hear me now?" sense of needing to find a spot with good cell signal. Naturally, these two senses converge: the medium inside could fill patients with a sense of dread or anxiety about being dropped emotionally; the medium outside could break down at just the right moment, exacerbating, augmenting, and interacting with the emotional need to be heard, held, and seen in therapeutic treatment. As Marshall McLuhan argues, "All media are *active* metaphors in their power to translate experience into new forms."[14] We can extend this, and say all media are *active* metaphors in their power to translate old psychical experiences onto new forms, into teletherapeutic encounters.

The interactions are different for those seeking either ongoing therapy or one-off helping encounters for the first time. The situation produced by COVID-19 has called on people on both sides of the dyad to make use of all kinds of media to keep together. In doing so, mental health professionals have drawn on most of the media in the history of teletherapy. The Italian Psychoanalytic Institute opened a hotline, inviting children, adults, families, couples, and—perhaps especially—doctors and nurses to call for psychoanalytic advice and listening.[15] By March 26, 2020, 6,175 mental health professionals had signed up to provide their services for free via telephone in New York State alone. Al-Anon and AA went digital, keeping a space for peer support, but had to confront the tension between the importance of open meetings and what that openness is vulnerable to: Zoom bombers. The Pandemic Check-in Podcast began broadcasting on March 18 over Spotify, out of the Brooklyn Minds Clinic in Brooklyn, taking questions over text and voicemail, both anonymously and named.

Corporate teletherapy companies like Talkspace have used their proprietary platforms to target those without ongoing therapies who were looking to begin during the pandemic. Newly, the major draw (and for some, the drawback) to specifically electing a teletherapy app is essentially neutralized: all therapy is teletherapy for now. Dr. Neil Leibowitz, Chief Medical Officer of Talkspace, reported in early April that he had seen a massive increase in therapists seeking to partner with the app, as well as a 65 percent increase in people seeking therapy. He added, "The majority of clients coming through are nurses. We're also seeing a large number of couples start to come in, as well as clients relating severe loneliness from the isolation, clients feeling stuck and trapped, and a large number of grocery store workers and other miscellaneous retailers struggling with feelings of fear and anxiety about their exposure, bringing it home to their family, coupled with guilt as they grapple with trying to still feel grateful they have a job."[16] Crisis lays bare the market's drive to capture new consumers and users, increasing its niche offerings to target the moment (for more on Talkspace, see chapter 5).

The multiplicity of avenues for receiving and providing care during the crisis of COVID-19 recalls all the other crises that have rendered teletherapy temporarily prominent: Freud demanding mental health care for all at the close of World War I (and after the 1918 pandemic of Spanish influenza, to which he lost his daughter Sophie); World War II, during which analysts reached patients via the advice column, via groups, via the airwaves; Hurricane Maria and Trump's 2016 election. In addition to international or national crisis, there is the permanent crisis of suicidality—both historical and contemporary—that resulted in the hotline and its related forms. Teletherapy has always been thought a crisis measure—whether that crisis is collective or private, or the private iteration of the collective. Teletherapy will, in all likelihood, acquire an even more pervasive, ongoing, palliative afterlife post-pandemic as a modality of care. Many have argued that we were inevitably heading that way. On the other hand, listservs have been dominated by therapists already preparing to return to the office as swiftly as possible.

* * *

There are several adages that get tossed around in my corner of academe:

The personal is political.
Always already.
It's turtles all the way down.
The medium is the message.

Another one, increasingly popular when I started graduate school, goes something like: rupture lays bare the conditions we wouldn't see otherwise. In disruption, we become painfully aware of our dependencies. This was part of the larger "infrastructural turn" in media studies and attendant fields, as well as disruption discourse in Silicon Valley, but was applied metaphorically, as well as to material infrastructures. For teletherapy, what was revealed by the sudden shutdown of daily life was the bias against working remotely, as well as how easily that bias could be overcome in a moment of need.

For some people, rupture was the start of the story of COVID-19. For some, the story of rupture started long, long ago, as partially evidenced by the riots and mass protests against anti-Blackness that emerged sixty-six days into lockdown.[17] By March 2020 or, in some places in the world, earlier, depending on togetherness for anything had become impossible. By late May, forms of togetherness were doubly restarted in the United States: for commerce and for resistance. In that interval, when togetherness was disrupted, when one couldn't depend on bodies being in any close proximity, when the only thing certain was that we would all be traumatized (and thus already were), the pandemic identified those for whom COVID served as a revelation, a reckoning, and those for whom it did not. The riots and their political effects too show this: distinguishing those for whom George Floyd's death was a revelation, an awakening, a "white surprise," to borrow Jim Perkinson's term, from those for whom it was not.[18]

A meme on Twitter in the early moments of COVID-19 featured growing lists of all the things we could "*suddenly*" have, that pre-COVID-19 were an inconvenience or impossible or somewhere in between. COVID-19 swiftly (though not swiftly enough from a public health standpoint) changed the very fabric of social and economic life. This, in some ways, presaged the uprisings of summer 2020 and their demands, which in part emerged from seeing just how quickly and for what reason the United States was willing, however reluctantly, to change life dramatically, where it was willing to change at all. If one pandemic can change the order of the world, why not longer-standing health issues, like racist policing and the larger forces of white supremacy? The meme was multiple: remote participation at conferences and online education was named by many disability activists as something that they had advocated for ad nauseam but that their institutions had regularly derided and rejected. Now it is the only way forward and thus acceptable. Free testing for COVID-19, no matter someone's insurance status, was pushed by the same bodies that frequently worked to deny community health care. Other customary impossibilities became thinkable, however briefly: the ending of imprisonment for failing to make bail; Universal Basic Income. Relaxed policing appeared early and often as a move that now appeared to be reasonable. As Joshua Clover writes, "The April First revelation that you could just . . . not pay your rent was surely an important tear in the ideological veil; the historically unique collapse down to a labor participation rate of barely 50% ripped the veil further."[19] It also turned out that we couldn't have nearly any of this despite these ruptures. Evictions restarted in pockets of the country on June 1. Policing didn't relax, it intensified, again unevenly. Masks still aren't mandated at a federal level. A second stimulus check has yet to be cut.

* * *

The overwhelming need for mental health care doesn't mean that teletherapeutic modalities should be exempt from critical consideration. Most critiques of teletherapy center around the body in its absence. They go like this: you need the body to be in the room because embodiment *does* things. And that is certainly true—there are effects that come from being together, much like there are effects that follow from being apart. The most devastating logic deployed in service of this critique I've ever heard of was articulated by the Lacanian Gerard Pommier, who claimed that for an analyst (granted, only one form of therapy and by no means the default) to be an analyst, and for a patient to be in analysis, the analyst's body must be proximate to the patient's body so that the patient can fear and *fantasize* being raped.[20] Without that particular fear, no analysis. Without the proximity, no fear.[21] Without physical presence, the absence of analysis.

Moving far away from this incendiary, violent, and misogynist form of the argument for bodies in rooms together, Sherry Turkle, Gillian Isaacs Russell, and Todd Essig write of the importance of being together physically in the therapeutic scenario, arguing that there is power and intimacy in "nonverbal communication, of eye contact, of smell, gesture, touch" and even trust.[22] For each patient, the meanings of liveness, of distance, of coming together or being held apart, and of those situations being dictated as opposed to chosen, are all relevant for therapeutic treatment that contends with the psyche.

This critique is not just focused on the workings of therapy but of "human empathy."[23] Again, the absence of empathy, its loss. This subset of critiques is often evidence based: screen-based communication has been proven to lower empathy scores, which correlate with a whole host of other psychological problems.[24] If the work of therapy is to produce a more feeling, in-touch, empathetic subject, then how can screen-based teletherapy not be antagonistic to the very aims of the treatment?[25] But empathy, which is held up as an eternal ethical value, one we impart to children, one we may chastise ourselves and others for failing to manifest, is complicit in structures of white supremacy and racism, misogyny, classism, homophobia, transphobia, and ableism.

I would argue that empathy only exists on a spectrum of failure. Or that when it succeeds, its success is defined by a failure; as Saidiya Hartman says, empathy "fails to expand the space of the other but merely places the self in its stead."[26] As the critic and novelist Namwali Serpell writes of empathy in art, "The empathy model of art can bleed too easily into the relishing of suffering by those who are safe from it. It's a gateway drug to white saviorism, with its familiar blend of propaganda, pornography, and paternalism. It's an emotional palliative that distracts us from real inequities, on the page and on screen, to say nothing of our actual lives. And it has imposed upon readers and viewers the idea that they can and ought to use art to inhabit others, especially the marginalized."[27] Applying Serpell's critique of empathy in art to the clinical relationship, not only is white or male saviorism a likely outcome of what passes for *successful* empathy, but empathy's *failure* allows for the categorical denial of humanity where it cannot be produced. Empathy is then the wrong goal. Perhaps a more radical feeling or, echoing Foucault's call for "new relational modes," something like solidarity needs to be our aim. Empathy functions like charity—it is a privatization of what should be a collective form of care; in this, it's like psychoanalysis's focus on the individual, which can turn its back on the social conditions that produce subjects. As Leo Bersani writes, "There is no solution easily recognizable as 'political' to the political horrors . . . because no recognizably political solution can be durable without something approaching a mutation in our most intimate relational system."[28] Empathy is not that mutation—it is the norm.

Before the pandemic, across the therapeutic landscape, reactions to teletherapy were, on a foundational level, about the aforementioned fantasized freedom from mediation: the purity of two bodies together in a room. As I laid out in the introduction to this book, the reaction against technology in the therapeutic scene is a reaction against the intrusion of an unknown third—media—and its effects on the communication it makes possible. A second and actual "purity" politic is also currently being exposed, although it is too soon to tell how far and deep the revision prompted by this most recent exposure will go: that of therapy's nearly exclusive whiteness, on both sides of the communication cure, and its ties, complicities, and active participation in the systematic oppression of marginalized groups and people. Sarah Ackerman writes of this historical formation as having a relationship to the aftermath of World War II: "The American psychoanalytic—in spite of being populated by a brotherhood of Jews who had escaped World War II—contrived reasons for excluding vast groups of people from diverse backgrounds, so that it remained a largely white, male organization."[29] It is not just the whiteness or maleness of psychology as a field, but its complicity and inextricability with white supremacy that must continue to be reevaluated, from the role race plays in diagnosis and prescription, to institutionalization, to the fantasies of white saviorism, to the very core of what it means to be in a "helping" profession seeking to impart empathy across the distance of difference.

The last genre of teletherapy critique concerns commerce, capital, and "Big Tech," sometimes spoken of as the neoliberal turn in mental health care, and I've advanced this critique, especially over the last two chapters of this book. In short, algorithms are not neutral.[30] Neither are corporations. "Big Tech" corporations and start-ups that make use of algorithmic treatment of patients and clients expose those users to all kinds of vulnerabilities, biases, and mistreatment, furthering inequalities via medical redlining (see chapters 4 and 5). Essig says, "There's a differentiation taking place in the therapy world between people who are doing whatever they can to make it work and be helpful, and people who are viewing this as an opportunity to promote a particular product to sell. There is an assumption among some of the mental health technology entrepreneurs that this will result in an explosion in the products they're selling."[31] This can be true even when the algorithm is in the hands of a nonprofit staffed by volunteers.[32] No amount of technologization or lay mental health care is protection against human bias and its presence in digital tools.

This group of critiques—the effects of disembodiment, destruction of empathy, and the overwhelming presence of neoliberal "Big Tech"—are not just leveled at teletherapy. The broad strokes of these critiques can be applied to any mediated or technologized intimacy or site of care when media are under intense scrutiny, especially those that involve screens. The absence of bodies, the absence of empathy becomes attached to the presence of screens. These critiques of teletherapy sometimes confuse symptom for cause, the medium outside for the medium inside, or vice versa: the problem with contemporary human relations is not the screen. Or not primarily the screen. Or not only the screen. I would not argue that the screen has no effects, nor that it is inherently good (see chapters 4 and 5), but the critiques that are leveled at screen-dependent relations are themselves a screen. Screens don't destroy empathy, they host its contemporary loss, which is an effect of despair, loneliness, and alienation.

These three words are not synonymous and all three are in play in the pandemic, because they always are, and have been for at least the last six hundred years or so. Each has its own connotations, lineage, and history, from the Christian feeling of God's grace leaving (despair) to the behavioral and quantifiable (loneliness) to the Marxist diagnosis (alienation, which is a result of economic conditions, but also an emotion). All three feelings are attributed to *mediated* encounters, even as they deeply predate and subtend the kinds of mediated encounters critiqued here. They are, in essence, the feelings that attend life under capital, not just life transpiring over communicative distance. Despair, loneliness, and alienation didn't start with heavy screen use or the pandemic and obviously haven't gone away during this moment.

In John Brunner's 1975 science fiction novel, *The Shockwave Rider*, the United States, and particularly California, is imagined as an overwhelmingly technological society—networked, monitored, and policed. Suppression is the norm. On the edges of this imagined society also exist various forms of resistance. One of them is the "Hearing Aid"—a collectively operated anonymous telephone service reachable at 999-999-9999. The Hearing Aid (or "Ten Nines," as it is also called) works much like a crisis hotline does in reality. Callers use it to talk freely, to scream—some callers even use it as a witnessing function and holding space at the end of their lives as they commit suicide. Telecare is imagined as functioning even at the bitterest of ends, in the most dystopian of societies. There is a major difference between a hotline and the Hearing Aid: Hearing Aid operators don't talk back to the callers. Instead, they end every call uniformly: "Only I heard that. I hope it helped." The Hearing Aid works because it offers a unique form of communication in the midst of crisis and suffering: the strictest confidentiality is promised. No one but the caller and the listener has access to what transpires over the call. Much like the monologue function that the written letter or the radio broadcast is, talking—or just being—in the distanced presence of someone who is "there" as the steady breath of a stranger on the other end of the phone does something. Even in the absence of reply, in the absence of embodiment, (tele)care does something.

Teletherapy cannot fix that which is systemic—it addresses and ameliorates the individual, not the crisis, even if it attends crisis, becomes available in crisis, and is used as a tool in crisis conditions. Screens, too, are part of human relations. Anything can and will travel across them: violence and trust; empathy, however slight or temporary; connection and disconnection; presence and absence. The feeling structures associated with teletherapy, that extraordinary version of an ordinary communicative relationship, determine the possibilities for relating over distance, a distance that is currently everywhere.

June 2020
Berkeley, CA

Notes

INTRODUCTION

1. Crisis Text Line, "Board and Advisors," https://www.crisistextline.org/board-advisors, last accessed February 1, 2018.

2. John Durham Peters, *Speaking into the Air: A History of the Idea of Communication* (Chicago: University of Chicago Press, 2001), 5.

3. Plato, *Charmides*, trans. T. West (New York: Hackett, 1986).

4. Cognitive, group, and other therapies also don't delimit the curative to communication; particular actions and interactions are also deeply important.

5. For the many wonderful books that *do* assess teletherapy and make direct recommendations to clinicians, see Jill S. Scharff's series, *Psychoanalysis Online: Mental Health, Teletherapy, and Training*, vols. 1–3 (London: Karnac 2013, 2015, 2017); Stephen Goss and Kate Anthony, eds., *Technology in Counselling and Psychotherapy: A Practitioner's Guide* (London: Palgrave, 2003). In addition, several recent books focus on the psychoanalytic use of digital technology, either by clinicians or by patients: Gillian Isaacs Russell, *Screen Relations: The Limits of Computer-Mediated Psychotherapy* (New York: Routledge, 2015), and Ricardo Carlino, *Distance Psychoanalysis: The Theory and Practice of Using Communication Technology in the Clinic* (London: Karnac, 2011).

6. Sigmund Freud, "On Beginning the Treatment (Further Recommendations on the Technique of Psychoanalysis I)" (1913), *The Standard Edition*, vol. 12 (London: Hogarth Press, 1966). For more on the status of the frame see *Reconsidering the Moveable Frame in Psychoanalysis*, ed. Isaac Tymlin and Adrienne Harris (New York: Routledge, 2017).

7. Christer Sjoödin, "Quality Assurance and Quality Assessment as Internal Ongoing Aspects of Psychoanalysis and Psychotherapy," *International Forum of Psychoanalysis* 3, no. 3 (1994): 183–193.

8. Sjoödin, "Quality Assurance and Quality Assessment." Soundproofing reemerges as an issue to discuss once the mediation of an analytic encounter becomes more apparent, or

with the arrival of additional technologies that allow for teletherapy, such as Skype. Skype itself gives assurances of its encryption but is not HIPAA compliant (other video teleconferencing platforms are deemed to be "medical grade"). Zoom does offer a HIPAA-compliant room but, anecdotally, not many practitioners of therapy purchase it because it is extremely expensive. Nonetheless, the fact that Zoom does offer such a room may be part of the reason why Zoom therapy was popular in pre-COVID one-to-one teletherapy, and why it dominated the move to remote therapy during the COVID pandemic. For more on teletherapy and its ubiquity during the pandemic, see coda.

9. The couch as an instrument, perhaps a legacy of Freud's work under Charcot as a hypnotist, has been rationalized as key to the analytic scenario in a number of ways: the couch reduces visual and other external stimulation, allowing the analysand to focus on the world of the mind; it makes impossible (regular) viewing of the analyst's face and her reactions to the patient's content; it asks the patient to lie down, which is said to allow the patient to relax and better access unconscious fantasy; it keeps the patient in a fixed place. For more on the history of the couch in psychoanalysis and beyond, see Nathan Kravis's *On the Couch: A Repressed History of the Analytic Couch from Plato to Freud* (Cambridge, MA: MIT Press, 2017).
10. The frame was later codified in Sigmund Freud's "On Beginning the Treatment."
11. Debra Neuman, "The Frame for Psychoanalysis in Cyberspace," in *Psychoanalysis Online: Mental Health, Teletherapy, Training* (London: Karnac Books, 2013), 174.
12. Janine Puget, "Revisiting the Concept of the Frame," in *Reconsidering the Moveable Frame*, 188–189.
13. Freud, "On Beginning the Treatment," 126.
14. Freud, 126–127.
15. Freud, 126–127.
16. Freud, 126–127.
17. Freud, 126–127.
18. Freud, 126–127 (emphasis added).
19. Freud, 132.
20. There is a perhaps apocryphal story told in psychoanalytic circles about the French psychoanalyst Jacques Lacan, who once terminated a patient's treatment but told the patient to keep paying for one year *as if* he were coming into treatment still—to really make sure the *gains* of the treatment stuck. There, the treatment ended but the fee went on, outliving it.
21. Freud, "On Beginning the Treatment," 133.
22. Sigmund Freud, "Lines of Advance in Psycho-Analytic Therapy" (1919), *The Standard Edition*, vol. 17 (London: Hogarth Press, 1955), 167. For more on this speech and its consequences, see Elizabeth Danto's *Freud's Free Clinics: Psychoanalysis and Social Justice 1918–1938* (New York: Columbia University Press, 2005).

23. Freud, “Lines of Advance in Psycho-Analytic Therapy,” 168.

24. Danto, *Freud's Free Clinics*, 3.

25. Danto notes that it was at the Berlin Poliklinik, the first psychoanalytic clinic to offer free and short-term treatment, that child analysis was first debated. I would like to strongly link the ability to think free treatment with thinking about children making use of psychoanalysis. That is, when we rethink the most basic elements of the frame (time and money), we can rethink doxologies surrounding the therapeutic dyad, triad, and tetrad. In this case, being open to short-term and free treatment coincided with being open to child patients. It is also worth noting, then, that Anna Freud and Melanie Klein—both pioneers in child analysis—also treated patients for free. Danto, *Freud's Free Clinics*, 2. For more on the relationship between class and psychoanalysis, see Joanna Ryan, *Class and Psychoanalysis: Landscapes of Inequality* (New York: Routledge, 2017).

26. The Freudian activist generation was just that—a generation. Other experiments with fee reduction and reconfiguration of therapeutic value were conducted along varying political and theoretical commitments: from the psychosocial and low-fee treatments of Harlem's Black community at the Lafargue Mental Hygiene Clinic in the late 1940s, to Félix Guattari's antipsychiatry schizoanalysis practice at the residential clinic La Borde in France (in which the therapeutic dyad was dissipated in favor of the group), to feminist peer-counseling efforts in the 1970s, to unorganized individuals with liberal or radical sliding-scale policies in private practices. For more on radical psychoanalysis specifically, see Daniel Jose Gaztambide, *A People's History of Psychoanalysis: From Freud to Liberation Psychology* (New York: Lexington Books, 2019).

27. Sigmund Freud, “Three Essays on the Theory of Sexuality” (1905), *The Standard Edition*, vol. 7 (London: Hogarth Press, 1953), 222.

28. Elizabeth Wilson, *Affect and Artificial Intelligence* (Seattle: University of Washington Press, 2010), 85.

29. Wilson, *Affect and Artificial Intelligence*, 85.

30. Sherry Turkle, *Alone Together: Why We Expect More from Technology and Less from Each Other* (New York: Basic Books, 2012), 1.

31. Telegram, Dorothy Parker to Pascal Covici, Viking Press, June 28, 1945.

32. Jonathan Steuer, “Defining Virtual Reality: Dimensions Determining Telepresence,” *Journal of Communication* 42, no. 4 (Autumn 1992): 76.

33. Peters, *Speaking into the Air*, 2.

34. Cait McKinney, “Calling to Talk and Listening Well: The Multimedia Practices of Feminist Telephone Hotlines” (presentation delivered at FemTechNet, University of Michigan, Ann Arbor, April 8, 2016).

35. Gabriele Balbi and Richard John define telecommunication networks more specifically as having three distinguishing features. The first feature “concerns users”: the telecommunication

network is point-to-point, and transmits messages "between a relatively small number of nodes" with the *aim* of privacy (Balbi and John point out that this is a misguided assumption as opposed to a reality). Given this feature, Balbi and John exclude broadcast networks such as radio and television. They name the second feature of telecommunications as the transmission of a coded signal over a network. The last requisite feature is that users on both ends can respond to messages in a timely fashion—or, as they put it, telecommunication requires interactivity. I diverge slightly from Balbi and John and extend teletherapy to include "as-if" instances, where actual use and lived experience proceed as though telecommunication were occurring, or to therapies that import the fantasy of private, human-to-human conversation and response. See Gabriele Balbi and Richard John, "Point-to-Point: Telecommunications Networks from the Optical Telegraph to the Mobile Telephone," in *Communication and Technology, 5th Volume of the Handbook of Communication Science* (Berlin: De Gruyter Mouton, 2014).

CHAPTER 1

1. Elliott Oring, *The Jokes of Sigmund Freud: A Study in Humor and Jewish Identity* (Lanham, MD: Jason Aronson, 1984), 87.

2. Eva Brabant, Ernst Falzeder, and Paula Giampieri-Deutsch, eds., and P. T. Hoffer, trans., *The Correspondence of Sigmund Freud and Sándor Ferenczi*, vol. 1, *1908–1914* (Cambridge, MA: Belknap Press, 1993), 79.

3. Oring, *The Jokes of Sigmund Freud*, 87.

4. Some of this material on thought transference and Freud previously appeared in my article, "Freud's Séance," *American Imago* 75, no. 1 (Spring 2018): 53–65.

5. See Jeffrey Sconce, *Haunted Media: Electronic Presence from Telegraphy to Television* (Durham, NC: Duke University Press, 2000), 76. Originally self-published in 1930, Upton Sinclair's *Mental Radio* focused on testing the telepathic capabilities of his wife, Mary Craig Kimbrough Sinclair. Lana Lin has connected the work of the Sinclairs to Freud's writings on telepathy by framing telepathy as related to the invasiveness of the analytic relationship and to the transference proper to it ("Are These Thoughts My Own? A Psychoanalytic Reading of Upton Sinclair's *Mental Radio*," paper presented at the Society for Cinema and Media Studies 2014 Conference, Seattle, WA).

6. See Pamela Thurschwell, "Ferenczi's Dangerous Proximities: Telepathy, Psychosis, and the Real Event," *differences: A Journal of Feminist Cultural Studies* 11 (1999): 150–178.

7. The group was comprised of Karl Abraham, Max Eitingon, Sándor Ferenczi, Otto Rank, Hans Sachs, and Ernest Jones.

8. Sigmund Freud, "Psycho-Analysis and Telepathy," *The Standard Edition*, vol. 18 (London: Hogarth Press, 1955), 175.

9. Freud, "Psycho-Analysis and Telepathy," 179.

10. Sigmund Freud, "Dreams and Telepathy" (1922), *The Standard Edition*, 18:197.

11. Sigmund Freud, "New Introductory Lectures on Psycho-Analysis," *The Standard Edition*, vol. 22 (London: Hogarth Press, 1964), 39.

12. Freud, "New Introductory Lectures on Psycho-Analysis," 55.

13. Ludwig Börne as quoted in Ernest Jones, *The Life and Work of Sigmund Freud* (New York: Penguin, 1964), 219.

14. Masud Khan, "Preface" in *Freud's Self-Analysis* (Madison, CT: International Universities Press, 1986), xiii.

15. Khan, "Preface," xiii.

16. The Freud–Fliess correspondence also contains telegrams and postcards—these other postal forms are not included in any published volume of their letters. However, these objects are referenced throughout the collection, and it seems as if letters are used to respond to these other forms at greater length.

17. Jeffrey M. Masson, ed. and trans., *The Complete Letters of Sigmund Freud to Wilhelm Fliess, 1887–1904* (New York: Belknap Press, 1985).

18. Masud Khan, *The Privacy of the Self* (London: Karnac Books, 1996), 108.

19. Emma Eckstein was a patient of Freud's and a practicing psychoanalyst, who was referred to Fliess for surgery. The procedure was a disaster and Fliess forgot to remove the surgical gauze. Eckstein bled profusely and was disfigured. Freud at first blamed these effects on the surgery but quickly decided they were hysterical symptoms. See Khan, *Privacy of the Self*, 108.

20. Letter from Freud to Fliess, in *The Origins of Psychoanalysis: Letters to Wilhelm Fliess, Drafts and Notes: 1887–1902*, ed. Marie Bonaparte, Anna Freud, and Ernst Kris (New York: Basic Books, 1954), 324.

21. Esther Milne, "Email and Epistolary Technologies: Presence, Intimacy, Disembodiment," *FibreCulture Journal* 2 (2003): http://two.fibreculturejournal.org/fcj-010-email-and-epistolary-technologies-presence-intimacy-disembodiment/.

22. Sigmund Freud, *Civilization and Its Discontents* (1930), *The Standard Edition*, vol. 21 (London: Hogarth Press, 1961), 91.

23. Roger Chartier, Alain Boureau, and Cécile Dauphin, *Correspondence: Models of Letter-Writing from the Middle Ages to the Nineteenth Century* (Princeton, NJ: Princeton University Press, 1997), 138.

24. David M. Henkin, *The Postal Age: The Emergence of Modern Communications in Nineteenth-Century America* (Chicago: University of Chicago Press, 2007), 100.

25. Chartier, Boureau, and Dauphin, *Correspondence*, 139.

26. John Durham Peters, *Speaking into the Air: A History of the Idea of Communication* (Chicago: University of Chicago Press, 2001), 165.

27. Letter from Freud to Fliess, January 3–4, 1888.

28. William Merrill Decker, *Epistolary Practices: Letter Writing in America before Telecommunications*, (Chapel Hill, NC: University of North Carolina Press, 1998), 46–47.

29. Milne, "Email and Epistolary Technologies."

30. Milne.

31. E. H. Erikson, *Life History and the Historical Moment* (New York: Norton, 1975), 51.

32. Lori Lebow, "Woman of Letters: Narrative Episodes in the Letters of Emily Dickinson," *The Emily Dickinson Journal* 8, no. 1 (1999): 73–96.

33. Claudio Guillén, "On the Edge of Literariness: The Writing of Letters," *Comparative Literature Studies* 31, no. 1 (1994): 2.

34. Letter from Freud to Fliess, November 14, 1897.

35. Khan, *Privacy of the Self*, 108.

36. Letter from Freud to Fliess, May 18, 1898.

37. Ernst Kris, "Introduction," in *Origins of Psychoanalysis*, 4.

38. Peter Rudnytsky, *Freud and Oedipus* (New York: Columbia University Press, 1992).

39. Walter Ong, *Orality and Literacy: The Technologizing of the World* (New York: Routledge, 1982).

40. Chartier, Boureau, and Dauphin, *Correspondence*, 116.

41. Henkin, *The Postal Age*, 94.

42. Grande Encylopedie du XIX siècle, quoted by Chartier, Boureau, and Dauphin, *Correspondence: Models of Letter-Writing from the Middle Ages to the Nineteenth Century*, 132.

43. Henkin, *The Postal Age*, 100.

44. Chartier, Boureau, and Dauphin, *Correspondence*, 137.

45. Chartier, Boureau, and Dauphin, 137.

46. Chartier, Boureau, and Dauphin, 137.

47. Letter from Freud to Fliess, May 21, 1894.

48. Decker, *Epistolary Practices*, 45.

49. Letter from Freud to Fliess, January 3–4, 1888.

50. Letter from Freud to Fliess, November 2, 1896.

51. Sigmund Freud, Letter 70, October 3, 1897, Extracts from the Fliess Papers, *The Standard Edition*, vol. 1 (London: Hogarth Press, 1953), 261–263.

52. Letter from Freud to Fliess, November 5, 1897.

53. Letter from Freud to Fliess, May 21, 1894.

54. Letter from Freud to Fliess, May 18, 1898.

55. Henkin, *The Postal Age*, 100.

56. Letter from Freud to Fliess, December 8, 1895.

57. Peter Gay, *Freud: A Life for Our Time* (New York: Norton, 1988), 613.

58. This work catalogs Freud's research into parapraxes from 1887 to the text's publication in 1901—nearly the exact same time span as his epistolary relationship with Fliess (1887–1902).

59. Gay, *Freud*, 126.

60. Sigmund Freud, *The Psychopathology of Everyday Life*, *The Standard Edition*, vol. 6 (London: Hogarth Press, 1960), 132.

61. Ben Kafka, *The Demon of Writing: Powers and Failures of Paperwork* (New York: Zone Books, 2012), 138.

62. The supporting communication network that allows for letter circulation—the mailbox, the post office, stamps, and addresses—also routinely enters Freud's reading of the psychopathology of daily life. Freud's work on inhibition in relation to carrying out actions and the forgetting of intentions relies heavily on scenes of letter writing and mailing. He writes of forgetting to post his mail:

> If I am going for a walk and take a letter with me which has to be posted, it is certainly not necessary for me, as a normal individual, free from neurosis, to walk all the way with it in my hand and to be continually on the look-out for a letter-box in which to post it; on the contrary I am in the habit of putting it in my pocket, of walking along and letting my thoughts range freely, and I confidently expect that one of the first letter-boxes will catch my attention and cause me to put my hand in my pocket and take out the letter. Normal behaviour after an intention has been formed coincides fully with the experimentally-produced behaviour of people to whom what is described as a "post-hypnotic suggestion at long range" has been given under hypnosis. This phenomenon is usually described in the following way. The suggested intention slumbers on in the person concerned until the time for its execution approaches. Then it awakes and impels him to perform the action.

Freud, *The Psychopathology of Everyday Life*, 152. The envelope containing the finished letter is internally prohibited from being mailed. Freud understands this as a motivated forgetting—he must have wanted *not* to post it. The mailing of letters becomes a representative site of resistance, or an oppositional action or behavior. Bernhard Siegert writes of this kind of pervasive forgetfulness in posting letters after prepaid postage had taken effect in Vienna, "The effect of this evasion of consciousness was that Freud . . . would be able to found a psychopathology of this everyday life produced by mailboxes. The distinction between normal and abnormal individuals depends precisely on the question of whether or not neighborhood mailboxes made the leap over the threshold of consciousness." Bernhard Siegert, *Relays: Literature as an Epoch of the Postal System*, trans. Kevin Repp (Stanford, CA: Stanford University Press, 1999), 111.

63. Kafka, *The Demon of Writing*, 138.

64. Peter Galison writes that Freud "felt the weight of this self-limitation in his correspondence acutely, commenting to his friends and acquaintances how oppressive he found the necessity of sending unsealed letters (prominently labeled *offen*) so that the censors would not tear them up in their effort to surveil contents. Freud could see that his correspondence was being twice inspected—the stamps were there for all the world to see: "inspected in Vienna" and then "inspected in Königsberg, for example" (Peter Galison, "The Theater of Forgetting," *Cabinet Magazine* 42 [2011]: http://cabinetmagazine.org/issues/42/galison.php).

65. I take this term from David Henkin's *The Postal Age*. There, he applies "the myth of epistolary privacy" to the antebellum South, taking it to encompass aspects that I attribute to security.

66. Howard Robinson, *The British Post Office: A History* (Princeton, NJ: Princeton University Press, 1948), 337–353.

67. Siegert, *Relays*, 38.

68. Siegert.

69. Peter Galison, "Self-Censorship in the Digital Age: We Won't Be Able to Recognize Ourselves," *Frankfurter Allgemeine Feuilleton*, July 7, 2014, 3.

70. The postal service appears as a key metaphor in Freud's early attempt at understanding the process and scope of inhibition in dreams (see Sigmund Freud, *The Interpretation of Dreams* [1900], *The Standard Edition*, vol. 4 [London: Hogarth Press, 1953], 141; Galison, "Theater of Forgetting"). Figurations of censorship (as repression, in reality-testing) are littered throughout Freud's work. In two editions of *The Interpretation of Dreams*, Freud suggests that the mind contains mechanisms for censorship that parallel the mode of postal censors. In the 1900 edition of *The Interpretation of Dreams*, Freud makes an analogy between dream censorship and a political dissident who, unable to write *exactly* as he pleases, systematically disguises his content. This representation of the writer is parallel to the dreamer who is unable to make his true meaning clear right away and yet leaves traces of it to be recalled and worked with upon waking. *The Standard Edition* notes that this model has previously appeared in two other earlier and unrelated Freud texts, both times as a way of describing defensiveness. Freud writes,

> A similar difficulty confronts the political writer who has disagreeable truths to tell to those in authority. If he presents them undisguised, the authorities will suppress his words. . . . A writer must beware of the censorship and on its account he must soften and distort the expression of his opinion. According to the strength and sensitiveness of the censorship he finds himself compelled either merely to refrain from certain forms of attack. . . . The stricter the censorship the more far-reaching will be the disguise and the more ingenious too may be the means employed for putting the reader on the scent of the true meaning.

Freud, *Interpretation of Dreams*, 141. Here, the censor is depicted as the controller of content and the writer lives in fear of being detected. This also prefigures the censor as hermeneut; before he can blot out and blacken passages, he must first read them. The dreamer, in an attempt to both keep his true meaning somewhat available and prevent it from being "read," creates a disguise both effective and ineffective enough to wend its way to consciousness. (For further exploration of the political influences on *The Interpretation of Dreams*, see Carl E. Schorske's *Fin-De-Siècle Vienna: Politics and Culture* [New York: Vintage, 1980].) This also appeared in Freud's clinical work, as he famously writes, the "royal road to knowledge of the unconscious" is paved with censors, the path to psychic understanding superimposed on national infrastructure and state permission (Freud, *Interpretation of Dreams*, 613). What can be communicated or inhibited in dreaming—a most important topography for psychoanalysis—not just to another but to one's own self, is schematized through Freud's experience with violations of his wished-for epistolary security. No form is free from intercession, whether it be carried out by an outside force or by internal redaction. See also Galison, "Theater of Forgetting."

71. Letter from Freud to Lou Andres-Salome, July 30, 1915, *The International Psychoanalytical Library* 89: 32–33. For further discussion of this marking on Freud's letters, see Galison, "Theater of Forgetting."

72. For further consideration of the letter as metaphor in Freud's clinical works, see Jacques Derrida's *The Postcard: From Socrates to Freud and Beyond* (Chicago: University of Chicago, 1987), especially "To Speculate—On Freud." For Lacan's work on the letter, Freud, and the unconscious, see "Seminar on the Purloined Letter" in Jacques Lacan, *Ecrits: The First Complete Translation in English*, trans. Bruce Fink (New York: W. W. Norton, 2007), 6–50.

73. Henkin, *The Postal Age*, 105.

74. Henkin, *The Postal Age*, 103.

75. Letter from Freud to Fliess, March 11, 1902.

76. It is not known whether the analysis of "Little Hans" is Freud's only full therapy via letter or other media. Freud certainly corresponded with former patients after they stopped seeing him in person. In "On Beginning the Treatment," Freud writes of a Russian woman who sought treatment from him: "She hopes to be completely cured by psycho-analysis, which she has read about, but her illness has already cost her family so much money that she cannot manage to come to Vienna for longer than six weeks or two months. Another added difficulty is that she wishes from the very start to 'explain' herself in writing only, since any discussion of her complexes would cause an explosion of feeling in her or 'render her temporarily unable to speak.'" Freud seemingly refused to participate in this treatment. Freud, "On Beginning the Treatment," 128.

77. This ulterior motive is seen as a large impetus for taking on the first ever child analysis. Freud openly states in the introduction to the Hans case that his aim in collecting experiences of children and child rearing from his circle is to provide, in his own words, "direct . . . proof of these fundamental theorems." Sigmund Freud, *Analysis of a Phobia in a Five-Year-Old Boy*, *The Standard Edition*, vol. 10 (London: Hogarth Press, 1955), 6. See Jennifer Stuart, "Little Hans and Freud's Self-Analysis: A Biographical View of Clinical Theory in the Making," *Journal of the American Psychoanalytic Association* 55, no. 3 (2007): 799–819.

78. Stuart, *Little Hans and Freud's Self-Analysis.*

79. Freud, *Analysis of a Phobia in a Five-Year-Old Boy*, 10.

80. Freud, 6.

81. Freud, 22.

82. Freud, 22–23.

83. Freud, 32.

84. Herbert Graf, as a child patient, didn't quite consent to be a patient, let alone have an entire case study published on his early psychic life. Herbert recalled in 1959—fifty years after the publication of "Hans"—the moment at which he understood that an entire Freud case study was devoted to *him* and his material. He was in his father's library and began to read "Little Hans" and although his name was changed, his aunts' names weren't. He asked his father if it were so, "And he said 'yes, it is all true.' I said I would like to meet Professor Freud now. And he said, 'of course, you should.' And I called Professor Freud and made an appointment. I came to him and I went to his studio, and he looked at me, of course, not recognizing me. And I said, 'I am the little Hans,' I said." According to Graf, Freud responded that "it [the analysis] must have done some good because I spoke or acted—at least in his presence—quite normally. And I went home. And later I heard that some sort of post-script lately added that I came to him after so many years and this was the best proof of the correctness of his theory to see me in the flesh, and so forth." (Herbert Graf, "Sigmund Freud Papers: Interviews and Recollections, 1914–1998; Set A, 1914–1998; Interviews and; Graf, Herbert, 1959" [manuscript/mixed material], 3, https://www.loc.gov/item/mss3999001476/.) It was only the second time they had ever seen each other in person.

85. Freud, *Analysis of a Phobia in a Five-Year-Old Boy*, 56.

86. Freud, 43.

87. Freud, 43.

88. Freud, *Civilization and Its Discontents*, 85–91.

89. See Jonathan Sterne, *The Audible Past* (Durham, NC: Duke University Press, 2003), especially pages 31–38 for intersections in the history of deaf education and the production of Alexander Graham Bell's telephone; for women's construction of telephone use, in its interpretive flexibility and adaptation, see Michelle Martin's *Hello, Central?: Gender, Technology, and Culture in the Formation of Telephone Systems* (Montreal, QC: McGill-Queens Press, 1991).

90. Sigmund Freud, "Recommendations to Physicians Practicing Psycho-Analysis," *The Standard Edition*, vol. 12 (London: Hogarth Press, 1966), 380.

91. Freud, "Recommendations to Physicians Practicing Psycho-Analysis," 381.

92. Peters, *Speaking into The Air*, 264.

93. In *Gramophone, Film, Typewriter* (Stanford, CA: Stanford University Press, 1999), Friedrich Kittler famously takes up Freud's metaphor and claims that Freud made a critical error of theorization.

94. Freud uses the metaphor of the telephone to illuminate the fantasy of returning to the womb in *The Future of an Illusion*, as well as in his work on telepathy, quoted above.

95. Sigmund Freud, *Psycho-Analytic Notes on an Autobiographical Account of a Case of Paranoia*, *The Standard Edition*, 12:11n1.

96. Freud, *Analysis of a Phobia in a Five-Year-Old Boy*, 6.

97. Lisa Farley, "Analysis on Air: A Sound History of Winnicott on Air in Wartime," *American Imago* 68, no. 4 (Winter 2012): 449.

98. Sigmund Freud, BBC broadcast recorded at Maresfield Gardens, December 7, 1938.

CHAPTER 2

1. Peter Gay, *Freud: A Life for Our Time* (New York: Norton, 1988), 650.

2. Newspaper Columns, Susan Isaacs file, Personal Papers, British Psychoanalytical Society, FAA 19.

3. Newspaper Columns, Susan Isaacs file, FAA 19.

4. Newspaper Columns, Susan Isaacs file, FAA 19.

5. Newspaper Columns, Susan Isaacs file, FAA 19.

6. Harold Bridger, "The Discovery of the Therapeutic Community: The Northfield Experiments," in *The Social Engagement of Social Science, A Tavistock Anthology*, ed. Eric Trist and Hugh Murray, vol. 1 (London: Tavistock Publications, 1990), 67.

7. Simultaneously, experiments with group therapy were being conducted in US military hospitals, where 20 percent of all veterans returning home were diagnosed with some neuropsychological disorder. These treatment courses focused more on medical intervention and made use of electroshock and insulin therapies as well as hypnosis, work, and group therapies. The treatments typically lasted six weeks before the men were considered rehabilitated. See John Huston's 1946 film *Let There Be Light.*

8. Wilfred Bion, *Experiences in Groups* (London: Tavistock Publications, 1961), 11.

9. Wilfred Bion, "The Leaderless Group Project," *Bulletin of the Menninger Clinic* 10 (1946): 77–81.

10. Bion, "The Leaderless Group Project," 77–81.

11. Bion, *Experiences in Groups*, 13–16.

12. Bridger, "The Discovery of the Therapeutic Community," 73.

13. Bion, *Experiences in Groups*, 14.

14. Bion, 22.

15. Bion, 22.
16. Bion, 22.
17. Bion, 81.
18. Bion, 80–81.
19. Melanie Klein, *Narrative of a Child Analysis* (London: Karnac Books, 1961).
20. Phyllis Grosskurth, *Melanie Klein: Her World and Her Work* (Maryland: Jason Aronson, 1977), 265.
21. Klein, *Narrative of a Child Analysis*, 462.
22. The speech was so derided by members of the BPAS that he was forced to resign from his position as deputy chairman and gave up his membership in its entirety. Despite his important administrative position within the BPAS, Glover was made to print a retraction via a vote at an extraordinary meeting. See: Business Meetings Minutes, Extraordinary Business Meeting, February 23, 1944, Society & Institute Records, British Psychoanalytical Society, FAA.
23. Though Klein's largest work on war and children was *Narrative of a Child Analysis*, she also spoke on European Radio in October 1944 about the horrific effects of war on children. Klein delivered this address from a layperson's standpoint, urging parents to consider the resonances between the inner, psychic life of children and the outer, war-torn reality of occupied Europe. Klein is also very careful to ground this address as absolutely indebted to Freud, as if partially a propaganda piece for the battle going on inside the BPAS. She stated, "It is widely acknowledged that children need good food and vitamins. But they just as much need steady opportunities for play . . . we can therefore hope to mitigate the ill effects of the tragic experiences that this war has brought to children in occupied Europe if we help them to gain inner security. All of us who are in close touch with children can help contribute to this urgent task if we keep in mind the most essential need of the child."
24. Donald W. Winnicott, *Talking to Parents* (Boston: Da Capo Press, 1994), xiii.
25. For more on Winnicott's broadcasts, see Lisa Farley, "Analysis on Air: A Sound History of Winnicott on Air in Wartime," *American Imago* 68, no. 4 (Winter 2012): 449–471; Michal Shapira, *The War Inside: Psychoanalysis, Total War, and the Making of the Democratic Self in Postwar Britain* (Cambridge: Cambridge University Press, 2013); and Ann Karpf's "Constructing and Addressing the 'Ordinary Devoted Mother,'" *History Workshop Journal* 78 (2004): 27.
26. Sian Nicholas, "The People's Radio: The BBC and Its Audience, 1939–1945," in *Millions Like Us?: British Culture in the Second World War*, ed. Nick Hayes and Jeff Hill (Liverpool, UK: Liverpool University Press, 1999), 72.
27. Brian Kane, *Sound Unseen: Acousmatic Sound in Theory and Practice* (Oxford: Oxford University Press, 2014), 4.

28. Masud Khan reports that Winnicott listened to his patients while obscuring his face with his hands, looking at them only through "the chinks" between his fingers. Khan, *The Long Wait and Other Psychoanalytic Narratives* (London: Summit Press, 1989), 38.

29. Donald W. Winnicott, "Children in the War," in *Deprivation and Delinquency* (New York: Routledge, 2011), 26.

30. Farley, "Analysis on Air," 456.

31. Shapira notes that these lines were revised out of "Where Does Dad Come In"—not the first or only censorship of Winnicott's broadcasts. For more on the role of production and of editing Winnicott's broadcasts, please see Karpf's "Constructing and Addressing the 'Ordinary Devoted Mother.'"

32. Donald W. Winnicott, "The Ordinary Devoted Mother and Her Baby: Nine Broadcast Talks." Distributed privately, produced by Miss I. D. Benzie. 1949. Courtesy of The Wellcome Library and The Winnicott Trust, 3.

33. Winnicott, "The Ordinary Devoted Mother and Her Baby," 16.

34. Farley, "Analysis on Air."

35. Winnicott, "The Ordinary Devoted Mother and Her Baby," 9, 43.

36. Winnicott, 9, 43.

37. Winnicott, 3.

38. Winnicott, 4.

39. Shapira, *The War Inside*, 134. For more on the reaction of the audience to Winnicott, please see Ann Karpf's "Constructing and Addressing the 'Ordinary Devoted Mother,'" 27.

40. This follows Winnicott's advancement of the notion that mothers only need to be "good enough" or "ordinarily devoted" to succeed as a parent.

41. Business Meetings Minutes, the Annual Meeting of the BPAS, July 21, 1943, Society & Institute Records, British Psycho-Analytical Society, FAA.

42. Business Meetings Minutes, the Annual Meeting of the BPAS, July 21, 1943.

43. Business Meetings Minutes, courtesy of The Archives of the British Psycho-Analytical Society. It is not clear if "Ms. Sharpe" is the renowned psychoanalyst Ella Sharpe (which is most likely), or someone more junior at the Society.

44. Theodor Adorno also briefly participated in the Radio Research Project at Princeton under the leadership of Paul F. Lazarsfeld and was funded by the Rockefeller foundation. The Project sought to identify "The Essential Value of Radio to All Types of Listeners"—and Adorno worked predominantly on music. Additionally, he wrote a short monograph, *The Psychological Technique of Martin Luther Thomas' Radio Addresses*, taking on ascendant American fascism, the religious right and anti-Semitism, and the radio as method for dissemination of ideology (see Theodor Adorno, *The Psychological Technique of Martin Luther Thomas' Radio Addresses* [Palo Alto, CA: Stanford University Press, 2000]). After completing

the volume, in 1950 Adorno returned to Germany after exile in the United States and began giving radio addresses on a wide range of topics from music and literature, to psychoanalytic and sociopolitical lectures on postwar recovery via Hessian Broadcasting (Anna Parkinson, "Adorno on the Airwaves: Feeling Reason, Educating Emotions," in "West Germany's Cold War Radio: The Crucible of the Transatlantic Century," special issue, *German Politics and Society* 32, no. 1 [110] [Spring 2014]: 44). He gave more than 100 addresses between his return and his death. For more on the radio, trauma, and psychoanalysis, see Amit Pinchevski and Tamar Liebes, "Severed Voices: Radio and the Mediation of Trauma in the Eichmann Trial," *Public Culture* 22, no. 2 (2010): 265–291.

45. Frantz Fanon, "This is the Voice of Algeria," in *A Dying Colonialism*, trans. Haackon Chevalier (New York: Grove Press, 1994), 71.

46. Fanon, "This is the Voice of Algeria," 88.

47. Fanon, 87.

48. Fanon, 87.

49. For more on Fanon and his theories of the radio, radio as technique, and participatory broadcasting, see Ian Baucom's "Frantz Fanon's Radio: Solidarity, Diaspora, and the Tactics of Listening," *Contemporary Literature* 42, no. 1 (Spring 2001): 15–49. For more on its relationship to psychoanalysis and Fanon's other theoretical work, see John Mowitt, "Stations of Exception," in *Radio: Essays in Bad Reception* (Berkeley: University of California Press, 2011).

50. For an extended and theoretical reading of Guattari's involvement with radical psychoanalysis and radio, see John Mowitt, "Phoning in Analysis," in *Radio: Essays in Bad Reception.*

51. Francois Dosse, *Intersecting Lives: Gilles Deleuze and Félix Guattari* (New York: Columbia University Press, 2011), 304.

52. Dosse, *Intersecting Lives*, 302–303.

53. Félix Guattari, *Soft Subversions*, ed. Sylvère Lotringer (Cambridge, MA: MIT Press, 1996), 76.

54. Guattari, *Soft Subversions.*

55. Radio-based psychoeducation began in the United States in the interwar period, and the earliest interwar psychology radio show appeared on WEAF in September 1927, where weekly on Tuesdays an hour-long show addressed parents about how to raise their children (under different titles like "Concerning Parents" and "Parents Talk"). Other shows in this moment tended to be just fifteen-minute slots, also in an educational format, also particularly focused on children and aimed at mothers, tuning in during the afternoon from home. For more on this precursor, see Peter J. Behrens, "Psychology Takes to the Airways: American Radio Psychology between the Wars, 1926–1939," *The American Sociologist* 40, no. 3 (September 2009): 217.

56. Sally C. Clarke, Division of Vital Statistics, Centers for Disease Control and Prevention and the National Center for Health Statistics, "Advance Report of Final Divorce Statistics, 1989 and 1990," *Monthly Vital Statistics Report* 43, no. 9 (March 22, 1995).

57. De Angelis, Schlessinger, and Kagan all moved from broadcast to the small screen, joining other long-running para-therapeutic programs hosted by the likes of Dr. Joyce Brothers, Dr. Phil, Dr. Ruth, and other daytime television hosts that traffic in various forms of self-help. These shows have been pervasive since the start of the television talk show, and although each of these shows brands, formats, advertises, and presents itself somewhat differently and offers different perspectives on many of the same questions, Mimi White collects them under the sign of "tele-advising" (see Mimi White, *Tele-Advising: Therapeutic Discourse in American Television* [Chapel Hill: University of North Carolina Press, 1992]). Most frequently, these shows too discuss romantic and sexual relationships, though not exclusively, and do so in a way that invites the audience in, either literally—by filming in front of a live audience—or in the same mode as the call-in, sourcing problems, and therefore participants, via the larger audience at home, bringing these participants on stage in an ever-rotating cast. Of course, no matter how the audience participates—either as a witness, or more overtly—these shows removed anonymity completely, relying on the one stand-in to again become the case study and learning object for the whole audience via the conduit of the host.

    While I focus on broadcast and podcast shows about therapy, or that describe themselves as therapy, shows that focus fictionally on therapy abound—and the recent golden age of television has provided us with many such narratives (including *The Sopranos*, *In Treatment*, and, most recently, *Gypsy*). In parallel, out of the public eye, clinicians developed practices of filming real sessions with real patients. Filming therapy would seem to allow us to overhear the private confessional that therapy is, accessing that intimate scene and therapeutic relationship as well as all the confidential details of the lives under mutual investigation there. There is a longstanding audiovisual culture and history of the mind sciences, which are often theorized as being entirely aural while devaluing the visual, though practitioners of therapeutic techniques have made extensive use of audio and visual recording to document and witness since Charcot's work with hysterical patients in the late 1800s. In the mid- and late twentieth century, these experiments with documenting and witnessing psychologically were wide-ranging in clinical aim and scope and include R. D. Laing's video tapings of his therapeutic communities in the late 1960s, in which clinicians and patients lived side by side in a controlled residence; Milton Berger's innovative use of videotaping in psychotherapeutic training and treatment—with a particular focus on couples therapy—and psychoanalyst Dori Laub's work with videotaping Holocaust survivors' testimonies, which became the Fortunoff Archive at Yale University. Most recently, Dr. Orna Guralnik has developed a couples' counseling reality television show for Showtime called *Couples Therapy*, in which an entire season is devoted to several couples in treatment. For more on this show, see coda.

58. Andrea Higbie, "From Confidentiality to Anybody Who Tunes In," *New York Times*, October 31, 1999.

59. James Brown, "Radio: Relating to People in a Caring Way," *Los Angeles Times*, November 27, 1977.

60. Brown, "Radio: Relating to People in a Caring Way."

61. De Angelis also holds a PhD in psychology, although she is not licensed. She would go on to author nine best-selling self-help books on the subject of marital sex, equality, and fulfilment.

62. "Therapist Toni Grant Departing KFI-AM," *Los Angeles Times*, August 26, 1989.

63. "Therapist Toni Grant Departing KFI-AM."

64. *Biographical Dictionary of Radio*, ed. Christopher H. Sterling (New York: Routledge, 2010), 317.

65. Daniel Patrick Foley, "The Moral and Ethical Judgments of Dr. Laura," *Journal of Religion and Health* 39, no. 1 (Spring 2000): 42.

66. Marilyn Kagan, Call-in Show, The Internet Archive, December 21, 1992, https://archive.org/details/ACs9212s021a13Track13_201706/a+-+cs9212s021a+-+07+-+Track07.mp3, last accessed June 2, 2020.

67. Jeannine Stein, "Keeping in Touch: A Viscott Primer: With Hugs and Quick Answers, Radio Shrink has Built Himself a Mini-Empire," *Los Angeles Times*, March 17, 1988.

68. This kind of scripted relation is also reminiscent of helpers on hotlines, who are there in large part to affirm their callers. For more on the scripts used by hotline volunteers, see chapter 3.

69. Paddy Scannell, "For Someone-as-Anyone-Structures," *Media, Culture, and Society* 22, no. 1 (2000): 5–24.

70. Barbara De Angelis, *Ask Barbara: The 100 Most Asked Questions About Love, Sex, and Relationships* (New York: Random House, 1997).

71. Brown, "Radio: Relating to People in a Caring Way."

72. Scannell, "For Someone-as-Anyone-Structures."

73. John Durham Peters, "Broadcasting and Schizophrenia," *Media, Culture, and Society* 32, no. 1 (2010): 127.

74. Peters, "Broadcasting and Schizophrenia," 132.

75. Peters, 132.

76. Application for *Where Should We Begin?*, https://docs.google.com/forms/d/e/1FAIpQLScvP6TQ79f3iK4bjO5F4gAhE-mEnYcOKjLBZccYzfAiBeNd5g/viewform, last accessed June 7, 2020.

77. Nicholas Quah, "How Esther Perel Makes Her Intensely Intimate Podcasts," *New York Magazine*, January 9, 2020.

78. Quah, "How Esther Perel Makes Her Intensely Intimate Podcasts."

79. Esther Perel, *Where Should We Begin?*, Episode One, Season One, October 8, 2017.

80. White, *Tele-Advising*, 55.

81. Alexandra Schwartz, "Esther Perel Lets Us Listen in on Couple's Secrets," *New Yorker*, May 31, 2017.

CHAPTER 3

1. Chad Varah, *The Samaritans* (New York: MacMillan, 1965), 10.
2. Chad Varah, "Why I Started the Samaritans," Samaritans, http://www.samaritans.org/about-us/history-samaritans/how-and-why-i-started-samaritans-chad-varah, accessed June 15, 2016.
3. Chad Varah, *Before I Die Again: The Autobiography of the Founder of the Samaritans* (London: Constable, 1992), 151.
4. Varah, *Before I Die Again*, 151.
5. Varah, 151.
6. Varah, 150.
7. Varah, *The Samaritans*, 20.
8. Varah, *Before I Die Again*, 154.
9. Varah, 157.
10. Varah, *The Samaritans*, 22.
11. "Telephone Used as Counseling Aid," *Christian Science Monitor*, September 18, 1962.
12. "Telephone Used as Counseling Aid."
13. I use this term from Erica Robles-Anderson, whose work on the Garden Grove Community Church has been especially useful for this chapter.
14. Later, Dr. Smiley Blanton would use this quote as a justification for the psycho-religious work he took up with Norman Vincent Peale. (Dr. Smiley Blanton, "A Pioneering Partnership: The American Foundation of Religion and Psychiatry," The Dr. Smiley Blanton Papers, MS.0739, Box 10, Folder 46. Special Collections, University of Tennessee—Knoxville Libraries.)
15. "Conversion" is the term used by psychoanalysts to describe the shift from seeing a patient upright to having the patient recline on the couch, as well as the shift from seeing patients for a particular crisis in their life to seeing them in a more long-term, open-ended way.
16. The American Association of Suicidology recommends a minimum of forty hours training to become a crisis worker; San Francisco Suicide Prevention's volunteer training currently takes thirty hours, New Hope's hotline required a fifty-hour training.
17. Mark Lukach, "Exquisite Listening: America's First Suicide Hotline Celebrates 50 Years," *GOOD*, July 21, 2012, https://www.good.is/articles/exquisite-listening-america-s-first-suicide-prevention-hotline-celebrates-50-years, accessed June 15, 2016.
18. For more on the history of loneliness and despair, see coda.
19. Lukach, "Exquisite Listening."
20. *The Bible*, King James Version, Exodus 20.

21. George Makari, *Soul Machine: The Invention of the Modern Mind* (New York: W. W. Norton, 2015), 164.
22. John T. McNeill, ed., and Ford Lewis Battle, trans., *Calvin: Institutes of the Christian Religion* (Louisville, KY: Westminster Press, 1960), 3.22.10.
23. J. Tobin Grant, "Measuring Aggregate Religiosity in The United States, 1952–2005," *Sociological Spectrum* 28, no. 5 (2008): 460–476.
24. Dana L. Farnsworth and Francis J. Braceland, eds., *Psychiatry, the Clergy, and Pastoral Counseling: The St. John's Story* (Collegeville, MN: Saint John's University Press, 1969), 6.
25. Arthur Gordon, *One Man's Way: The Story and Message of Norman Vincent Peale* (New York: Prentice-Hall, 1972), 155.
26. Gordon, *One Man's Way*, 155.
27. Gordon, 174.
28. Gordon, 177.
29. Blanton wrote *Diary of My Analysis with Sigmund Freud* (New York: Hawthorne Books, 1971), an account by a practicing clinician about being in treatment with the founder of psychoanalysis. The two had their last session together in 1938, the day Freud was to go for one of the final treatments for his terminal jaw cancer.
30. Blanton, *Diary of My Analysis with Sigmund Freud*, 15.
31. Gordon, *One Man's Way*, 177.
32. Smiley Blanton, "The Religio-Psychiatric Clinic of the Marble Collegiate Church," The Dr. Smiley Blanton Papers, MS.0739, Box 11, Folder 16. Special Collections, University of Tennessee.
33. Blanton, "Religio-Psychiatric Clinic."
34. Smiley Blanton, "A Pioneering Partnership: The American Foundation of Religion and Psychiatry," The Dr. Smiley Blanton Papers, MS.0739, Box 10, Folder 46. Special Collections, University of Tennessee.
35. Blanton, "A Pioneering Partnership."
36. Blanton.
37. "Dr. Smiley Blanton Dead Here; Psychiatrist and Author Was 84," *New York Times*, October 31, 1966.
38. Roy M. Anker, *Self-Help and Popular Religion in Modern American Culture: An Interpretive Guide*, vol. 2 (Westport, CT: Greenwood Publishing Group, 1999), 111.
39. Anker, *Self-Help and Popular Religion.*
40. "Healing of Mind Linked to Spirit," *New York Times*, March 14, 1955.
41. "Healing of Mind Linked to Spirit."
42. "Healing of Mind Linked to Spirit."

43. Peale's success in growing, mediating, and reaching his congregation over distance is only one of many similar stories of the expansion of church participation in the United States in the 1940s and 1950s. In 1940, only some 49 percent of Americans had membership in a church. By 1953, that figure was reported at 60 percent and climbing ("Healing of Mind Linked to Spirit"). *Life Magazine* attributed this fact to twelve representative preachers—one of them Peale. And while Blanton's clinic, and his ongoing partnership with Peale, was unique for his moment, Peale's use of mass media (in nearly every available form) was not (for more on this moment in American religious radio history, see Tona Hangen, *Redeeming the Dial: Radio, Religion, and Popular Culture in America* (Chapel Hill: University of North Carolina Press, 2002). For more on religious self-help, see Micki McGee, *Self-Help, Inc.: Makeover Culture in American Life* (Oxford: Oxford University Press, 2005).

44. For more on ritual and transmission views of communication, see James W. Carey, *Communication As Culture: Essays on Media and Society* (New York: Routledge, 1988); for more on the history of Early Christianity and the Spiritualist understandings of "soul-to-soul" communication, see John Durham Peters's *Speaking into the Air: A History of the Idea of Communication* (Chicago: University of Chicago Press, 2001), especially chapter 2.

45. Mara Mills, "The Audiovisual Telephone: A Brief History," in *Handheld? Music Video Aesthetics for Portable Devices*, ed. Henry Keazor (Heidelberg, Germany: ART-Dok, 2012), 34–47.

46. Hidenori Tomita, "*Keitai* and the Intimate Stranger," in *Personal, Portable, Pedestrian: Mobile Phones in Japanese Life*, ed. Mizuko Ito, Daisuke Okabe, and Misa Matsuda (Cambridge, MA: MIT Press, 2005), 184.

47. Tomita, "*Keitai* and the Intimate Stranger," 183.

48. For more on this, please see Lisa Stevenson's discussion of the delight and horror of the suicide prevention volunteer in *Life beside Itself: Imagining Care in the Canadian Arctic* (Berkeley: University of California Press, 2014).

49. For some examples of this kind of warm line and referral service, see Cait McKinney, "Calling to Talk and Listen Well: Information as Care at Telephone Hotlines," in *Information Activism: A Queer History of Lesbian Media Technologies* (Durham, NC: Duke University Press, 2020).

50. Aves Middleton, Jane Gunn, Bridget Bassilios, and Jane Pirkis, "Systematic Review of Research into Frequent Callers to Crisis Helplines," *Journal of Telemedicine and Telecare* 20, no. 2 (2014): 89–98. Separate from this kind of caller is another category of user, "the exploit caller." "The exploit caller" uses the hotline for various kinds of pranking or abuse of the hotline, including masturbating while speaking a false scenario. For more on this, see David Lester, "Counseling and Crisis Usage," in *The Social Impact of the Telephone*, ed. Ithiel de Sola Pool (Cambridge, MA: MIT University Press, 1977), 455–456; and David Lester and James C. Rogers, eds., *Crisis Intervention and Counseling by Telephone and the Internet* (Springfield, IL: Charles C. Thomas Publishing, 2012).

51. David Lester, "Counseling and Crisis Usage," 460.

52. Lester, 460.

53. Suicide.org, accessed August 25, 2017. In his book *We Are Data*, John Cheney-Lippold looks at these kinds of scripted communications critically—so critically that he doesn't consider them communications. For more, see Cheney-Lippold, *We Are Data* (New York: New York University Press, 2018).

54. Tom Long, "Obituary: Rev. Kenneth B. Murphy, at 78; Pastor Founded Suicide Hot Line," *Boston Globe*, May 26, 1999.

55. Long, "Obituary: Rev. Kenneth B. Murphy."

56. Lukach, "Exquisite Listening."

57. Bernard Duncan Mayes, *Escaping God's Closet: The Revelations of a Queer Priest* (Charlottesville: University of Virginia Press, 2001), 138.

58. Mayes would go on to have an extensive career in media practice and scholarship, first volunteering at KPFA in Berkeley before becoming NPR's first chairman, lecturing at Stanford's Institute for Mass Media from 1972 to 1984, and then becoming a professor at the University of Virginia in Communications Studies.

59. Mayes, *Escaping God's Closet*, 123.

60. Mayes, 123.

61. Mayes, 128.

62. Dr. E. S. Shneidman Papers, Box 6, Folder 10. UCLA Special Collections, Charles E. Young Research Library, University of California, Los Angeles.

63. Dr. E. S. Shneidman Papers, Box 6, Folders 9–12. UCLA Special Collections, Charles E. Young Research Library, University of California, Los Angeles.

64. Dr. E. S. Shneidman Papers, Box 6, Folder 10.

65. Dr. E. S. Shneidman Papers, Box 6, Folder 10.

66. Mayes, *Escaping God's Closet*, 128.

67. Sarah Baughey-Gill, "When Gay Was Not Okay with the APA: A Historical Overview of Homosexuality and Its Status as Mental Disorder," *Occam's Razor* 1 (2011): https://cedar.wwu.edu/orwwu/vol1/iss1/2 (last accessed September 30, 2020).

68. Mayes, *Escaping God's Closet*, 128.

69. Mayes, 132.

70. Mayes, 135.

71. Nan Alamilla Boyd, "San Francisco's Castro District: From Gay Liberation to Tourist Destination," *Journal of Tourism and Cultural Change* 9, no. 3 (2011): 237–248.

72. Mayes, *Escaping God's Closet*, 136.

73. Mayes, 136.

74. Mayes, 138.

75. “Thinking of Suicide? Bernard Mayes Interviewed by Elsa Knight Thomson,” March 19, 1963. Courtesy of the Pacifica Radio Archives.

76. Mayes, *Escaping God's Closet*, 145.

77. Lukach, “Exquisite Listening.”

78. “Thinking of Suicide?”

79. Patricia McBroom, “24-Hour Suicide Services Winning Attention of Cities,” November 10, 1965. Dr. E. S. Shneidman Papers, Box 31, Folder 8. UCLA Special Collections, Charles E. Young Research Library, University of California, Los Angeles.

80. McBroom, “24-Hour Suicide Services.”

81. Sam Whiting, “Bernard Mayes to be Honored as Lifeline to Suicidal,” *SF Gate*, April 28, 2012.

82. For more on this please consult Kara Kvaran's “Super Gay” in Annessa Babic's *Comics as History, Comics as Literature* (Madison, NJ: Fairleigh Dickinson University Press, 2013).

83. Mayes, *Escaping God's Closet*, 144.

84. “History,” San Francisco Suicide Prevention, http://www.sfsuicide.org/about-sfsp/history, last accessed June 15, 2016.

85. Eyder Peralta, “Bernard Mayes, NPR's First Chairman, Founder of Suicide Hotline, Dies,” *National Public Radio*, October 27, 2014.

86. “History,” San Francisco Suicide Prevention.

87. Erica Robles-Anderson, “The Crystal Cathedral: Architecture for a Mediated Congregation,” *Public Culture* 24, no. 3 (2012): 581.

88. Robles-Anderson, “The Crystal Cathedral,” 580; Robert H. Schuller, “Garden Grove Community Church History,” H93–1188, Crystal Cathedral Ministries Collection, Joint Archives of Holland (1977).

89. Suzanne Keller, “The Telephone in New (and Old) Communities,” in *The Social Impact of the Telephone*, 282.

90. Hosting a crisis hotline is in keeping not only with generalized Protestant doctrine, but the specific message that Schuller preached to his congregation. Schuller argued that acts that lowered another's self-esteem were true sins and as bad as doing someone physical harm. Where despair, or loneliness, depression, and anxiety were the hallmarks of damnation, Schuller thought that self-esteem came through prayer and good works and that it was crucial for being saved. He argued that literal Hell follows the emotional hell that comes when a person is separated from God and has lost his self-esteem.

91. For more on the history of AT&T and telephonic sociability, see Claude S. Fischer, “‘Touch Someone’: The Telephone Industry Discovers Sociability,” *Technology and Culture* 29, no. 1 (1988): 32.

92. Schuller, “Garden Grove Community Church History.”

93. Raymond E. Beckering, Collection W12–1398, Joint Archives of Holland.
94. Robert H. Schuller, "New Hope Telephone Counseling Service," Pamphlet used for outreach, H93–1188, Crystal Cathedral Ministries Collection, Joint Archives of Holland.
95. Schuller, "Garden Grove Community Church History."
96. Robert H. Schuller, Call Logs H93–1188, Crystal Cathedral Ministries Collection, Joint Archives of Holland.
97. Raymond E. Beckering, Collection W12–1398.
98. Schuller, "Garden Grove Community Church History."
99. Schuller, "Call Logs."
100. Schuller.
101. Schuller.
102. Schuller. As a note, I have access to call logs with callers' real names, personal data, and call content. Where I discuss particular calls, all identifying data have been removed. For more on this consideration, see "A Note on Method" in the introduction.
103. Lester, "Counseling and Crisis Usage," 455–456.
104. Russell Leigh Sharman, *The Tenants of East Harlem* (Berkeley: University of California Press, 2006), 64.
105. Jose B. Rivera, "Rafael Flores in Remembrance," East-Harlem.com, 2003, https://www.east-harlem.com/index.php/News/view/rafael_flores_in_remembrance/, last accessed May 6, 2020.
106. Carole Haymes Howard, "Rest in Power Elbert 'Big Man' Howard, Founding Father of the Black Panther Party," *San Francisco Bay View*, July 18, 2018. For more on the radical health care services and initiatives of the Black Panthers, see Alondra Nelson, *Body and Soul: The Black Panther Party and the Fight against Medical Discrimination* (Minneapolis: University of Minnesota Press, 2011).
107. Varah, *Before I Die Again*, 153.
108. Mayes, *Escaping God's Closet*, 137.
109. Raymond E. Beckering, Collection W12–1398.
110. However, psychological studies show that it is much more difficult to perform phone therapy for the majorly depressed than for those with anxiety disorders—let alone for those who are paranoid and worry that their phone conversation may be recorded or tapped.

CHAPTER 4

1. Alan Turing, "Computing Machinery and Intelligence," *MIND* 59, no. 236 (October 1950): 434.
2. Turing, "Computing Machinery and Intelligence," 434.

3. Turing, 455.

4. Warner V. Slack, *Cybermedicine: How Computing Empowers Doctors and Patients for Better Care*, 2nd ed. (San Francisco: Jossey-Bass, 2001), 49.

5. Charles's brother, Dr. Warner Slack, recounts this story in his book *Cybermedicine*. Warner Slack was perhaps the first person ever to put a patient into conversation with a machine and is discussed in his own right later in this chapter. Slack, *Cybermedicine*, 49.

6. Slack, *Cybermedicine*, 50.

7. Slack, 50.

8. I. M. Marks, "Self-Administered Behavioural Treatment," *Behavioural Psychotherapy* 19, no. 1 (1991): 42–46. As quoted in Fjóla Dögg Helgadóttir, Ross G. Menzies, Mark Onslow, Ann Packman, and Sue O'Brian, "Online CBT I: Bridging the Gap between Eliza and Modern Online CBT Treatment Packages," *Behaviour Change* 26, no. 4 (2009): 245.

9. Sherry Turkle, *Life on the Screen* (New York: Simon and Schuster, 1995), 26.

10. Turkle, *Life on the Screen*, 103 (emphasis added).

11. For more on ELIZA, please see Elizabeth Wilson's *Affect and Artificial Intelligence* (Seattle: University of Washington Press, 2010); Turkle's *Life on the Screen*; Lucy Suchman's *Human-Machine Reconfigurations: Plans and Situated Actions* (Cambridge: Cambridge University Press, 1987); and Lydia Liu's *The Freudian Robot: Digital Media and the Future of the Unconscious* (Chicago: University of Chicago Press, 2011).

12. Joel Epstein and William D. Klinkenberg, "From Eliza to Internet: A Brief History of Computerized Assessment," *Computers in Human Behavior* 17, no. 3 (2001): 295–314.

13. Joseph Weizenbaum, *Computer Power and Human Reason* (New York: W. H. Freeman, 1976), 3.

14. Carl R. Rogers, *Counseling and Psychotherapy* (Cambridge, MA: Riverside Press, 1942).

15. Weizenbaum, *Computer Power and Human Reason*, 5.

16. Weizenbaum, 2.

17. Weizenbaum, 6.

18. Turkle notes that there are other reasons to remove the therapist from therapy. In the early 1990s, after a scandalous case of boundary violation in the Boston psychoanalytic community, her students at MIT began to remark that there would be no such violations if therapists were computers. For more, see *Life on the Screen*, 113. For more on violence (especially rape) and therapy, see coda.

19. Liu, *The Freudian Robot*, 210. Liu argues that Weizenbaum here is "not only implying that only women are susceptible to such delusions, but the popularity of his story within the communities of computer science and artificial intelligence does reveal something about shared assumptions about gender and intelligence" (210).

20. Liu, 210.

21. Weizenbaum, *Computer Power and Human Reason*, 6–7 (emphasis added).

22. Turkle, *Life on the Screen*, 108.

23. Turkle, 109.

24. Wilson, *Affect and Artificial Intelligence*, 94.

25. For more on the psychological relation to anthropomorphized artifacts, especially children's toys and robots, see Sherry Turkle, *The Second Self: Computers and the Human Spirit* (Cambridge, MA: MIT Press, 1985), 289–290.

26. Anna Freud, "The Psychoanalytic Study of Infantile Feeding Disturbances," *Psychoanalytic Studies of the Child* 2 (1946): 127.

27. Intrinsic to the conversation here, but beyond the purview of this book, is a deeper engagement with the "digital unconscious." For more on theorization of the relations between the unconscious and the digital, see Patricia Ticineto Clough, *Autoaffection: Unconscious Thought in the Age of Technology* (Minneapolis: University of Minnesota Press, 2000), and *The User Unconscious: On Affect, Media, and Measure* (Minneapolis: University of Minnesota Press, 2018); Aaron Balick, *The Psychodynamics of Social Networking: Connected-up Instantaneous Culture and Self* (New York: Routledge, 2013); Alessandra Lemma, *The Digital Age on the Couch: Psychoanalytic Practice and New Media* (New York: Routledge, 2017); Jacob Johanssen, *Psychoanalysis and Digital Culture: Audiences, Social Media, and Big Data* (New York: Routledge, 2018).

28. Weizenbaum, *Computer Power and Human Reason*, 5.

29. Weizenbaum, 5–6.

30. Weizenbaum, 5–6.

31. Weizenbaum, 5–6.

32. Turkle, *Life on the Screen*, 107. For more on this feud from Colby's perspective, see Kenneth Colby, "Dialog Programs I Have Known and Loved over 33 Years," in *Machine Conversations*, ed. Yorick Wilks (New York: Springer Nature, 1999).

33. K. M. Colby, J. B. Watt, and J. P. Gilbert, "A Computer Method of Psychotherapy: Preliminary Communication," *Journal of Nervous and Mental Disease* 142 (1966): 146.

34. Wilson, *Affect and Artificial Intelligence*, 96.

35. Turkle, *Life on the Screen*, 289n8.

36. Colby, Watt, and Gilbert, "A Computer Method of Psychotherapy," 149.

37. Colby, as quoted in Weizenbaum, *Computer Power and Human Reason*, 5.

38. Colby, as quoted in Weizenbaum, 5.

39. Wilson, *Affect and Artificial Intelligence*, 96.

40. Wilson, 96.

41. Wilson, 98.

42. Wilson, 98.

43. Wilson, 97.

44. Slack, *Cybermedicine*, 46.

45. Slack, 13.

46. Warner V. Slack and Lawrence J. Van Cura, "Patient Reaction to Computer-Based Medical Interviewing," *Computers and Biomedical Research* 1 (1968): 527–531.

47. Warner Slack, Phone Interview, September 13, 2017.

48. Slack, Phone Interview.

49. Slack, *Cybermedicine*, 46.

50. Slack and Van Cura, "Patient Reaction to Computer-Based Medical Interviewing."

51. Warner Slack, Phone Interview, September 13, 2017.

52. Slack and Van Cura, "Patient Reaction to Computer-Based Medical Interviewing."

53. Warner Slack, Phone Interview, September 13, 2017.

54. Harold P. Erdman, John J. Greist, Marjorie H. Klein, James W. Jefferson, and Carl Getto, "The Computer Psychiatrist: How Far Have We Come? Where Are We Heading? How Far Dare We Go?," *Behavior Research Methods and Instrumentation* 13, no. 4 (1981): 394 (emphasis added).

55. Slack, *Cybermedicine*, 46.

56. Wilson, *Affect and Artificial Intelligence*, 101.

57. Theodore Nadelson, "The Inhuman Computer, the Too Human Therapist," *American Journal of Psychotherapy* 41, no. 4 (October 1987): 490.

58. Tomas Rozbroj, Anthony Lyons, Marian Pitts, Anne Mitchell, and Helen Christensen, "Assessing the Applicability of E-Therapies for Depression, Anxiety, and Other Mood Disorders among Lesbians and Gay Men: Analysis of 24 Web- and Mobile Phone-Based Self-Help Interventions," *Journal of Medical Internet Research* 16, no. 7 (2014): e166.

59. Paulette Selmi, "Computer-Assisted Cognitive-Behavior Therapy in the Treatment of Depression" (PhD diss., Illinois Institute of Technology, 1990).

60. Weizenbaum, *Computer Power and Human Reason*, 6.

61. But, in one key way, this division isn't as clear as it seems. Freud himself worked to establish the scienticity of psychoanalysis (see chapter 1) and psychoanalysis has, by and large, failed to produce evidence-based accounts of its successes.

62. For more on the Macy Conferences, see N. Katherine Hayles, *How We Became Posthuman: Virtual Bodies in Cybernetics, Literature, and Informatics* (Chicago: University of Chicago Press, 1999); Wilson's *Affect and Artificial Intelligence*; Luke Stark, "That Signal Feeling: Emotion and Interaction Design from Social Media to the 'Anxious Seat,'" (PhD diss., New York University, 2016); Todd Essig's "Psychoanalysis Lost—and Found—in Our Culture

of Simulation and Enhancement," *Psychoanalytic Inquiry* 32 (2012): 438–453. For more on the history of psychoanalysis in this moment, see Jonathan Metzl, *Prozac on the Couch: Prescribing Gender in the Era of Wonder Drugs* (Durham, NC: Duke University Press, 2005).

63. Essig, "Psychoanalysis Lost—and Found."

64. In 1917, the American Psychological Association released a precursor to the DSM: the *Statistical Manual for the Use of Institutions for the Insane*. This volume contained only twenty-two categories of diagnosis. See American Psychiatric Association—Mental Hospital Service, *The Diagnostic and Statistical Manual of Mental Disorders* (Washington, DC: American Psychiatric Association—Mental Hospital Service, 1952).

65. Robert Spitzer and Joseph Fliess, "A Re-analysis of the Reliability of Psychiatric Diagnosis," *British Journal of Psychiatry* 125, no. 4 (1974): 321–347.

66. Spitzer and Fliess, "A Re-analysis of the Reliability of Psychiatric Diagnosis."

67. Liu, *The Freudian Robot*, 234–235.

68. Liu, 345.

69. Liu, 345.

70. Liu, 345.

71. "Parry Encounters the Doctor," https://tools.ietf.org/html/rfc439, last accessed August 15, 2017.

72. "Parry Encounters the Doctor."

73. Weizenbaum, *Computer Power and Human Reason*, 6.

74. Albert Ellis, as quoted in Oliver Burkeman, "Albert Ellis," *Guardian*, August 10, 2007.

75. Burkeman, "Albert Ellis."

76. Rachel Rosner challenges the notion that Beck totally broke with psychoanalysis. According to her research, while Beck presented as anti-Freudian publicly, privately he was still interested and attached to psychoanalytic theory. For more, see Rachel Rosner, "Aaron T. Beck's Drawings and the Psychoanalytic Origin Story of Cognitive Therapy," *History of Psychology* 15, no. 1 (2012): 1–18. See also Erica Goode, "Scientist at Work: Aaron T. Beck, Pragmatist, Embodies His No-nonsense Therapy," *New York Times*, 2011.

77. Goode, "Scientist at Work."

78. As Luke Stark observes, "Ellis' Rational Emotional Behavioral Therapy teach[es] patients to become self-sufficient through positive reinforcement—in effect, practicing self-therapy" ("That Signal Feeling," 114).

79. Luke Stark writes that, even in the earliest moments of REBT, Ellis was interested in other media channels including the audio recording, and that such efforts to make REBT multimedial should be contrasted with the genre of self-help; but I would argue that Norman Vincent Peale and Smiley Blanton had already paved the way in the preceding decades for

taking a kind of psychological self-help and delivering it over every imaginable medium and modality (see chapter 3).

80. Erica Robles-Anderson, "Blind Spots: Religion in Media," *Flow Journal* 17 (2012): http://flowtv.org/2012/12/blind-spots/, last accessed June 15, 2016.

81. Albert Ellis, Correspondence with Jeffrey Caine, as quoted in Stark, "That Signal Feeling," 114–115.

82. Turkle, *Life on the Screen*, 112.

83. Boris Kachka, "The Power of Positive Publishing," *New York Magazine*, January 6, 2013.

84. Turkle, *Life on the Screen*, 103–104.

85. Burkeman, "Albert Ellis."

86. Philippe Lejeune, *On Diary* (Honolulu: University of Hawaii Press, 2009), 51.

87. Lejeune also recounts that, in the nineteenth century, young women laid out their religious books, taking their formatting from accounting books with "one page for each week and one line for each day with two columns, one marked 'V' for victories (over the Devil) and the other marked 'D' for defeats" (*On Diary*, 51).

88. Harold Innis, *The Bias of Communication* (Toronto: University of Toronto Press, 1951).

89. Lejeune, *On Diary*, 179.

90. The handwritten diary is assumed to be a private autobiographical writing, for the self, even if it's published later or posthumously. It is a genre that continues to be in use and flourish online, beginning with Claudio Pinhanez's "Open Diary" published at MIT in 1994, to Xanga, Livejournal, and other web-based diary keeping platforms in the late 1990s and early 2000s. Much like their analogue counterparts, these digital diaries could either be closed and private or published. Even when digital autobiographical forms begin to exist alongside the handwritten diaries, entries get time stamped, words get counted; this kind of self-monitoring (and self-tracking) migrates to the digital as an automated feature.

91. Witold Gombrowicz, *Diary*, trans. Lilian Vallee (New Haven, CT: Yale University Press, 2012), 1.

92. Lejeune, *On Diary*, 31.

93. Lejeune, 326.

94. Stark, "That Signal Feeling," 121.

95. "Diary Writing Turns a New Leaf," *New York Times*, 1981.

96. "Diary Writing Turns a New Leaf."

97. Lejeune, *On Diary*, 289 (emphasis added).

98. Lejeune, 289 (emphasis added).

99. Lejeune, 289–90.

100. Turkle, *The Second Self,* 5.

101. Roger Gould, In-Person Interview, September 8, 2017.

102. Gould, In-Person Interview.

103. Gould, In-Person Interview.

104. Gould, In-Person Interview.

105. Roger Gould, "Therapeutic Learning Program," http://www.drrogergould.com/software/therapeutic-learning-program, last accessed October 11, 2017.

106. Patricia Ward Biderman, "Feeling Depressed? Here's a Program That Could Help: Computers: A Psychiatrist Has Developed Dr. Software, Which Lets People Pour Out Their Problems as Fast as Their Fingers Can Type on Their PCs," *Los Angeles Times,* November 15, 1990.

107. Biderman, "Feeling Depressed?"

108. Kenneth Colby, "Human-Computer Conversation in a Cognitive Therapy Program," in *Machine Conversations,* 12.

109. Colby, "Human-Computer Conversation," 11.

110. Lawrence Magid, "Psychological Software Programs Come with Their Own Shortcomings," *Washington Post,* November 19, 1990.

111. A copy of the program is housed at Stanford University in the Edward Feigenbaum papers. The disks could be opened in order to see a list of files but the files themselves could not be accessed because the disks are considered "extremely obsolete." The description that follows comes from the paper materials included in the program that were also sent by Colby to Feigenbaum. Floppy Disks and Instruction Manual of Overcoming Depression. Edward A. Feigenbaum Papers, ACCN 2005–101, SC 340 Box 59, Folder 3, Stanford Special Collections, Stanford University, California.

112. Biderman, "Feeling Depressed?"

113. Colby, "Human-Computer Conversation," 11.

114. Kenneth Colby, Floppy Disks and Instruction Manual of Overcoming Depression 2.0, Edward A. Feigenbaum Papers, ACCN 2005–101, SC 340 Box 59, Folder 3, Stanford Special Collections, Stanford University, California.

115. Colby, Manual of Overcoming Depression 2.0.

116. Kenneth Colby, Malibu Artifactual Intelligence, https://web.archive.org/web/19970529035521/http://maiw.com:80/program.html, last accessed via the Internet Archive, August 15, 2017.

117. Colby, Manual of Overcoming Depression 2.0.

118. Colby, Malibu Artifactual Intelligence.

119. Biderman, "Feeling Depressed?"

120. Bureau of Labor Statistics, "Computer Ownership in the 1990s," April 5, 1999, https://www.bls.gov/opub/ted/1999/apr/wk1/art01.htm, last accessed July 1, 2017.

121. Colby, Manual of Overcoming Depression 2.0. For more on this program, see Sherry Turkle, "Taking Things at Interface Value," in *Life on the Screen.*

122. Colby, Malibu Artifactual Intelligence.

123. Colby, Manual of Overcoming Depression 2.0.

124. Colby.

125. Colby, "Human-Computer Conversation," 11.

126. Colby, "Comments on Human-Computer Conversation," 6.

127. Colby, 3.

128. Margaret A. Boden, *Mind as Machine: A History of Cognitive Science* (Oxford: Oxford University Press, 2006).

129. Joseph Weintraub, "History of the PC Therapist," http://www.cis.umassd.edu/~ivalova/Spring09/cis412/Old/therapist.pdf, last accessed July 1, 2017.

130. For more on this and other 1990s software for depression, and user reactions to it, see Turkle, *Life on the Screen*, 102–127.

131. Selmi, "Computer-Assisted Cognitive-Behavior Therapy."

132. Wayne Bowers, Scott Stuart, Robin Macfarlane, and Laura Gorman, "Use of Computer-Administered Cognitive-Behavior Therapy with Depressed Patients," *Depression* 1, no. 6 (1993): 293–299.

133. Another one of DARPA's DCAPS projects is Bravemind, a virtual reality therapy for returning veterans. For more on this therapy and its history, see Marisa Renee Brandt's "Simulated War: Remediating Trauma Narratives in Military Psychotherapy," *Catalyst Journal* 2, no. 1 (2016).

134. Talkspace, "The Future of Therapy: Can You Have a Relationship with a Machine?" (conference presented by Talkspace, April 5, 2016).

135. For more on listening and monitoring software, see Jessica Feldman's "The Problem of the Adjective: Affective Computing of the Speaking Voice," *Transposition: Music et sciences sociales*, no. 6 (2016): https://doi.org/10.4000/transposition.1640.

136. Ann Robinson, "Meet Ellie, the Machine That Can Detect Depression," *The Guardian*, September 17, 2005.

137. Talkspace, "The Future of Therapy."

138. Robinson, "Meet Ellie."

139. Robinson, "Meet Ellie."

140. As with Ellie, Tess's creators are all white men, and yet Tess is feminized in the lineage that begins with ELIZA and ends with other feminized listening objects and "assistants" like Siri

and Alexa. Much like users of Ask Uncle Ezra (see chapter 5) couldn't imagine a man providing such therapy (despite the masculine "Uncle" and proper name), it seems that from ELIZA forward, chatbots with and without avatars are to be women.

141. "x2.ai," https://x2.ai/, last accessed July 1, 2017.

142. "Ethics," https://x2.ai/ethics, last accessed August 23, 2017 (page no longer available).

143. "Ethics."

144. "Introducing Tess," https://x2.ai/, last accessed July 1, 2017.

145. Talkspace, "The Future of Therapy."

146. everbliss, http://www.everbliss.com/, last accessed May 10, 2017.

147. Uli Cohen and Yoon Im Kane, Phone Interview, November 5, 2016.

148. "Joyable," https://joyable.com/how-it-works, last accessed July 1, 2017.

149. Stark, "That Signal Feeling," 112.

150. "Psychological Therapies, Annual Report on the Use of IAPT Services—England, 2014–15," November 24, 2015, http://content.digital.nhs.uk/catalogue/PUB19098/psyc-ther-ann-rep-2014-15.pdf, last accessed July 15, 2017.

151. Ian Bogost, "Gamification is Bullshit," 2001, http://bogost.com/writing/blog/gamification_is_bullshit/, last accessed July 1, 2017.

152. Natasha Schull, "Data for Life: Wearable Technology and the Design of Self-Care," *BioSocieties* 11 (2016): 317–333.

153. Schull, "Data for Life."

154. "Koko," https://itskoko.com/, last accessed July 1, 2017.

155. Attif Sulyeman, "DARPA to Plug Computers into Brains to Talk Directly to People," *The Independent*, July 12, 2017.

CHAPTER 5

1. Jerry Feist and Steven Worona, *The Best of Uncle Ezra*, vol. 1, *Fall 1988* (Ithaca, NY: Cornell University, 1988), 92.

2. Feist and Worona, *The Best of Uncle Ezra*, 1:92.

3. Steven Worona, Phone Interview, October 23, 2016.

4. Feist and Worona, *The Best of Uncle Ezra*, vol. 2, *Fall 1991* (Ithaca, NY: Cornell University, 1991), Foreword.

5. Worona, Phone Interview, October 23, 2016.

6. Worona, Phone Interview.

7. Feist and Worona, *The Best of Uncle Ezra*, 1:92.

8. Martha Ainsworth, "E-Therapy: A History and Survey," last retrieved May 10, 2017, from https://metanoia.org/imhs/.

9. C. Atkins, "A 2011 Recap of the 1996 Telemedicine Development Act: The Therapist" (November/December 2011), last retrieved May 10, 2017, from https://archive.camft.org/COS/The_Therapist/Legal_Articles/Cathy/A_2011_Recap_of_the_1996_Telemedicine_Development_Act.aspx.

10. David Sommers, Mental Health Cyber-Clinic (1996), last retrieved May 10, 2017, from https://web.archive.org/web/19990116231713/http://www.dcez.com:80/~davids/pageone.htm.

11. B. Monegain, "Telemedicine Market to Soar Past $30B," *Health Care IT News*, August 4, 2015, https://www.healthcareitnews.com/news/telemedicine-poised-grow-big-time, last accessed May 10, 2017.

12. Jerry Feist, Phone Interview, October 17, 2016.

13. The Cornell community had its suspicions that Uncle Ezra was a woman, and that no man could produce that voice and that kind of care. When Feist retired from running that service, and therefore acknowledged his role in it, students were surprised that he had been their anonymous ear. Some users alerted Feist in turn that they had written particular questions.

14. Feist and Worona, *The Best of Uncle Ezra*, vol. 2, Back cover.

15. Feist and Worona, *The Best of Uncle Ezra*, vol. 1, Foreword.

16. Feist and Worona, 99.

17. Feist and Worona, *The Best of Uncle Ezra*, vol. 2, Foreword.

18. Worona, Phone Interview, October 23, 2016.

19. Feist and Worona, *The Best of Uncle Ezra*, vol. 1, Foreword.

20. Feist and Worona, Foreword.

21. Feist and Worona, Foreword.

22. Laura Finley, ed., *The Encyclopedia of School Crime and Violence*, vol. 1, *A–N* (Oxford: ABC-CLIO, 2011), 12.

23. Martha Ainsworth, "My Life as an E-Patient," in *e-Therapy: Case Studies, Guiding Principles, and the Clinical Potential of the Internet* (New York: W. W. Norton, 2002), 195.

24. Ainsworth, "My Life as an E-Patient," 196.

25. Ainsworth, 196.

26. Ainsworth, 197.

27. Ainsworth, 197.

28. David Sommers, Phone Interview, December 14, 2016.

29. Sommers, Phone Interview.

30. Sommers.

31. Sommers, Mental Health Cyber-Clinic.

32. Sommers.

33. Sommers.

34. Moira Weigel, *Labor of Love: The Invention of Dating* (New York: Farrar, Strauss, Giroux, 2016), 201.

35. Weigel, *Labor of Love.*

36. Sommers, Mental Health Cyber-Clinic.

37. Ainsworth, "My Life as an E-Patient," 198.

38. Eric Cohen, "Shrinks Aplenty Online, but Are They Credible?," *New York Times*, January 17, 1997.

39. Sommers, Mental Health Cyber-Clinic.

40. For an in-depth reading of these spaces, see Joe Dumit, "Illnesses You Have to Fight to Get: Facts as Forces in Uncertain, Emergent Illnesses," *Social Science and Medicine* (February 2006): 577–590.

41. John Grohol, Phone Interview, October 21, 2016.

42. Over the course of Internet 1.0 and 2.0, there are radically shifting conventions of anonymity on the web. One such indicator is handle culture, which is not static and goes from featuring pseudonyms to frequently being identity tied or representative. For teletherapy, questions of anonymity are perhaps connected to the status of the fee in therapeutic interaction; that is, on the Internet you can have free peer-to-peer, or even free expert-to-patient help without names. But names seem to reintroduce billing and the fee.

43. John Grohol, "Our Dedication to Mental Health," June 7, 2016, https://psychcentral.com/about/our-dedication-to-mental-health, last retrieved May 10, 2017.

44. Grohol, Phone Interview, October 21, 2016.

45. John Ashbery, "Self-Portrait in a Convex Mirror," in *Self-Portrait in a Convex Mirror* (New York: Viking Press, 1975), 82.

46. Sommers, Mental Health Cyber-Clinic.

47. Ainsworth, "My Life as an E-Patient," 198.

48. Sommers, Mental Health Cyber-Clinic.

49. Ainsworth, "My Life as an E-Patient," 198.

50. Sommers, Mental Health Cyber-Clinic.

51. Sommers.

52. Sommers, Phone Interview, December 14, 2016.

53. Ainsworth, "My Life as an E-Patient," 199.

54. Ainsworth, 199.

55. Sherry Turkle, *Alone Together: Why We Expect More from Technology and Less from Each Other* (New York: Basic Books, 2011), 1.

56. Sommers, Phone Interview, December 14, 2016.

57. Sommers.

58. Sommers, Mental Health Cyber-Clinic.

59. Sommers.

60. Sigmund Freud, *Fragment of an Analysis of a Case of Hysteria* (1905), *The Standard Edition*, vol. 7 (London: Hogarth Press, 1953), 1–122, 77.

61. M. Kleine and G. Gale, "The Elusive Presence of the Word: An Interview with Walter Ong," *Composition FORUM* (1996): 81.

62. Kleine and Gale, "The Elusive Presence of the Word," 80.

63. Jacques Derrida has written much about the relationship between speech and writing, most notably perhaps in *Of Grammatology*, trans. Gayatri Chakravorty Spivak (Baltimore, MD: Johns Hopkins University Press, 1998). For more on the supposed primacy of speech over writing, and Derrida's revision to this argument, see "Chapter 1: The End of The Book and Beginning of Writing."

64. Cohen, "Shrinks Aplenty Online, but Are They Credible?"

65. Letter from Sigmund Freud to Wilhelm Fliess, May 21, 1894, in *The Complete Letters of Sigmund Freud to Wilhelm Fliess, 1887–1904*, ed. and trans. Jeffrey M. Masson (Cambridge, MA: Belknap Press, 1985).

66. Virginia Shea, *Netiquette* (San Francisco: Albion Books, 1994).

67. Kleine and Gale, "The Elusive Presence of the Word," 81.

68. Mara Mills, "The Audiovisual Telephone: A Brief History," in *Handheld? Music Video Aesthetics for Portable Devices*, ed. Henry Keazor (Heidelberg, Germany: ART-Dok, 2012), 44–45.

69. Naomi Baron, *Always On: Language in an Online and Mobile World* (New York: Oxford University Press, 2008), 48.

70. Baron, *Always On*, 7. For more on plural and World Englishes, see Kingsley Bolton and Braj B. Kachru, *World Englishes: Critical Concepts in Linguistics* (New York: Routledge, 2006).

71. Baron, *Always On*, 172.

72. Feist, Phone Interview, October 17, 2016.

73. Naomi Baron uses the term "volume control" in regard to online communications with a different meaning. Instead of implied volume of speech, she takes it to mean the number of communications one is dealing with at any given time. One can turn up the volume, she argues, by "incessantly checking email" or turn down the volume by blocking someone from a messaging service. For more on this, see chapter 3, "Controlling the Volume," in *Always On*.

74. Ainsworth, "My Life as an E-Patient," 201.

75. Tom Shortis, *The Language of ICT* (London: Psychology Press, 2001), 88.

76. Baron, *Always On*, 14–15.

77. For more on this, see Baron's *Always On*, 66–70; Ainsworth, "My Life as an E-Patient," 194.

78. Ainsworth, 194.

79. Ainsworth, 194.

80. Therese Örnberg Berglund, "Disrupted Turn Adjacency and Coherence Maintenance in Instant Messaging Conversations," *Language @ Internet* 6 (2009): https://www.languageatinternet.org/articles/2009/2106.

81. Netiquette manuals even mention the remediation of the dead letter office as a possible culprit for disjoined communications between correspondents: "Somewhere in cyberspace, there's a limbo of lost email messages. Like the souls of unbaptized babies, these notes wait, unread, for the end of time. The Post Office has always had its dead letter office. Mail delivery in cyberspace is no more foolproof." Shea, *Netiquette*, 55.

82. Shea, *Netiquette*, 55.

83. Kleine and Gale, "The Elusive Presence of the Word," 81.

84. Berglund, "Disrupted Turn Adjacency."

85. Gary Stofle, "Chat Room Therapy," in *e-Therapy: Case Studies, Guiding Principles, and the Clinical Potential of the Internet* (New York: W. W. Norton, 2002), 101.

86. Stofle, "Chat Room Therapy."

87. Ainsworth, "My Life as an E-Patient," 202.

88. Mills, "The Audiovisual Telephone," 34–47.

89. Talkspace, https://talkspace.workable.com/?fv=social, last retrieved May 10, 2017.

90. "Talkspace x Michael Phelps: How Therapy Saved His Life," https://www.youtube.com/watch?v=e8cBl9pKES4, last retrieved July 2, 2018.

91. Baron, *Always On*, 32.

92. Thomas D. Hull and Kush Mahan, "Telemedicine and e-Health," October 2016 (ahead of print), https://doi.org/10.1089/tmj.2016.0114.

93. Talkspace even features gift cards where you can "gift therapy to a loved one."

94. Talkspace, "Frequently Asked Questions," https://help.talkspace.com/hc/en-us, last retrieved May 10, 2017.

95. Todd Essig, "Talkspace Reveals Clients Emails Violating Clinical Confidentiality," *Forbes Magazine*, August 18, 2016.

96. Essig, "Talkspace Reveals Clients Emails."

97. Essig.

98. Yoon Im Kane, Email Interview, April 1, 2020.

99. Uli Cohen and Yoon Im Kane, Phone Interview, November 5, 2016.

100. Cohen and Kane, Phone Interview, November 5, 2016.

101. Cohen and Kane, Phone Interview.

102. Cohen and Kane.

103. Cohen and Kane.

104. Reddit Suicide Watch, https://www.reddit.com/r/SuicideWatch/, last retrieved May 10, 2017.

105. Reddit Suicide Watch.

106. Alice Gregory, "R U There?," *New Yorker*, February 9, 2015.

107. Mara Mercurio, Mark Larsen, Hannah Wisniewski, Philip Henson, Sarah Lagan, and John Torous, "Longitudinal Trends in the Quality, Effectiveness and Attributes of Highly Rated Smartphone Health Apps," *BMJ: Evidence-Based Mental Health* (April 2020): 1–5, https://ebmh.bmj.com/content/ebmental/early/2020/04/20/ebmental-2019-300137.full.pdf.

108. Sommers, Mental Health Cyber-Clinic (emphasis in the original).

109. Gregory, "R U There?"

CODA

1. Melanie Klein, *Narrative of a Child Analysis* (London: Karnac Books, 1961), 35. Some of what follows was previously reported in "Therapists Are Doing Sessions in Locked Bathrooms While Patients Call in from Their Cars," *Slate*, April 10, 2020.

2. Michal Shapira, *The War Inside: Psychoanalysis, Total War, and the Making of the Democratic Self in Postwar Britain* (Cambridge: Cambridge University Press, 2013).

3. As a disclosure, I provided peer mental health care during the pandemic via a mutual aid group set up in Berkeley.

4. Eric Linsker, Personal Communication, March 18, 2020.

5. Michael Garfinkle, Phone Interview, March 31, 2020.

6. Giuseppe Civiterese, Personal Communication, March 30, 2020.

7. Connie Scozzarro, Personal Communication, March 26, 2020.

8. Orna Guralnick, Phone Interview, March 29, 2020.

9. Bruce Weitzman, Personal Communication, March 31, 2020.

10. Guralnick, Phone Interview, March 29, 2020.

11. Hannah Black, https://twitter.com/nanpansky/status/1243142287820980226, last accessed June 12, 2020.

12. Carina del Valle Schorske, *April 20, 2020*, Pandemic Diary, https://www.nybooks.com/daily/2020/05/15/pandemic-journal-april-13-20/#del%20valle%20schorske.

13. Guralnick, Phone Interview, March 29, 2020.

14. Marshall McLuhan, *Understanding Media: The Extensions of Man* (Berkeley, CA: Gingko Press, 2013), 47 (emphasis added).

15. Civiterese, Personal Communication, March 30, 2020.

16. Neil Leibowitz, Personal Communication, March 31, 2020.

17. Joshua Clover, "66 Days," June 2, 2020, https://www.versobooks.com/blogs/4734-66-days.

18. Jim Perkinson, "Beyond Occasional Whiteness," *CrossCurrents* 47, no. 2 (1997): 195–209.

19. Clover, "66 Days."

20. Gerard Pommier, "What Constitutes an Interpretation?" (presented at the Psychoanalysis on Ice Conference, Reykjavik, Iceland, July 27, 2018).

21. When Sherry Turkle interviewed her undergraduates about Eliza in "Taking Things at Interface Value" in *Life on the Screen*, she pointed out that a recent series of boundary violations in the Boston psychiatric community influenced the thinking of her students about computer psychotherapy. "'Well, the computer therapist might not be involved with you the way a human would be, but that has a good side, too. These doctors who have sex with their patients are involved but in a bad way. . . .' For generations, machine metaphors had been used when humans were heartless toward other humans. Now it was the machines that could be counted on for civility." Turkle, *Life on the Screen* (New York: Simon and Schuster, 1995), 113.

22. Sherry Turkle, Gillian Isaacs Russell, and Todd Essig, "Bodies in the Room: Keeping Talk Therapy Real" May 29, 2018, https://medium.com/@sturkle/bodies-in-the-room-ca07d196e0d9, last accessed June 14, 2020.

23. Turkle, Russell, and Essig, "Bodies in the Room."

24. Jean M. Twenge and W. Keith Campbell, "Associations between Screen Time and Lower Psychological Well-being among Children and Adolescents: Evidence from a Population-based Study," *Preventive Medicine Reports* 12 (2018): 271–283.

25. For more on empathy and its centrality to conceptions of therapy, see Heinz Kohut, "Introspection, Empathy, and Psychoanalysis—an Examination of the Relationship between Mode of Observation and Theory," *Journal of the American Psychoanalytic Association* 7 (1959): 459–483; Elizabeth Lunbeck's "Empathy as a Psychoanalytic Mode of Observation: Between Sentiment and Science," in *Histories of Scientific Observation*, ed. Lorraine Daston and Elizabeth Lunbeck (Chicago: University of Chicago Press, 2011).

26. Saidiya Hartman, *Scenes of Subjection: Terror, Slavery, and Self-Making in Nineteenth-Century America* (Oxford: Oxford University Press, 1997), 20.

27. Namwali Serpell, "The Banality of Empathy," *New York Review of Books*, March 2, 2019.

28. Leo Bersani and Adam Phillips, *Intimacies* (Chicago: University of Chicago Press, 2008), 66–67.

29. Sarah Ackerman, "A Diagnosis for Psychoanalysis in the 21st Century: Freud as Medicine," *Psychoanalytic Quarterly* (October 2020), 670.

30. For work being done on this incredibly important phenomenon, see Safiya Noble's *Algorithms of Oppression: How Search Engines Reinforce Racism* (New York: New York University Press, 2018); Catherine D'Ignazio and Lauren F. Klein's *Data Feminism* (Cambridge, MA: MIT Press, 2020); Ruha Benjamin's *Race after Technology* (New York: Wiley, 2018); Virginia Eubanks's *Automating Inequality: How High-Tech Tools Profile, Police, and Punish the Poor* (New York: St. Martin's, 2018).
31. Todd Essig, Phone Interview, March 31, 2020.
32. As just one example from the first several months in pandemic, the Crisis Text Line, which at the start of COVID placed calls for more volunteers due to an increase in usage, has just publicly ousted its CEO, Nancy Lublin, for fostering a racist and abusive environment as well as evaluating the effectiveness of its volunteer crisis counselors by race and ethnicity.

Bibliography

Ackerman, Sally. "A Diagnosis for Psychoanalysis in the 21st Century: Freud as Medicine." *Psychoanalytic Quarterly* (October 2020): 667–688.

Adorno, Theodor. *The Psychological Technique of Martin Luther Thomas' Radio Addresses*. Palo Alto, CA: Stanford University Press, 2000.

Ainsworth, Martha. "E-Therapy: A History and Survey." Last retrieved May 10, 2017, from https://metanoia.org/imhs/.

Ainsworth, Martha. "My Life as an E-Patient." In *e-Therapy: Case Studies, Guiding Principles, and the Clinical Potential of the Internet*. New York: W. W. Norton, 2002.

American Psychiatric Association—Mental Hospital Service. *The Diagnostic and Statistical Manual of Mental Disorders*. Washington, DC: American Psychiatric Association—Mental Hospital Service, 1952.

Anker, Roy M. *Self-Help and Popular Religion in Modern American Culture: An Interpretive Guide*. Vol. 2. Westport, CT: Greenwood Publishing Group, 1999.

Anzieu, Didier. *Freud's Self-Analysis*. Madison, CT: International Universities Press, 1986.

Application for *Where Should We Begin?*, https://docs.google.com/forms/d/e/1FAIpQLScvP6TQ79f3iK4bjO5F4gAhE-mEnYcOKjLBZccYzfAiBeNd5g/viewform. Last accessed June 7, 2020.

Ashbery, John. "Self-Portrait in a Convex Mirror." In *Self-Portrait in a Convex Mirror*. New York: Viking Press, 1975.

Atkins, C. "A 2011 Recap of the 1996 Telemedicine Development Act: The Therapist." November/December 2011. Last retrieved May 10, 2017, from https://archive.camft.org/COS/The_Therapist/Legal_Articles/Cathy/A_2011_Recap_of_the_1996_Telemedicine_Development_Act.aspx.

Balbi, Gabriele, and Richard John. "Point-to-Point: Telecommunications Networks from the Optical Telegraph to the Mobile Telephone." In *Communication and Technology, 5th Volume of the Handbook of Communication Science*. Berlin: De Gruyter Mouton, 2014.

Balick, Aaron. *The Psychodynamics of Social Networking: Connected-up Instantaneous Culture and Self.* New York: Routledge, 2013.

Baron, Naomi. *Always On: Language in an Online and Mobile World.* New York: Oxford University Press, 2008.

Baucom, Ian. "Frantz Fanon's Radio: Solidarity, Diaspora, and the Tactics of Listening." *Contemporary Literature* 42, no. 1 (Spring, 2001): 15–49.

Baughey-Gill, Sarah. "When Gay Was Not Okay with the APA: A Historical Overview of Homosexuality and Its Status as Mental Disorder." *Occam's Razor* 1 (2011): https://cedar.wwu.edu/orwwu/vol1/iss1/2. Last accessed September 30, 2020.

Beckering, Raymond W. Collection, W12–1398. Joint Archives of Holland.

Behrens, Peter J. "Psychology Takes to the Airways: American Radio Psychology between the Wars, 1926–1939." *The American Sociologist* 40, no. 3 (September 2009): 214–227.

Benjamin, Ruha. *Race after Technology.* New York: Wiley, 2018.

Berglund, Therese Örnberg. "Disrupted Turn Adjacency and Coherence Maintenance in Instant Messaging Conversations." *Language @ Internet* 6 (2009): https://www.languageatinternet.org/articles/2009/2106.

Bersani, Leo, and Adam Phillips. *Intimacies.* Chicago: University of Chicago Press, 2008.

The Bible, King James Version.

Biderman, Patricia Ward. "Feeling Depressed? Here's a Program That Could Help: Computers: A Psychiatrist Has Developed Dr. Software, Which Lets People Pour Out Their Problems as Fast as Their Fingers Can Type on Their PCs." *Los Angeles Times*, November 15, 1990.

Bion, Wilfred. *Experiences in Groups.* London: Tavistock Publications, 1961.

Bion, Wilfred. "The Leaderless Group Project." *Bulletin of the Menninger Clinic* 10 (1946): 77–81.

Black, Hannah. https://twitter.com/nanpansky/status/1243142287820980226. Last accessed June 12, 2020.

Blanton, Smiley. *Diary of My Analysis with Sigmund Freud.* New York: Hawthorne Books, 1971.

Blanton, Smiley. "A Pioneering Partnership: The American Foundation of Religion and Psychiatry." The Dr. Smiley Blanton Papers, MS.0739, Box 10, Folder 46. Special Collections, University of Tennessee.

Blanton, Smiley. "The Religio-Psychiatric Clinic of the Marble Collegiate Church." The Dr. Smiley Blanton Papers, MS.0739, Box 11, Folder 16. Special Collections, University of Tennessee.

Boden, Margaret A. *Mind as Machine: A History of Cognitive Science.* Oxford: Oxford University Press, 2006.

Bogost, Ian. "Gamification is Bullshit." 2001. http://bogost.com/writing/blog/gamification_is_bullshit/. Accessed July 1, 2017.

Bolton, Kingsley, and Braj B. Kachru. *World Englishes: Critical Concepts in Linguistics*. New York: Routledge, 2006.

Bowers, Wayne, Scott Stuart, Robin Macfarlane, and Laura Gorman. "Use of Computer-Administered Cognitive-Behavior Therapy with Depressed Patients." *Depression* 1, no. 6 (1993): 293–299.

Boyd, Nan Alamilla. "San Francisco's Castro District: From Gay Liberation to Tourist Destination." *Journal of Tourism and Cultural Change* 9, no. 3 (2011): 237–248.

Brabant, Eva, Ernst Falzeder, and Paula Giampieri-Deutsch, eds., and P. T. Hoffer, trans. *The Correspondence of Sigmund Freud and Sándor Ferenczi*. Vol. 1, *1908–1914*. Cambridge, MA: Belknap Press, 1993.

Brandt, Marisa Renee. "Simulated War: Remediating Trauma Narratives in Military Psychotherapy." *Catalyst Journal* 2, no. 1 (2016): https://doi.org/10.28968/cftt.v2i1.28829.

Bridger, Harold. "The Discovery of the Therapeutic Community: The Northfield Experiments." In *The Social Engagement of Social Science, A Tavistock Anthology*. Edited by Eric Trist and Hugh Murray. Vol. 1. London: Tavistock Publications, 1990.

Brown, James. "Radio: Relating to People in a Caring Way." *Los Angeles Times*, November 27, 1977.

Bureau of Labor Statistics. "Computer Ownership in the 1990s." April 5, 1999. https://www.bls.gov/opub/ted/1999/apr/wk1/art01.htm. Accessed July 1, 2017.

Burkeman, Oliver. "Albert Ellis." *The Guardian*, August 10, 2007.

"Business Meetings Minutes of the British Psycho-Analytical Society." Courtesy of the Archives of the British Psycho-Analytical Society.

Carey, James. *Communication as Culture: Essays on Media and Society*. New York: Routledge, 1988.

Carlino, Ricardo. *Distance Psychoanalysis: The Theory and Practice of Using Communication Technology in the Clinic*. London: Karnac, 2011.

Chartier, Roger, Alain Boureau, and Cécile Dauphin. *Correspondence: Models of Letter-Writing from the Middle Ages to the Nineteenth Century*. Princeton, NJ: Princeton University Press, 1997.

Cheney-Lippold, John. *We Are Data*. New York: New York University Press, 2018.

Civiterese, Giuseppe. Personal Communication. March 30, 2020.

Clarke, Sally C. Division of Vital Statistics, Centers for Disease Control and Prevention and the National Center for Health Statistics. "Advance Report of Final Divorce Statistics, 1989 and 1990." *Monthly Vital Statistics Report* 43, no. 9 (March 22, 1995).

Clough, Patricia Ticineto. *Autoaffection: Unconscious Thought in the Age of Technology*. Minneapolis: University of Minnesota Press, 2000.

Clough, Patricia Ticineto. *The User Unconscious: On Affect, Media, and Measure*. Minneapolis: University of Minnesota Press, 2018.

Clover, Joshua. "66 Days." June 2, 2020. https://www.versobooks.com/blogs/4734-66-days.

Cohen, Eric. "Shrinks Aplenty Online, but Are They Credible?" *New York Times*, January 17, 1997.

Cohen, Uli, and Yoon Im Kane. Joint Phone Interview. November 5, 2016.

Colby, Kenneth. "Dialog Programs I Have Known and Loved over 33 Years." In *Machine Conversations*. Edited by Yorick Wilks. New York: Springer Nature, 1999.

Colby, Kenneth. Floppy Disks and Instruction Manual of Overcoming Depression 2.0. Edward A. Feigenbaum Papers, ACCN 2005–101, SC 340 Box 59, Folder 3. Stanford Special Collections, Stanford University, California.

Colby, Kenneth. "Human-Computer Conversation in a Cognitive Therapy Program." In *Machine Conversations*. Edited by Yorick Wilks. New York: Springer Nature, 1999.

Colby, Kenneth. Malibu Artifactual Intelligence. https://web.archive.org/web/19970529035521/http://maiw.com:80/program.html.Accessed via the Internet Archive, August 15, 2017.

Colby, Kenneth, J. B. Watt, and J. P. Gilbert. "A Computer Method of Psychotherapy: Preliminary Communication." *Journal of Nervous and Mental Disease* 142 (1966): 148–152.

Crisis Text Line. "Board and Advisors." https://www.crisistextline.org/board-advisors. Last accessed February 1, 2018.

Danto, Elizabeth. *Freud's Free Clinics: Psychoanalysis and Social Justice 1918–1938*. New York: Columbia University Press, 2005.

De Angelis, Barbara. *Ask Barbara: The 100 Most Asked Questions about Love, Sex, and Relationships*. New York: Random House, 1997.

Decker, William Merrill. *Epistolary Practices: Letter Writing in America before Telecommunications*. Chapel Hill: University of North Carolina Press, 1998.

del Valle Schorske, Carina. *April 20, 2020*. Pandemic Diary. https://www.nybooks.com/daily/2020/05/15/pandemic-journal-april-13-20/#del%20valle%20schorske. Last accessed October 4, 2020.

Derrida, Jacques. *Of Grammatology*. Translated by Gayatri Chakravorty Spivak. Baltimore, MD: Johns Hopkins University Press, 1998.

Derrida, Jacques. *The Postcard: From Socrates to Freud and Beyond*. Chicago: University of Chicago, 1987.

"Diary Writing Turns a New Leaf." *New York Times*, 1981.

D'Ignazio, Catherine, and Lauren F. Klein. *Data Feminism*. Cambridge, MA: MIT Press, 2020.

Dosse, Francois. *Intersecting Lives: Gilles Deleuze and Félix Guattari*. New York: Columbia University Press, 2011.

"Dr. Smiley Blanton Dead Here; Psychiatrist and Author Was 84." *New York Times*, October 31, 1966.

Dumit, Joe. "Illnesses You Have to Fight to Get: Facts as Forces in Uncertain, Emergent Illnesses." *Social Science and Medicine* (February 2006): 577–590.

Epstein, Joel, and William D. Klinkenberg. "From Eliza to Internet: A Brief History of Computerized Assessment." *Computers in Human Behavior* 17, no. 3 (2001): 295–314.

Erdman, Harold P., John J. Greist, Marjorie H. Klein, James W. Jefferson, and Carl Getto. "The Computer Psychiatrist: How Far Have We Come? Where Are We Heading? How Far Dare We Go?" *Behavior Research Methods and Instrumentation* 13, no. 4 (1981): 393–398.

Erikson, E. H. *Life History and the Historical Moment.* New York: Norton, 1975.

Essig, Todd. Phone Interview. March 31, 2020.

Essig, Todd. "Psychoanalysis Lost—and Found—in Our Culture of Simulation and Enhancement." *Psychoanalytic Inquiry* 32 (2012): 438–453.

Essig, Todd. "Talkspace Reveals Clients Emails Violating Clinical Confidentiality." *Forbes Magazine*, August 18, 2016.

Eubanks, Virginia. *Automating Inequality: How High-Tech Tools Profile, Police, and Punish the Poor.* New York: St. Martin's, 2018.

everbliss. http://www.everbliss.com/. Retrieved May 10, 2017.

Fanon, Frantz. *A Dying Colonialism.* Translated by Haackon Chevalier. New York: Grove Press, 1994.

Fanon, Frantz. "This Is the Voice of Algeria." In *A Dying Colonialism.* Translated by Haackon Chevalier. New York: Grove Press, 1994.

Farley, Lisa. "Analysis on Air: A Sound History of Winnicott on Air in Wartime." *American Imago* 68, no. 4 (Winter 2012): 449–471.

Farnsworth, Dana L., and Francis J. Braceland, eds. *Psychiatry, the Clergy, and Pastoral Counseling: The St. John's Story.* Collegeville, MN: Saint John's University Press, 1969.

Feist, Jerry. Phone Interview. October 17, 2016.

Feist, Jerry, and Steven Worona. *The Best of Uncle Ezra.* Vol. 1, *Fall 1988.* Ithaca, NY: Cornell University, 1988.

Feist, Jerry, and Steven Worona. *The Best of Uncle Ezra.* Vol. 2, *Fall 1991.* Ithaca, NY: Cornell University, 1991.

Feldman, Jessica. "The Problem of the Adjective: Affective Computing of the Speaking Voice." *Transposition: Music et sciences sociales*, no. 6 (2016): https://doi.org/10.4000/transposition.1640.

Finley, Laura, ed. *The Encyclopedia of School Crime and Violence.* Vol. 1, *A–N.* Oxford: ABC-CLIO, 2011.

Fischer, Claude S. "'Touch Someone': The Telephone Industry Discovers Sociability." *Technology and Culture* 29, no. 1 (1988): 32.

Foley, Daniel Patrick. "The Moral and Ethical Judgments of Dr. Laura." *Journal of Religion and Health* 39, no. 1 (Spring 2000): 39–42.

Freud, Anna. "The Psychoanalytic Study of Infantile Feeding Disturbances." *Psychoanalytic Studies of the Child* 2 (1946): 119–132.

Freud, Sigmund. *Analysis of a Phobia in a Five-Year-Old Boy. The Standard Edition*. Vol. 10. London: Hogarth Press, 1955.

Freud, Sigmund. BBC Broadcast Recorded at Maresfield Gardens, December 7, 1938.

Freud, Sigmund. *Civilization and Its Discontents* (1930). *The Standard Edition*. Vol. 21. London: Hogarth Press, 1961.

Freud, Sigmund. "Dreams and Telepathy" (1922). *The Standard Edition*. Vol. 18. London: Hogarth Press, 1955.

Freud, Sigmund. *Fragment of an Analysis of a Case of Hysteria* (1905). *The Standard Edition*. Vol. 7. London: Hogarth Press, 1953.

Freud, Sigmund. *The Interpretation of Dreams* (1900). *The Standard Edition*. Vol. 4. London: Hogarth Press, 1953.

Freud, Sigmund. Letter from Sigmund Freud to Lou Andres-Salome, July 30, 1915. The International Psychoanalytical Library, 89:32–33.

Freud, Sigmund. Letter from Sigmund Freud to Wilhelm Fliess, May 21, 1894. In *The Complete Letters of Sigmund Freud to Wilhelm Fliess, 1887–1904*. Edited and translated by Jeffrey M. Masson. Cambridge, MA: Belknap Press, 1985.

Freud, Sigmund. Letter 70, October 3, 1897. Extracts from the Fliess Papers. *The Standard Edition*. Vol. 1. London: Hogarth Press, 1953.

Freud, Sigmund. "Lines of Advance in Psycho-Analytic Therapy" (1919). *The Standard Edition*. Vol. 17. London: Hogarth Press, 1955.

Freud, Sigmund. "New Introductory Lectures on Psycho-Analysis." *The Standard Edition*. Vol. 22. London: Hogarth Press, 1964.

Freud, Sigmund. "On Beginning the Treatment (Further Recommendations on the Technique of Psychoanalysis I)" (1913). *The Standard Edition*. Vol. 12. London: Hogarth Press, 1966.

Freud, Sigmund. *The Origins of Psychoanalysis: Letters to Wilhelm Fliess, Drafts and Notes: 1887–1902*. Edited by Marie Bonaparte, Anna Freud, and Ernst Kris. New York: Basic Books, 1954.

Freud, Sigmund. "Psycho-Analysis and Telepathy." *The Standard Edition*. Vol. 18. London: Hogarth Press, 1955.

Freud, Sigmund. "Psycho-Analytic Notes on an Autobiographical Account of a Case of Paranoia." *The Standard Edition*. Vol. 12. London: Hogarth Press, 1966.

Freud, Sigmund. *The Psychopathology of Everyday Life. The Standard Edition*. Vol. 6. London: Hogarth Press, 1960.

Freud, Sigmund. "Recommendations to Physicians Practicing Psycho-Analysis." *The Standard Edition*. Vol. 12. London: Hogarth Press, 1966.

Freud, Sigmund. "Three Essays on the Theory of Sexuality" (1905). *The Standard Edition*. Vol. 7. London: Hogarth Press, 1953.

Galison, Peter. “Self-Censorship in the Digital Age: We Won’t Be Able to Recognize Ourselves.” *Frankfurter Allgemeine Feuilleton*, July 7, 2014.

Galison, Peter. “The Theater of Forgetting.” *Cabinet Magazine* 42 (2011): http://cabinetmagazine.org/issues/42/galison.php.

Garfinkle, Michael. Phone Interview. March 31, 2020.

Gay, Peter. *Freud: A Life for Our Time*. New York: Norton, 1988.

Gaztambide, Daniel Jose. *A People’s History of Psychoanalysis: From Freud to Liberation Psychology*. New York: Lexington Books, 2019.

Gombrowicz, Witold. *Diary*. Translated by Lilian Vallee. New Haven, CT: Yale University Press, 2012.

Goode, Erica. “Scientist at Work: Aaron T. Beck, Pragmatist, Embodies His No-nonsense Therapy.” *New York Times*, 2011.

Gordon, Arthur. *One Man’s Way: The Story and Message of Norman Vincent Peale*. New York: Prentice-Hall, 1972.

Goss, Stephen, and Kate Anthony, eds. *Technology in Counselling and Psychotherapy: A Practitioner’s Guide*. London: Palgrave, 2003.

Gould, Roger. In-Person Interview. September 8, 2017.

Gould, Roger. “Therapeutic Learning Program.” http://www.drrogergould.com/software/therapeutic-learning-program. Accessed October 11, 2017.

Graf, Herbert. “Sigmund Freud Papers: Interviews and Recollections, 1914–1998; Set A, 1914–1998; Interviews and; Graf, Herbert, 1959.” Manuscript/mixed material. https://www.loc.gov/item/mss3999001476/.

Grant, J. Tobin. “Measuring Aggregate Religiosity in The United States, 1952–2005.” *Sociological Spectrum* 28, no. 5 (2008): 460–476.

“Great Preachers.” *Life Magazine*, April 6, 1953.

Gregory, Alice. “R U There?” *New Yorker*, February 9, 2015.

Grob, Gerald. *From Asylum to Community: Mental Health Policy in Modern America*. Princeton, NJ: Princeton University Press, 1991.

Grohol, John. “Our Dedication to Mental Health.” June 7, 2016. https://psychcentral.com/about/our-dedication-to-mental-health. Last retrieved May 10, 2017.

Grohol, John. Phone Interview. October 21, 2016.

Grosskurth, Phyllis. *Melanie Klein: Her World and Her Work*. Lanham, MD: Jason Aronson, 1977.

Guattari, Félix. *Soft Subversions*. Edited by Sylvère Lotringer. Cambridge, MA: MIT Press, 1996.

Guillén, Claudio. “On the Edge of Literariness: The Writing of Letters.” *Comparative Literature Studies* 31, no. 1 (1994): 1–24.

Guralnick, Orna. Phone Interview. March 29, 2020.

Hangen, Tona. *Redeeming the Dial: Radio, Religion, and Popular Culture in America*. Chapel Hill: University of North Carolina Press, 2002.

Hartman, Saidiya. *Scenes of Subjection: Terror, Slavery, and Self-Making in Nineteenth-Century America*. Oxford: Oxford University Press, 1997.

Hayles, Katherine N. *How We Became Posthuman: Virtual Bodies in Cybernetics, Literature, and Informatics*. Chicago: University of Chicago Press, 1999.

"Healing of Mind Linked to Spirit." *New York Times*, March 14, 1955.

Helgadóttir, Fjóla Dögg, Ross G. Menzies, Mark Onslow, Ann Packman, and Sue O'Brian. "Online CBT I: Bridging the Gap between Eliza and Modern Online CBT Treatment Packages." *Behaviour Change* 26, no. 4 (2009): 245.

Henkin, David M. *The Postal Age: The Emergence of Modern Communications in Nineteenth-Century America*. Chicago: University of Chicago Press, 2007.

Higbie, Andrea. "From Confidentiality to Anybody Who Tunes In." *New York Times*, October 31, 1999.

"History." San Francisco Suicide Prevention. http://www.sfsuicide.org/about-sfsp/history. Accessed June 15, 2016.

Howard, Carole Haymes. "Rest in Power Elbert 'Big Man' Howard, Founding Father of the Black Panther Party." *San Francisco Bay View*, July 18, 2018.

Hull, Thomas D., and Kush Mahan. "Telemedicine and e-Health." October 2016, ahead of print. https://doi.org/10.1089/tmj.2016.0114.

Innis, Harold. *The Bias of Communication*. Toronto: University of Toronto Press, 1951.

Isaacs, Susan. Archival Files. Courtesy of the Archives of the British Psycho-Analytical Society.

Isaacs Russell, Gillian. *Screen Relations: The Limits of Computer-Mediated Psychotherapy*. New York: Routledge, 2015.

Johanssen, Jacob. *Psychoanalysis and Digital Culture: Audiences, Social Media, and Big Data*. New York: Routledge, 2018.

Jones, Ernst. *The Life and Work of Sigmund Freud*. New York: Penguin, 1964.

"Joyable." https://joyable.com/how-it-works. Accessed July 1, 2017.

Kachka, Boris. "The Power of Positive Publishing." *New York Magazine*, January 6, 2013.

Kafka, Ben. *The Demon of Writing: The Powers and Failures of Paperwork*. New York: Zone Books, 2012.

Kagan, Marilyn. Call-in Show. December 21, 1992. https://archive.org/details/ACs9212s021a13Track13_201706/a+-+cs9212s021a+-+07+-+Track07.mp3. Last accessed June 2, 2020.

Kane, Brian. *Sound Unseen: Acousmatic Sound in Theory and Practice*. Oxford: Oxford University Press, 2014.

Kane, Yoon Im. E-mail Interview. April 1, 2020.

Karpf, Ann. "Constructing and Addressing the 'Ordinary Devoted Mother.'" *History Workshop Journal* 78 (2004): 27.

Keller, Suzanne. "The Telephone in New (and Old) Communities." In *The Social Impact of the Telephone*. Edited by Ithiel de Sola Pool. Cambridge, MA: MIT University Press, 1977.

Khan, Masud. *The Long Wait and Other Psychoanalytic Narratives*. London: Summit Press, 1989.

Khan, Masud. *The Privacy of the Self.* London: Karnac Books, 1996.

Kittler, Freidrich. *Gramophone, Film, Typewriter*. Palo Alto, CA: Stanford University Press, 1999.

Klein, Melanie. *Narrative of a Child Analysis*. London: Karnac Books, 1961.

Kleine, M., and G. Gale. "The Elusive Presence of the Word: An Interview with Walter Ong." *Composition FORUM* (1996): 65–86.

Kohut, Heinz. "Introspection, Empathy, and Psychoanalysis—an Examination of the Relationship between Mode of Observation and Theory." *Journal of the American Psychoanalytic Association* 7 (1959): 459–483.

"Koko." https://itskoko.com/. Accessed July 1, 2017.

Kravis, Nathan. *On the Couch: A Repressed History of the Analytic Couch from Plato to Freud.* Cambridge, MA: MIT Press, 2017.

Krueger, D. W. "Money Meanings and Madness: A Psychoanalytic Perspective." *Psychoanalytic Review* 78, no. 2 (2009): 209–224.

Kvaran, Kara. "Super Gay." In *Comics as History, Comics as Literature*. Edited by Annessa Babic. Madison, NJ: Fairleigh Dickinson University Press, 2013.

Lacan, Jacques. *Ecrits: The First Complete Translation in English*. Translated by Bruce Fink. New York: W. W. Norton, 2007.

Lacan, Jacques. *The Four Fundamental Concepts of Psycho-Analysis*. Translated by Alan Sheridan. London: W. W. Norton, 1981.

Lebow, Lori. "Woman of Letters: Narrative Episodes in the Letters of Emily Dickinson." *Emily Dickinson Journal* 8, no. 1 (1999): 73–96.

Leibowitz, Neil. Personal Communication. March 31, 2020.

LeJeune, Philippe. *On Diary*. Honolulu: University of Hawaii Press, 2009.

Lemma, Alessandra. *The Digital Age on the Couch: Psychoanalytic Practice and New Media*. New York: Routledge, 2017.

Lester, David. "Counseling and Crisis Usage." In *The Social Impact of the Telephone*. Edited by Ithiel de Sola Pool. Cambridge, MA: MIT University Press, 1977.

Lester, David, and James C. Rogers, eds. *Crisis Intervention and Counseling by Telephone and the Internet*. Springfield, IL: Charles C. Thomas Publishing, 2012.

Lin, Lana. "Are These Thoughts My Own? A Psychoanalytic Reading of Upton Sinclair's *Mental Radio*." Paper presented at the Society for Cinema and Media Studies 2014 Conference, Seattle, WA.

Linsker, Eric. Personal Communication. March 18, 2020.

Liu, Lydia. *The Freudian Robot: Digital Media and the Future of the Unconscious*. Chicago: University of Chicago Press, 2011.

Long, Tom. "Obituary: Rev. Kenneth B. Murphy, at 78; Pastor Founded Suicide Hot Line." *Boston Globe*, May 26, 1999.

Lukach, Mark. "Exquisite Listening: America's First Suicide Hotline Celebrates 50 Years." *GOOD*, July 21, 2012. https://www.good.is/articles/exquisite-listening-america-s-first-suicide-prevention-hotline-celebrates-50-years. Accessed June 15, 2016.

Lunbeck, Elizabeth. "Empathy as a Psychoanalytic Mode of Observation: Between Sentiment and Science." In *Histories of Scientific Observation*. Edited by Lorraine Daston and Elizabeth Lunbeck. Chicago: University of Chicago Press, 2011.

Magid, Lawerence. "Psychological Software Programs Come with Their Own Shortcomings." *Washington Post*, November 19, 1990.

Makari, George. *Soul Machine: The Invention of the Modern Mind*. New York: W. W. Norton, 2015.

Marks, I. M. "Self-Administered Behavioural Treatment." *Behavioural Psychotherapy* 19, no. 1 (1991): 42–46.

Martin, Michelle. *Hello, Central?: Gender, Technology, and Culture in the Formation of Telephone Systems*. Montreal: McGill-Queens Press, 1991.

Masson, Jeffrey M., ed. and trans. *The Complete Letters of Sigmund Freud to Wilhelm Fliess, 1887–1904*. New York: Belknap Press, 1985.

Mayes, Bernard Duncan. *Escaping God's Closet: The Revelations of a Queer Priest*. Charlottesville: University of Virginia Press, 2001.

Mayes, Bernard Duncan. "Thinking of Suicide: Bernard Mayes Interviewed by Elsa Knight Thomson." March 19, 1963. Courtesy of the Pacifica Radio Archives.

McBroom, Patricia. "24-Hour Suicide Services Winning Attention of Cities." November 10, 1965. Dr. E. S. Shneidman Papers, Box 31, Folder 8. UCLA Special Collections, Charles E. Young Research Library, University of California, Los Angeles.

McGee, Micki. *Self-Help, Inc.: Makeover Culture in American Life*. Oxford: Oxford University Press, 2005.

McKinney, Cait. "Calling to Talk and Listening Well: The Multimedia Practices of Feminist Telephone Hotlines." Presentation delivered at FemTechNet, University of Michigan, Ann Arbor, April 8, 2016.

McKinney, Cait. "Calling to Talk and Listen Well: Information as Care at Telephone Hotlines." In *Information Activism: A Queer History of Lesbian Media Technologies*. Durham, NC: Duke University Press, 2020.

McLuhan, Marshall. *Understanding Media: The Extensions of Man*. Berkeley, CA: Gingko Press, 2013.

McNeill, John T., ed., and Ford Lewis Battle, trans. *Calvin: Institutes of the Christian Religion.* Louisville, KY: Westminster Press, 1960.

Mercurio, Mara, Mark Larsen, Hannah Wisniewski, Philip Henson, Sarah Lagan, and John Torous. "Longitudinal Trends in the Quality, Effectiveness and Attributes of Highly Rated Smartphone Health Apps." *BMJ: Evidence-Based Mental Health* (April 2020): 1–5, https://ebmh.bmj.com/content/ebmental/early/2020/04/20/ebmental-2019-300137.full.pdf.

Metzl, Jonathan. *Prozac on the Couch: Prescribing Gender in the Era of Wonder Drugs.* Durham, NC: Duke University Press, 2005.

Middleton, Aves, Jane Gunn, Bridget Bassilios, and Jane Pirkis. "Systematic Review of Research into Frequent Callers to Crisis Helplines." *Journal of Telemedicine and Telecare* 20, no. 2 (2014): 89–98.

Mills, Mara. "The Audiovisual Telephone: A Brief History." In *Handheld? Music Video Aesthetics for Portable Devices.* Edited by Henry Keazor. Heidelberg, Germany: ART-Dok, 2012.

Milne, Esther. "Email and Epistolary Technologies: Presence, Intimacy, Disembodiment." *FibreCulture Journal* 2 (2003): http://two.fibreculturejournal.org/fcj-010-email-and-epistolary-technologies-presence-intimacy-disembodiment/.

Monegain, B. "Telemedicine Market to Soar Past $30B." *Health Care IT News*, August 4, 2015. https://www.healthcareitnews.com/news/telemedicine-poised-grow-big-time. Last retrieved May 10, 2017.

Mowitt, John. "Phoning in Analysis." In *Radio: Essays in Bad Reception.* Berkeley: University of California Press, 2011.

Mowitt, John. *Radio: Essays in Bad Reception.* Berkeley: University of California Press, 2011.

Mowitt, John. "Stations of Exception." In *Radio: Essays in Bad Reception.* Berkeley: University of California Press, 2011.

Nadelson, Theodore. "The Inhuman Computer, the Too Human Therapist." *American Journal of Psychotherapy* 41, no. 4 (October 1987): 489–498.

Nead, Lynda. *Myths of Sexuality: Representations of Women in Victorian Britain.* Oxford: Basil Blackwell, 1988.

Nelson, Alondra. *Body and Soul: The Black Panther Party and the Fight against Medical Discrimination.* Minneapolis: University of Minnesota Press, 2011.

Neuman, Debra. "The Frame for Psychoanalysis in Cyberspace." In *Psychoanalysis Online: Mental Health, Teletherapy, Training.* London: Karnac Books, 2013.

Nicholas, Sian. "The People's Radio: The BBC and Its Audience, 1939–1945." In *Millions Like Us?: British Culture in the Second World War.* Edited by Nick Hayes and Jeff Hill. Liverpool, UK: Liverpool University Press, 1999.

Noble, Safiya. *Algorithms of Oppression: How Search Engines Reinforce Racism.* New York: New York University Press, 2018.

Ong, Walter. *Orality and Literacy: The Technologizing of the World.* New York: Routledge, 1982.

Oring, Elliott. *The Jokes of Sigmund Freud: A Study in Humor and Jewish Identity*. Lanham, MD: Jason Aronson, 1984.

Parker, Dorothy. Telegram to Pascal Covici, Viking Press. June 28, 1945.

Parkinson, Anna. "Adorno on the Airwaves: Feeling Reason, Educating Emotions." In "West Germany's Cold War Radio: The Crucible of the Transatlantic Century," special issue, *German Politics and Society* 32, no. 1 (110) (Spring 2014): 44.

"Parry Encounters the Doctor." https://tools.ietf.org/html/rfc439. Accessed August 15, 2017.

Peralta, Eyder. "Bernard Mayes, NPR's First Chairman, Founder of Suicide Hotline, Dies." *National Public Radio*, October 27, 2014.

Perel, Esther. *Where Should We Begin?* Episode One, Season One. October 8, 2017.

Perkinson, Jim. "Beyond Occasional Whiteness." *CrossCurrents* 47, no. 2 (1997): 195–209.

Peters, John Durham. "Broadcasting and Schizophrenia." *Media, Culture, and Society* 32, no. 1 (2010): 132.

Peters, John Durham. *Speaking into the Air: A History of the Idea of Communication*. Chicago: University of Chicago Press, 2001.

Pinchevski, Amit, and Tamar Liebes. "Severed Voices: Radio and the Mediation of Trauma in the Eichmann Trial." *Public Culture* 22, no. 2 (2010): 265–291.

Plato. *Charmides*. Translated by T. West. New York: Hackett, 1986.

Pommier, Gerard. "What Constitutes an Interpretation?" Presented at the Psychoanalysis on Ice Conference, Reykjavik, Iceland, July 27, 2018.

"Psychological Therapies, Annual Report on the Use of IAPT Services—England, 2014–15." November 24, 2015. http://content.digital.nhs.uk/catalogue/PUB19098/psyc-ther-ann-rep-2014-15.pdf. Accessed July 15, 2017.

Puget, Janine. "Revisiting the Concept of the Frame." In *Reconsidering the Moveable Frame in Psychoanalysis*. Edited by Isaac Tymlin and Adrienne Harris. New York: Routledge, 2017.

Quah, Nicholas. "How Esther Perel Makes Her Intensely Intimate Podcasts." *New York Magazine*, January 9, 2020.

Reddit Suicide Watch. https://www.reddit.com/r/SuicideWatch/. Last retrieved May 10, 2017.

Rivera, Jose B. "Rafael Flores in Remembrance." East-Harlem.com, 2003. https://www.east-harlem.com/index.php/News/view/rafael_flores_in_remembrance/. Last accessed May 6, 2020.

Robinson, Ann. "Meet Ellie, the Machine That Can Detect Depression." *The Guardian*, September 17, 2005.

Robinson, Howard. *The British Post Office: A History*. Princeton, NJ: Princeton University Press, 1948.

Robles-Anderson, Erica. "Blind Spots: Religion in Media." *Flow Journal* 17 (2012): http://flowtv.org/2012/12/blind-spots/. Accessed June 15, 2016.

Robles-Anderson, Erica. "The Crystal Cathedral: Architecture for a Mediated Congregation." *Public Culture* 24, no. 3 (2012): 577–599.

Rogers, Carl R. *Counseling and Psychotherapy*. Cambridge, MA: Riverside Press, 1942.

Rosner, Rachel. "Aaron T. Beck's Drawings and the Psychoanalytic Origin Story of Cognitive Therapy." *History of Psychology* 15, no. 1 (2012): 1–18.

Rozbroj, Tomas, Anthony Lyons, Marian Pitts, Anne Mitchell, and Helen Christensen. "Assessing the Applicability of E-Therapies for Depression, Anxiety, and Other Mood Disorders among Lesbians and Gay Men: Analysis of 24 Web- and Mobile Phone-Based Self-Help Interventions." *Journal of Medical Internet Research* 16, no. 7 (2014): e166.

Rudnytsky, Peter. *Freud and Oedipus*. New York: Columbia University Press, 1992.

Ryan, Joanna. *Class and Psychoanalysis: Landscapes of Inequality*. New York: Routledge, 2017.

Scannell, Paddy. "For Someone-as-Anyone-Structures." *Media, Culture, and Society* 22, no. 1 (2000): 5–24.

Scharff, Jill S. *Psychoanalysis Online: Mental Health, Teletherapy, and Training*, vols. 1–3. London: Karnac, 2013, 2015, 2017.

Schorke, Carl E. *Fin-De-Siècle Vienna: Politics and Culture*. New York: Vintage, 1980.

Schull, Natasha. "Data for Life: Wearable Technology and the Design of Self-Care." *BioSocieties* 11 (2016): 317–333.

Schuller, Robert H. Call logs. H93–1188. Crystal Cathedral Ministries Collection. Joint Archives of Holland.

Schuller, Robert H. "Garden Grove Community Church History." H93–1188. Crystal Cathedral Ministries Collection. Joint Archives of Holland, 1977.

Schuller, Robert H. "New Hope Telephone Counseling Service." Pamphlet used for outreach. H93–1188. Crystal Cathedral Ministries Collection. Joint Archives of Holland.

Schwartz, Alexandra. "Esther Perel Lets Us Listen in on Couple's Secrets." *New Yorker*, May 31, 2017.

"Scientific Meetings Minutes." Courtesy of the Archives of the British Psycho-Analytical Society.

Sconce, Jeffrey. *Haunted Media: Electronic Presence from Telegraphy to Television*. Durham, NC: Duke University Press, 2000.

Scozzaro, Connie. Personal Communication. March 26, 2020.

Selmi, Paulette. "Computer-Assisted Cognitive-Behavior Therapy in the Treatment of Depression." PhD diss., Illinois Institute of Technology, 1990.

Serpell, Namwali. "The Banality of Empathy." *New York Review of Books*, March 2, 2019.

Shafer, Roy. "Listening in Psychoanalysis." *Narrative* 13, no. 3 (2005): 271–280.

Shapira, Michal. *The War Inside: Psychoanalysis, Total War, and the Making of the Democratic Self in Postwar Britain*. Cambridge: Cambridge University Press, 2013.

Sharman, Russell Leigh. *The Tenants of East Harlem*. Berkeley: University of California Press, 2006.

Shea, Virginia. *Netiquette*. San Francisco: Albion Books, 1994.

Shneidman, Edwin S. Papers, Box 6, Folders 9–12. UCLA Special Collections, Charles E. Young Research Library, University of California, Los Angeles.

Shneidman, Edwin S. Papers, Box 31, Folder 8. UCLA Special Collections, Charles E. Young Research Library, University of California, Los Angeles.

Shortis, Tom. *The Language of ICT*. London: Psychology Press, 2001.

Siegert, Bernhard. *Relays: Literature as an Epoch of the Postal System*. Translated by Kevin Repp. Palo Alto, CA: Stanford University Press, 1999.

Sjoödin, Christer. "Quality Assurance and Quality Assessment as Internal Ongoing Aspects of Psychoanalysis and Psychotherapy." *International Forum of Psychoanalysis* 3, no. 3 (1994): 183–193.

Slack, Warner V. *Cybermedicine: How Computing Empowers Doctors and Patients for Better Care*. 2nd ed. San Francisco: Jossey-Bass, 2001.

Slack, Warner V. Phone Interview. September 13, 2017.

Slack, Warner V., and Lawrence J. Van Cura. "Patient Reaction to Computer-Based Medical Interviewing." *Computers and Biomedical Research* 1 (1968): 527–531.

Sommers, David. Mental Health Cyber-Clinic. 1996. Last retrieved May 10, 2017, from https://web.archive.org/web/19990116231713/http://www.dcez.com:80/~davids/pageone.htm.

Sommers, David. Phone Interview. December 14, 2016.

Spitzer, Robert, and Joseph Fliess. "A Re-analysis of the Reliability of Psychiatric Diagnosis." *British Journal of Psychiatry* 125, no. 4 (1974): 321–347.

Stark, Luke. "That Signal Feeling: Emotion and Interaction Design from Social Media to the 'Anxious Seat.'" PhD diss., New York University, 2016.

Stein, Jeannine. "Keeping in Touch: A Viscott Primer: With Hugs and Quick Answers, Radio Shrink has Built Himself a Mini-Empire." *Los Angeles Times*, March 17, 1988.

Sterling, Christopher H., ed. *Biographical Dictionary of Radio*. New York: Routledge, 2010.

Sterne, Jonathan. *The Audible Past*. Durham, NC: Duke University Press, 2003.

Steuer, Jonathan. "Defining Virtual Reality: Dimensions Determining Telepresence." *Journal of Communication* 42, no. 4 (Autumn 1992): 73–93.

Stevenson, Lisa. *Life beside Itself: Imagining Care in the Canadian Arctic*. Berkeley: University of California Press, 2014.

"Stigma." http://sur.ly/i/getstigma.com/. Accessed July 1, 2017.

Stofle, Gary. "Chat Room Therapy." In *e-Therapy: Case Studies, Guiding Principles, and the Clinical Potential of the Internet*. New York: W. W. Norton, 2002.

Stuart, Jennifer. "Little Hans and Freud's Self-Analysis: A Biographical View of Clinical Theory in the Making." *Journal of American Psychological Association* 55, no. 3 (Summer 2007): 799–819.

Suchman, Lucy. *Human-Machine Reconfigurations: Plans and Situated Actions.* Cambridge: Cambridge University Press, 1987.

"Suicide." http://suicide.org/. Accessed August 25, 2017.

Sulyeman, Attif. "DARPA to Plug Computers into Brains to Talk Directly to People." *The Independent,* July 12, 2017.

Talkspace. https://talkspace.workable.com/?fv=social. Last retrieved May 10, 2017.

Talkspace. "The Future of Therapy: Can You Have a Relationship with a Machine?" Conference presented by Talkspace, April 5, 2016.

"Talkspace x Michael Phelps: How Therapy Saved His Life." https://www.youtube.com/watch?v=e8cBl9pKES4. Last retrieved July 2, 2018.

"Telephone Used as Counseling Aid." *Christian Science Monitor,* September 18, 1962.

"Therapist Toni Grant departing KFI-AM." *Los Angeles Times,* August 26, 1989.

Thurschwell, Pamela. "Ferenczi's Dangerous Proximities: Telepathy, Psychosis, and the Real Event." *differences: A Journal of Feminist Cultural Studies* 11 (1999): 150–178.

Tomita, Hidenori. "*Keitai* and the Intimate Stranger." In *Personal, Portable, Pedestrian: Mobile Phones in Japanese Life.* Edited by Mizuko Ito, Daisuke Okabe, and Misa Matsuda. Cambridge, MA: MIT Press, 2005.

Turing, Alan. "Computing Machinery and Intelligence." *MIND* 59, no. 236 (October 1950): 433–460.

Turkle, Sherry. *Alone Together: Why We Expect More from Technology and Less from Each Other.* New York: Basic Books, 2012.

Turkle, Sherry. *Life on the Screen.* New York: Simon and Schuster, 1995.

Turkle, Sherry. *The Second Self: Computers and the Human Spirit.* Cambridge, MA: MIT Press, 1985.

Turkle, Sherry. "Taking Things at Interface Value." In *Life on the Screen.* New York: Simon and Schuster, 1995.

Turkle, Sherry, Gillian Isaacs Russell, and Todd Essig. "Bodies in the Room: Keeping Talk Therapy Real." May 29, 2018. https://medium.com/@sturkle/bodies-in-the-room-ca07d196e0d9. Last accessed June 14, 2020.

Twenge, Jean M., and W. Keith Campbell. "Associations between Screen Time and Lower Psychological Well-being among Children and Adolescents: Evidence from a Population-Based Study." *Preventive Medicine Reports* 12 (2018): 271–283.

Varah, Chad. *Before I Die Again: The Autobiography of the Founder of the Samaritans.* London: Constable, 1992.

Varah, Chad. *The Samaritans.* New York: MacMillan, 1965.

Varah, Chad. "Why I Started the Samaritans." Samaritans. http://www.samaritans.org/about-us/history-samaritans/how-and-why-i-started-samaritans-chad-varah. Accessed June 15, 2016.

Watson, Nicholas. "Despair." In *Cultural Reformations: Medieval and Renaissance in Literary History*. Edited by James Simpson and Brian Cummings. Oxford: Oxford University Press, 2010.

Weigel, Moira. *Labor of Love: The Invention of Dating*. New York: Farrar, Strauss, Giroux, 2016.

Weintraub, Joseph. "History of the PC Therapist." http://www.cis.umassd.edu/~ivalova/Spring09/cis412/Old/therapist.pdf. Accessed July 1, 2017.

Weitzman, Bruce. Personal Communication. March 31, 2020.

Weizenbaum, Joseph. *Computer Power and Human Reason*. New York: W. H. Freeman, 1976.

White, Mimi. *Tele-Advising: Therapeutic Discourse in American Television*. Chapel Hill: University of North Carolina Press, 1992.

Whiting, Sam. "Bernard Mayes to be Honored as Lifeline to Suicidal." *SF Gate*, April 28, 2012.

Wilks, Yorick. *Machine Conversations*. New York: Springer Nature, 1999.

Wilson, Elizabeth. *Affect and Artificial Intelligence*. Seattle: University of Washington Press, 2010.

Winnicott, D. W. "Children in the War." In *Deprivation and Delinquency*. New York: Routledge, 2011.

Winnicott, D. W. *Deprivation and Delinquency*. New York: Routledge, 2011.

Winnicott, D. W. *On the Child*. Cambridge, MA: Perseus Publishing, 2002.

Winnicott, D. W. "The Ordinary Devoted Mother and Her Baby: Nine Broadcast Talks." Distributed Privately, Produced by Miss I. D. Benzie. 1949. Courtesy of the Wellcome Library and the Winnicott Trust.

Winnicott, D. W. *The Piggle: An Account of the Psychoanalytic Treatment of a Little Girl*. London: Hogarth Press and Institute of Psycho-Analysis, 1980.

Winnicott, D. W. *Talking to Parents*. Boston: Da Capo Press, 1994.

Worona, Steven. Phone Interview. October 23, 2016.

"x2.ai." https://x2.ai/. Accessed July 1, 2017.

Zeavin, Hannah. "Freud's Séance." *American Imago* 75, no. 1 (Spring 2018): 53–65.

Zeavin, Hannah. "Therapists Are Doing Sessions in Locked Bathrooms While Patients Call in from Their Cars." *Slate*, April 10, 2020.

Index

Page numbers in italics refer to a figure.